Photogrammetry

Photogrammetry

second edition

Francis H. Moffitt

Professor of Civil Engineering
University of California

International Textbook Company
Scranton, Pennsylvania

International Textbooks in Civil Engineering

Consulting Editor

Russell C. Brinker

Professor of Civil Engineering
Texas Western College

Preface to Second Edition

Since the first edition of this text was introduced in 1959, the science of photogrammetry has experienced a tremendous advance in the technology of photographic measurement, instrument development, automation, numerical methods, improved materials, and diversity of applications of this most fascinating system of measurement. In the opinion of the author, the most significant advance has been made in the area of numerical photogrammetry, based on highly sophisticated plate coordinate measurement of the photographic image, depending for its practicality on the progress made in high-speed computers and programming for these computers, and made meaningful by the study of error propagation and evaluation in various systems.

Perhaps the second most productive area has been in the development of ingenious and workable automatic instruments for the solutions to photogrammetric problems, most notably for the rapid compilation of reliable topographic maps. Progress in this area is in large part due to the successful cooperation between the photogrammetrists, systems engineers, and electronic engineers.

In order to provide the student with a comprehensive foundation for further study of photogrammetry as well as to allow those in other disciplines such as civil engineering, geology, cartography, and forestry to become familiar with the potential of photogrammetry to the solution of their problems, the author has introduced material in this edition which reflects the advances made in photogrammetry since the first edition.

In Chapter 1 are introduced many of the latest types of comparators and stereocomparators as well as devices for marking points for comparator measurements. These instruments are the basis for analytic or numerical photogrammetry. New aerial camera lenses, methods of camera calibration, and more complete plate coordinate corrections are given in Chapter 2.

Chapter 3 has been expanded to include the rotational formulae in matrix notation and the development of the projective transformation equations. These are the foundations of analytic photogrammetry as presently developed. These principles are applied to the determination of the orientation of an aerial photograph in Chapter 9, and to the analytical treatment of terrestrial photographs in Chapter 14.

Chapter 12 has been expanded considerably to present some of the principles of automation and of the analytical plotters. The operation and orientation of so-called first-order plotters has been enlarged upon.

The necessity for precise, well-marked control to be used in numerical photogrammetric systems is recognized. Thus, in Chapter 5, targeting of ground control points is discussed fairly extensively. The airborne control system of the U.S. Geological Survey is also described in this chapter.

The author has attempted to make the presentation of this new subject matter as simple and uncomplicated as possible, with the idea in mind that the reader will be able to grasp the significance of the basic principles of photogrammetry on his own. In order to extend his knowledge in this field, he will then presumably be in a position to study the reference material cited in the greatly expanded bibliographies following each chapter.

The author wishes to express his thanks to the instrument manufacturers who most generously furnished photographs for many of the illustrations, and also to the many critics of the first edition who influenced the preparation of text for this second edition.

Francis H. Moffitt

Berkeley, California
October, 1967

Preface to First Edition

Photogrammetry, as a system of measuring data recorded on photographs, is applicable to all sciences that depend on reliable geometric measurements of physical quantities in a fixed or transitory state. Its widest application thus far has been in the field of topographic mapping of the surface of the earth. Initially, photogrammetry was confined to the measuring of terrestrial or ground photographs for map-making purposes. The advent of the airplane brought about the development of a new system of airborne cameras and recording devices, and the associated measuring and plotting devices used in the laboratory.

Photogrammetry is becoming more and more a part of instrumentation engineering, principally in fields where measurements of transitory phenomena must be made. The cameras may be either airborne or earthbound. Nevertheless, the principles of photogrammetry apply equally in both cases.

This book has been written primarily as a college text to fill a need for a simple but complete coverage of the principles of photogrammetry. The book is designed to provide answers to a great many questions pertaining to these principles which it is difficult, if not impossible, to obtain from existing texts and references. No previous knowledge of photogrammetry is assumed.

Because of the intense development of the art and science of aerial photogrammetry as applied to mapping, this book undertakes to explain that phase first, placing the subject of terrestrial photogrammetry in the final chapter. If the book is to be used for a course in terrestrial photogrammetry, Chapters 1, 2, 3, and 7 should be carefully studied to provide a background for the study of Chapter 14 on Terrestrial Photogrammetry.

One of the difficulties encountered in developing a course or a series of courses in photogrammetry in a college or university is the expense of equipping the laboratory with the necessary measuring devices. Except for some of the more elaborate plotting instruments discussed in Chapter 12 and the rectifiers discussed in Chapter 10, however, the equipment described in this book is available to colleges and universities at moderate expense. The reader must realize that some of the basic instruments discussed in the book are not practical in map production. But the reader should understand that the principles applied to the simple instruments are essentially the same as those which underly the operation of the more elaborate production equipment designed for photogrammetry.

A bibliography located at the end of each chapter has been prepared from a selected list of textbooks, manuals, and articles from periodicals. With few exceptions, the articles have been chosen from Volumes XIII to XXIV (1947-1958) of *Photogrammetric Engineering*, which is the journal of the American Society of Photogrammetry. These volumes, together with other literature cited in the bibliographies, are readily available to the reader through the college or university libraries. It is from these references that a student is expected to expand his knowledge and increase his understanding of the diverse applications of the principles of photogrammetry discussed in this book.

In studying the examples in this book and in working the numerical problems at the ends of the chapters, the reader will note frequent occasions in which the given values are expressed as numbers with only one or two significant figures. The values in examples and problems are presented in this manner simply for convenience. In actual photogrammetric problems, especially in the planning phases, some of the data will be taken to few significant figures, and the reader is cautioned to consider the precision of the given and computed values.

The author wishes to thank the instrument manufacturers, the federal mapping and charting agencies, and the American Society of Photogrammetry, who kindly furnished photographs or granted permission to use diagrams on which some illustrations in this book are based.

This book is dedicated to the late Earl Church, Professor of Photogrammetry at Syracuse University, and to Mr. Alfred O. Quinn, former Professor of Photogrammetry at Syracuse University. Because of their inspirational teaching and professional guidance, the author has himself enjoyed many fruitful years of teaching photogrammetry.

FRANCIS H. MOFFITT

Berkeley, California
June, 1959

Contents

Control by Radial-Line Plotting. Errors in Radial-Line Plotting Due to Tilt. Azimuth Point as Center of Rays. Slotted Templets. Metal-Arm Templets. Photo Control Requirements for Radial-Line Plotting. Map Revision by Radial-Line Principle. Vertical Photograph Versus Planimetric Map. Planimetric Features by Direct Tracing. Planimetric Features by Camera Lucida. Planimetric Features by Projection of Photograph. Planimetric Features by Using Radial Plotter. Bibliography. Problems.

Introduction 1

1–1. Photogrammetry

In its restricted sense, the term photogrammetry means the measuring of images on a photograph. This definition is inadequate, however, since photogrammetry is understood to mean the science and art of using photographs for various purposes, such as the following:

The construction of planimetric and topographic maps.
The determination of the space position of objects by measurements on photographs.
The evaluation of timber stands.
The classification of soils.
The interpretation of geology.
The acquisition of military intelligence.
The preparation of composite pictures of the ground.

The term *aerial photogrammetry* denotes that branch of photogrammetry wherein photographs of the terrain in an area are taken by a precision camera mounted in an aircraft flying over the area. The term *terrestrial photogrammetry* denotes that branch of photogrammetry wherein photographs are taken from a fixed, and usually known, position on or near the ground and with the camera axis horizontal or nearly so. The term *space photogrammetry* embraces all aspects of extraterrestrial photography and subsequent measurement wherein the camera may be fixed on earth, contained in an artificial satellite, or positioned on the moon or a planet. The term *photo interpretation* is applied to that branch of photogrammetry wherein aerial or terrestrial photographs are used to evaluate, analyze, classify, and interpret images of objects which can be seen on the photographs. In the process of photo interpretation, measuring may not be essential, but some measurements must usually be made. Also, in the practice of aerial, terrestrial, and space photogrammetry, a certain amount of interpretation must be performed in addition to making measurements. Consequently, photogrammetry must be considered as a combination of measurement and interpretation.

The major use of aerial photogrammetry is in the preparation of planimetric maps, topographic maps, *photo maps*, and *mosaics*. A photo map is understood to be an orthographic representation of the ground in the form of a continuous tone picture, whereas a mosaic is an assembly of a series of aerial photographs into one continuous picture. With certain exceptions, the aerial photographs used in preparing maps and mosaics are taken with a single-lens camera having the optical axis pointed vertically downward or nearly so. The photographs are taken in a planned sequence along parallel flight lines and from a predetermined height above a datum, such as sea level.

In special mapping where a great area is to be covered from a limited flying height, use may be made of a camera with several lenses whose optical axes are inclined to the vertical, or of a group of cameras whose optical axes are inclined to the vertical. The nine-lens camera of the U. S. Coast and Geodetic Survey, briefly described in Chapter 2, is used to advantage in photographing shore-line areas for mapping and charting. Because the extensive coverage of such a camera embraces off-shore features at the same time that it photographs the mainland, the off-shore features can be more easily charted in their correct positions with respect to the shore line.

By the use of three cameras mounted in a fixed relationship with one another so that one axis points vertically downward and the other two axes point off to the sides of the flight line, a very wide band of terrain can be photographed along a single flight line. This procedure is known as the *trimetrogon* system of photography for small-scale charting and mapping, and is discussed in Chapter 13.

Photographs made from known positions or stations on the ground were employed in the past, and are still used to a limited extent, for the preparation of topographic maps of rather inaccessible areas such as mountains and canyons. Such terrestrial photographs are also successfully employed to furnish supplementary ground control for aerial-photogrammetric mapping. Terrestrial photogrammetry embraces also the use of cameras at ground stations in known positions for the following purposes:

> To reproduce plan and elevation views of buildings and structures.
> To obtain reliable measurements in experimental research in engineering, medicine, and the other arts and sciences.
> By means of motion-picture photography, to make measurements involving transitory phenomena such as wave motion, currents, moving machinery, and humans and animals in motion.

Literature citing the application of photogrammetry to fields other than map-making commonly uses the term *nontopographic* photogrammetry to describe the measuring process.

1—2. Classification of Aerial Photographs

An aerial photograph taken with the optical axis of the camera held in a vertical or nearly vertical position is classified as a *vertical photo-*

graph. See Fig. 1–1. When the geometry of a vertical photograph is considered, the photograph is assumed to be taken with the optical axis truly vertical. An unintentional and unavoidable inclination of the optical axis from the vertical produces what will be called a *tilted photograph.*

Fig. 1–1. Vertical photograph. (Courtesy of Clyde Sunderland Aerial Photographs, Oakland, Calif.)

An *oblique photograph,* or an *oblique,* is a photograph taken with the optical axis intentionally inclined to the vertical. In the trimetrogon system, the two side photographs are obliques. An oblique which contains the apparent horizon of the earth is termed a *high oblique.* A *low oblique* is one on which the apparent horizon does not appear. Both a high oblique and a low oblique are shown in Fig. 1–2. A pair of low obliques taken in sequence along a flight line in such manner that both

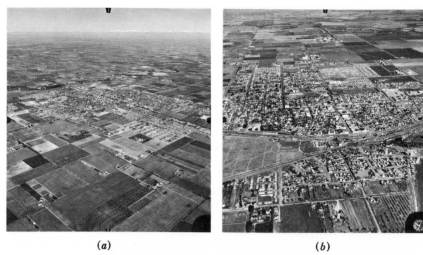

(a)   (b)

FIG. 1–2. (<i>a</i>) High oblique. (<i>b</i>) Low oblique. (Courtesy of Clyde Sunderland
Aerial Photographs, Oakland, Calif.)

photographs cover essentially the same area, as shown in Fig. 1–3, are
called *convergent photographs.*

Aerial photographs may be classified according to their size. Most
photographs taken for photogrammetric operations are 9 in. by 9 in. in
size. Cameras which take photographs 5½ by 5½, 7 by 7, 7 by 9, and
9 by 18 in. in size are used also. Of these four sizes, the 5½- by 5½-in.
and the 7- by 7-in. sizes are associated with precision cameras. The other
two sizes are typical of reconnaissance-type cameras, where precise
metrical characteristics of the camera are not paramount.

Photography may be classified as *normal-angle, wide-angle,* or *ultra
wide-angle* photography. The angle is measured at the apex of the usable

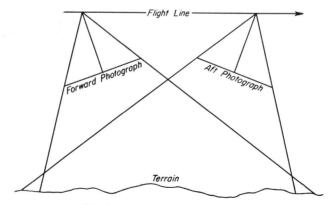

FIG. 1–3. Convergent photography.

cone of rays entering the lens of the camera. A normal angle is one between 50° and 70°. In wide-angle photography the usable apex angle is between approximately 80° and 100°. Conventional wide-angle precision cameras have an angular coverage of about 90° or slightly less. The angular coverage of ultra wide-angle photography ranges between 100° and 130°. Photographs having relatively narrow angular coverage are taken for purposes of military intelligence and for other photo interpretation. These photographs are not used in the preparation of maps, but are excellent for use in the construction of mosaics if taken expressly for that purpose.

1–3. Solution of Photogrammetric Problems

Because photogrammetry is basically a science of measurement, almost every problem involves some measurement of images. The problem may be solved by geometry, trigonometry, or analytics, the arithmetic being based on the use of the measurements together with known factors surrounding the problem. Problems involving the determination of the space positions of discrete points in space, whether in aerial, space, or terrestrial photogrammetry, are solved by analytics. The photographic scale, flying heights, ground distances, and elevations may be determined by geometry.

Many problems in photogrammetry are approached on a purely graphical basis. In Chapter 6 is discussed the process of obtaining horizontal control for photographs by graphical methods. The construction of mosaics can be considered as a graphical solution to the problem of assembling a series of aerial photographs in their proper positions.

The majority of photogrammetric problems are solved by instrumentation which combines optical and mechanical devices to produce an analog solution. In Chapter 12 are discussed stereoscopic plotting instruments which are used to produce topographic maps as well as to obtain and extend ground control or to determine the space positions of objects that have been photographed. The analytical, graphical, and instrumental methods are quite often combined in a given photogrammetric process.

1–4. Making Linear Measurements on Photographs

Both linear measurements and angular measurements can be made on a photograph. A linear measurement is made between consecutive points as a photographic distance, or from an axis to a point. Distances to a point from a pair of axes are the photographic coordinates of the point. Measurements can be made on the original negative, on a paper photograph made from the negative, or on a photograph printed from the negative onto a sensitized glass plate. The negative itself may be a sensitized emulsion on a glass plate or on a flexible film base, the type depending on the camera.

Before a measurement is made between two points, the points may be identified by lightly pricking through the emulsion of the negative or through the photograph with a fine needle at their precise positions. If the points are satisfactorily identified by the appearance of their images as seen under magnification, identification by pricking may be unnecessary. When a simple scale is used to measure the coordinates of points on a photograph, the photographic axes must be marked on the negative or the positive. This is done by lightly indenting the emulsion by drawing a fine needle along a straightedge aligned with the *fiducial marks* on the photograph which define these coordinate axes. (See Chapter 2.) Distances on a photograph are measured with greatest facility by placing the photograph on a light table equipped preferably with cold light tubes. The lines identifying the coordinate axes then show plainly as fine scratches, and the pricked image points appear as fine pin points of light.

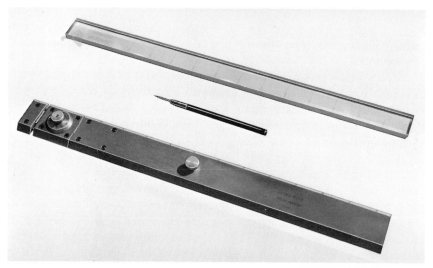

FIG. 1–4. Scales used for measuring on photographs.

Two types of scales for making measurements are shown in Fig. 1–4. The glass scale is marked at every inch, and an extra inch at the zero end is graduated in hundredths. The fine markings are etched on the bottom face of the scale to eliminate the effect of parallax between the photograph and the graduations. If the points have been pricked satisfactorily, a distance can be estimated to the nearest 0.002 in. with ease under magnification.

The metal scale, if properly calibrated for index error, also gives excellent results. There is a V-notch at every inch and in the extra subdivided inch at every tenth of an inch. This extra inch can be moved through an entire tenth of an inch parallel with the scale by turning the dial, which is graduated into 100 divisions. Since one complete rotation of the dial moves the end of the scale through 0.10 in., each graduation on the dial represents 0.001 in. A pin point of light or a fine etched line appearing on the photograph can be centered in the V-notches with great facility. So the scale is ideal for photographic measurements. The index error should be checked from time to time to prevent any otherwise unknown error from affecting the measurements.

The scales shown in Fig. 1–5 are graduated on the bottom face of a glass strip which is fixed to the plastic frame. The scale is graduated to either 0.1 mm or 0.005 in., with the graduations continuous throughout the length of the scale. The scale is viewed through 7-diameter magnifiers which slide in grooves in the frame. A distance between two pricked points is thus obtained by reading the positions of the points with respect to the scale and subtracting the two readings.

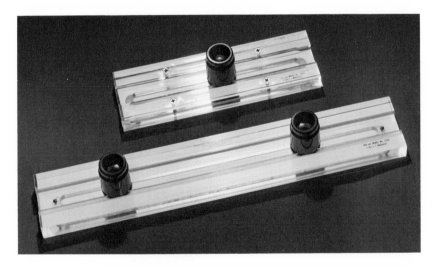

Fig. 1–5. Gurley rapid comparator. (Courtesy of W. and L.E. Gurley Company.)

If the measurement of a photographic distance is repeated several times with a scale of a type illustrated in Fig. 1–4 and Fig. 1–5, all the values should agree with one another. This agreement is to be expected because the random errors involved in the measurements should be smaller than the least reading of the scale. The limiting accuracy of a scaled measurement is, in general, one-half the least reading of the scale, provided that the last figure in the measurement has not been estimated.

If the last figure has been obtained by estimation to one-tenth of a scale division, then the limiting accuracy of a measurement is somewhat smaller than one-half the least reading.

1—5. Comparator

A refined type of measuring device designed expressly for making measurements on photographs is shown in Fig. 1–6. This instrument is known as a *comparator*. Three motions are incorporated in the comparator. One motion allows the photograph holder, or stage, to be rotated in azimuth and is provided with a slow-motion screw for fine adjustments. The other two motions allow the stage to be transported along two pairs of mutually perpendicular ways. These two movements are actuated by precision lead screws turned by hand wheels, the peripheries of which are graduated to read the advance of the lead screw to 0.001 mm, or 1 micron. A microscope containing a set of cross hairs is mounted above the stage so that its optical axis is perpendicular to the plane of travel of the stage.

Fɪɢ. 1-6. Mann comparator. (Courtesy of David Mann Co.)

To measure a photographic distance between two points, the photograph is placed on the stage, which is lighted from below, and the stage is rotated until the two points are approximately aligned with one pair of ways. By moving the photograph back and forth along this pair of ways and using a slow-motion adjustment of the stage rotation, the two points are made to coincide with the cross hairs of the microscope. This procedure aligns the line to be measured with the direction of travel of the stage.

One point is brought on the cross hairs, and the main-scale reading of the comparator and the drum reading are recorded. The second point is then brought on the cross hairs, and the readings are again recorded. The difference between the two readings is the length of the line in millimeters.

When it is desired to measure the coordinates of a point, the photograph is placed in the stage and the stage is rotated and adjusted so that one of the photo axes is parallel with one set of ways. This adjustment is made with reference to fiducial marks which appear on the photograph. The y-reading of the x-axis fiducial marks and the x-reading of the y-axis fiducial marks are taken by bringing the marks under the microscope. In this way the values of the x-reading and y-reading for the origin of the photo axes are found. The points to be located are next brought under the microscope, and the readings of the x-scale and drum and the y-scale and drum are observed and recorded. The coordinate readings of the origin are then subtracted from the coordinate readings of the points to give the point coordinates with respect to an origin of $x=0$, $y=0$. Typical comparator readings are shown in the accompanying tabulation. The readings have been reduced so that the intersection of the photographic axes is the origin of coordinates.

COMPARATOR READINGS AND PHOTOGRAPHIC COORDINATES

Point	x-reading (mm)	y-reading (mm)	x-coordinate (mm)	y-coordinate (mm)
x-axis mark		122.414		0.000
y-axis mark	119.816		0.000	
1	94.110	29.552	− 25.706	− 92.862
2	42.326	182.502	− 77.490	+ 60.088
3	178.212	164.416	+ 58.396	+ 42.002

The comparator is the basic measuring instrument for computing photogrammetric problems analytically. In practice, more than one set of readings are taken on each point to eliminate as much as possible the chance for sizable random errors. Also, readings on the two fiducial marks defining the y-axis are never the same because of the virtual impossibility of setting the marks defining the two axes exactly 90° apart. (See Chapter 2.) Consequently, the average of the x-readings of the two y-axis fiducial marks is adopted as the x-reading of the y-axis.

A comparator of similar design to that shown in Fig. 1–6, but with an altogether different external appearance is shown in Fig. 1–7. The opera-

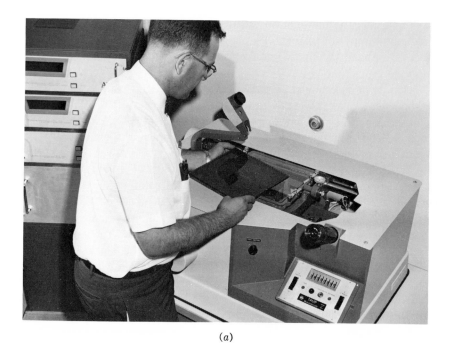

(a)

(b)

Fig. 1–7. OMI-Nistri TA1/P comparator. (Courtesy of OMI Corp.)

tor is shown in Fig. 1–7(a) placing the photographic plate onto the stage in preparation for measurement of coordinates. In Fig. 1–7(b), the operator is at the viewing microscope and controlling the position of the stage and microscope objective by means of handwheels. The readings are automatically read out and recorded. The automatic recording of coordinate values, adapted to many types of photogrammetric instruments, has several advantages. First, the system eliminates human mistakes; second, it increases the speed of reading points; and third, it presents the data in a form ready for data reduction in a computer (e.g., punched cards, perforated tape, etc).

Quite often, it becomes essential to mark a point on one photograph for comparator measurement and to precisely transfer the point to an adjacent photograph for comparator measurement. The instrument shown in Fig. 1–8 and known as the Wild PUG point transfer device centers on a

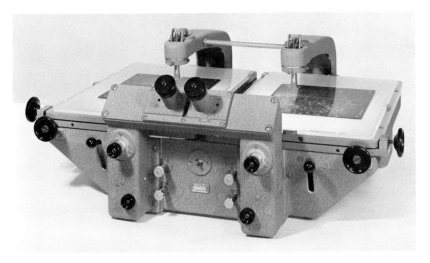

Fig. 1–8. PUG point transfer device. (Courtesy of Wild-Heerbrugg Instruments, Inc.)

point on two adjacent photographs by means of stereoscopic viewing of the point. (See Chapter 7.) When the centering has been perfected, a small drill approximately 0.1 mm in diameter drills a hole through the emulsion of each photograph. The operator can then verify the accuracy of the position of the point on each photograph by viewing the two drill holes stereoscopically.

The point-marking device shown in Fig. 1–9 is used in conjunction with a separate stereoscope for marking and transfering points in prepara-

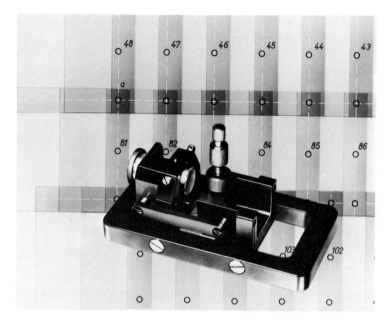

FIG. 1–9.   Zeiss point marker. (Courtesy of Carl Zeiss, Oberkochen.)

tion for comparator measurement.   Its function is similar to that of the PUG device.

1—6. Stereocomparator

If the photographic coordinates of points are to be measured on successive photographs without resorting to some form of point transfer instrument, a *stereocomparator* is employed.   The stereocomparator shown in Fig. 1–10 contains two photograph stages each containing X- and Y-lead screws for reading the position of a point on both photographs simultaneously.   The measuring principle is the same as that of the comparator of Fig. 1–6.   In the instrument shown in Fig. 1–10, provision is made for automatic readout and recording of the screw readings.

The measuring principle of the stereocomparator shown in Fig. 1–11 is different from that of those shown in Figs. 1–6 and 1–10.   In this instrument, the position of a point appearing on each photograph is located by reference to a pair of precise grids on glass rather than rotations of a lead screw.   The grid spacing is 5 mm.   Thus, the absolute positional accuracy of a point need be controlled in an area only 5 mm square rather than over the entire area of the photograph.   Also since both grid and photograph are on glass, temperature fluctuations are not as serious as

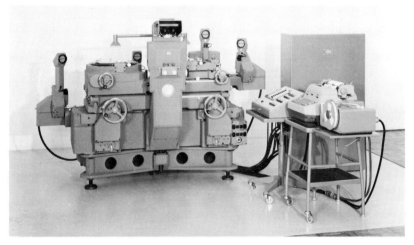

FIG. 1–10. Wild STK-1 stereocomparator. (Courtesy of Wild-Heerbrugg Instruments, Inc.)

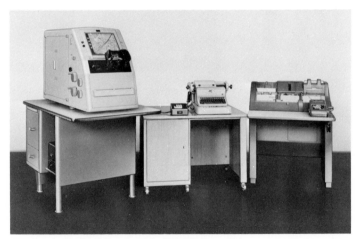

FIG. 1–11. Zeiss PSK stereocomparator. (Courtesy of Carl Zeiss, Oberkochen.)

with metal lead screws. This instrument also contains automatic coordinate readout facilities.

The stereocomparator shown in Fig. 1–12 contains three stages. This design allows a point appearing on one photograph to be identified and measured on the photographs lying both to the right and to the left (see Sec. 4–1). This instrument contains automatic coordinate readout facilities.

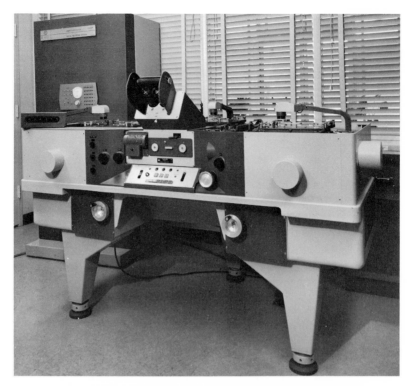

Fig. 1–12.   OMI-Nistri TA-3P stereocomparator. (Courtesy of OMI Corp.)

1–7. Making Angular Measurements on Photographs

Angles are measured at the perspective center of the photograph, as point p in Fig. 1–13, between the lines through that center and two points, between a horizontal plane and the line through the center and a point, or between a vertical plane and the line through the center and a point. In Fig. 1–13, the line $b'oa'$ is a horizon line on a terrestrial photograph. The line po is the optical axis of the photograph which is here assumed to be a horizontal line. The horizontal angle formed between the lines pb and po is $\angle\ b'po$. The horizontal angle between the lines po and pa is $\angle\ opa'$. If the principal distance po is known, these two angles can be determined by measuring the coordinates of the two points a and b, and applying principles of trigonometry. The vertical angles bpb' and $a'pa$ can also be computed by trigonometry.

Angles may be measured directly in an instrument called a *photogoniometer*. In principle, this instrument is similar to a transit or a theodolite in that it contains a horizontal circle and a vertical circle. A photograph to be used for the measurements is placed in a frame in front

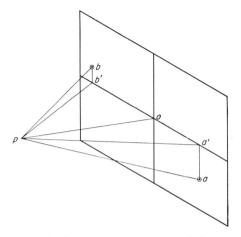

FIG. 1–13. Angles at perspective center of photograph.

of the telescope of the goniometer and is oriented to conform with its orientation at the moment of exposure. The perspective center of the photograph is located at the center of the goniometer, that is, at the intersection of its horizontal and vertical axes. In effect, there is recreated a view of the landscape in front of the goniometer identical to that which

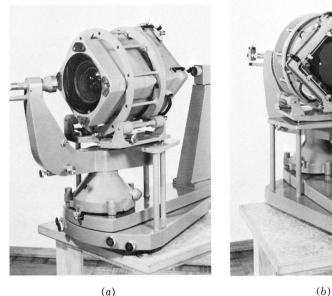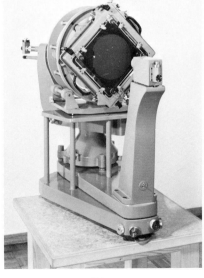

(a)   (b)

FIG. 1–14. Goniometer. (Courtesy of Wild-Heerbrugg Instruments, Inc.)

would be seen at the camera exposure station in the field. The telescope of the goniometer contains cross hairs similar to those of a theodolite. The operator directs the line of sight to the various points on the photograph and reads the horizontal and vertical circles for each pointing.

A goniometer used to measure lens distortion (see Chapter 2) is shown in Fig. 1–14. A glass plate containing a calibrated grid is placed in the focal plane of the lens being tested. The front perspective center of the lens is placed on the axis of rotation of the goniometer telescope. Sighting through the lens at the targets on the plate allows the angles between these targets to be measured by reading the goniometer circle. In this instrument, no provision is made for measuring vertical angles. Instead, the entire camera assembly to be tested is rotated 90°, thus bring-

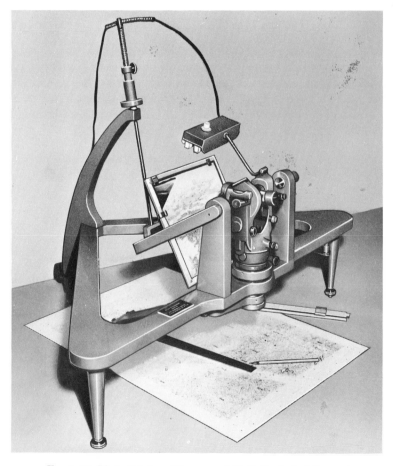

FIG. 1–15. Photoalidade. (Courtesy of U. S. Geological Survey.)

ing a heretofore vertical plane into a horizontal position. Thus, only one goniometer circle is required.

In Fig. 1–15 is shown an instrument called a *photoalidade*. This instrument was originally developed to measure horizontal and vertical angles on oblique photographs, as shown in the illustration, but it can be used also with terrestrial photographs. The only basic difference between the photoalidade and the photogoniometer is the addition of the alidade blade mounted directly beneath the theodolite of the photoalidade. The blade rotates in azimuth as the alidade is rotated. Thus, lines representing horizontal directions to points on the photograph may be drawn on the supporting table beneath. The photoalidade is used to solve problems of the intersection of horizontal lines graphically.

1–8. Instrumentation

The graduated scale, the comparator, and the goniometer are the basic instruments used for making photogrammetric measurements. Virtually any problem in photogrammetry can be solved to varying degrees of accuracy by using these basic instruments. However, the labor involved in compiling a topographic map, for example, by using only the basic instruments would be so ponderous as to be impractical. Specialized instruments, such as the stereoscopic plotting instruments discussed in Chapter 12, have been developed for automatic or semiautomatic solution of various problems in photogrammetry. These instruments will be described as the problems are discussed in subsequent chapters.

Bibliography

AMERICAN SOCIETY OF PHOTOGRAMMETRY. *Manual of Photogrammetry.* New York: Pitman Publishing Corp., 1944.

AMERICAN SOCIETY OF PHOTOGRAMMETRY. *Manual of Photogrammetry.* Menasha, Wisc.: George Banta Co., 1952.

AMERICAN SOCIETY OF PHOTOGRAMMETRY. *Manual of Photogrammetry* (Menasha, Wisc.: George Banta Co., 1966), Chapters 1, 10, 20, and 22.

AMERICAN SOCIETY OF PHOTOGRAMMETRY. *Manual of Photographic Interpretation.* Menasha, Wisc.: George Banta Co., 1960.

ANSTIS, A. N. "An Automatic Recording Stereocomparator," *Photogrammetric Record,* Vol. III (1960), p. 298.

ARTHUR, D. W. G. "Lunar Cartography and Photogrammetry," *Photogrammetric Record,* Vol. III (1961), p. 408.

BODNAR, B. J. "Instrumentation for Analytical Triangulation," *Photogrammetric Engineering,* Vol. XXIII (1957), p. 957.

BRANDENBERGER, A. J. "Photogrammetry, Navigation, and Space Problems," *Photogrammetric Engineering,* Vol. XXVII (1961), p. 41.

———. "The Use of Baker-Nunn Cameras for Tracking of Artificial Earth Satellites," *Photogrammetric Engineering,* Vol. XXVIII (1962), p. 727.

BRUCKLACHER, W. "Instruments for Marking Natural Points and Producing Artificial Points in the Preparation of Aerial Photography and Aerotriangulation," *Photogrammetric Engineering,* Vol. XXIX (1963), p. 800.

CANNELL, W. D. "The New Air Force Photoalidade," *Photogrammetric Engineering,* Vol. XXI (1955), p. 664.

CHURCH, E., and QUINN, A. O. *Elements of Photogrammetry,* Syracuse University Press, 1948.

DE METER, E. R. "Automatic Point Identification Marking and Measuring Instrument," *Photogrammetric Engineering,* Vol. XXVIII (1962), p. 82.

DVORIN, M. "The C-D Method of Point Marking," *Photogrammetric Engineering,* Vol. XXXII (1966), p. 1016.

GUGEL, R. A. "Comparator Calibration," *Photogrammetric Engineering,* Vol. XXXI (1965), p. 853.

HALLERT, BERTIL. *Photogrammetry.* New York: McGraw-Hill Book Co., 1960.

———. "Test Measurements in Comparators and Tolerances for Such Instruments," *Photogrammetric Engineering,* Vol. XXIX (1963), p. 301.

HARLEY, I. A. "Some Notes on Stereocomparators," *Photogrammetric Record,* Vol. IV (1963), p. 218.

HERNDON, R. E. "Aerospace Cartography," *Surveying and Mapping,* Vol. XXI (1961), p. 31.

KRISHNAMURTY, V., and SMIALOWSKI, A. J. "Investigations Into the Accuracy of the N.R.C. Monocomparator," *Canadian Surveyor,* Vol. XX (1966), p. 300.

LANDON, DAVID. "History of Photogrammetry in the United States," *Photogrammetric Engineering,* Vol. XVIII (1952), p. 854.

LOEWEN, E. G. "Coordinate Measurement—The Elusive Micron," *Photogrammetric Engineering,* Vol. XXX (1964), p. 962.

LOWMAN, PAUL D. "Space Photography—A Review," *Photogrammetric Engineering,* Vol. XXXI (1965), p. 76.

MERRITT, E. L. "The MM 100 Optical Comparator," *Photogrammetric Engineering,* Vol. XXI (1955), p. 56.

———, and LUNDAHL, A. C. "A Reconsideration of Terrestrial Photogrammetry," Part I, *Photogrammetric Engineering,* Vol. XIII (1947), p. 295.

———. Ibid., Part II, Vol. XIV (1948), p. 561.

NORWICKI, A. L. "Topographic Lunar Mapping," *Canadian Surveyor,* Vol. XVI (1962), p. 141.

O'NEILL, H., and NAGEL, W. "The O'Neill-Nagel Light Table," *Photogrammetric Engineering,* Vol. XVIII (1952), p. 134.

Photogrammetric Engineering, Vol. XIII, No. 4, 1947.

ROSENFIELD, G. H. "Calibration of a Precision Coordinate Comparator," *Photogrammetric Engineering,* Vol. XXIX (1963), p. 161.

SCHMID, H. H. "Accuracy Aspects of a World-Wide Passive Satellite Triangulation System," *Photogrammetric Engineering,* Vol. XXXI (1965), p. 104.

———. "Precision Photogrammetry a Tool of Geodesy," *Photogrammetric Engineering,* Vol. XXVII (1961), p. 779.

SCHWIDEFSKY, K. *An Outline of Photogrammetry.* New York: Pitman Publishing Corp., 1959.

SMAILOWSKI, A. J. "N.R.C. Monocomparator," *Canadian Surveyor,* Vol. XVII (1963), p. 224.

SMITH, H. T. U. *Aerial Photographs and Their Applications,* New York: Appleton-Century-Crofts Co., 1943.

STANTON, J. W. "The Wild A-7 Autograph as a Comparator," *Photogrammetric Engineering,* Vol. XXVIII (1962), p. 455.

STREES, L. V. "A Satellite's View of the Earth," *Photogrammetric Engineering,* Vol. XXVII (1961), p. 37.

TAGGART, C. I. "Satellite Photography," *Canadian Surveyor,* Vol. XVIII (1964). p. 105.

TRAGER, H. "The New Zeiss Stereocomparator," *Photogrammetric Engineering,* Vol. XXVII (1961), p. 112.

U. S. COAST and GEODETIC SURVEY. "Topographic Manual," Part II, *Special Publication* No. 249. Washington, D. C.: Government Printing Office, 1949.

VON GRUBER, O. *Photogrammetry.* Boston: American Photographic Publishing Co., 1942.

WILLIAMS, O. W. "ANNA Satellite Yields Photogrammetric Parameters," *Photogrammetric Engineering,* Vol. XXXI (1965), p. 340.

ZELLER, M. *Textbook of Photogrammetry.* London: H. K. Lewis and Co., Ltd., 1952.

Aerial Cameras 2

2–1. Requirements of Camera

Since the first portion of this text is concerned with aerial photogrammetry, the aerial camera will be described in this chapter to the exclusion of the terrestrial camera. The two types of cameras perform the same function, which is that of taking pictures, but their requirements are quite different. The more important differences in the requirements of the two types of cameras are as follows.

The terrestrial camera remains stationary during the exposure. So a slow-speed, fine-grained emulsion can be used for the film. The aerial camera is in motion during the exposure, and the exposure must therefore be of as short a duration as possible. Such a camera needs a fast lens; a high-speed, efficient, dependable shutter; and high-speed emulsion for the film. As a rule the terrestrial camera does not need a shutter, a lens cap being sufficient to control exposure time. However, for many applications of non-topographic photogrammetry in which the camera is stationary, the phenomenon being measured is in a state of continual change. Water waves generated in a hydraulics laboratory is an example. In such a situation, the terrestrial camera must be equipped with a shutter. Furthermore, the system may require two cameras to be triggered simultaneously in order to photographically freeze the phenomenon to be measured in three dimensions.

Because aerial photographs must be taken in rapid succession, a magazine is required to hold large rolls of film or a great number of photographic plates. Furthermore, this magazine must be an integral part of the camera. Terrestrial photographs are taken at the convenience of the photographer. Consequently, the plate holders may be stored separately from the camera, and there is no necessity for an intricately designed magazine.

The camera is the instrument which gathers the data necessary for subsequent photogrammetric processes and operations. It can be considered as a surveying instrument of great precision. The orientation of critical parts of the camera with one another must be determined by calibration before the data can be used. As indicated in Sec. 1–7, horizontal and vertical angles can be measured at the perspective center of the photograph. Thus, when a photograph has been made from an aircraft flying over the terrain, it is equivalent to having a transit occupy the exposure station and measure an infinite number of horizontal and vertical angles to points on the terrain and record them for subsequent use. Although the photograph will not in general give results so accurately as will the transit record, the photographic record of the terrain is nevertheless more complete.

2–2. Component Parts of Aerial Camera

To describe in detail the various parts of a camera, or to describe the wide variety of precision cameras used at present, is outside the scope or intent of this book. This chapter is intended to give to the student information concerning cameras which is needed to understand the principles of photogrammetry set forth in subsequent chapters.

The principal parts of the camera are: 1) the *lens assembly*, which includes the camera lens, the diaphragm, the shutter, and the filter; 2) the *focal plane;* 3) the *camera cone;* 4) the *camera body;* 5) the *drive mechanism;* and 6) the *magazine.* These parts, except for the drive mechanism, are shown in Fig. 2–1, which is a schematic diagram of an

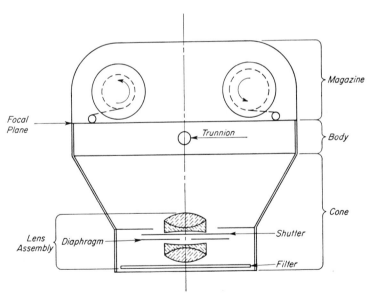

Fig. 2–1. Schematic diagram of aerial camera.

aerial camera. Several different camera designs exist for bringing the component parts of a camera together to make it operate as a precision camera.

2–3. Lens Assembly

The function of the lens is to gather a selected bundle of light rays for each of an infinite number of points on the terrain and to bring each bundle to focus as a point in the focal plane, as illustrated for three points in Fig. 2–2. Points A, O, and C in the object space appear as point images a, o, and c in the plane of focus in the image space. Because the aircraft is at a considerable distance from the terrain, and because the

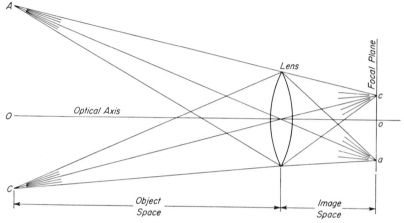

Fig. 2–2. Focusing a point as an image.

diameter of each bundle of rays entering and passing through the lens is small, all the rays in one bundle in the object space are for all practical purposes parallel with one another, and the point is considered to be at an infinite distance from the lens. Hence, the focal plane of the aerial camera can be fixed at one location. The aerial camera is thus a fixed-focus camera, the focus being set for infinity.

In Fig. 2–3 is shown a simple lens system composed of four elements, with an air space between the two doublets. The optical axis is the line Oo. The lens system contains two principal planes which are normal to the optical axis and are pierced by the optical axis at the two cardinal points N and N'. These are called the *nodal points* of the lens system. Point N, normally on the object-space side, is called the front nodal point; point N', normally on the image-space side, is called the rear nodal point, or emergent nodal point. The significance of the nodal points is as follows: If a ray of light in the object space is directed at the front nodal point, it is so bent, or refracted, by the lens system that it appears to emerge from the rear nodal point without having undergone a change in direction. The paths of two such rays are shown in Fig. 2–3 from A to a and from C to c. In geometric optics, the common practice is to represent an entire bundle of rays by the single ray which is directed

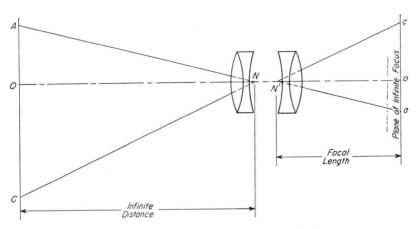

Fɪɢ. 2–3. Simple lens system showing nodal points.

toward the nodal point. This is called the chief ray for the point. Thus, the rays Aa and Cc are chief rays. The ray Oo is also a chief ray. Since it coincides with the optical axis, it is also called the axial ray.

If points A, O, and C in Fig. 2–3 lie far enough away to be considered as lying at infinity, the images a, o, and c of the three points will come to focus as points in the focal plane which lies at a distance $N'o$ from the rear nodal point, where the distance $N'o$ is the focal length of the lens. The *focal length* is defined as the distance from the rear nodal point to the plane of infinite focus. In photogrammetry, the focal length is not directly measured. Instead, it is arrived at by computation based on calibration data, as described in Sec. 2–11.

When a lens designer computes the properties of a lens for a modern photogrammetric camera, he must take into consideration all the various aberrations characteristic of a lens. He must design for an effective coverage of a rather wide angle; he must design a fast lens; and he must design for a certain minimum resolution of the lens throughout the effective area of coverage in the focal plane. Resolution is here defined as the number of black lines separated by white spaces of equal width which may be identified in a 1-mm distance after rays have passed through the lens system and been registered in the focal plane of the camera. In photographic parlance, resolution is a measure of the "sharpness" or "crispness" of a lens.

Because of the lengthy computations involved in the design of a lens, the manner of grinding lenses, the human limitations in assembling the lens system, and other factors, a lens will invariably exhibit a certain amount of residual distortion. Residual distortion is simply the inability of the lens to bring an image to focus in its theoretically correct position in the focal plane.

Residual distortions are of two forms, radial distortion and tangential distortion. Each has an effect on different photogrammetric processes. Fortunately, because of the nature of design and manufacture of lenses, both of these distortions show a remarkable symmetry, and they can be measured and corrected, either by instrumentation or by computation. In general, radial distortion is the greater.

In Fig. 2–4 the ray from A, after passing through the lens, does not follow its original direction to a', but is bent outward from the optical axis to a. The amount of the distortion is $a'a$, and it is considered positive. The ray from C has been distorted inward from c' to c. Hence, the

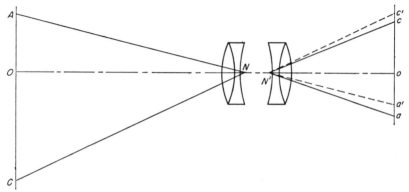

FIG. 2–4. Radial distortion.

distortion $c'c$ is a negative distortion. The ray Oo, being the axial ray, has suffered no distortion. The distortions appear in the focal plane along radial lines from the center of the focal plane at o through points a and c. So the designation radial distortion is used.

Tangential distortion is the displacement of the image of a point normal to a radial line through the point. As shown in Fig. 2–5, the image d has suffered no tangential distortion; image e has suffered a clockwise tangential distortion; image f has suffered a counterclockwise tangential distortion. This type of lens distortion seems to result from faulty centering of the lens elements during assembly.

Some of the lenses used in precision aerial cameras are shown in cross section in Fig. 2–6. The Bausch and Lomb *Metrogon* wide-angle lens

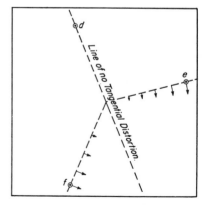

FIG. 2–5. Tangential distortion.

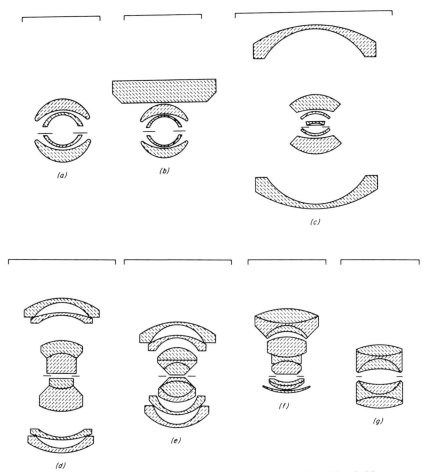

Fig. 2-6. Sections through aerial camera lenses. (a) Bausch and Lomb Metrogon, f/6.3, 93° coverage; (b) Zeiss Topogon, f/6.3, 93° coverage; (c) Zeiss Pleogon, f/5.6, 93° coverage; (d) Wild Aviogon, f/5.6, 93° coverage; (e) Wild Super-Aviogon, f/5.6, 120° coverage; (f) Wild Aviotar, f/4.6, 60° coverage; (g) Goertz Aerotar, f/6.8, 75° coverage.

with 93° coverage, was the most common lens in use in the United States until about 1955. Its radial distortion is substantially greater than that of the *Topogon* lens. The Zeiss *Pleogon* and the Wild *Aviogon* lenses have remarkably low distortion considering their wide angular coverage. These two lenses are used for the majority of mapping in the United States at present. The *Super-Aviogon* lens is used at present for small scale mapping. The great coverage of this lens is its chief advantage. The *Aviotar* and *Aerotar* lenses, both containing negligible distortion, are examples of normal-angle lenses.

The diaphragm of the lens assembly is the physical opening of the lens system. It is made up of a series of leaves which can be rotated to increase or decrease the size of the opening. It is located between the elements at approximately the mid-position, being placed there to eliminate certain aberrations of the lens. The function of the diaphragm is to restrict the size of the bundle of rays which may pass through the lens and in this way to control the amount of light striking the emulsion in the focal plane. Generally, lens resolution is greatest when the diaphragm is wide open. Also, shutter speeds may be correspondingly greater as the diaphragm opening becomes larger.

The shutter is located between the lens elements and as close to the plane of the diaphragm as physical limitations will permit. The shutter controls the interval of time during which light is allowed to pass through the lens. In aerial cameras this interval varies from 1/100 second to 1/1000 second. The settings of both shutter speed and diaphragm opening depend on the amount of available light reflected from the terrain, and on the speed of the film or plate emulsion. The shutter is usually set for a fast speed to prevent blurring of the image caused by camera vibrations and the forward motion of the aircraft.

The filter, although not actually a part of the physical lens assembly, is included in this discussion because it is involved in the passage of light from the terrain to the focal plane. Stray light in the atmosphere caused by haze and moisture is predominantly blue and violet. These are colors to which photographic emulsions are rather sensitive. If stray light is not filtered out, therefore, it causes a clouded effect on the film and reduces the definition of the terrain images. The filter, placed in front of the lens to filter out the blue and violet light, is a piece of colored glass, both surfaces of which are plane and presumably parallel with one another. The color varies from yellow through orange to deep red, the choice depending on the intensity of filtration desired. An incidental benefit from use of the filter is the protection afforded the front surface of the lens from flying particles which might damage the lens or reduce its effectiveness.

2–4. Camera Cone

The functions served by the camera cone depend on the camera design. It supports the entire lens assembly, including the filter, and prevents any light except that transmitted by the lens from striking the focal plane. In some cameras the cone together with the camera body, holds the lens at the proper distance from the focal plane, which is then defined by the upper surface of the camera body. In other cameras the cone supports an inner frame called the inner cone, or spider. This inner cone, shown in Fig. 2–7, holds the lens assembly and also contains the

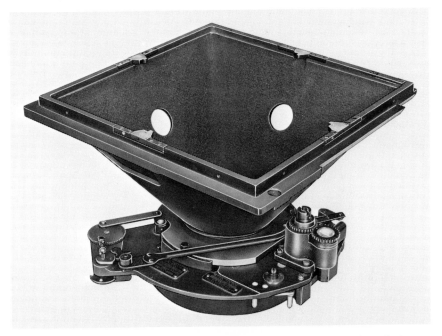

FIG. 2–7. Inner cone showing lens assembly at bottom and fiducial marks in upper surface. (Courtesy of Fairchild Camera & Instrument Corp.)

fiducial marks which define the coordinate axes of the photograph.

The inner cone is made of a metal with a relatively low coefficient of thermal expansion so that the lens, the lens axis, the focal plane defined by the upper surfaces of the fiducial marks, and the fiducial marks themselves are all held in the same relative positions at most operating temperatures. The relative positions of the above-mentioned components fix the elements of interior orientation of the camera, the negatives, or the photographs. The inner cone is calibrated as a unit to determine these orientation elements.

2–5. Camera Body

The camera body can be an integral part of the camera cone, or detachable as shown in Fig. 2–8. If the camera does not contain an inner cone, the camera body, together with the cone, fixes the position of the lens with respect to the focal plane. In some types of cameras, the fiducial marks are located in the upper surface of the body and the body defines the focal plane. The cone and the body must then be one integral part in order to preserve interior orientation once the camera is calibrated.

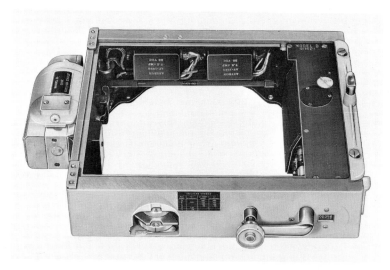

Fig. 2-8. Detachable camera body. (Courtesy of Fairchild Camera & Instrument Corp.)

The camera body houses the drive mechanism, the camera level bubble, the hand-turned operating crank, the handles, and other appurtenances shown in Fig. 2–8. It also provides the support for the film magazine.

2–6. Camera Drive Mechanism

The drive mechanism provides the motion necessary to wind and trip the shutter, to operate the vacuum system or pressure-plate system for flattening the film in the focal plane, and to wind the film or change plates between exposures. It is driven either manually by means of a hand crank and tripping lever or by a small electric motor which derives its power from the aircraft. A complete cycle of the drive mechanism includes releasing the film-flattening device, advancing the film (or changing the plate), winding the shutter, actuating the film-flattening device, and finally tripping the shutter. The frequency of this cycle depends on the forward speed of the aircraft, the flying height, and the desired amount of overlap between successive photographs. (See Sec. 4–1.)

2–7. Magazine

The magazine serves to hold the exposed and unexposed film (or plates), advance the necessary amount of film (or change plates) between exposures, and house the film-flattening device. The magazine is detachable on most cameras and is equipped with a dark slide for covering the focal-plane opening when the magazine is to be detached outside a dark-room. The necessary amount of film is metered out by a roller, which is turned as the film is advanced. A fixed number of turns of the roller disengages the film advance mechanism at the proper time. Power for operation of the movable parts of the magazine is supplied from the drive mechanism through a coupling.

In a precision aerial camera that uses film, there are two methods for keeping the film flat in the focal plane during exposure. The first method is by inserting a piece of optical glass in the focal-plane opening so that the upper surface of the glass itself is the focal plane. When the unexposed film has been drawn into place over the glass, a pressure plate from above is pressed down onto the back surface of the film. Small holes in the pressure plate allow the air to escape from between the film and the pressure plate. After exposure, the pressure plate is released to allow the film to be advanced. With such an arrangement, the glass plate becomes a part of the lens system, and the lens must be designed to allow for the thickness of the plate.

The second method of keeping the film flat is by applying a vacuum to a ribbed plate which is crisscrossed with tiny grooves. The grooves lead to small conduits in the plate, and all the conduits lead off to an external vacuum line. A cross section of the vacuum back is shown in Fig. 2–9. With the vacuum back raised, the film is drawn through the focal-plane opening. The vacuum back is then lowered, forcing the film down against the focal-plane frame. This frame is either the upper surface of the camera body or the upper surface of the inner cone, depending on the camera. It contains the fiducial marks. With a vacuum now applied to the vacuum line so that the air is exhausted from the conduits and grooves in the vacuum back, the film is drawn up flat against the lower surface, or platen, of the vacuum back. Once the exposure has been made and the vacuum broken, the vacuum back is raised to allow the film to be advanced for the next exposure.

In a camera which uses glass plates instead of film, flatness of the emulsion is maintained by the rigidity of the glass plate itself. The

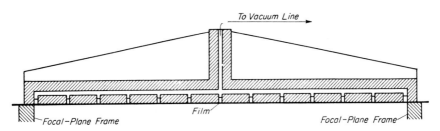

Fɪɢ. 2–9. Vacuum back.

glass plates used in precision aerial cameras are thick enough to prevent undue flexure at the middle, this thickness increasing the durability of the plate. The magazine mechanism lowers the plate, with the emulsion side down, onto the focal-plane frame, and holds it in place by a slight pressure applied over the frame. The distinct disadvantage of glass plates is their bulk and weight as compared with the compactness and light weight of photographic film. Also the danger of breakage always exists.

2–8. Focal Plane

The focal plane, as previously mentioned, is defined by the upper surfaces of the fiducial marks together with the upper surface of the focal-plane frame. It is located at such a distance from the rear nodal point of the lens as to give the best possible over-all image definition. The actual fixed distance between the rear nodal point and the focal plane in a camera may not coincide with the focal length as defined previously. The focal length is determined by calibrating the camera after assembly.

2–9. Variations in Cameras and Features

In the foregoing sections are described the general features of a single-lens precision aerial camera. This type of camera, which is used primarily for obtaining photographs for use in topographic mapping, has a focal

Fig. 2–10. Wild RC8 wide-angle camera. (Courtesy of Wild-Heerbrugg Instruments, Inc.)

Fig. 2–11. Zeiss RMK15/23 wide-angle camera with interval-ometer. (Courtesy of Carl Zeiss, Oberkochen.)

length between 3½ and 8.25 in. The Wild RC8 and the Zeiss RMK 15/23 cameras shown in Figs. 2–10 and 2–11 contain nominal 6-in. focal length lenses and take photographs on film 9 by 9 in. in size. The lenses are respectively the Aviogon and Pleogon shown in Fig. 2–6. The Wild RC7a camera shown in Fig. 2–12 uses glass plates about 5½ by 5½ in. It is

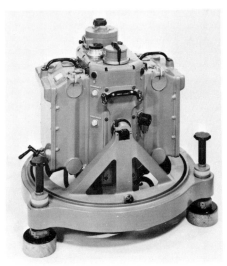

Fig. 2–12. Wild RC7a glass plate camera. (Courtesy of Wild-Heerbrugg Instruments, Inc.)

Fig. 2–13. Wild RC9 super-wide-angle
camera. (Courtesy of Wild-Heerbrugg
Instruments, Inc.)

fitted with the Aviotar lens. The Wild RC9 shown in Fig. 2–13 is the
super-wide-angle camera using the Super-Aviogon lens, and takes photographs on film 9 by 9 in. in size.

Cameras designed for military reconnaissance, for photo interpretation, and for the construction of mosaics contain lenses with focal lengths
of 12, 24, and 36 in. They are consequently narrow-angle cameras. The
requirement for precise and permanent location of the fiducial marks with
respect to the lens and the optical axis, as demanded in mapping cameras,
is not so rigorous in reconnaissance cameras. The fiducial marks in these
reconnaissance cameras are frequently located in the bottom surface of the
magazine. When so located, they are moved each time the magazine is
removed and replaced.

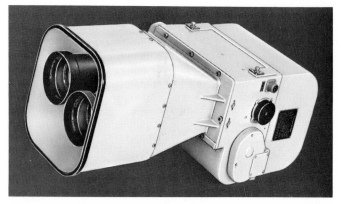

Fig. 2–14. Sonne continuous-strip camera. (Courtesy of Chi-
cago Aerial Industries.)

In Fig. 2–14 is shown an unusual reconnaissance camera which takes two continuous photographs of a strip of terrain. This is called a *continuous-strip* aerial camera. Since it contains no shutters, the lenses are open at all times. The film moves continuously past two narrow slits in the focal plane at the same rate of speed as the terrain image moves. The image movement is caused by the forward motion of the aircraft, and it depends on the flying height above the terrain. The two slits are so arranged that one lens photographs the forward view of the terrain while the second lens photographs the aft view. This camera therefore provides a continuous and different viewpoint of the terrain necessary for stereoscopic viewing of the strips. (See Chapter 7.) The resultant photographs are uninterrupted pictures of two narrow bands of the

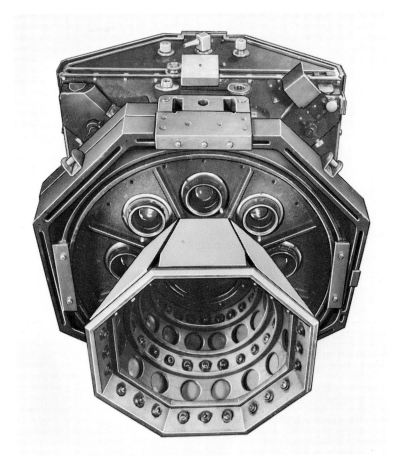

FIG. 2–15. Nine-lens camera. (Courtesy of U. S. Coast & Geodetic Survey.)

terrain. The continuous-strip camera is used for reconnaissance, but cannot be used for mapping.

Another unusual camera is the U.S. Coast and Geodetic Survey's nine-lens mapping camera shown in Fig. 2–15. A central lens photographs the terrain directly beneath the aircraft, and the resulting photograph is a near-vertical. Each of the eight mirrors arranged around the periphery of the camera is inclined to the vertical at an angle of 19°, as shown in Fig. 2–16. The eight lens axes, although mounted parallel with the axis of the central lens, are bent at the mirrors so that each one makes an angle of 38° with the vertical. All eight peripheral photographs are therefore low obliques. The total angular coverage of

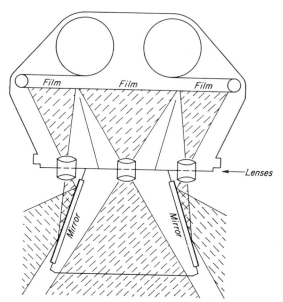

FIG. 2–16. Diagram of U. S. Coast & Geodetic
Survey 9-lens camera.

the nine lenses is 130° by 130°. Each lens has a focal length of 8.24 in. The film used in the camera is 23 in. wide, and the composite photograph after being transformed into a single near-vertical is approximately 36 in. square. The camera assembly contains a total of 45 fiducial marks. These marks are necessary to orient each of the nine separate negatives in the transformer printer when the composite photograph is made.

These are but a few variations in aerial-camera designs and features. The reader is referred to current literature found in *Photogrammetric*

Engineering, the journal of the American Society of Photogrammetry, for a more exhaustive discussion of aerial cameras.

2–10. Camera Accessories

Accessories needed for the proper functioning of an aerial camera include a viewfinder, camera mount, intervalometer, power supply, vacuum line, and in some operations a heating jacket.

The view finder is similar to a small aerial camera, but it has no shutter and no magazine. In the focal plane there is a piece of frosted glass whose dimensions are such that the area covered by the glass is the same as the area covered by the aerial camera in one exposure. The photographer views the image of the terrain on the frosted glass, and can control the interval between exposures by means of properly spaced lines ruled on the glass. The photographer can also correct for crabbing of the aerial camera (see Chapter 4) by noting the passage of the terrain image over the viewfinder's focal plane.

The camera mount is secured to the aircraft frame directly over a hole in the bottom of the fuselage. The connection between the mount and the aircraft frame is provided with sponge-rubber shock absorbers to lessen the effect of aircraft vibration on the camera. The camera is suspended in the mount by two trunnions on the sides of the camera cone or body, and is free to rotate about three axes, which are the fore-and-aft axis, a transverse axis, and the optical axis of the lens.

In recent years, camera mounts have been designed to maintain the orientation of the camera during flight. These stabilized mounts hold the camera axis nearly vertical by means of gyroscopes.

For fully automatic or semiautomatic operation of the camera, the intervalometer is connected to the power line and is set to trip the shutter at regular intervals of time corresponding to the intervals between successive exposures. When using the intervalometer, the photographer needs only to correct for crabbing and for camera tilt. Without the intervalometer, he must either use a watch to time the exposure intervals or follow the ground image as it crosses the lines ruled on the viewfinder.

In order to overcome the variation in the speed with which the image moves over the focal plane due to variation in ground elevation, some camera viewfinders are coupled to the intervalometer for continuous monitoring on the part of the photographer. (See Chapter 3.) Depending on the design, a series of lines is caused to move over the ground glass of the viewfinder at a rate controlled at the intervalometer. Also, the proper amount of overlap is set on the intervalometer. (See Chapter 4.) The photographer then continuously controls the speed of the lines to coincide with the movement of the images across the ground glass. The intervalometer then causes the camera shutter to be tripped at the proper interval.

The power supply to operate the intervalometer and the drive mechanism is obtained from the aircraft-engine generator. A vacuum line is necessary for exhausting air from the vacuum back. Some of the accessories just mentioned are shown in Fig. 2–17.

Fig. 2–17. Fairchild T-11 precision cartographic camera with accessories. (Courtesy of Fairchild Camera & Instrument Corp.)

Some aerial cameras contain a mechanism for shifting the film through a small distance during the instant of exposure. The movement of the film is made to coincide with that of the images in the focal plane caused by the forward motion of the camera during the exposure. The device for compensating for the motion of the image thus prevents blurring of a photograph taken at a relatively low flying height and at high aircraft speed.

A heating jacket is used when aerial photographs are taken in subzero temperatures, to insure proper functioning of the moving parts of the camera and to prevent inordinate stresses set up by excessive contraction of the metal components of the camera.

2–11. Camera-Calibration Data

The purpose of this section is not to describe how an aerial camera is calibrated, but to indicate what data are derived from the calibration itself. Cameras are calibrated by the camera manufacturers including the Fairchild Camera and Instrument Company, and also by the U.S. Bureau of Standards and the U.S. Geological Survey. Camera calibration is necessary before the photographs can be used in photogrammetric operations, whether these operations be analytical, graphical, or instrumental. It consists in determining 1) the focal length of the camera lens; 2) the radial distortion of the camera lens; 3) the resolution of the lens; 4) the positions of the fiducial marks with respect to the optical axis; 5) the flatness of the focal plane; and 6) the dimensions of the focal-plane opening.

The first four values are determined by measurements made on a negative plate which has been exposed through the lens when the lens is set in a certain position in front of two banks of collimators that are located in planes at right angles to each other. In the camera calibrator of the U.S. Bureau of Standards, the axes of the collimators in each bank are spaced 7.5° from one another, as illustrated in Fig. 2–18. Each bank

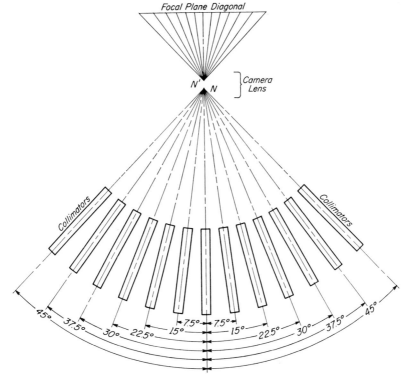

Fig. 2–18. Bank of collimators for calibrating aerial camera.

makes an exposure across each diagonal of the focal plane. A reticule at the principal focus of each collimator contains a small cross, together with a series of resolution patterns. Since the reticule is at the principal focus, the light rays are leaving the collimators and entering the camera lens along parallel paths. And since the camera lens is focused for infinity, these rays are therefore brought to focus in the focal plane of the camera.

In order to give an idea of the physical appearance of the collimators, reference is made to Fig. 2–19. These are not part of the Bureau of Standards calibrator but rather of the Wild Co. calibrator located in Heerbrugg, Switzerland. The angular coverage of this particular bank is approximately 150° which will accommodate ultra-wide-angle lenses. The arrangement for lighting and focusing each reticule can be seen in the figure.

Fig. 2–19.   Collimators of Wild camera calibrator. (Courtesy of
Wild-Heerbrugg Instruments, Inc.)

The camera is oriented so that its focal plane is exactly normal to the axis of the central collimator, and is moved parallel with the axis of the central collimator until the best average resolution is obtained in the focal plane. A sensitized plate is placed in the focal plane, and lights are arranged to expose the positions of the fiducial marks in the focal plane. An exposure is made, and the plate is developed, resulting in the generalized array shown in Fig. 2–20. Each small square contains the image of the small cross and the resolution pattern coming from the corresponding collimator.

The angle formed between lines joining opposite fiducial marks is determined by measurements on the exposed plate. In a precision camera, this angle should be between 89°59′ and 90°01′.

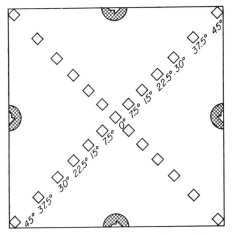

Fig. 2-20. Exposure array during calibration.

The intersection of the lines joining opposite fiducial marks is called the *center of collimation*. The fiducial marks are thus sometimes referred to as *collimation* marks. The position of the image of the small cross from the central collimator with respect to the center of collimation is determined by plate measurements of the distances a and b in Fig. 2-21. These two distances are very small and represent the amounts by which a ray of light coming from infinity and normal to the focal plane fails to strike the center of collimation.

The next point whose position is to be determined is the *principal point* of the photograph. The principal point, designated by the symbol

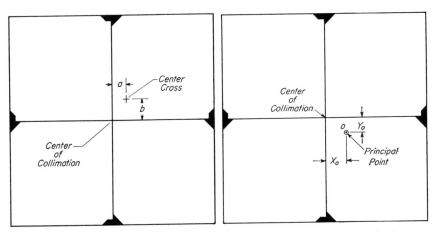

Fig. 2-21. Cross of central collimator referred to center of collimation.

Fig. 2-22. Principal point referred to center of collimation.

o, is the point where a perpendicular dropped from the rear nodal point
of the lens strikes the focal plane. Its position with respect to the image
of the small cross coming from the central collimator is computed from
measurements on the plate. Finally, its position with respect to the center
of collimation is established as the distances x_o and y_o shown in Fig. 2–22.
Since the lines joining opposite fiducial marks are the coordinate
axes of the photograph, the distances x_o and y_o are the photographic
coordinates of the principal point.

The focal length of the camera lens can be determined by measuring
the distance from the central cross to each of the four crosses coming
from the 7.5° collimators, dividing each distance by tan 7.5°, and adopting
an average of the four values. As shown in Fig. 2–23, the nodal point
subtends an angle of 7.5° between the central cross and one 7.5° cross.
The distance $N'p$, from the rear nodal point N' to the focal plane, is the
focal length, and the distances pa and pb are the distances measured to
two 7.5° crosses. Thus, the focal length f is given by the relationship

$$f = N'p = \frac{ap}{\tan 7.5°} = \frac{bp}{\tan 7.5°}$$

Averaging four computed values of f tends to compensate for certain
instrumental errors in the calibration process. The focal length thus

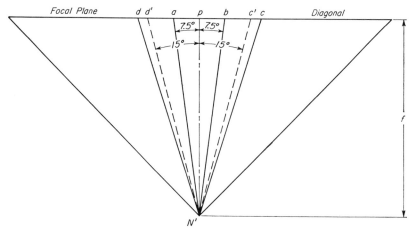

FIG. 2–23. Determination of focal length.

obtained is effective only in the central portion of the negative or photograph. Suppose that in Fig. 2–23 the rays from the 15° collimators came
to focus at c and d, rather than at their theoretically correct positions
c' and d'. These displacements of rays $N'c$ and $N'd$ are caused by radial
distortion of the lens. A focal length computed from cp/tan 15° or
dp/tan 15° would be different from that previously computed. As may

be expected, a different focal length would be obtained if the computations were based on images of the 22.5°, 30°, 37.5°, and 45° cross marks. That focal length which is effective at the center of the photograph is called the *equivalent focal length*.

Based on the equivalent focal length, the amount of distortion can be computed at each of the 15°, 22.5°, 30°, 37.5°, and 45° cross marks. A distortion curve typical of the Metrogon lens and based on the equivalent focal length is shown in Fig. 2–24. The abscissa is the angular distance out along the diagonal of the focal plane, and the ordinate is the radial distortion (either plus or minus) of a corresponding point. It will be noted that the positive distortion greatly exceeds the negative distortion. This is not a rational distribution of radial distortion. For

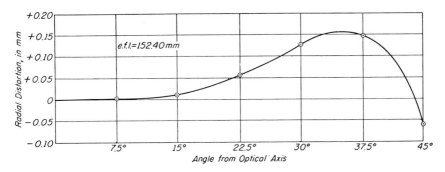

Fig. 2–24. Distortion curve based on equivalent focal length.

photogrammetric processes, it is advisable to compute an adjusted focal length, called the *calibrated focal length*, which will make the maximum positive distortion equal to the maximum negative distortion. This distribution is shown in Fig. 2–25. The symbol f used throughout the remainder of this book denotes the calibrated focal length as herein defined.

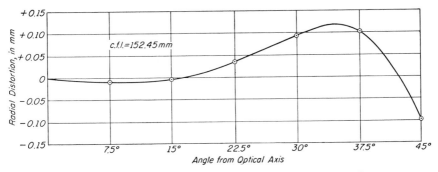

Fig. 2–25. Distortion curve based on calibrated focal length.

The resolution of the lens at each of several angular distances out from the center is determined by analyzing the images of the resolution patterns formed on the plate. Lens resolution tends to fall off as the distance from the center increases.

The lack of flatness of the vacuum-back platen is determined by means of a sensitive dial, or feeler, gage which is passed over the platen along selected lines or diameters. The focal-plane support must be flat to within ± 0.0005 in. in a precision aerial camera.

The size of the focal-plane opening is measured directly by means of a specially designed comparator. The dimensions are measured from points located in the vicinity of the fiducial marks, as shown in Fig. 2–26. The purpose of measuring these two dimensions is to detect differential film shrinkage resulting from processing, temperature, and humidity, and to correct for these effects in subsequent computations or instrumentation.

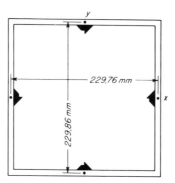

Fig. 2–26. Dimensions of focal-plane opening.

As an example of the use of some of the camera-calibration data just discussed, consider the following example.

EXAMPLE 2–1. A photograph, taken with a camera whose focal length is 152.45 mm and whose distortion curve is as shown in Fig. 2–25, is printed on a glass plate. The dimensions of the focal-plane opening are as given in Fig. 2–26. The coordinates of the principal point are $x_o = -0.05$ mm, $y_o = +0.03$ mm. When the plate is placed in a comparator and its x-axis is oriented parallel with the x-direction of the comparator, and readings are made on the numbered points shown in Fig. 2–27, the results are given in the tabulation.

It is required to determine the angle formed at the rear nodal point, or the perspective center, between lines to the principal point o and the photo point p.

Solution: To find the angle, make the principal point the origin of coordinates, determine the coordinates of point p with respect to this origin, compute the distance between the principal point and point p, and finally divide this distance by the focal length of the lens to obtain the tangent of the required angle.

First, the comparator readings of point p are reduced to x- and y-coordinates with respect to the lines joining the fiducial marks, as discussed in Sec. 1–5.

COMPARATOR READINGS FOR EXAMPLE 2–1

Point Number	Location of Point	x-reading (mm)	y-reading (mm)
1	x-fiducial mark	—	139.22
2	Upper y-fiducial mark	134.65	—
3	Lower y-fiducial mark	134.71	—
4	Left edge of focal plane	19.68	—
5	Right edge of focal plane	249.78	—
6	Upper edge of focal plane	—	254.09
7	Lower edge of focal plane	—	24.39
8	Photo point p	195.44	92.16

Since the y-reading of the x-axis is 139.22 mm, the y-coordinate of point p is $92.16 - 139.22 = -47.06$ mm. The x-value of the y-axis is $(134.65 + 134.71)/2 = 134.68$ mm, since the readings for the upper and lower ends are different. The x-coordinate of point p is therefore $195.44 - 134.68 = +60.76$ mm.

Next, the coordinates of point p are computed with respect to the principal point as origin. Thus, $x_p = 60.76 - (-0.05) = +60.81$ mm; $y_p = -47.06 - 0.03 = -47.09$ mm.

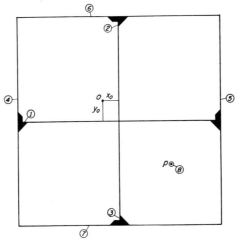

FIG. 2–27. Points for comparator readings.

The photograph has undergone differential shrinkage as determined by subtracting the reading for point *4* on the left edge of the focal plane from the reading for point *5* on the right edge. The difference is $249.78 - 19.68 = 230.10$ mm in the x-direction, whereas the calibrated distance in the x-direction is 229.76 mm, according to Fig. 2–26. Therefore, the x-coordinate of p must be multiplied by the factor $229.76/230.10$, and the value of x_p corrected for film shrinkage is 60.72 mm. Subtracting the lower-edge reading from the upper-edge reading gives $254.09 - 24.39 = 229.70$ mm in the y-direction. The calibrated distance in the y-direction, according to Fig. 2–26, is 229.86 mm. Therefore, the y-coordinate of p must be multiplied by the factor 229.86/229.70, and the value of y_p corrected for film shrinkage is −47.12 mm. If several photo points have been measured, the x- and y-coordinates of each such point would be multiplied by these same two factors, respectively.

To determine the amount by which point p has been displaced because of lens distortion, the angle β from the center is computed by applying the relationship tan $\beta = \sqrt{x_p{}^2 + y_p{}^2}/f$, or by dividing the radial distance out by the focal length. The radial distance is computed to be 76.86 mm, and $\beta = \tan^{-1} 76.86/152.45 = 27°$ approximately. Since the first value of the angle is used only to determine the radial distortion at the point, the nearest degree is sufficiently accurate. The value of the distortion at 27°, as obtained from Fig. 2–25, is +0.07 mm. The corrected radial distance from the principal point to point p is therefore 76.86−0.07=76.79 mm. The value of the angle at the rear nodal point between lines to the principal point and point p is $\beta = \tan^{-1} 76.79/152.45 = 26° \ 44' \ 05''$. Had the intersection of lines joining fiducial marks been taken as the principal point, and had the film shrinkage and lens distortion been neglected, the value of the angle would be 26° 45′ 10″.

When the coordinates of points are adjusted to eliminate lens distortion, each point must be treated separately because of the varying distances from the principal point. The position of point p, Fig. 2–27, with respect to the principal point o is shown in Fig. 2–28. The distance

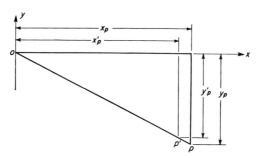

Fig. 2–28. Coordinates corrected for lens distortion.

$op = 76.86$ mm; the distance $op' = 76.79$ mm, where p' is the position of p after the correction for distortion has been applied. The corrected x-coordinate of p, or x'_p, is $(76.79/76.86)x_p$; the corrected y-coordinate of p, or y'_p, is $(76.79/76.86)y_p$.

A variation in the use of collimator images for computing radial lens distortion is the direct measurement, at the perspective center, of the angles between reference marks located in the focal plane of the lens by means of the goniometer shown in Fig. 1–14. The front nodal point of the lens is located on the vertical axis of rotation of the goniometer telescope. The operator then sights directly through the camera lens, bringing the line of sight of the telescope into coincidence with the successive reference marks of the glass plate held in the focal plane. The known spacing between the center reference mark and the next adjacent mark together with the angle measured between these marks allows for computing an equivalent focal length. Letting s_1 equal this known spacing and α_1 equal the measured angle, the equivalent focal length is then given by

$$\text{e.f.l.} = \frac{s_1}{\tan \alpha_1}$$

The distortion at any other reference mark, based on the e.f.l., is then obtained by subtracting the computed distance from the central mark to the reference mark from the actual distance. The computed distance, s'_i, is given by

$$s'_i = \text{e.f.l. } \tan \alpha_i$$

and the distortion at point i becomes

$$d_i = s_i - s'_i = s_i - \text{e.f.l. } \tan \alpha_i$$

Finally, the distribution of the lens distortion over the area of coverage is put on a rational basis by an adjustment procedure, the solution of which results in the calibrated focal length.

A variation in the form and location of the fiducial marks is to be found in some of the Wild aerial cameras. The fiducial marks are composed of optically-projected fine crosses located in the corners of the focal plane frame. These are supplemented by the usual shadowgraph marks located at the midpoint of the sides of the focal plane opening. As part of the calibration data, the rectangular coordinates of these corner fiducial marks as well as the coordinates of the principal point are computed. The reference coordinate axes can be taken quite arbitrarily, but the most convenient method is to assume an origin in one corner, pass the x-axis through the corner to the right, thus defining the y-axis of a right-hand system.

The calibrated coordinates of the corner fiducials together with their measured coordinates allows the coordinates of any point to be corrected for film shrinkage or deformation. An analysis of the results of comparator readings of the corner fiducials will indicate the amount of shrinkage in the x- and y-directions and whether the shrinkage is or is not uniform. Indicating the fixed values by primes ($'$), then (see Fig. 2–29), if

$$\frac{x'_3 - x'_2}{x'_1 - x'_4} = \frac{x_3 - x_2}{x_1 - x_4}$$

shrinkage in the x-direction must be assumed uniform. A similar analysis can be made in the y-direction. If shrinkage is found to be non-uniform in either or both directions, an approximation can be made by averaging the shrinkage indicated along opposite sides. A better approximation can be

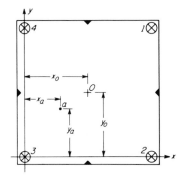

FIG. 2–29. Corner fiducial marks.

made by taking into account the actual position of the point to be corrected.

In Fig. 2–29, if shrinkage in the x-direction is greater along line 3–2
than along 4–1, then the x-reading at a can be corrected in an amount
proportionate to its y-coordinate. The same holds for correction to the
y-reading of a. This would be corrected in proportion to x_a.

Reference is made to the U.S. Coast and Geodetic Survey Technical
Bulletin No. 25, March 1965, entitled "Aerotriangulation: Image Coordinate Refinement," for a method of reducing comparator readings based
on the readings of the four corner fiducial marks. This method, in effect,
translates, rotates, scales, and warps the comparator readings to force a
fit at the fiducial marks. This method is most satisfactory, and is to be
preferred over an approximate procedure when accuracy warrants it.

Bibliography

ADELSTEIN, P. Z., and LEISTER, D. A. "Nonuniform Dimensional Changes in Topo-
graphic Aerial Films, *Photogrammetric Engineering,* Vol. XXIX (1963), p. 149.
———, JOSEPHSON, P. R., and LEISTER, D. A. "Nonuniform Film Deformational
Changes," *Photogrammetric Engineering,* Vol. XXXII (1966), p. 1028.
AMERICAN SOCIETY OF PHOTOGRAMMETRY. *Manual of Photogrammetry* (Menasha,
Wisc: George Banta Publishing Co., 1952), Chapter 2 and 3.
AMERICAN SOCIETY OF PHOTOGRAMMETRY. *Manual of Photogrammetry* (Menasha,
Wisc: George Banta Co., 1966), Chapters 3 and 4.
A Symposium on Camera Calibration, Photogrammetric Record, Vol. IV (1962), p.
139.
BARTH, W. "The Determination of the Angle Between the Fiducial Axes," *Photo-
grammetric Engineering,"* Vol. XXVII (1961), p. 128.
BROWN, D. C., "Decentering Distortion of Lenses," *Photogrammetric Engineering,*
Vol. XXXII (1966), p. 444.
CALHOUN, J. M., KELLER, L. E., and NEWELL, R. F. "A Method for Studying Pos-
sible Local Distortions in Aerial Films," *Photogrammetric Engineering,* Vol.
XXVI No. 4 (Sept. 1960), p. 661.

CARMAN, P. D., and BROWN, H. "Camera Calibration in Canada," *Canadian Surveyor,* Vol. XV (1961), p. 425.

CROUCH, L. W. "High Performance Mapping Equipment and Materials," *Photogrammetric Engineering,* Vol. XXVII (1961), p. 105.

EDEN, J. A. "Super-Wide Angle Photography and its Application with Various Techniques," *Photogrammetric Record,* Vol. V (1966), p. 150.

FISH, R. W. "Image Location," *Photogrammetric Record,* Vol. IV (1964), p. 379.

FLEMING, E. A. "Recognition of Air Survey Lens Types," *Canadian Surveyor,* Vol. XV (1960), p. 107.

GARDNER, I. C. "New Developments in Photogrammetric Lenses," *Photogrammetric Engineering,* Vol. XV (1949), p. 36.

GODDARD, G. W. "New Developments for Aerial Reconnaissance," *Photogrammetric Engineering,* Vol. XV (1949), p. 51.

HALLERT, B. *Photogrammetry.* New York: McGraw-Hill Book Co., 1960, Chapter 1.

———. "Some Preliminary Results of the Determination of Radial Distortion In Aerial Pictures," *Photogrammetric Engineering,* Vol. XXII (1956), p. 169.

———. "The Method of Least Squares Applied to Multicollimator Camera Calibration," *Photogrammetric Engineering,* Vol. XXIX (1963), p. 836.

HELAVA, U. V. "New Significance of Errors of Inner Orientation," *Photogrammetric Engineering,* Vol. XXIX (1963), p. 126.

HOTHMER, J. "Possibilities and Limitations for Elimination of Distortion in Aerial Photographs," *Photogrammetric Engineering,* Vol. XXVII (1961), p. 136.

HOVEY, S. T. "Panoramic Possibilities and Problems," *Photogrammetric Engineering* Vol. XXXI (1965), p. 727.

KASPER, H. C. "The Wild RC 7 Automatic Plate Camera with Aviotar Lens," *Photogrammetric Engineering,* Vol. XV (1949), p. 334.

KENNEDY, D. "Airborne Photographic Equipment," *Photogrammetric Engineering,* Vol. XXXI (1965), p. 971.

LAMPTON, B. F. "Film Distortion Compensation," *Photogrammetric Engineering,* Vol. XXXI (1965), p. 874.

———, and UMBACH, M. J. "Film Distortion Compensation Effectiveness," *Photogrammetric Engineering,* Vol. XXXII (1966), p. 1035.

LIVINGSTON, R. G. "A History of Military Mapping Camera Development," *Photogrammetric Engineering,* Vol. XXX (1964), p. 97.

———. "Airborne Mapping Equipment Quality Development," *Photogrammetric Engineering,* Vol. XXXII (1966), p. 390.

MATOS, R. A. "Aerial Camera for Photogrammetric Research," *Photogrammetric Engineering,* Vol. XXXI (1965), p. 978.

McNEIL, G. T. "Film Distortion," *Photogrammetric Engineering,* Vol. XVII (1951), p. 605.

———. "Normal Angle Camera Calibrator," *Photogrammetric Engineering,* Vol. XXVIII (1962), p. 633.

MERRITT, E. L. "Field Camera Calibration," *Photogrammetric Engineering,* Vol. XIV (1948), p. 303.

———. "Methods of Field Camera Calibration," *ibid.,* Vol. XVII (1950), p. 610.

MOLINEUX, C. E. "Multiband Spectral System for Reconnaissance," *Photogrammetric Engineering,* Vol. XXXI (1965), p. 131.

NELSON, ROBERT. "Quality Control in Precision Camera Manufacturing," *Photogrammetric Engineering,* Vol. XIX (1953), p. 59.

"New Development in Photogrammetric Equipment" (A Symposium), *Photogrammetric Engineering,* Vol. XX (1954), p. 621.

NORTON, CLARICE L. "The Fairchild Precision Camera Calibrator," *Photogrammetric Engineering,* Vol. XVI (1950), p. 688.

———. "The 'Multi.' Fairchild's Vertical Reconnaissance Camera Test Equipment," *ibid.,* Vol. XXI (1955), p. 445.

ODLE, J. E. "The Williamson F49 Mark 4 Air Survey Camera," *Photogrammetric Record,* Vol. V (1965), p. 37.

PENNINGTON, J. T. "Tangential Distortion and Its Effect on Photogrammetric Extension of Control," *Photogrammetric Engineering,* Vol. XIII (1947), p. 135.

"Photogrammetric Optics Panel," *Photogrammetric Engineering,* Vol. XX (1954), p. 487.

PODEYN, G. J., JR. "The Fairchild Cartographic Camera," *Photogrammetric Engineering,* Vol. XV (1949), p. 374.

———. "The Fairchild T-9 Camera," Ibid., p. 377.

RICHTER, R. "Development and Perfection of the Topogon Lens," *Photogrammetric Engineering,* Vol. XXII (1956) p. 868.

SANDERS, R. G. "A Commercial Laboratory for the Calibration of Photogrammetric Cameras," *Photogrammetric Engineering,* Vol. XVI (1950), p. 686.

SCHWIDEFSKY, K. *An Outline of Photogrammetry.* New York: Pitman Publishing Corp., 1959, Chapter 4.

SEWELL, E. D. "Distortion—Planigon Versus Metrogon," *Photogrammetric Engineering,* Vol. XX (1954), p. 54.

———. "Field Calibration of Aerial Mapping Cameras," *ibid.,* Vol. XIV (1948), p. 363.

TAYLOR, E. A., and LAMPTON, B. F. "A Report on the Camera Calibration Phase of the C. and G. S. Satellite Geodesy Program," *Photogrammetric Engineering,* Vol. XXX (1964), p. 245.

TOWNS, V. W. H., and DANIELSON, E. "The FX 105 Survey Camera," *Photogrammetric Record,* Vol. III (1960), p. 183.

U. S. COAST and GEODETIC SURVEY. "Topographic Manual," Part II, *Special Publication* No. 249 (Washington, D. C.: Government Printing Office, 1949), Chapter 2.

WASHER, F. E. "A Simplified Method of Locating the Point of Symmetry," *Photogrammetric Engineering,* Vol. XXIII (1957), p. 75.

———. "Calibration of Photogrammetric Lenses and Cameras at the National Bureau of Standard," *Photogrammetric Engineering,* Vol. XXIX (1963), p. 113.

———. "Prism Effect, Camera Tipping and Tangential Distortion," *Photogrammetric Engineering,* Vol. XXIII (1957), p. 721.

WASHER, F. E. "The Precise Evaluation of Lens Distortion," *Photogrammetric Engineering,* Vol. XXIX (1963), p. 327.

———, and CASE, F. A. "Calibration of Precision Airplane Mapping Cameras," *Photogrammetric Engineering,* Vol. XVI (1950), p. 502.

———, and TAYMAN, W. P. "Location of the Plane of Best Average Definition for Airplane Camera Lenses," *Photogrammetric Engineering,* Vol. XXVI (1960), p. 475.

ZELLER, M. *Textbook of Photogrammetry* (London: H. K. Lewis and Co., Ltd., 1952), Chapter 1.

Problems

2-1. An aircraft flying at the speed of sound carries an aerial camera whose shutter is set for 1/175 second. Air temperature is assumed to be 32° F. How many feet will the aircraft have traveled in the time during which the shutter is open?

2-2. The distance to the 7.5°, 15°, 22.5°, 30°, 37.5°, and 45° marks, measured along a diagonal from the principal point out to the corner of a photographic plate, are as follows: 20.223, 41.177, 63.663, 88.726, 117.866, and 153.435 mm, respectively. Compute the focal length based on the distance to 7.5° mark, and compute the radial distortion at the remaining angular distances. Plot the distortion curve for this focal length.

2-3. From the data in Prob. 2-2, compute the individual focal lengths based on the distances to the 15°, 22.5°, 30°, 37.5°, and 45° marks. Compute the individual distortions and plot the distortion curves.

2-4. In addition to the comparator readings shown in the table for Example 2-1, the following values were observed:

Point	x-reading (mm)	y-reading (mm)
a	42.45	195.82
b	124.60	144.25
c	174.44	135.41
d	158.28	43.16

Using the data in Example 2-1, compute the adjusted photographic coordinates of the points a, b, c, and d, based on the photographic axes defined by the fiducial marks.

2-5. When the diaphragm opening of a camera lens is 27.2 mm in diameter, the proper amount of light is admitted if the shutter is set for 1/500 second. What must be the diameter of the diaphragm opening if the shutter is set for 1/100 second?

2-6. A ray of light leaving the rear nodal point of an aerial-camera lens and passing through a glass-plate focal plane will be bent in toward the center before striking the negative. If the focal-plane glass is 12.000 mm thick, and the index of refraction of the glass is 1.515, how much will a ray forming an angle of 5° with the optical axis be displaced inward? 15°? 30°? 45°? 60°?

2-7. Plot the distortion curve caused by the glass plate of Prob. 2-6, based on a camera focal length of 88 mm.

2-8. At the time of calibration, the focal plane dimensions of a cartographic camera measures 230.10 mm in the x-direction and 230.15 mm in the y-direction. A photograph taken with the camera measures 9.094 in. in the x-direction and 9.040 in. in the y-direction. Correct the following measured coordinates for film and paper distortion.

Point	x-coordinate (in.)	y-coordinate (in.)
a	−1.462	−2.585
b	+3.144	−2.506
c	−2.150	−0.902
d	+3.466	+1.442
e	−0.015	+2.972

2-9. The coordinates of the five points listed in Prob. 2-8 are referred to the principal point as the origin, and the focal length of the camera is 152.68 mm. Compute the angles at the rear nodal point between a line perpendicular to the photograph and lines directed to the five points, first uncorrected for film and paper distortion and then corrected for this distortion.

2-10. Assume that the vacuum failed during an exposure, and the film buckled 5 mm out from the focal plane at a point whose x- and y-coordinates are measured as 102.45 mm and 78.24 mm respectively. The focal length of the camera is 151.80 mm. What are the magnitude and direction of the displacement of the point due to the buckling?

2-11. The comparator readings for the four fiducial marks measured on a glass "flash" plate used in calibrating a camera are as follows:

Point	x-reading (mm)	y-reading (mm)
left x-mark	20.144	132.204
right x-mark	248.432	128.156
upper y-mark	138.400	247.450
lower y-mark	134.308	19.050

What is the angle between the photographic axes defined by the fiducial marks?

2-12. The optical axis of a camera lens is truly vertical when the camera is at rest and the level bubble is centered. At what angle is the optical axis inclined to the vertical at the instant of exposure if the level bubble is centered and the aircraft which carries the camera is accelerating horizontally with a force equal to 5 per cent of gravity?

2-13. Assume that the four corner fiducial marks of an aerial camera form a perfect square 230.000 mm on a side, and that the position of the principal point lies on the intersection of the diagonals of the square. Comparator readings on the four fiducial marks of a photograph are (see Fig. 2–29)

Point	x-reading (mm)	y-reading (mm)
1	245.294	242.552
2	245.662	12.452
3	15.462	12.452
4	15.494	242.352
a	105.568	208.167

Compute the photographic coordinates of point a.

Geometry of the Aerial Photograph 3

3–1. Assumptions

An aerial photograph that has been exposed in a precision aerial camera can be treated analytically, because the camera has been calibrated to obtain certain metrical characteristics. These are inherent in the photograph. Perhaps the most important calibration factor is the focal length of the camera lens. In actuality, the negative which lies in the image space behind the lens receives the exposure of the terrain being photographed, and the focal length of the camera is considered as the principal distance of the negative. Since the negative produces a reversal of all object points on the terrain, it is more convenient to consider the positive produced by direct contact of the negative with a sensitized piece of paper, this positive being the photograph itself. A positive printed on glass is referred to as a diapositive, but it is nevertheless considered as a photograph.

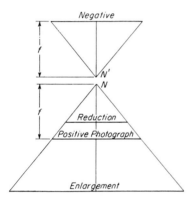

Fig. 3–1. Focal length and principal distance.

In Fig. 3–1, the negative is shown behind the lens at a distance f from the rear nodal point. The positive photograph is shown to lie in front of the lens at a distance f from the front nodal point. Hence, the focal length is considered as the principal distance of the photograph. Were an enlargement to be made of the negative, greater in size than the positive photograph, the principal distance of the enlargement would be greater than the focal length by an amount proportionate to the enlargement factor. If there were a reduction in size of the negative, the principal distance of the reduction would be correspondingly smaller than the focal length. In the discussion of the geometry of the photograph in this and succeeding chapters, the photograph is considered to be of the same size as the negative with a principal distance equal to f, unless otherwise stated.

In Fig. 3–2 (*a*) is shown a negative receiving rays representing terrain points. Since the rays entering the front nodal point N leave the rear nodal point N' unchanged in direction, except for the deflection caused by lens distortions, the geometry of the negative is identical with that of the photograph in all respects. The photograph in Fig. 3–2(*b*) is shown to receive rays representing terrain points. The front nodal point of the lens, being the perspective center of the photograph, is called the exposure station and is denoted by the symbol L. As will be observed, L in view (*b*) and N in view (*a*) are in reality the same point. In Fig. 3–2(*c*) is shown a vertical section through the photograph and the terrain. This portrayal is common in the discussion of basic principles.

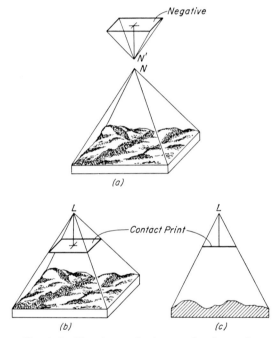

(*a*)

(*b*)   (*c*)

Fɪɢ. 3–2. Negative and photograph of terrain.

At the moment of exposure, a projective relation exists between points on the ground and any plane intersecting the optical axis. The perspective center is imagined to be the front nodal point of the lens system. However, since the lens transmits light, the projection of points on the ground to the front node as light rays is upset by refraction of the light rays as they pass through the atmosphere. Then, in passing through the lens system, the light rays are deflected by the lens abberations in the form of distortions. After being imaged in the focal plane on the negative emulsion, a further distortion takes place in the film processing.

Four assumptions are made to simplify the presentation of the geometry of the photograph. 1) The intersection of the lines joining opposite fiducial marks defines the principal point. It is assumed here that the positions or coordinates of all points have been corrected to allow for x_0 and y_0. (See Sec. 2–11.) 2) Lens distortion either does not exist or has been allowed for. 3) Film shrinkage either does not exist or has been allowed for. 4) Atmospheric refraction either does not exist or has been allowed for. Under these four assumptions, projective relations between the points on the ground and their corresponding images on the photograph are considered to be preserved.

3–2. Definitions

Some of the following definitions have been given previously, but are grouped here for convenience.

Vertical photograph. A photograph taken with the optical axis coinciding with the direction of gravity.

Tilted photograph or *near-vertical.* A photograph taken with the optical axis unintentionally tilted from the vertical by a small amount, usually less than 3°. The photograph shown in Fig. 3–3 is a tilted photograph.

Focal length. The distance from the front nodal point of the lens to the plane of the photograph, as the distance Lo in Fig. 3–3.

Exposure station. The space position of the front nodal point at the instant of exposure, as the point L in Fig. 3–3.

Flying height. The elevation of the exposure station above sea level or above the stated datum.

The x-axis of the photograph. The line on the photograph between opposite fiducial marks which most nearly parallels the direction of flight, as the line so designated in Fig. 3–3.

The y-axis of the photograph. The line on the photograph between opposite fiducial marks which lies normal to the x-axis, as the line so designated in Fig. 3–3.

Principal point. The point where a perpendicular dropped from the front nodal point strikes the photograph, as the point o in Fig. 3–3. The principal point is considered to coincide with the intersection of the x-axis and the y-axis.

Nadir point. The point where a plumb line dropped from the front nodal point pierces the photograph, as the point n in Fig. 3–3. It is the point on the photograph vertically beneath the exposure station.

Tilt. The angle formed between the optical axis and a plumb line, as $\angle\,oLn = t$ in Fig. 3–3. It is the angle which the plane of the photograph makes with a horizontal plane.

Principal plane. The vertical plane containing the optical axis, as the plane nLo or the plane NLO in Fig. 3–3.

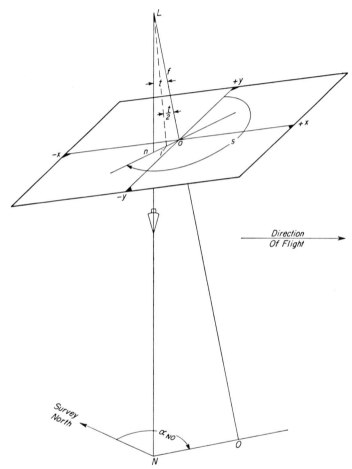

Fig. 3–3. Near-vertical photograph.

Principal line. The intersection of the principal plane with the plane of the photograph, as the line no in Fig. 3–3.

Swing. The angle measured in the plane of the photograph from the positive y-axis clockwise to a radial line from the principal point to the nadir point, as the angle s in Fig. 3–3. The angle of swing is the direction of tilt with respect to the photographic axes.

Ground nadir point. The point on the ground vertically beneath the exposure station, as the point N in Fig. 3–3.

Azimuth of the principal plane. The clockwise horizontal angle measured about the ground nadir point from the ground-survey north meridian to the principal plane of the photograph, as the angle α_{NO} in Fig. 3–3. The azimuth of the principal plane, sometimes referred to as the azimuth of the photograph, is the ground-survey direction of the tilt.

Isocenter. The point where the bisector of the angle of tilt strikes the photograph, as the point i in Fig. 3–3. Since the angle of tilt lies in the principal plane, the isocenter lies on the principal line and at a distance $f \tan (t/2)$ from the principal point.

Axis of tilt. The line in the plane of the photograph perpendicular to the principal line and passing through the isocenter. The axis of tilt is a horizontal line, as are all lines perpendicular to the principal line.

The tilt, the swing, and the azimuth of the principal plane are the elements of *outer,* or *exterior, orientation* of the protograph. These three angles define the attitude or orientation of the photograph in space with respect to the ground-survey axes.

On a vertical photograph, the isocenter and the nadir point coincide with the principal point. Also, the swing and the azimuth of the principal plane are indeterminate, and the axis of tilt does not exist. There is, however, a definite relationship between the ground-survey axes and the coordinate axes of a vertical photograph.

The exterior orientation of a photograph is also expressed in terms of three sequential rotations about a set of axes parallel with the ground-survey axis and whose origin is at the exposure station. These rotations, when completed, result in the x and y photographic axes as shown in Fig. 3–3 together with the photographic z-axis which is taken as the optical axis oL. The first, or primary, rotation taken about the original x-axis is designated omega (ω). The second, or secondary, rotation, taken about the once-rotated y-axis is designated phi (ϕ). The third, or tertiary rotation, taken about the twice-rotated z-axis (which now coincides with the optical axis) is designated kappa (κ). The two different systems of exterior orientation are discussed more fully in Secs. 3–13 and 3–14.

3–3. Scale of a Vertical Photograph

The common concept of scale is the ratio of a distance measured on a map or drawing to the corresponding distance on the ground. For example, if 1 in. on the map represents 100 ft on the ground, the scale of the map is expressed as 1 in. = 100 ft. If a distance on this map between two map features is measured and found to be 2.30 in., the corresponding survey or ground distance between the two points is 2.30 in. × 100 ft/in. = 230 ft.

The scale of a map may be expressed as a fraction, with the numerator and the denominator in the same units. For example, if 1 in. on the map equals 24,000 in. on the ground, the scale may be expressed as 1 in./24,000 in., which is the same ratio as 1 ft/24,000 ft. Since the common units may be eliminated, the scale is expressed simply as 1/24,000, which means that 1 unit of length on the map represents 24,000 of the same units of length on the ground. This form of scale expression is called a representative fraction.

The scale of a map may be expressed in the form of a ratio such as 1:10,000, read "1 to 10,000." This means that 1 unit on the map represents 10,000 of the same units on the ground. From the foregoing, it can be deduced that the expressions 1 in. = 2,000 ft, 1/24,000, and 1:24,000 are all equivalent. The first is an engineer's scale, the second is a representative fraction, and the third is a ratio, but all express the same scale.

A map is an orthographic projection of the ground surface. So all the points on the map are in their true relative horizontal positions. In fact, the term *map position* means true horizontal position. As a consequence, the scale of a given map is uniform throughout its entire extent. This is not true of a vertical photograph, except under rare circumstances. Because a photograph is a perspective projection, areas of the terrain lying closer to the camera at the instant of exposure will appear larger than corresponding areas lying farther from the camera. The scale of a vertical photograph will vary from point to point on the photograph, as it depends on the elevation of the points on the terrain. The greater the elevation of the ground area, the greater will be the scale of the photograph for that area.

In Fig. 3–4, it is assumed that a vertical photograph is taken from a flying height H above sea level. The focal length of the camera is f, and the principal point of the photograph is at o. The elevation of ground point A is h_A, and that of ground point B is h_B. Point A appears as an image on the photograph at a; point B is imaged at b. At an elevation h_A, the scale of the photograph is the ratio ao/AO_A. By similar triangles, $ao/AO_A = f/(H-h_A)$. At an elevation h_B, the scale of the photograph is the ratio ob/O_BB. By similar triangles, $ob/O_BB = f/(H-h_B)$. Thus, the scale of a photograph for any elevation may be found from the relationship

$$S_h = \frac{f}{H-h} \tag{3-1}$$

where S_h is the scale at elevation h; f is the focal length, in inches or in feet; H is the flying height above the vertical datum, in feet; and h is

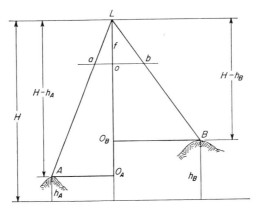

Fig. 3–4. Scale of photograph.

the elevation of the point above the vertical datum, in feet. In the numerical result, the numerator of the fraction is reduced to unity. Then, if f is expressed in inches, the scale is an engineer's scale; if f is expressed in feet, the scale is a representative fraction.

EXAMPLE 3–1. The exposure station in Fig. 3–4 is 2,900 ft above sea level. The elevation of A is 250 ft, and the elevation of B is 720 ft. The focal length is 6 in. Determine the scale of the photograph for terrain lying at these two elevations, first as an engineer's scale and then as a representative fraction.

Solution: By Eq. 3–1, the scale at elevation 250 ft, expressed as an engineer's scale, is

$$S_{250} = \frac{6 \text{ in.}}{(2,900 - 250) \text{ ft}} = \frac{1 \text{ in.}}{442 \text{ ft}}$$

or 1 in. = 442 ft.

As a representative fraction, the scale is

$$S_{250} = \frac{(6/12) \text{ ft}}{(2,900 - 250) \text{ ft}} = \frac{1}{5,300}$$

Also, by Eq. 3–1, the scale at elevation 720 ft, expressed as an engineer's scale, is

$$S_{720} = \frac{6 \text{ in.}}{(2,900 - 720) \text{ ft}} = \frac{1 \text{ in.}}{363 \text{ ft}}$$

or 1 in. = 363 ft.

As a representative fraction, the scale is

$$S_{720} = \frac{(6/12) \text{ ft}}{(2,900 - 720) \text{ ft}} = \frac{1}{4,360}$$

When the scale of a photograph for a given area is referred to, the scale can be considered uniform over that area only if the area lies at a constant elevation. Similarly, when reference is made to the scale along a line appearing on a photograph, it is presumed that the line on the ground lies at the same elevation throughout its length. Otherwise, the scale will change from point to point along the line.

The datum scale of a photograph is that scale which would be effective over the entire photograph if all points were projected vertically downward to the datum before being photographed. The datum scale is given by the relationship

$$S_D = \frac{f}{H} \qquad (3\text{-}2)$$

where the units correspond to those given for Eq. 3–1.

Of general use in planning photography is the average scale of the photograph. The average scale is that which would be effective over the entire photograph if all points were projected vertically upward or downward to the surface representing the average elevation of the terrain before being photographed. The average scale is given by the relationship

$$S_{\text{avg}} = \frac{f}{H - h_{\text{avg}}} \qquad (3\text{-}3)$$

where h_{avg} is the average elevation of the area.

The average scale computed from Eq. 3–3 is not, in fact, effective over the entire area. This scale will be too small for areas whose elevations are greater than h_{avg} and too large for areas whose elevations are less than h_{avg}. The average scale is nevertheless convenient in photogrammetry to describe the best single scale to use for a photograph or group of photographs.

EXAMPLE 3–2. What is the height above sea level at which an aircraft must fly in order to procure photography at an average scale of 1:10,000, if the average elevation of the area is 4,000 ft and the camera to be used has a focal length of 8.24 in.?

Solution: By Eq. 3–3,

$$\frac{1}{10,000} = \frac{(8.24/12) \text{ ft}}{(H - 4,000) \text{ ft}}$$

Hence,

$$H = \frac{8.24 \times 10,000}{12} + 4,000$$

The flying height should be 10,870 ft above sea level.

3–4. Determination of Scale

The datum scale of a photograph can be determined directly by Eq. 3–2 if the focal length is known and if the aircraft altimeter reading is available. The altimeter may be in error by as much as 2 per cent, however, and cannot be relied on for precise measurements. The average scale can be determined directly by Eq. 3–3 if, in addition to the focal length and flying height, the average elevation of the area is known. This elevation can be determined from a topographic map of the area if such a map is available. The scale at any point on a photograph can be determined directly by Eq. 3–1 if f and H are known and, in addition, the elevations of the points appearing on the photograph are determined. These elevations can be determined by reference to a topographic map of the area or by means of an aneroid barometer.

The scale of a photograph may be determined by comparing the length of a line measured on the photograph with the corresponding ground length. The ground length may be measured by taping or computed by triangulation or some other field method; or it may be a length of common knowledge, such as that of a section line, a city block, or a center stripe on a highway. To arrive at a fairly representative scale for the entire photograph, several known lines in different areas of the photograph should be scaled, and the average of the various resulting scales adopted.

EXAMPLE 3–3. The length of a section line lying at an elevation of about 1,000 ft scales 3.25 in. on a photograph for which the focal length is 6.02 in. Determine the scale of the photograph in an area the elevation of which is about 1,800 ft.

Solution: By Eq. 3–1,

$$S_{1,000} = \frac{3.25 \text{ in.}}{5,280 \text{ ft}} = \frac{6.02 \text{ in.}}{(H - 1,000) \text{ ft}}$$

so $H = 10,780$ ft.

Again by Eq. 3–1,

$$S_{1,800} = \frac{6.02 \text{ in.}}{(10,780 - 1,800) \text{ ft}}$$

Hence, $S_{1,800}$ is 1 in. = 1,500 ft.

The scale of a photograph can be determined very readily when a reliable map of the area is available. By measuring on the photograph the distance between two well-defined points which can also be identified on the map and then measuring the map distance, data are obtained for computing the photographic scale by the following relationship:

$$\frac{\text{Photo scale}}{\text{Map scale}} = \frac{\text{photo distance}}{\text{map distance}} \qquad (3\text{--}4)$$

Both the photo distance and the map distance are measured in the same units. If the map scale is given as an engineer's scale, the photo scale will be expressed as an engineer's scale. If the map scale is given as a representative fraction, the photo scale will also be expressed as a representative fraction.

EXAMPLE 3–4. A map scale is 1 in.=800 ft and a photograph covers a portion of the map area. The distance between two road intersections measures 4.34 in. on the photograph and 1.55 in. on the map. Determine the scale of the photograph.

Solution: By Eq. 3–4,

$$\frac{1 \text{ in.}/X \text{ ft}}{1 \text{ in.}/800 \text{ ft}} = \frac{4.34 \text{ in.}}{1.55 \text{ in.}} = \frac{800 \text{ ft}}{X \text{ ft}}$$

Hence, $X=285$ ft and the scale of the photograph in the vicinity of the line is 1 in.=285 ft.

EXAMPLE 3–5. A distance of 4.70 in. is scaled on a photograph for which the focal length is 8.25 in. and the corresponding distance of 1.07 in. is scaled on a map which is to a scale of 1/62,500. The area in question lies at an elevation of approximately 300 ft above sea level. Determine the flying height of the aircraft, above sea level, when the photograph was taken.

Solution: The scale at an elevation of 300 ft can be found by Eq. 3–4. Thus

$$\frac{1/X}{1/62,500} = \frac{4.70 \text{ in.}}{1.07 \text{ in.}} = \frac{62,500}{X}$$

So $X = 14,230$ approximately.

By Eq. 3–1,

$$S_{300} = \frac{1}{14,230} = \frac{(8.25/12) \text{ ft}}{(H - 300) \text{ ft}}$$

Hence, $H = 10,080$ ft above sea level.

3–5. Ground Coordinates from Measurements on a Vertical Photograph

A direct determination of the ground length of a line cannot be made by measuring the corresponding photographic distance unless the points at the two ends of the line lie at the same elevation. This difficulty can be overcome by determining the ground coordinates of the points with respect to a set of ground rectangular axes, and then determining the distance by the Pythagorean Theorem.

In Fig. 3–5, the vertical photograph is taken at a flying height H above the datum. The ground coordinate X- and Y-axes coincide in direction with the photographic coordinate x- and y-axes. The origin of ground coordinates at O lies directly beneath the exposure station. It is desired to determine the ground coordinates of two points A and B whose elevations are h_A and h_B, respectively. Points a and b are the corresponding photographic images whose measured coordinates are (x_a, y_a) and (x_b, y_b). The ground coordinates of points A and B are (X_A, Y_A) and (X_B, Y_B). They can be determined in the following manner.

By similar triangles,

$$\frac{Lo}{LO_A} = \frac{x_a}{X_A} = \frac{y_a}{Y_A} = \frac{f}{H - h_A} \quad \text{and} \quad \frac{Lo}{LO_B} = \frac{x_b}{X_B} = \frac{y_b}{Y_B} = \frac{f}{H - h_B}$$

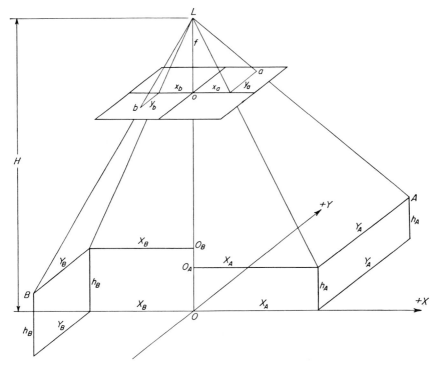

Fig. 3-5. Ground coordinates from photographic coordinate measurements.

Therefore,

$$X_A = \frac{H - h_A}{f} x_a \qquad \text{and} \qquad Y_A = \frac{H - h_A}{f} y_a$$

Also,

$$X_B = \frac{H - h_B}{f} x_b \qquad \text{and} \qquad Y_B = \frac{H - h_B}{f} y_b$$

The ground coordinates of a general point are given by the following expressions:

$$X = \frac{H - h}{f} x \tag{3-5}$$

$$Y = \frac{H - h}{f} y \tag{3-6}$$

where X and Y are the ground coordinates of the point, in feet, with respect to a set of axes whose directions are parallel with the photographic axes and whose origin is directly beneath the exposure station; H is the flying height above sea level, in feet; h is the elevation of the point, in feet; x and y are the coordinates of the point measured on a vertical photograph, in inches or millimeters; and f is the focal length, in the same units as x and y.

EXAMPLE 3–6. In Fig. 3–6 is represented a vertical photograph showing the images of three ground points A, B, and C at a, b, and c, respectively. The elevations of these points, and their coordinates measured on the photograph with a micro-rule and corrected for film shrinkage and lens distortion, are given in the accompanying tabulation. The focal length is 8.212 in., and the flying height is 7,810 ft above

PHOTOGRAPHIC COORDINATES AND ELEVATIONS

Point	x (in.)	y (in.)	Elevation (ft)
a	− 1.954	− 3.502	974
b	− 3.106	+ 2.250	146
c	+ 2.155	+ 2.775	420

sea level. Determine the lengths of the ground lines AB, BC, and CA; the area of the triangle ABC, in acres; and the horizontal angle at A from B to C.

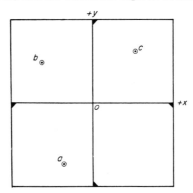

FIG. 3–6. Image points on photo-graph.

Solution: For convenience, a portion of the solution is set up in tabular form as shown. The X- and Y-coordinates are computed by Eqs. 3–5 and 3–6. The

TABULAR SOLUTION FOR COORDINATES AND GROUND DISTANCES

Point	x (in.)	y (in.)	$H-h$ (ft)	$(H-h)/f$	X (ft)	Y (ft)	Line	ΔX (ft)	ΔY (ft)	Dist. (ft)
a	− 1.954	− 3.502	6,836	832.4	− 1,627	− 2,915	AB	1,272	5,015	5,174
b	− 3.106	+ 2.250	7,664	933.3	− 2,899	+ 2,100	BC	4,838	397	4,854
c	+ 2.155	+ 2.775	7,390	899.9	+ 1,939	+ 2,497	CA	3,566	5,412	6,481

ground distances are computed by the relationship $D=\sqrt{(\Delta X)^2+(\Delta Y)^2}$. The area can be computed by any one of several formulas for the area of a triangle.

COMPUTATION OF AREA

$a =$ 5,174 ft	8,255	8,255	8,255
$b =$ 4,854 ft	− 5,174	− 4,854	− 6,481
$c =$ 6,481 ft	3,081	3,401	1,774
Sum = 16,509			
$s =$ 8,255			

$$s(s-a)(s-b)(s-c)=1.5345\times10^{14}$$

$$\text{Area}=12{,}387{,}000 \text{ sq ft}=284.37 \text{ acres}$$

The formula used is $A = \sqrt{s(s-a)\ (s-b)\ (s-c)}$, where a, b, and c are the lengths of the sides and $s = \frac{1}{2}\ (a+b+c)$.

The angle at A from B to C is determined by computing the ground azimuths of AB and AC and substracting one from the other. The azimuth of each line is found by the formula $\alpha = \tan^{-1}\ (\Delta X/\Delta Y)$. Thus,

$$\tan \alpha_{AC} = \frac{+3{,}566}{+5{,}412} = +0.65891 \qquad \text{or} \qquad \alpha_{AC} = 33° 23'$$

$$\tan \alpha_{AB} = \frac{-1{,}272}{+5{,}015} = -0.25364 \qquad \text{or} \qquad \alpha_{AB} = 345° 46'$$

$$\alpha_{AC} - \alpha_{AB} = 47° 37'$$

Equations 3–5 and 3–6 allow a complete survey to be made from measurements on a vertical photograph, provided that the focal length and flying height are known and that the elevations of the points involved in the survey have been determined either by field work or from a topographic map.

3–6. Flying Height for a Vertical Photograph from Ground Control Line

The flying height can be precisely determined (within the limitations of the refinement of measurement of the photographic coordinates) from the known distance on the ground between two points which can be positively identified on the photograph. The elevations of these two points must also be known. By the Pythagorean Theorem,

$$D^2 = (X_B - X_A)^2 + (Y_B - Y_A)^2$$

From Eqs. 3–5 and 3–6,

$$D^2 = \left[\frac{H-h_B}{f} x_b - \frac{H-h_A}{f} x_a\right]^2 + \left[\frac{H-h_B}{f} y_b - \frac{H-h_A}{f} y_a\right]^2$$

where the ground length D, the elevations h_A and h_B, and the focal length f are known, and where the photographic coordinates (x_a, y_a) and (x_b, y_b) have been measured. This takes the form of the quadratic equation $aH^2 + bH + c = 0$, where a, b, and c represent numbers obtained by substituting known values in the expression for D^2. The solution of the quadratic is

$$H = \frac{-b + \sqrt{b^2 - 4ac}}{2a}$$

This method provides a direct solution for H, but formation of the quadratic equation is rather awkward and time consuming.

An indirect solution for H by successive approximation is, in most instances, quicker and easier than the direct solution. By the scale relationship of Eq. 3–1, the distance ab measured directly on the photograph is used to determine an approximate value of H. Thus,

$$\frac{f}{\text{Approx. } H - h_{AB}} = \frac{ab}{AB}$$

where f and ab are in the same units; the approximate height H and AB, the known ground distance, are in feet; and h_{AB} is the average elevation of points A and B, in feet. The approximate value of H is used to solve for the coordinates (X_A, Y_A) and (X_B, Y_B) by applying Eqs. 3–5 and 3–6, in which the elevation of each point is taken into consideration. A value is computed for the distance AB by using the approximate value of H, and this computed distance is compared with the correct distance AB to obtain a better value of H by the following relationship:

$$\frac{H - h_{AB}}{\text{Approx. } H - h_{AB}} = \frac{\text{correct } AB}{\text{computed } AB}$$

All values are in feet.

With the new value of H, Eqs. 3–5 and 3–6 are again solved and a new value for the length is computed and compared with the true length. This iteration is performed until the necessary precision has been obtained, usually within 1 part in 5,000.

EXAMPLE 3–7. The ground length is known to be 8,527 ft between point A whose elevation above sea level is 580 ft and point B whose elevation is 860 ft. A vertical photograph on which the images a and b of the two ground points appear is taken with a camera having a focal length of 6.008 in. The coordinates of a are measured as $x_a = -2.154$ in. and $y_a = +3.320$ in.; the coordinates of b are measured as $x_b = +1.954$ in. and $y_b = -0.104$ in. The distance ab scaled directly from the photograph measures 5.350 in. Compute the flying height above sea level.

Solution: By Eq. 3–1,

$$\frac{5.350 \text{ in.}}{8,527 \text{ ft}} = \frac{6.008 \text{ in.}}{(\text{approx. } H - 720) \text{ ft}}$$

The first approximate height is 10,296 ft. Then by Eqs. 3–5 and 3–6,

$$X_A = \frac{10,296 - 580}{6.008}(-2.154) = -3,483.4 \text{ ft}$$

$$Y_A = \frac{10,296 - 580}{6.008}(+3.320) = +5,369.0 \text{ ft}$$

$$X_B = \frac{10,296 - 860}{6.008}(+1.954) = +3,068.9 \text{ ft}$$

$$Y_B = \frac{10,296 - 860}{6.008}(-0.104) = -163.3 \text{ ft}$$

The ground length based on the approximate height is $\sqrt{6,552.3^2 + 5,532.3^2} = 8,575$ ft. A second approximate height is computed as follows:

$$\frac{\text{Approx. } H - 720}{10,296 - 720} = \frac{8,527}{8,575}$$

from which the new approximate height is 10,242 ft. Then, by Eqs. 3–5 and 3–6,

$$X_A = \frac{10,242 - 580}{6.008}(-2.154) = -3,464.0 \text{ ft}$$

$$Y_A = \frac{10,242 - 580}{6.008}(+3.320) = +5,339.2 \text{ ft}$$

$$X_B = \frac{10{,}242 - 860}{6.008}(+1.954) = +3{,}051.3 \text{ ft}$$

$$Y_B = \frac{10{,}242 - 860}{6.008}(-0.104) = -162.4 \text{ ft}$$

The new ground length is $\sqrt{6{,}515.3^2 + 5{,}501.6^2} = 8{,}527$ ft, which agrees with the correct ground length. The true flying height is therefore 10,242 ft above sea level, or 10,240 ft within the accuracy of the data.

Precise determination of flying heights always requires at least one ground control line in each photograph. The flying height fixed in the complex stereoscopic plotting instruments described in Chapter 12 depends on ground control established by field surveys. This control can be somewhat extended over several consecutive photographs, both by analytical methods and by instrumental methods. Such control is achieved very successfully in actual photogrammetric production.

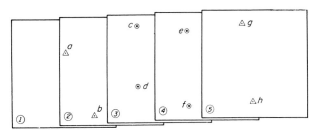

FIG. 3–7. Extension of flying heights from one control line.

Assume that all the overlapping photographs (see Sec. 4–1) in Fig. 3–7 are vertical, and that established ground control points appear at a, b, g, and h. The flying heights for photographs 1 and 2 can be determined from control line ab. If the elevations of identifiable points C and D, appearing on photograph 2 at c and d, are known, the ground length of line CD may be determined from the computed coordinates of C and D. Since the images at c and d appear also on photograph 3, the flying height for photograph 3 may be determined. This extension of ground lengths and flying heights may be continued until a known ground length is reached. By comparing the computed length of the new control line GH with its known length, a basis for adjusting intermediate flying heights is established. It is to be noted that the elevations of all the points A through H must be known.

The extension of ground control to determine flying heights as just described breaks down quite rapidly in actuality, because each of the photographs contains a certain amount of tilt. This tilt renders Eqs. 3–5 and 3–6 invalid, since these two equations are based on vertical photographs. In the stereoscopic plotting instruments, however, the tilt of each photograph is recreated directly in the instrument, and a successful extension is possible. Methods have been developed for extending control analytically by basing computations on photographic coordinate measurements; the elements of exterior orientation are computed for each photograph in the series. But such methods go beyond the scope of this book.

3–7. Relief Displacement on a Vertical Photograph

A vertical photograph taken over a ground area which lies at sea level at all points would be a planimetric map of the area with a scale equal to f/H. This scale would be effective over the entire area, since the elevation is constant throughout. A vertical photograph taken over an area all of which lies at a constant elevation h above sea level would be a planimetric map of the area with a scale equal to $f/(H-h)$ As discussed in Sec. 3–3, a vertical photograph, except in the rare circumstances just mentioned, does not have a constant scale. Virtually every

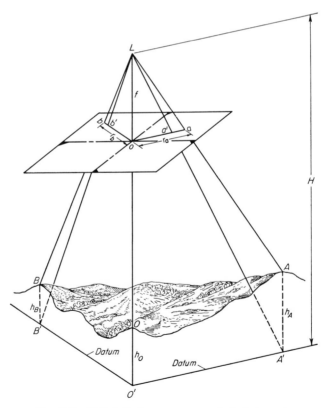

FIG. 3–8. Relief displacement on vertical photograph.

point on the photograph is displaced from its datum photograph position because of its elevation above or below the datum. This displacement is called *relief displacement*.

In Fig. 3–8 is represented a photograph of focal length f taken at exposure station L, which is H feet above the datum. Here A, O, and B are points on the terrain whose elevations are h_A, h_O, and h_B, respectively. The images of these three terrain points appear at a, o, and b, respectively. Point o is the principal point. The datum positions of these three points lie at A', O', and B', respectively. If they could be photographed as lying on the datum, their images would appear at the datum photograph positions a', o, and b', respectively. As seen in Fig. 3–8, point a has been displaced from its datum photograph position outward along the radial line oa a distance $a'a$; point b has been displaced outward along the radial line ob a distance $b'b$. These two small distances are the relief displacements of the two points. Point o has not been displaced at all. From Fig. 3–8, the following conclusion may be stated: On a vertical photograph, relief displacement takes place on a line radially from the principal point, and there is no relief displacement of the principal point.

In Fig. 3–9 is shown a vertical section through the photograph of

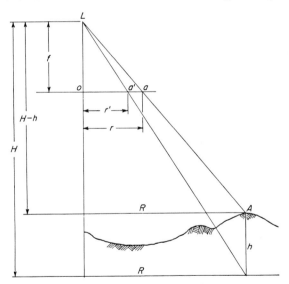

Fig. 3–9. Relief displacement of a point.

Fig. 3–8 along the line oa. Let A designate a general point. Its elevation is $h;$ the radial distance from the principal point to its image at a is $r;$ and the radial distance from the principal point to its datum photograph position is r'. By similar triangles,

$$\frac{f}{H-h}=\frac{r}{R} \quad \text{and} \quad \frac{f}{H}=\frac{r'}{R}$$

Hence,

$$r=\frac{Rf}{H-h} \quad \text{and} \quad r'=\frac{Rf}{H}$$

Also,

$$R=\frac{r(H-h)}{f} \quad \text{and} \quad R=\frac{r'H}{f}$$

The relief displacement, designated d, is $r-r'$. Therefore,

$$d=\frac{Rf}{H-h}-\frac{Rf}{H}=\frac{Rfh}{H(H-h)}$$

Substituting the value of $r(H-h)/f$ for R gives

$$d=\frac{rh}{H} \tag{3-7}$$

Substituting the value of $r'H/f$ for R gives

$$d=\frac{r'h}{H-h} \tag{3-8}$$

In Eqs. 3–7 and 3–8, d is the relief displacement of a point, in inches; r is the radial distance from principal point to the image of the ground point, in inches; r' is the radial distance from the principal point to the datum photograph position of the point, in inches; h is the elevation of the point above the datum, in feet; and H is the flying height above the same datum, in feet.

For a given elevation, the relief displacement of a point increases as the distance from the principal point increases. Also, all other things being equal, an increase in flying height causes a decrease in the relief displacement of a point. This fact is important in considering photography for mosaic work as will be discussed in Chapters 4 and 11.

If the ground point lies above the datum, as in Fig. 3–8, the relief displacement will be outward, or positive. If the ground point lies below the datum, h has a negative sign and the relief displacement will be inward, or negative. When relief displacement is computed by applying Eq. 3–7 or Eq. 3–8, it must be borne in mind that the flying height is measured above the same datum above or below which the elevations are measured.

EXAMPLE 3–8. What is the relief displacement, on a vertical photograph, of a point whose elevation is 2,800 ft above sea level, if the focal length of the camera is 6.000 in., the datum scale is 1:16,000, and the image of the point lies 3.50 in. from the principal point?

Solution: By Eq. 3–2,

$$S_D=\frac{1}{16,000}=\frac{(6/12)\text{ ft}}{H\text{ ft}}$$

So $H = 8,000$ ft above sea level. By Eq. 3–7,

$$d = \frac{3.50 \times 2,800}{8,000} = 1.225 \text{ or } 1.23 \text{ in.}$$

EXAMPLE 3–9. When a vertical photograph of a flat area lying at an average elevation of 650 ft above sea level is compared with a map, the scale of the photograph determined by applying Eq. 3–4 is 1 in.=850 ft. The focal length is 8.250 in. As indicated in Fig. 3–10, a tower in the area appears on the photograph. The distance from the image b on the bottom of the tower to the image t of the top of the tower measures 0.152 in. The distance from the principal point o to the image of the top of the tower is 2.845 in. Determine the height of the tower.

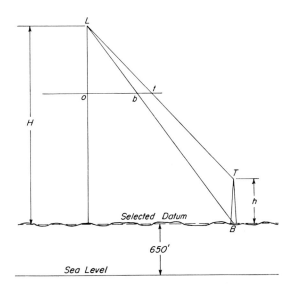

FIG. 3–10. Height of object from relief displacement.

Solution: In solving this problem, the datum is selected at the 650-ft elevation. Consequently, both H and h are measured from this datum, as shown in Fig. 3–10. Furthermore, the distance r in Eq. 3–7 is measured to the image of the top of the tower. It is to be noted that in this case both the image and its datum photograph position (which coincides with b) can be identified on the photograph. Hence, the relief displacement of the top with respect to the bottom can be measured directly.

By Eq. 3–2,

$$S_D = \frac{1 \text{ in.}}{850 \text{ ft}} = \frac{8.250 \text{ in.}}{H \text{ ft}}$$

from which $H = 7,013$ ft. By Eq. 3–7,

$$0.152 = \frac{2.845 \, h}{7,013}$$

So $h = 375$ ft and the tower is therefore 375 ft high.

3–8. Scale of a Tilted Photograph

In the case of a vertical photograph taken over terrain whose elevation varies from point to point, the scale of the photograph varies from point to point, as discussed in Sec. 3–3. If a vertical photograph is taken over an area with no relief, then the scale is uniform throughout the

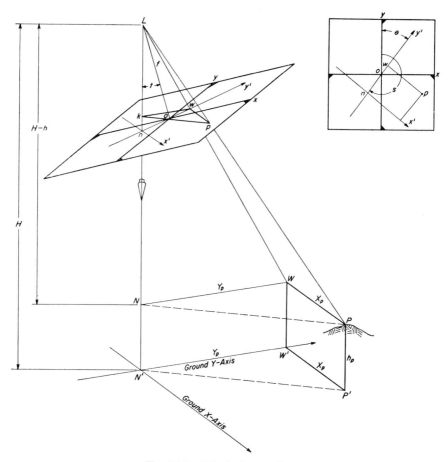

Fig. 3–11. Tilted photograph.

entire photograph. However, a tilted photograph taken over terrain with no relief will not have a uniform scale, because the plane of the photograph is tilted to the terrain and the downward half will have a larger scale than will the upward half.

The scale situation is further complicated when a tilted photograph is taken over terrain whose elevation varies from point to point. In order to determine the scale at a particular point on such a photograph, not only must the elevation of the point be known, but its position on the photograph must be known with respect to both the axis of tilt and the principal line, because the tilt takes place in the direction of the principal line. The positions of the principal line and the nadir point, which is on the downward half of the photograph (see Fig. 3–3), are fixed by the angle of swing. To determine the scale of a tilted photograph at a point, it is therefore necessary to know the tilt and swing, as well as the flying height, focal length, and elevation of the point.

In Fig. 3–11, P is a point lying at an elevation h_P above the datum. The image of the point appears on a tilted photograph at p, the photographic coordinates x and y of which are measured with respect to the axes defined by the fiducial marks. The principal point is at o, and the nadir point is at n. The angle of swing is shown as the angle s. Let the positive y-axis be rotated until the new y-axis, or the y'-axis, coincides with the principal line having a positive direction no as shown. The rotation is considered positive if in a counterclockwise direction, as in analytic geometry. The amount of rotation θ is given by the relationship

$$\theta = 180° - s \qquad (3\text{–}9)$$

Since the rotation in Fig. 3–11 is clockwise, θ must be negative. From analytic geometry, the new coordinates of p are

$$x' = x \cos \theta + y \sin \theta$$
$$y' = -x \sin \theta + y \cos \theta$$

Let the x'-axis be translated from o to n, as shown in Fig. 3–11. Since the distance on equals $f \tan t$, the coordinates of p, after this translation, are

$$x' = x \cos \theta + y \sin \theta \qquad (3\text{–}10)$$

$$y' = -x \sin \theta + y \cos \theta + f \tan t \qquad (3\text{–}11)$$

Let the line wk be constructed perpendicular to the line Ln. This is a horizontal line, since Ln is a vertical line. Since wp is perpendicular to the principal line, it is also a horizontal line (see Sec. 3–2 under axis of tilt). The plane kwp is therefore a horizontal plane. Each of the vertical lines PP', WW', and NN' being equal to h_P, the plane NWP also is a horizontal plane. The scale relationship between the planes kwp and NWP can be derived by similar triangles.

In the triangles Lkp and LNP,

$$\frac{kp}{NP} = \frac{Lk}{LN} = \frac{Lk}{H - h}$$

But $Lk = Ln - kn = f \sec t - y' \sin t$.   Therefore,

$$\frac{kp}{NP} = \frac{f \sec t - y' \sin t}{H - h}$$

The ratio kp/NP is the scale of any point at elevation h lying in the plane kwp.   Since p lies in this plane, the scale at p is given by the relationship

$$S_t = \frac{f \sec t - y' \sin t}{H - h} \tag{3-12}$$

in which S_t is the scale of a tilted photograph at a point whose elevation is h; f is the focal length; t is the tilt of the photograph; H is the flying height above the datum, in feet; h is the elevation, in feet; and y' is the y-coordinate of the point with respect to a set of axes whose origin is at the nadir point and whose y'-axis coincides with the principal line. The units of f and y' must be the same.   If they are expressed in inches, the scale is an engineer's scale; if they are expressed in feet, the scale is a representative fraction.

3–9. Ground Coordinates from Measurements on a Tilted Photograph

If the data needed to compute the scale at a point on a tilted photograph have been obtained, the ground coordinates of the point may be computed.   The scale data needed for this computation are the tilt, the swing, and the flying height above sea level.   Chapter 9 discusses two methods for determining these data.   The Y-coordinate axis lies in the principal plane, and the X-coordinate axis passes through the ground nadir point, as shown in Fig. 3–11.   Thus, the ground nadir point is the origin of coordinates.

In Fig. 3–11, $wp = x'$ and $WP = X$.   The scale relationship between the planes kwp and NWP is given by Eq. 3–12.   Therefore,

$$\frac{wp}{WP} = \frac{x'}{X} = \frac{f \sec t - y' \sin t}{H - h}$$

and

$$X = \frac{H - h}{f \sec t - y' \sin t} x' \tag{3-13}$$

in which X is the ground X-coordinate of the point, in feet; x' is the x'-coordinate of the point with respect to a set of axes whose origin is at the nadir point and whose y'-axis coincides with the principal line, in the same units as f and y'; and the other quantities have the same meanings as in Eq. 3–12.

In Fig. 3–11,

$$\frac{kw}{NW} = \frac{kw}{Y} = \frac{nw \cos t}{Y} = \frac{y' \cos t}{Y} = \frac{f \sec t - y' \sin t}{H - h}$$

Therefore,

$$Y = \frac{H-h}{f \sec t - y' \sin t} y' \cos t \tag{3-14}$$

in which Y is the ground Y-coordinate of the point, in feet, and the other quantities have the same meanings as in Eq. 3–12.

From the foregoing discussion, it is seen that a complete survey of the ground covered by a tilted aerial photograph may be performed by coordinate measurements of the points involved in the survey, if the scale data for the photograph are known. The elevations of the points must be determined either from a map or by a field survey. Any problem of lengths, angles, or areas which can be solved by using ground coordinates can be solved by photographic measurements as well.

EXAMPLE 3-10. For a near-vertical the tilt is 3°27′, the swing is 272°, and the flying height is 7,850 ft above sea level. The focal length of the camera is 6.000 in. The elevations of two ground points A and B, whose images appear on the photograph, are 160 ft and 720 ft, respectively. The photographic coordinates of these two points, measured with respect to lines joining opposite fiducial marks, are $x_a = +3.154$ in., $y_a = -1.002$ in., $x_b = -2.866$ in., and $y_b = -2.010$ in. Compute the true ground length between the two points.

Solution: By Eq. 3–9, $\theta = 180° - 272° = -92°$. Then

$\sin \theta = -0.99939$	$\cos t = 0.99819$
$\cos \theta = -0.03490$	$\tan t = 0.06029$
$\sin t = 0.06018$	$\sec t = 1.00181$

By Eqs. 3–10 and 3–11,

$x'_a = (3.154)(-0.03490) + (-1.002)(-0.99939) = +0.891$ in.

$y'_a = -(3.154)(-0.99939) + (-1.002)(-0.03490) + (6.000)(0.06029) = +3.549$ in.

$x'_b = (-2.866)(-0.03490) + (-2.010)(-0.99939) = +2.109$ in.

$y'_b = -(-2.866)(-0.99939) + (-2.010)(-0.03490) + (6.000)(0.06029) = -2.432$ in.

By Eqs. 3–13 and 3–14,

$$X_A = \frac{7,850 - 160}{(6.000)(1.00181) - (3.549)(0.06018)} \times (+0.891) = +1,182 \text{ ft}$$

$$Y_A = \frac{7,850 - 160}{(6.000)(1.00181) - (3.549)(0.06018)} \times (+3.549)(0.99819) = +4,700 \text{ ft}$$

$$X_B = \frac{7,850 - 720}{(6.000)(1.00181) - (-2.432)(0.06018)} \times (+2.109) = +2,442 \text{ ft}$$

$$Y_B = \frac{7,850 - 720}{(6.000)(1.00181) - (-2.432)(0.06018)} \times (-2.432)(0.99819) = -2,812 \text{ ft}$$

Finally, $AB = \sqrt{1,260^2 + 7,512^2} = 7,617$ ft, or 7,620 ft within the accuracy of the data.

The computations for determining the coordinates of several points should be arranged in tabular form in order to increase the efficiency of this work.

3–10. Flying Height for a Tilted Photograph from Ground Control Line

The method described in Sec. 3–6 for determining the precise flying height for a vertical photograph by using a ground line of known length can be applied for finding the flying height for a tilted photograph, provided that the tilt and swing for the photograph are also known. The general procedure is as follows: Photographic coordinates of the end points of the control line are measured with respect to the axes defined by the fiducial marks. The photographic length of the line is then scaled directly. (The length of the line can be computed from the photographic coordinates, but scaling is more convenient than computing.) The ratio of the photographic length to the known ground length is used to compute the first approximate value of the flying height by the scale relationship of Eq. 3–1. Thus,

$$\frac{f}{\text{Approx. } H - h_{AB}} = \frac{ab}{AB}$$

in which h_{AB} is the average elevation of the two end points, in feet; f is the focal length; ab is the scaled photographic length; and AB is the known ground length, in feet. The distances f and ab must be in the same units, inches or millimeters. The approximate height is in feet.

By using the approximate height, together with the other scale data, Eqs. 3–9, 3–10, 3–11, 3–13, and 3–14 are solved in turn, and the distance based on the first set of ground coordinates is computed. This computed distance is compared with the known ground distance to determine a better value of H. Thus,

$$\frac{H - h_{AB}}{\text{Approx. } H - h_{AB}} = \frac{\text{correct } AB}{\text{computed } AB}$$

in which H is the new value of the flying height, and computed AB is the value of the length based on the first approximate height. All distances are in feet.

The new value of H and the other scale data are used in applying Eqs. 3–13 and 3–14 again and a new ground length is computed. This iteration is continued until the computed value of the ground length agrees with the known ground length within the desired precision.

3–11. Relief Displacement on a Tilted Photograph

The relief displacement of a point on a tilted photograph with respect to its datum photograph position is shown in Fig. 3–12. The exposure station is at L, the principal point is at o, the nadir point is at n, the isocenter is at i, and the focal length is Lo. The line no is the principal line, and the line perpendicular to no at i is the axis of tilt. Ground point A

is imaged at a; ground point B is imaged at b. The datum photograph positions of the datum points A' and B' are at a' and b', respectively. Since LN is a vertical line containing the nadir point n, the planes LN_AA and LNA' containing the line LN are vertical planes. They are, in fact, the same plane. Furthermore, since points n, a', and a all lie in the

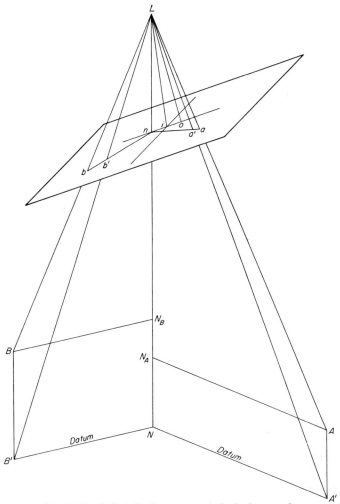

Fig. 3-12. Relief displacement on tilted photograph.

same vertical plane, and since they all lie in the plane of the photograph, these three points all lie on the same line. Also, the points n, b', and b all lie on the same line. Therefore, on a tilted photograph, relief displacement takes place along a line running radially from the nadir point.

The amount of relief displacement on a tilted photograph depends not only on the flying height, the distance from the nadir point to the image, and the elevation of the ground point, but also on the position of the point with respect to the principal line and to the axis of tilt. Compared with the equivalent relief displacement on a vertical photograph, the relief displacement on a tilted photograph will be less on the half of the photograph upward from the axis of tilt, identical for points lying on the axis of tilt, and greater on the downward half of the photograph. As will be shown, image displacements due to tilt will tend to compensate relief displacement on the upward half and will be added to relief displacement on the downward half of the photograph. Because the tilts of near-vertical photographs are rarely over 3°, the value of the relief displacement is given with sufficient accuracy by Eqs. 3–7 and 3–8, although the radial distance should be measured from the nadir point rather than from the principal point.

3–12. Displacement of Images Due to Tilt

A tilted photograph and a corresponding vertical photograph taken with the same focal length and from the same flying height will match along the axis of tilt, where they intersect one another. At any other point on the tilted photograph, the image of the point will be displaced either outward or inward with respect to its equivalent position on a vertical photograph. As has been stated, if the point lies on the half of the photograph upward from the axis of tilt, it will be displaced inward; if the point lies on the downward half, it will be displaced outward.

In Fig. 3–13, points A, B, C, and D appear as images at a, b, c, and d, respectively, on the tilted photograph. The images of these four ground points would appear at a', b', c', and d', respectively, on an equivalent vertical photograph. If the vertical photograph is now rotated about the axis of tilt until it is in the plane of the tilted photograph, point a' would fall at a'', b' at b'', c' at c'', and d' at d''. The displacements of the four points are therefore seen to be $a''a$, $b''b$, $c''c$, and $d''d$. It is to be noted that these displacements occur along lines which radiate from the isocenter. The two points a and c have been displaced inward toward the isocenter, while the two points b and d have been displaced outward from the isocenter. On a tilted photograph, therefore, tilt displacement takes place along a line radially from the isocenter.

Note that in Fig. 3–13 points a and c both lie at the same distance from the axis of tilt, but the displacement of a is greater than that of c. The ratio is equal to the secant of angle cia. Also points b and d both

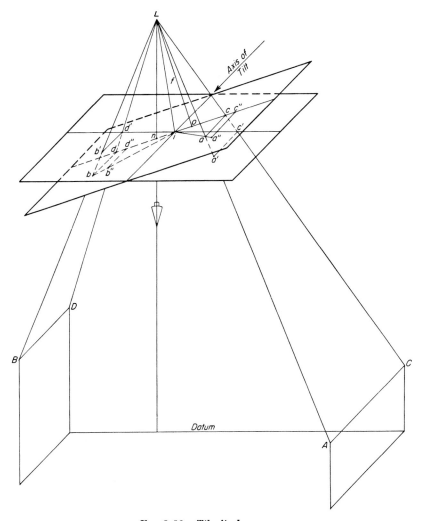

Fɪɢ. 3–13.   Tilt displacement.

lie at the same distance from the axis of tilt, but the displacement of b is greater than that of d and the ratio is equal to the secant of angle dib. Thus, tilt displacement depends on the position of the point with respect to both the axis of tilt and the principal line no.

In Fig. 3–14 is shown a vertical section through the principal line of the tilted photograph of Fig. 3–13. An expression for the tilt displacement $c''c$ of point c is deduced as follows:

$$c''c = ic'' - ic = ic' - ic = (n'c' - n'i) - (io + oc)$$

But

$$n'c' = f \tan (t+\alpha)$$
$$n'i = Ln' \tan (t/2) = f \tan (t/2)$$
$$io = f \tan (t/2)$$
$$oc = f \tan \alpha$$

Therefore,

$$c''c = [f \tan (t+\alpha) - f \tan (t/2)] - [f \tan (t/2) + f \tan \alpha]$$

or

$$c''c = f [\tan (t+\alpha) - 2 \tan (t/2) - \tan \alpha]$$

The angle α is obtained by measuring the distance to the point from a line through the principal point and parallel with the axis of tilt. When the point lies on the principal line, as does point c, the distance is measured from the principal point itself to the image point. This

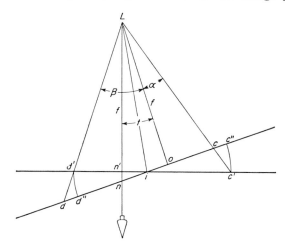

FIG. 3–14. Amount of tilt displacement.

distance is then divided by the focal length to obtain $\tan \alpha$. As indicated in Fig. 3–13, the tilt displacement of a point not lying on the principal line is greater than that of a corresponding point on the principal line. The ratio is equal to the secant of the angle at the isocenter from the principal line to the point. Therefore, the tilt displacement of a point on the upward half of a tilted photograph is inward and is given by the expression

$$d_U = f \sec I [\tan (t+\alpha) - 2 \tan (t/2) - \tan \alpha] \qquad (3\text{--}15)$$

For a point lying on the downward or nadir-point half, the tilt displacement is outward and is given by the expression

$$d_D = f \sec I [\tan \beta - \tan (\beta - t) - 2 \tan (t/2)] \qquad (3\text{--}16)$$

In Eqs. 3–15 and 3–16, d_U and d_D are, respectively, the tilt displacements for the upward and downward halves of the photograph, in inches or millimeters; f is the focal length, in inches or millimeters, corresponding to the desired units of d_U and d_D; I is the angle measured at the isocenter from the principal line to the point; t is the angle of tilt; α is the angle in the principal plane formed at the exposure station between the principal point and the projection onto the principal line of an image point on the upward half; and β is the angle in the principal plane formed at the exposure station between the principal point and the projection onto the principal line of an image point on the downward half.

EXAMPLE 3–11. A photograph with a focal length of 150 mm has a tilt of 2°30′. A point on the photograph lies on the half upward from the axis of tilt at a measured distance of 72.2 mm from a line through the principal point and parallel with the axis of tilt. The angle measured at the isocenter between the principal line and the point is 27°. Compute the tilt displacement.

Solution: Since tan α=72.2 mm/150 mm=0.48133, α=25° 42′. By Eq. 3–15,
$$d_U=150 \text{ sec } 27° \text{ [tan } (2° 30′+25° 42′)-2 \text{ tan } 1° 15′-\text{tan } 25° 42′]$$
$$=150×1.12233 \text{ [}0.53620-2×0.02182-0.48133]=1.89 \text{ mm}$$
Hence, the tilt displacement is 1.89 mm inward, or 1.89 mm toward the isocenter.

To gain some idea of the complexity of the combined effects of tilt and relief on the position of a point on a tilted photograph, consider Fig. 3–15. The position of each point marked *1* is the datum photograph position; that marked *2* is the position after the image has undergone

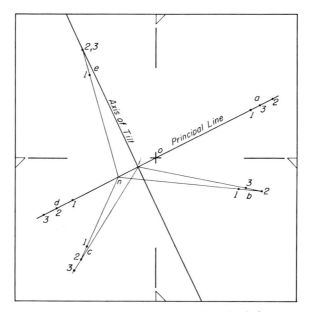

FIG. 3–15. Combined effects of tilt and relief.

relief displacement; and that marked *3* is the position after the image has been displaced due to tilt. For points *a* and *b*, the two displacements tend to cancel; for points *c* and *d*, the two displacements are cumulative; for point *e*, which lies on the axis of tilt, there is no tilt displacement. This complexity is compounded in photogrammetry by the fact that the amounts and directions of tilts are random and it is difficult to compute them.

In spite of scale variation, relief displacement, and tilt displacement, an aerial photograph taken with a calibrated precision aerial camera is a precise perspective view of the terrain. From such a photograph, precise measurements and highly accurate results may be obtained. This accuracy depends on adequate ground control surveys and calibrated photogrammetric instruments to be discussed later.

3–13. Orientation of a Photograph by Direction Cosines as Functions of Tilt, Swing, and Azimuth

Many problems in photogrammetry can be solved by application of the principles of solid analytic geometry. This approach to the solutions of problems in photogrammetry was introduced by the late Professor Earl Church in 1945 in *Photogrammetry Bulletin* No. 15, "Revised Geometry of the Aerial Photograph," published by the Syracuse University Press. The symbols used in this discussion are identical to those used in Bulletin 15, with the exception that n and N are used to denote the photograph nadir point and the ground nadir point, respectively, and α_{NO} is used to denote the azimuth of the principal plane.

Two sets of space coordinate axes are involved in the orientation of a photograph in space. In Fig. 3–16, the ground-survey coordinate axes are defined by the mutually perpendicular lines designated as X, Y, and Z. The Y-axis coincides with the ground-survey meridian or north-south line. The Z-axis is the direction in which elevations are measured. The photographic coordinate axes are defined by the lines joining opposite fiducial marks, together with the optical axis oL, and are designated as x, y, and z. The ground space coordinates of the exposure station are X_L, Y_L, and Z_L where Z_L is the flying height above the datum. The photographic space coordinates of the exposure station are the quantities $x_L = 0$, $y_L = 0$, and $z_L = +f$.

The elements of exterior orientation defined first in Sec. 3–2 are the tilt t, the swing s, and the azimuth α_{NO}. These angles are shown in Fig. 3–16. The orientation of the photograph with respect to the ground-survey axes can be defined by the relationship between the two sets of axes. In solid analytic geometry the direction of a line in space is defined by the angles which the line makes with the x-axis, y-axis, and z-axis, these angles being denoted by α, β, and γ. They are known as the direction angles of

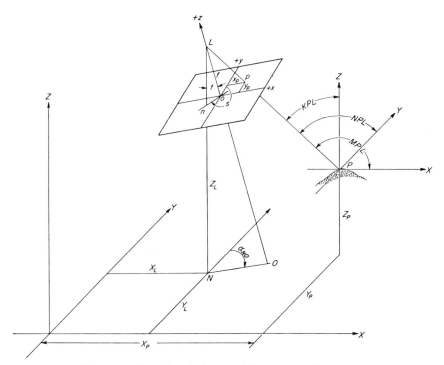

Fɪɢ. 3–16. Ground and photographic space coordinate axes.

the line; and their respective cosines, cos α, cos β, and cos γ, are called the direction cosines of the line.   Instead of using the Greek letters as symbols, Church designated the direction cosines of a line with respect to the photographic space coordinate axes as cos m, cos n, and cos k, where m, n, and k are, respectively, the angles formed between the line and the x-axis, y-axis, and z-axis.   For the direction cosines of a line with respect to the ground X-axis, Y-axis, and Z-axis, Church used the symbols cos M, cos N, and cos K, respectively.

The direction cosines of the angles formed between the photographic axes and the ground axes are derived in terms of the tilt, swing, and azimuth by rotational formulae of analytic geometry.   Imagine the ground X-, Y-, and Z-axes of Fig. 3–16 to be translated in space to a position in which the origin of this translated system coincides with the principal point of the photograph (the origin of the photographic axes). Each set of axes comprises a right-hand system in space.   The coordinates of a point referred to the photographic axes are designated x, y, z.   The coordinates of the same point referred to the translated ground axes are designated x_T, y_T, z_T.

In Fig. 3–17, the reader is assumed to be looking vertically downward

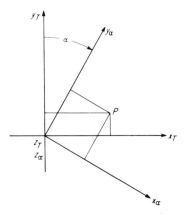

FIG. 3–17. Rotation through azimuth angle.

along the translated z_T axis. The coordinates of a point p are expressed as x_T, y_T, z_T. Imagine a set of axes rotated about the z_T axis in a clockwise direction through an angle α_{NO} to define a new set of axes x_a, y_a, z_a. This rotation is considered as a negative rotation in analytical geometry, resulting from the convention of measuring azimuths in a clockwise direction when looking down. Consequently, the coordinates of p referred to this rotated set of axes are

$$\left.\begin{aligned} x_a &= x_T \cos \alpha - y_T \sin \alpha \\ y_a &= x_T \sin \alpha + y_T \cos \alpha \\ z_a &= z_T \end{aligned}\right\} \tag{3–17}$$

The z-coordinate remains unchanged since the rotation took place about the z_T-axis. The y_a-axis lies in the direction of the principal plane.

In Fig. 3–18, the reader is assumed to be looking from the positive end of the x_a-axis toward the origin. The coordinates of point p are

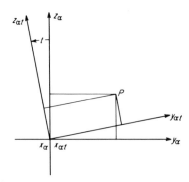

FIG. 3–18. Rotation through tilt angle.

x_a, y_a, z_a as defined by Eq. 3–17. Imagine a set of axes rotated about the x_a-axis through an angle t in a counterclockwise direction to a position in which the y_{at}-axis lies in the plane of the tilted photograph. This rotation must be counterclockwise in order to lower the nadir point side of the photograph (see Fig. 3–11). This makes the y_{at}-axis identical to the y'-axis of Fig. 3–11. The coordinates of p referred to this rotated set of axes are

$$\left.\begin{aligned} x_{at} &= x_a \\ y_{at} &= y_a \cos t + z_a \sin t \\ z_{at} &= -y_a \sin t + z_a \cos t \end{aligned}\right\} \quad (3\text{–}18)$$

The z_{at}-axis of Fig. 3–18 is now identical to the optical axis of the photograph (oL of Fig. 3–11).

In Fig. 3–19, the reader is assumed to be looking down on to the plane

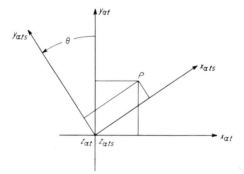

Fig. 3–19. Rotation through 180° minus swing angle.

of the photograph along the optical axis (the z_{at}-axis). The coordinates of point p are x_{at}, y_{at}, z_{at} as defined by Eq. 3–18. Imagine a set of axes rotated about the z_{at}-axis through a counterclockwise angle $\theta = 180° - s$ to a position in which the x_{ats}-axis and the y_{ats}-axis now coincide with the photographic x- and y-axes as defined by the fiducial marks. Since the z_{at}- and the z_{ats}-axes are identical, and since they coincide with the optical axis, then the z_{ats}-axis is the photographic z-axis. Thus, the coordinates of p become

$$\left.\begin{aligned} x &= x_{ats} = -x_{at} \cos s - y_{at} \sin s \\ y &= y_{ats} = x_{at} \sin s - y_{at} \cos s \\ z &= z_{ats} = z_{at} \end{aligned}\right\} \quad (3\text{–}19)$$

By combining the results of Eqs. 3–17, 3–18, and 3–19, the photographic coordinates x, y, z of a point, can be expressed in terms of the coordinates of the same point x_T, y_T, z_T, with respect to a set of axes parallel with the ground axes and having a common origin with the photographic coordinate axes, together with the tilt, swing, and azimuth of the principal plane, as follows:

$$
\left.
\begin{aligned}
x = &\ (-\cos s \cos \alpha_{NO} - \sin s \cos t \sin \alpha_{NO})x_T \\
 &\ + \quad (\cos s \sin \alpha_{NO} - \sin s \cos t \cos \alpha_{NO})y_T \\
 &\qquad\qquad\qquad + (-\sin s \sin t)z_T \\[6pt]
y = &\ (\sin s \cos \alpha_{NO} - \cos s \cos t \sin \alpha_{NO})x_T \\
 &\ + (-\sin s \sin \alpha_{NO} - \cos s \cos t \cos \alpha_{NO})y_T \\
 &\qquad\qquad\qquad + (-\cos s \sin t)z_T \\[6pt]
z = &\qquad\qquad\quad (-\sin t \sin \alpha_{NO})x_T \\
 &\ + \qquad\qquad\quad (-\sin t \cos \alpha_{NO})y_T \\
 &\qquad\qquad\qquad + \qquad (\cos t)z_T
\end{aligned}
\right\} \quad (3\text{--}20)
$$

The nine values in the parentheses are the direction cosines of the photographic axes with respect to the ground system of axes (a translation from ground origin to photo origin does not affect the direction angles), and can be tabulated in the form of an *orientation matrix* as follows:

$$
\mathbf{M} =
\begin{bmatrix}
\cos Mx & \cos Nx & \cos Kx \\
\cos My & \cos Ny & \cos Ky \\
\cos Mz & \cos Nz & \cos Kz
\end{bmatrix}
=
\begin{bmatrix}
m_{11} & m_{12} & m_{13} \\
m_{21} & m_{22} & m_{23} \\
m_{31} & m_{32} & m_{33}
\end{bmatrix}
\quad (3\text{--}21)
$$

in which $\cos Mx$ is the cosine of the angle which the photographic x-axis makes with the ground X-axis; $\cos Nx$ is the cosine of the angle which the photographic x-axis makes with the ground Y-axis; $\cos Kx$ is the cosine of the angle which the photographic x-axis makes with the ground Z-axis. Similarly, $\cos My$, $\cos Ny$, $\cos Ky$ are the cosines of the angles between the photographic y-axis and the ground X-, Y-, and Z-axes. Also, $\cos Mz$, $\cos Nz$, $\cos Kz$ are the cosines of the angles between the photographic z-axis (the optical axis) and the ground X-, Y-, and Z-axes.

In order to introduce the concept of matrix manipulations, particularly of multiplication, consider the form of Eq. 3–17. The coordinates x_a, y_a, and z_a are expressed as functions of the coordinates x_T, y_T, z_T. This equation can be stated in matrix form as

$$
\begin{bmatrix}
x_a \\
y_a \\
z_a
\end{bmatrix}
=
\begin{bmatrix}
\cos \alpha & -\sin \alpha & 0 \\
\sin \alpha & \cos \alpha & 0 \\
0 & 0 & 1
\end{bmatrix}
\begin{bmatrix}
x_T \\
y_T \\
z_T
\end{bmatrix}
\quad (3\text{--}22)
$$

The multiplication of the two matrices on the right side of Eq. 3–22 result in the terms of the right side of Eq. 3–17. Letting the matrix of the coefficients of Eq. 3–22 be denoted by $\mathbf{M}_a$, then

$$
\begin{bmatrix} x_a \\ y_a \\ z_a \end{bmatrix} = \mathbf{M}_a \begin{bmatrix} x_T \\ y_T \\ z_T \end{bmatrix} \tag{3-23}
$$

In similar fashion, Eq. 3–18 can be expressed as

$$
\begin{bmatrix} x_{at} \\ y_{at} \\ z_{at} \end{bmatrix} = \begin{bmatrix} 1 & 0 & 0 \\ 0 & \cos t & \sin t \\ 0 & -\sin t & \cos t \end{bmatrix} \begin{bmatrix} x_a \\ y_a \\ z_a \end{bmatrix} \tag{3-24}
$$

Then, letting the matrix of coefficients of Eq. 3–24 be denoted by $\mathbf{M}_t$, the resulting equation is

$$
\begin{bmatrix} x_{at} \\ y_{at} \\ z_{at} \end{bmatrix} = \mathbf{M}_t \begin{bmatrix} x_a \\ y_a \\ z_a \end{bmatrix} \tag{3-25}
$$

Also, Eq. 3–19 can be expressed in matrix form as

$$
\begin{bmatrix} x \\ y \\ z \end{bmatrix} = \begin{bmatrix} x_{ats} \\ y_{ats} \\ z_{ats} \end{bmatrix} = \begin{bmatrix} -\cos s & -\sin s & 0 \\ \sin s & -\cos s & 0 \\ 0 & 0 & 1 \end{bmatrix} \begin{bmatrix} x_{at} \\ y_{at} \\ z_{at} \end{bmatrix} \tag{3-26}
$$

Letting the matrix of coefficients of Eq. 3–26 be denoted by $\mathbf{M}_s$, the resulting equation is

$$
\begin{bmatrix} x \\ y \\ z \end{bmatrix} = \mathbf{M}_s \begin{bmatrix} x_{at} \\ y_{at} \\ z_{at} \end{bmatrix} \tag{3-27}
$$

Combining Eqs. 3–23, 3–25, and 3–27 gives

$$
\begin{bmatrix} x \\ y \\ z \end{bmatrix} = \mathbf{M}_s \mathbf{M}_t \mathbf{M}_a \begin{bmatrix} x_T \\ y_T \\ z_T \end{bmatrix} \tag{3-28}
$$

Multiplying the three coefficient matrices in the order shown in Eq. 3–28, gives the orientation matrix $\mathbf{M}$ defined by Eq. 3–21. The results are

$$
\begin{bmatrix} x \\ y \\ z \end{bmatrix} = \begin{bmatrix} -\cos s \cos \alpha_{NO} - \sin s \cos t \sin \alpha_{NO} \\ \sin s \cos \alpha_{NO} - \cos s \cos t \sin \alpha_{NO} \\ -\sin t \sin \alpha_{NO} \end{bmatrix}
$$

$$
\begin{matrix} \cos s \sin \alpha_{NO} - \sin s \cos t \cos \alpha_{NO} & -\sin s \sin t \\ -\sin s \sin \alpha_{NO} - \cos s \cos t \cos \alpha_{NO} & -\cos s \sin t \\ -\sin t \cos \alpha_{NO} & \cos t \end{matrix} \begin{bmatrix} x_T \\ y_T \\ z_T \end{bmatrix} \tag{3-29}
$$

or

$$
\begin{bmatrix} x \\ y \\ z \end{bmatrix} = \mathbf{M} \begin{bmatrix} x_T \\ y_T \\ z_T \end{bmatrix} \tag{3-30}
$$

The elements of the **M**-matrix can be identified by a comparison of Eqs. 3–21, 3–29, and 3–30. Thus,

$$\left.\begin{aligned}
\cos Mx &= -\cos s \cos \alpha_{N0} - \sin s \cos t \sin \alpha_{N0} \\
\cos Nx &= \cos s \sin \alpha_{N0} - \sin s \cos t \cos \alpha_{N0} \\
\cos Kx &= -\sin s \sin t \\
\cos My &= \sin s \cos \alpha_{N0} - \cos s \cos t \sin \alpha_{N0} \\
\cos Ny &= -\sin s \sin \alpha_{N0} - \cos s \cos t \cos \alpha_{N0} \\
\cos Ky &= -\cos s \sin t \\
\cos Mz &= -\sin t \sin \alpha_{N0} \\
\cos Nz &= -\sin t \cos \alpha_{N0} \\
\cos Kz &= \cos t
\end{aligned}\right\} \quad (3\text{–}31)$$

In the foregoing development, the photographic x, y, z, coordinates of a point are expressed as functions of $x_T y_T z_T$ coordinates of the point in a system which is parallel with the ground coordinate system together with the direction cosines of the photographic axes related to the ground system. The reverse relationship expresses the translated $x_T y_T z_T$ coordinates of a point as functions of the photographic coordinates of the point together with the direction cosines of the ground axes related to the photographic coordinate axis system.

The direction cosines given as elements of the matrix in Eq. 3–21 can be rearranged to form the orientation matrix for defining $x_T y_T z_T$ as functions of x, y, z. The following identities are obvious:

$$\left.\begin{aligned}
\cos Mx &= \cos mX & \cos Nx &= \cos mY & \cos Kx &= \cos mZ \\
\cos My &= \cos nX & \cos Ny &= \cos nY & \cos Ky &= \cos nZ \\
\cos Mz &= \cos kX & \cos Nz &= \cos kY & \cos Kz &= \cos kZ
\end{aligned}\right\} (3\text{–}32)$$

The orientation matrix for the reverse relationship is thus

$$\begin{bmatrix} \cos mX & \cos nX & \cos kX \\ \cos mY & \cos nY & \cos kY \\ \cos mZ & \cos nZ & \cos kZ \end{bmatrix} = \begin{bmatrix} m_{11} & m_{21} & m_{31} \\ m_{12} & m_{22} & m_{32} \\ m_{13} & m_{23} & m_{33} \end{bmatrix} = \mathbf{M}^T \quad (3\text{–}33)$$

The expression $\mathbf{M}^T$ signifies a matrix which is the transpose of the matrix **M** given by Eq. 3–21. It is obtained by putting rows of **M** into columns of $\mathbf{M}^T$. Because the matrix **M** is an orthogonal matrix, relating one set of axes to another (a line in one system does not change length when the end points are oriented to the other system), the translated coordinates can be stated as

$$\begin{bmatrix} x_T \\ y_T \\ z_T \end{bmatrix} = \mathbf{M}^T \begin{bmatrix} x \\ y \\ z \end{bmatrix} \quad (3\text{–}34)$$

This relationship can also be obtained by the rotational formulae. From Fig. 3–17,

$$\begin{matrix} x_T = x_a \cos \alpha + y_a \sin \alpha \\ y_T = -x_a \sin \alpha + y_a \cos \alpha \\ z_T = z_a \end{matrix} \quad \text{or} \quad \begin{bmatrix} x_T \\ z_T \\ y_T \end{bmatrix} = \begin{bmatrix} \cos \alpha & \sin \alpha & 0 \\ -\sin \alpha & \cos \alpha & 0 \\ 0 & 0 & 1 \end{bmatrix} \begin{bmatrix} x_a \\ y_a \\ z_a \end{bmatrix}$$

$$(3\text{-}35)$$

The matrix of coefficients of Eq. 3–35 is the transpose of the matrix of coefficients of Eq. 3–22. Thus,

$$\begin{bmatrix} x_T \\ y_T \\ z_T \end{bmatrix} = \mathbf{M}^T{}_a \begin{bmatrix} x_a \\ y_a \\ z_a \end{bmatrix} \qquad (3\text{-}36)$$

From Fig. 3–18,

$$\begin{matrix} x_a = x_{at} \\ y_a = y_{at} \cos t - z_{at} \sin t \\ z_a = y_{at} \sin t + z_{at} \cos t \end{matrix} \quad \text{or} \quad \begin{bmatrix} x_a \\ y_a \\ z_a \end{bmatrix} = \begin{bmatrix} 1 & 0 & 0 \\ 0 & \cos t & -\sin t \\ 0 & \sin t & \cos t \end{bmatrix} \begin{bmatrix} x_{at} \\ y_{at} \\ z_{at} \end{bmatrix}$$

$$(3\text{-}37)$$

The matrix of coefficients of Eq. 3–37 is the transpose of the matrix of coefficients of Eq. 3–24. Thus,

$$\begin{bmatrix} x_a \\ y_a \\ z_a \end{bmatrix} = \mathbf{M}^T{}_t \begin{bmatrix} x_{at} \\ y_{at} \\ z_{at} \end{bmatrix} \qquad (3\text{-}38)$$

From Fig. 3–19,

$$\begin{matrix} x_{at} = -x_{ats} \cos s + y_{ats} \sin s \\ y_{at} = -x_{ats} \sin s - y_{ats} \cos s \\ z_{at} = z_{ats} \end{matrix} \quad \text{or} \quad \begin{bmatrix} x_{at} \\ y_{at} \\ z_{at} \end{bmatrix} = \begin{bmatrix} -\cos s & \sin s & 0 \\ -\sin s & -\cos s & 0 \\ 0 & 0 & 1 \end{bmatrix} \begin{bmatrix} x_{ats} \\ y_{ats} \\ z_{ats} \end{bmatrix}$$

$$(3\text{-}39)$$

The matrix of coefficients of Eq. 3–39 is the transpose of the matrix of coefficients of Eq. 3–26. Therefore, since x_{ats}, y_{ats}, z_{ats} are the photographic coordinates,

$$\begin{bmatrix} x_{at} \\ y_{at} \\ z_{at} \end{bmatrix} = \mathbf{M}^T{}_s \begin{bmatrix} x \\ y \\ z \end{bmatrix} \qquad (3\text{-}40)$$

Combining Eqs. 3–36, 3–38, and 3–40 gives

$$\begin{bmatrix} x_T \\ y_T \\ z_T \end{bmatrix} = \mathbf{M}^T{}_a \mathbf{M}^T{}_t \mathbf{M}^T{}_s \begin{bmatrix} x \\ y \\ z \end{bmatrix} \qquad (3\text{-}41)$$

A comparison of Eq. 3–28 with Eq. 3–41 shows that if $\mathbf{M} = \mathbf{M}_s \mathbf{M}_t \mathbf{M}_a$, then

$$M^T = M^T_a M^T_t M^T_s \tag{3-42}$$

This demonstrates a rule of matrix operation which states that if a matrix **M** is the result of the multiplication of two or more matrices in a given order, the transpose matrix M^T is equal to the product of the transpose of each but taken in reverse order.

The orientation matrix M^T can be expressed as functions of the tilt, swing, and azimuth by the multiplication indicated in Eq. 3–42, in which the values of M^T_a, M^T_t, and M^T_s are obtained from Eqs. 3–35, 3–37, and 3–39.

$$M^T = \begin{bmatrix} \cos\alpha & \sin\alpha & 0 \\ -\sin\alpha & \cos\alpha & 0 \\ 0 & 0 & 1 \end{bmatrix} \begin{bmatrix} 1 & 0 & 0 \\ 0 & \cos t & -\sin t \\ 0 & \sin t & \cos t \end{bmatrix} \begin{bmatrix} -\cos s & \sin s & 0 \\ -\sin s & -\cos s & 0 \\ 0 & 0 & 1 \end{bmatrix}$$

$$\tag{3-43}$$

Finally, the translated coordinates x_T, y_T, z_T are expressed as functions of the photographic coordinates and the orientation angles according to the following:

$$\begin{bmatrix} x_T \\ y_T \\ z_T \end{bmatrix} = \begin{bmatrix} -\cos s \cos \alpha_{NO} - \sin s \cos t \sin \alpha_{NO} & \sin s \cos \alpha_{NO} - \cos s \cos t \sin \alpha_{NO} & -\sin t \sin \alpha_{NO} \\ \cos s \sin \alpha_{NO} - \sin s \cos t \cos \alpha_{NO} & -\sin s \sin \alpha_{NO} - \cos s \cos t \cos \alpha_{NO} & -\sin t \cos \alpha_{NO} \\ -\sin s \sin t & -\cos s \sin t & \cos t \end{bmatrix} \begin{bmatrix} x \\ y \\ z \end{bmatrix}$$

$$\tag{3-44}$$

Note that Eq. 3–44, which is the inverse of Eq. 3–29, can be obtained directly from Eq. 3–29 by transposing the rows of the former orientation matrix into columns of the latter.

An examination of Eqs. 3–31 and 3–32 give the elements of the M^T matrix as

$$\left. \begin{aligned} \cos mX &= -\cos s \cos \alpha_{NO} - \sin s \cos t \sin \alpha_{NO} \\ \cos nX &= \sin s \cos \alpha_{NO} - \cos s \cos t \sin \alpha_{NO} \\ \cos kX &= -\sin t \sin \alpha_{NO} \\ \cos mY &= \cos s \sin \alpha_{NO} - \sin s \cos t \cos \alpha_{NO} \\ \cos nY &= -\sin s \sin \alpha_{NO} - \cos s \cos t \cos \alpha_{NO} \\ \cos kY &= -\sin t \cos \alpha_{NO} \\ \cos mZ &= -\sin s \sin t \\ \cos nZ &= -\cos s \sin t \\ \cos kZ &= \cos t \end{aligned} \right\} \tag{3-45}$$

If the elements of the orientation matrix **M** or M^T are known, the elements of exterior orientation can be computed by the following formulae, deduced from Eqs. 3–31 and 3–45:

$$\cos t = \cos Kz = \cos kZ$$

$$\tan s = \frac{\cos Kx}{\cos Ky} = \frac{\cos mZ}{\cos nZ}$$

$$\tan \alpha_{NO} = \frac{\cos Mz}{\cos Nz} = \frac{\cos kX}{\cos kY}$$

$$(3\text{--}46)$$

The algebraic signs of sin s and cos s determine the quadrant in which the swing lies, and are obtained by the relationships

$$\sin s = -\frac{\cos Kx}{\sin t} = -\frac{\cos mZ}{\sin t}$$

and

$$\cos s = -\frac{\cos Ky}{\sin t} = \frac{\cos nZ}{\sin t}$$

The algebraic signs of sin α_{NO} and cos α_{NO} determine the quadrant in which the azimuth of the principal plane lies, and are obtained by the relationships

$$\sin \alpha_{NO} = -\frac{\cos Mz}{\sin t} = -\frac{\cos kX}{\sin t}$$

and

$$\cos \alpha_{NO} = -\frac{\cos Nz}{\sin t} = -\frac{\cos kY}{\sin t}$$

3–14. Orientation of a Photograph by Direction Cosines as Functions of the Rotation Angles ω, ϕ, and κ

Many problems in analytical photogrammetry depend for their solution on a set of approximate initial values of the elements of exterior orientation which are then corrected by successive iterations through the mathematical process. In aerial photogrammetry, the first approximation is usually an assumed truly vertical photograph. In this instant, the tilt angle is zero, but the swing and azimuth then are indeterminate or non-existant. For this reason, most photogrammetrists and mathematicians dealing with analytical aerial photogrammetry employ the rotational angles ω, ϕ, and κ defined in Sec. 3–2.

The rotational angles are used to designate the mechanical rotational axes of precise stereoscopic plotting instruments as discussed in Chapter 12. For this reason also, adoption of the angles ω, ϕ, and κ are convenient and advantageous.

The sequence of rotations employed to formulate the relations between the coordinates of a point in the photographic system to its coordinates in a system parallel with the ground axes is a matter of choice, but in order to conform to the practice in the United States, the sequence adopted in this discussion will be x-axis (ω) primary; y-axis (ϕ) secondary; and z-axis (κ) tertiary.

Consider a right-hand set of axes in space, parallel with the ground axes, and in which the origin of coordinates occupies the principal point of an aerial photograph. The coordinates of a point with respect to this set of axes is designated x_T, y_T, z_T, as shown in Fig. 3–20. The ω-, ϕ-, and

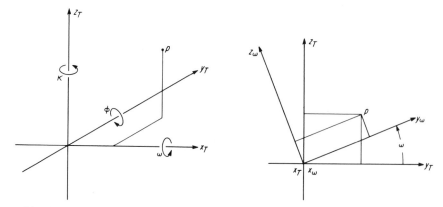

Fig. 3–20. The ω, ϕ, and κ rotations.   Fig. 3–21. Rotation through angle ω.

κ-rotations are indicated, together with the positive sense of rotation according to the right-hand rule. In Fig. 3-21, the reader is looking from the positive end of the x_T-axis toward the origin. A rotation about the x_T-axis through angle ω produces the x_ω-, y_ω-, and z_ω-coordinates of a point given by the following relation:

$$
\begin{aligned}
x_\omega &= x_T \\
y_\omega &= y_T \cos \omega + z_T \sin \omega \\
z_\omega &= -y_T \sin \omega + z_T \cos \omega
\end{aligned}
\quad \text{or} \quad
\begin{bmatrix} x_\omega \\ y_\omega \\ z_\omega \end{bmatrix}
=
\begin{bmatrix}
1 & 0 & 0 \\
0 & \cos \omega & \sin \omega \\
0 & -\sin \omega & \cos \omega
\end{bmatrix}
\begin{bmatrix} x_T \\ y_T \\ z_T \end{bmatrix}
$$

$$
= \mathbf{M}_\omega \begin{bmatrix} x_T \\ y_T \\ z_T \end{bmatrix}
\tag{3-47}
$$

In Fig. 3-22, the reader is looking from the positive end of the once-rotated y_ω-axis toward the origin. A rotation about the y_ω-axis through angle ϕ produces the $x_{\omega\phi}$-, $y_{\omega\phi}$-, and $z_{\omega\phi}$-coordinates of the point given by

$$x_{\omega\phi} = x_\omega \cos\phi - z_\omega \sin\phi$$
$$y_{\omega\phi} = y_\omega$$
$$z_{\omega\phi} = x_\omega \sin\phi + z_\omega \cos\phi$$

or

$$\begin{bmatrix} x_{\omega\phi} \\ y_{\omega\phi} \\ z_{\omega\phi} \end{bmatrix} = \begin{bmatrix} \cos\phi & 0 & -\sin\phi \\ 0 & 1 & 0 \\ \sin\phi & 0 & \cos\phi \end{bmatrix} \begin{bmatrix} x_\omega \\ y_\omega \\ z_\omega \end{bmatrix}$$

$$= \mathbf{M}_\phi \begin{bmatrix} x_\omega \\ y_\omega \\ z_\omega \end{bmatrix} \qquad (3\text{-}48)$$

In Fig. 3-23, the reader is looking from the positive end of the twice-rotated $z_{\omega\phi}$-axis (which coincides with the optical axis of the photograph)

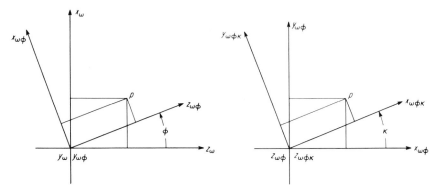

FIG. 3–22. Rotation through angle ϕ.   FIG. 3–23. Rotation through angle κ.

toward the origin. A rotation about the $z_{\omega\phi}$-axis through angle κ brings the final-rotated axes into coincidence with the photographic axes. The $x_{\omega\phi\kappa}$-, $y_{\omega\phi\kappa}$-, and $z_{\omega\phi\kappa}$-coordinates of the point are given by the rotation formulae as

$$x_{\omega\phi\kappa} = x_{\omega\phi} \cos\kappa + y_{\omega\phi} \sin\kappa$$
$$y_{\omega\phi\kappa} = -x_{\omega\phi} \sin\kappa + y_{\omega\phi} \cos\kappa$$
$$z_{\omega\phi\kappa} = z_{\omega\phi}$$

or

$$\begin{bmatrix} x_{\omega\phi\kappa} \\ y_{\omega\phi\kappa} \\ z_{\omega\phi\kappa} \end{bmatrix} = \begin{bmatrix} \cos\kappa & \sin\kappa & 0 \\ -\sin\kappa & \cos\kappa & 0 \\ 0 & 0 & 1 \end{bmatrix} \begin{bmatrix} x_{\omega\phi} \\ y_{\omega\phi} \\ z_{\omega\phi} \end{bmatrix}$$

$$= \mathbf{M}_\kappa \begin{bmatrix} x_{\omega\phi} \\ y_{\omega\phi} \\ z_{\omega\phi} \end{bmatrix} \qquad (3\text{-}49)$$

Remembering that $x_{\omega\phi\kappa}$, $y_{\omega\phi\kappa}$, and $z_{\omega\phi\kappa}$ are the photographic coordinates x, y, z, then combining Eqs. 3–47, 3–48, and 3–49 gives

$$\begin{bmatrix} x \\ y \\ z \end{bmatrix} = \mathbf{M}_\kappa \mathbf{M}_\phi \mathbf{M}_\omega \begin{bmatrix} x_T \\ y_T \\ z_T \end{bmatrix} = \mathbf{M} \begin{bmatrix} x_T \\ y_T \\ z_T \end{bmatrix} \qquad (3\text{-}50)$$

Multiplying the matrices $\mathbf{M}_\kappa$, $\mathbf{M}_\phi$, and $\mathbf{M}_\omega$ gives $\mathbf{M}$, thus

$$\mathbf{M} = \begin{bmatrix} \cos\kappa & \sin\kappa & 0 \\ -\sin\kappa & \cos\kappa & 0 \\ 0 & 0 & 1 \end{bmatrix} \begin{bmatrix} \cos\phi & 0 & -\sin\phi \\ 0 & 1 & 0 \\ \sin\phi & 0 & \cos\phi \end{bmatrix} \begin{bmatrix} 1 & 0 & 0 \\ 0 & \cos\omega & \sin\omega \\ 0 & -\sin\omega & \cos\omega \end{bmatrix}$$

$$\mathbf{M} = \begin{bmatrix} \cos\phi\cos\kappa & \cos\omega\sin\kappa + \sin\omega\sin\phi\cos\kappa \\ -\cos\phi\sin\kappa & \cos\omega\cos\kappa - \sin\omega\sin\phi\sin\kappa \\ \sin\phi & -\sin\omega\cos\phi \end{bmatrix}$$

$$\begin{matrix} \sin\omega\sin\kappa - \cos\omega\sin\phi\cos\kappa \\ \sin\omega\cos\kappa + \cos\omega\sin\phi\sin\kappa \\ \cos\omega\cos\phi \end{matrix} \Bigg] \qquad (3\text{-}51)$$

The orientation matrix $\mathbf{M}$ given by Eq. 3–51 comprises the nine direction cosines relating the photographic axes to the ground axes. For a photograph with a given position in space, this matrix is identical element for element with the matrix of coefficients given in Eq. 3–29. As a parallel to Eq. 3–21, the orientation matrix is stated as follows:

$$\mathbf{M} = \begin{bmatrix} \cos Xx & \cos Yx & \cos Zx \\ \cos Xy & \cos Yy & \cos Zy \\ \cos Xz & \cos Yz & \cos Zz \end{bmatrix} = \begin{bmatrix} m_{11} & m_{12} & m_{13} \\ m_{21} & m_{22} & m_{23} \\ m_{31} & m_{32} & m_{33} \end{bmatrix} \qquad (3\text{-}52)$$

The symbols Xx, Yx, Zx, etc., are used in place of Mx, Nx, Kx, etc., to conform with current terminology. Numerical values of these elements, however, are identical between the two matrices for any given aerial photograph.

The inverse of Eq. 3–50 is obtained by transposing each individual matrix and multiplying in reverse order. That is,

$$\mathbf{M}^T = \mathbf{M}^T_\omega \, \mathbf{M}^T_\phi \, \mathbf{M}^T_\kappa$$

and

$$\begin{bmatrix} x_T \\ y_T \\ z_T \end{bmatrix} = \mathbf{M}^T \begin{bmatrix} x \\ z \\ y \end{bmatrix} \qquad (3\text{-}53)$$

The elements of the $\mathbf{M}^T$ matrix in terms of functions of ω, ϕ, and κ can be obtained by transposing the rows of Eq. 3–51 to columns, thus

$$\mathbf{M}^T = \begin{bmatrix} \cos\phi\cos\kappa \\ \cos\omega\sin\kappa + \sin\omega\sin\phi\cos\kappa \\ \sin\omega\sin\kappa - \cos\omega\sin\phi\cos\kappa \end{bmatrix}$$

$$\begin{matrix} -\cos\phi\sin\kappa & \sin\phi \\ \cos\omega\cos\kappa - \sin\omega\sin\phi\sin\kappa & -\sin\omega\cos\phi \\ \sin\omega\cos\kappa + \cos\omega\sin\phi\sin\kappa & \cos\omega\cos\phi \end{matrix} \Bigg] \qquad (3\text{-}54)$$

3–15.   Direction of a Line by Photographic Coordinate Measurements

Let it be assumed that the orientation matrix $\mathbf{M}^T$ given by Eq. 3–33 the elements of which are given in Eq. 3–45 is known for the photograph shown in Fig. 3–16. This matrix fixes the ground coordinate axes with respect to the photographic space coordinate axes. The problem here is to determine the direction of the line PL of Fig. 3–16 with respect to the ground axes or, in other words, to establish cos MPL, cos NPL, and cos KPL, which stand for cos M of the line PL, cos N of the line PL, and cos K of the line PL. The angles MPL, NPL, and KPL are shown in Fig. 3–16.

The direction of the same line pL is first determined with respect to the photographic coordinate axes by finding cos mpL, cos npL, and cos

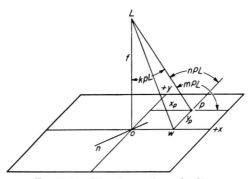

Fig. 3–24.   Direction cosines of a line.

kpL. The three direction angles are shown in Fig. 3–24. From analytic geometry, the length of a line in space is given by the equation

$$l = \sqrt{(x_2 - x_1)^2 + (y_2 - y_1)^2 + (z_2 - z_1)^2} \qquad (3\text{-}55)$$

Also, the direction cosines of the line are given by the following equations:

$$\cos \alpha = \frac{x_2 - x_1}{l} \qquad (3\text{-}56)$$

$$\cos \beta = \frac{y_2 - y_1}{l} \qquad (3\text{-}57)$$

$$\cos \gamma = \frac{z_2 - z_1}{l} \qquad (3\text{-}58)$$

As seen from Fig. 3–24, the photographic x-, y-, and z-coordinates of point p are x_p, y_p, and 0, and the photographic x-, y-, and z-coordinates of L are 0, 0, and $+f$. The values of x_p and y_p are measured on the photograph, and the value of f is obtained by camera calibration. The length of the line pL, by Eq. 3–55, is

$$pL = \sqrt{(0-x_p)^2 + (0-y_p)^2 + (f-0)^2} = \sqrt{x_p{}^2 + y_p{}^2 + f^2} \qquad (3\text{-}59)$$

The direction cosine of the line pL with respect to the photographic x-axis is, by Eq. 3-56,

$$\cos mpL = \frac{0-x_p}{\sqrt{x_p{}^2 + y_p{}^2 + f^2}} = \frac{-x_p}{pL} \qquad (3\text{-}60)$$

The direction cosine of the line pL with respect to the photographic y-axis is, by Eq. 3-57,

$$\cos npL = \frac{0-y_p}{\sqrt{x_p{}^2 + y_p{}^2 + f^2}} = \frac{-y_p}{pL} \qquad (3\text{-}61)$$

The direction cosine of the line pL with respect to the photographic z-axis is, by Eq. 3-58,

$$\cos kpL = \frac{f-0}{\sqrt{x_p{}^2 + y_p{}^2 + f^2}} = \frac{+f}{pL} \qquad (3\text{-}62)$$

Again, from analytic geometry, the angle θ formed between two lines *1* and *2* in space can be found from their direction cosines $\cos \alpha_1$, $\cos \beta_1$, and $\cos \gamma_1$ and $\cos \alpha_2$, $\cos \beta_2$, and $\cos \gamma_2$ by the equation

$$\cos \theta = \cos \alpha_1 \cos \alpha_2 + \cos \beta_1 \cos \beta_2 + \cos \gamma_1 \cos \gamma_2 \qquad (3\text{-}63)$$

In Fig. 3-16, it is seen that the lines pL and PL are identical. The cosine of the angle formed between the line PL and the ground coordinate X-axis can therefore be obtained by Eq. 3-59. This angle is MPL and its cosine is $\cos MPL$. Thus,

$$\cos MPL = \cos mpL \cos mX + \cos npL \cos nX + \cos kpL \cos kX \qquad (3\text{-}64)$$

Similarly, the equation for the cosine of the angle formed between the line PL and the ground coordinate Y-axis is

$$\cos NPL = \cos mpL \cos mY + \cos npL \cos nY + \cos kpL \cos kY \qquad (3\text{-}65)$$

Also, the equation for the cosine of the angle formed between the line PL and the ground coordinate Z-axis is

$$\cos KPL = \cos mpL \cos mZ + \cos npL \cos nZ + \cos kpL \cos kZ \qquad (3\text{-}66)$$

These three direction cosines completely fix the direction of the line PL in space with respect to the ground axes.

An examination of Eqs. 3-64, 3-65, and 3-66 indicates that the direction cosines of PL can be obtained by matrix multiplication as follows:

$$\begin{bmatrix} \cos MPL \\ \cos NPL \\ \cos KPL \end{bmatrix} = \begin{bmatrix} \cos mX & \cos nX & \cos kX \\ \cos mY & \cos nY & \cos kY \\ \cos mZ & \cos nZ & \cos kZ \end{bmatrix} \begin{bmatrix} \cos mpL \\ \cos npL \\ \cos kpL \end{bmatrix} \qquad (3\text{-}67)$$

or

$$\begin{bmatrix} \cos\ MPL \\ \cos\ NPL \\ \cos\ KPL \end{bmatrix} = \mathbf{M}^T \begin{bmatrix} \cos\ mpL \\ \cos\ npL \\ \cos\ kpL \end{bmatrix} \qquad (3\text{--}68)$$

Assume now that the ground space coordinates X_L, Y_L, and Z_L of the exposure station are known, together with the orientation matrix of the photograph. The equation of the line PL can then be formed from the general equation of a line in space given in analytic geometry. From analytic geometry,

$$\frac{x_2 - x_1}{\cos\ \alpha} = \frac{y_2 - y_1}{\cos\ \beta} = \frac{z_2 - z_1}{\cos\ \gamma} \qquad (3\text{--}69)$$

Therefore, the equation of the line PL can be written as follows:

$$\frac{X_L - X_P}{\cos\ MPL} = \frac{Y_L - Y_P}{\cos\ NPL} = \frac{Z_L - Z_P}{\cos\ KPL} \qquad (3\text{--}70)$$

Note that the quantity $Z_L - Z_P = H - h_P$.

If there is only a single photograph, the ground X- and Y-coordinates of a point P of known elevation can be found by applying Eq. 3–70 to formulate the equation of the line from the point P to the exposure station, and solving the resulting equation for the desired coordinates. Thus,

$$X_P = X_L - \frac{\cos\ MPL}{\cos\ KPL}(Z_L - Z_P) \qquad (3\text{--}71)$$

$$Y_P = Y_L - \frac{\cos\ NPL}{\cos\ KPL}(Z_L - Z_P) \qquad (3\text{--}72)$$

When two consecutive overlapping photographs of known orientation and position are available, the equation of two lines, one from each exposure station to a common ground point, can be written. These two equations can be solved simultaneously to determine the X-, Y-, and Z-coordinates of the point; the Z-coordinate is, of course, the elevation of the point.

3–16. Projective Transformation

Projectivity between a point on the ground (the object) and a point on a photograph (the image) can be defined in terms of the cooordinates of the point in the object coordinate system, the coordinates of the point in the photographic coordinate system, the coordinates of the perspective center in both systems, and the orientation matrix $\mathbf{M}$ relating the two coordinate systems.

In Fig. 3–25, two parallel systems of coordinate axes are shown, the

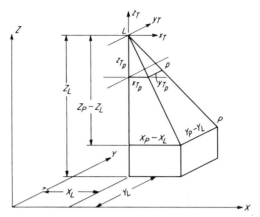

Fɪɢ. 3–25.   Coordinate axes defining projective transformation.

x_T, y_T, z_T system, and the ground X, Y, Z system.   The origin of coordinates of the x_T, y_T, z_T system is taken at the exposure station for the sake
of convenience and clarity of development.   This assumes, of course, that
the origin of coordinates of the photographic x, y, z system is also taken
at the exposure station.   The ground system coordinates of the exposure
station are X_L, Y_L, Z_L.

By similar triangles, it can be seen that

$$\frac{x_T}{X_P-X_L}=\frac{y_T}{Y_P-Y_L}=\frac{z_T}{Z_P-Z_L} \tag{3–73}$$

giving

$$x_T=\frac{X_P-X_L}{Z_P-Z_L}z_T$$

$$y_T=\frac{Y_P-Y_L}{Z_P-Z_L}z_T \tag{3–74}$$

$$z_T=\frac{Z_P-Z_L}{Z_P-Z_L}z_T$$

Then, by Eqs. 3–21 and 3–30,

$$
\begin{bmatrix} x \\ y \\ z \end{bmatrix}
=
\begin{bmatrix}
m_{11} & m_{12} & m_{13} \\
m_{21} & m_{22} & m_{23} \\
m_{31} & m_{32} & m_{33}
\end{bmatrix}
\begin{bmatrix}
\dfrac{X_P-X_L}{Z_P-Z_L}z_T \\[2ex]
\dfrac{Y_P-Y_L}{Z_P-Z_L}z_T \\[2ex]
\dfrac{Z_P-Z_L}{Z_P-Z_L}z_T
\end{bmatrix}
\tag{3–75}
$$

or

$$x = \frac{m_{11}(X_P - X_L)z_T}{(Z_P - Z_L)} + \frac{m_{12}(Y_P - Y_L)z_T}{(Z_P - Z_L)} + \frac{m_{13}(Z_P - Z_L)z_T}{(Z_P - Z_L)}$$

$$y = \frac{m_{21}(X_P - X_L)z_T}{(Z_P - Z_L)} + \frac{m_{22}(Y_P - Y_L)z_T}{(Z_P - Z_L)} + \frac{m_{23}(Z_P - Z_L)z_T}{(Z_P - Z_L)} \qquad (3\text{--}76)$$

$$z = \frac{m_{31}(X_P - X_L)z_T}{(Z_P - Z_L)} + \frac{m_{32}(Y_P - Y_L)z_T}{(Z_P - Z_L)} + \frac{m_{33}(Z_P - Z_L)z_T}{(Z_P - Z_L)}$$

from whence

$$\frac{x}{z} = \frac{(X_P - X_L)m_{11} + (Y_P - Y_L)m_{12} + (Z_P - Z_L)m_{13}}{(X_P - X_L)m_{31} + (Y_P - Y_L)m_{32} + (Z_P - Z_L)m_{33}}$$

$$\frac{y}{z} = \frac{(X_P - X_L)m_{21} + (Y_P - Y_L)m_{22} + (Z_P - Z_L)m_{23}}{(X_P - X_L)m_{31} + (Y_P - Y_L)m_{32} + (Z_P - Z_L)m_{33}} \qquad (3\text{--}77)$$

Equation 3–77 constitute the projective transformation equations expressing the relationship between a point on a photograph and its position on the ground. It expresses the condition of collinearity which states that the object point, the perspective center (exposure station or nodal point of lens) and the corresponding image point all lie on the same line. Since the origin of coordinates of the photograph has been assumed to occupy the exposure station, the value of the z-coordinate in Eq. 3–77 on the photograph is $-f$. The photographic x- and y-coordinates are assumed to be free of systematic effects of atmospheric refraction, lens distortion and film distortion.

If the photograph is truly vertical, the orientation matrix then becomes

$$\mathbf{M}_V = \mathbf{M}^T_V = \begin{bmatrix} 1 & 0 & 0 \\ 0 & 1 & 0 \\ 0 & 0 & 1 \end{bmatrix} \qquad (3\text{--}78)$$

Also, if X_L and Y_L are assumed to be zero, and $Z_L = H$, Eq. 3–77 reduces to Eqs. 3–5 and 3–6. It is of interest to note that in the tilt, swing, azimuth orientation system if a vertical photograph is assumed, the swing is then assumed to be 180° and the azimuth of the principal plane is assumed to be 0°. Compare Figs. 3–5 and 3–11.

The collinearity condition equations are extremely useful to many problems in photogrammetry for which the solution is based on plate coordinate measurements and analytic geometry. On examining these equations, it can be seen that they contain 12 quantities, two of which are measured in the photogrammetric process. These quantities are the measured x- and y-photographic coordinates of a point, the X-, Y-, and Z-ground coordinates of the point, the X-, Y-, and Z-ground coordinates of the exposure station, the focal length of the camera, and the orientation elements ω, ϕ, and κ or t, s, and α_{xo}. In some problems, only the ground coordinates of control points are presumed to be known. Plate coordinate measurements of the images of a sufficient number of ground points allows the determination of the interior orientation of the camera.

If the interior orientation is known, then a system of ground control points enables the solution of the space position and orientation of the photograph. On the other hand, if the interior and exterior orientations are known, then photographic plate coordinate measurements of image points permit the determination of ground coordinates.

Sections 3–13 through 3–16 are intended to give a brief introduction into the subject of analytic photogrammetry. The development of this subject has been extremely intensive in recent years, partly out of necessity due to restrictions imposed by photogrammetric instrumentation systems, and partly due to the facility with which automatic read-out systems and high-speed electronic computers can be employed. A wealth of literature is available on this subject, some of which is cited in the bibliography. The student should endeavor to appreciate fully the significance of these sections because they are fundamental to a better understanding of the principles of both analytic and instrumental photogrammetry.

Bibliography

AMERICAN SOCIETY OF PHOTOGRAMMETRY. *Manual of Photogrammetry* (Menasha, Wisc.: George Banta Co., 1952), Chapter 6.

———. *Manual of Photogrammetry* (Menasha, Wisc.: George Banta Co., 1966), Chapters 2 and 10.

ARTHUR, D. W. G. "Recent Developments in Analytical Aerial Triangulation at the Ordnance Survey," *Photogrammetric Record*, Vol. III (1959), p. 112.

BARROW, CRAN H. "Very Accurate Correction of Aerial Photographs for the Effects of Atmospheric Refraction and Earth's Curvature," *Photogrammetric Engineering*, Vol. XXVI (1960), p. 798.

BERTRAM, S. "Atmospheric Refraction," *Photogrammetric Engineering*, Vol. XXXII (1966), p. 76.

CHURCH, EARL. "Revised Geometry of the Aerial Photograph," *Photogrammetry Bulletin* No. 15, Syracuse University Press, 1945.

———, and QUINN, A. O. *Elements of Photogrammetry*, Syracuse University Press, 1948.

DOYLE, F. J. "The Historic Development of Analytical Photogrammetry," *Photogrammetric Engineering*, Vol. XXX (1964), p. 259.

EL-ASSAL, A. A. "Analytical Aerotriangulation at the University of Illinois," *Photogrammetric Engineering*, Vol. XXIX (1963), p. 199.

FAULDS, A. H., and BROCK, R. H. "Atmospheric Refraction and Its Distortion of Aerial Photographs," *Photogrammetric Engineering*, Vol. XXX (1964), p. 292.

HALLERT, B. *Photogrammetry* (New York: McGraw-Hill Book Co., 1960), Appendix A.

LIGHT, D. L. "The Orientation Matrix," *Photogrammetric Engineering,* Vol. XXXII (1966), p. 434.

LUCAS, J. R. "Differentiation of the Orientation Matrix by Matrix Multipliers," *Photogrammetric Engineering,* Vol. XXIX (1963), p. 708.

McNEIL G. T. "Two Methods of Determining Flying Height," *Photogrammetric Engineering,* Vol. XIV (1948), p. 311.

MIKHAIL, E. M. "Use of Triplets for Analytical Aerotriangulation," *Photogrammetric Engineering,* Vol. XXVIII (1962), p. 625.

———. "Use of Two-Directional Triplets in a Sub-Block Approach for Analytical Aerotriangulation," *Photogrammetric Engineering,* Vol. XXIX (1963), p. 1014.

ROSENFIELD, G. H. "The Application of Analytical Photogrammetry to Missile Trajectory Measurement," *Photogrammetric Engineering,* Vol. XXVII (1961). p. 547.

SCHUT, G. H. "Experiences with Analytical Methods in Photogrammetry," *Photogrammetric Engineering,* Vol. XXVI, No. 4 (Sept. 1960), p. 564.

WEIGHTMAN, J. A. "Analytical Procedures in Photogrammetry," *Photogrammetric Record,"* Vol. III (1961), p. 483.

WILSON, R. C. "The Relief Displacement Factor in Forest Area Estimates by Dot Templets on Aerial Photographs," *Photogrammetric Engineering,* Vol. XV (1949), p. 225.

WOOD, E. S., JR. "Photogrammetry for the Non-Photogrammetrist," *Photogrammetric Engineering,* Vol. XV (1949), p. 249.

Problems

3–1. A vertical photograph is taken with a lens having a focal length of 6 in. from a flying height of 9,000 ft above an airport whose elevation is 1,075 ft above sea level. Determine the representative fraction expressing the scale of the photograph at a point whose elevation above sea level is 1,525 ft.

3–2. How high above sea level must an aircraft fly in order that photographs at a scale of 1 in.=500 ft may be obtained, if the focal length is 8.25 in. and the average elevation of the terrain is 800 ft?

3–3. A distance measured on a vertical photograph between two points, both lying at a ground elevation of 850 ft, scales 3.255 in. The focal length of the camera is 6.020 in. The distance between the same two points measures 0.956 in. on a map which is at a scale of 1:24,000. Compute the flying height above sea level at which the photograph was taken. What is the datum scale of the photograph?

3–4. Photographs are to be taken for preparing a highway design map. The lowest elevation in the area to be photographed is 710 ft, and the highest elevation is 1,600 ft. The minimum photographic scale is to be 1:6000. What must be the flying height above sea level if the camera to be used contains a lens with a focal length of 152.4 mm? What will be the maximum scale?

3–5. A continuous-strip camera containing an 8.25 in. lens is to be used to photograph an existing highway from a low altitude in order to examine the condition of the pavement and the drainage ditches. The pavement, which is 36 ft wide, is to appear as a 1-in. band on the continuous-strip photograph. What must be the flying height?

3–6. In Prob. 3–5, the velocity of the aircraft is 180 mph (miles per hour). At what rate, in inches per minute, must the film negative pass the focal-plane slit in order to insure perfect definition, if both the roadway and the flight path are level?

3–7. The distance between two section corners is assumed to be exactly one mile. Both corners lie at an elevation of 450 ft. If the distance between the images of these two corners scales 3.342 in. on a vertical photograph taken with a lens having an 8.262-in. focal length, what is the flying height at which the photograph was taken?

3–8. The center stripes on a mountain road are alternate 9-ft white stripes and 15-ft unpainted spaces. In an area that is at an elevation of 4,250 ft, the distance on a vertical photograph between the beginning of one white stripe and the beginning of the twenty-sixth stripe measures 0.482 in. In a higher area the distance on the same photograph between the beginning of one white stripe and the beginning of the sixteenth white stripe measures 0.384 in. The camera focal length is 6.100 in. What is the elevation of the higher area?

3–9. The distance measured between two points on a map to a scale of 1:62,500 is 29.05 mm. The distance measured between the images of these same two points on a vertical photograph taken with a lens having a 152.14 mm focal length is 54.81 mm. Both points lie at an elevation of 240 ft as determined from the map. Compute the flying height for the photograph.

3–10. The roof of a rectangular building with vertical sides measures 1.050 in. by 0.482 in. on a vertical photograph taken with a lens having a focal length of 6.000 in. The long dimension of the building is 340 ft and on the photograph the base of the building measures 1.009 in. in the long direction. What is the approximate height of the building?

3–11. Three points A, B, and C appear on a vertical photograph which was taken from a flying height of 16,000 ft above sea level with a lens having a 6-in. focal length. Their photographic coordinates are $x_a = +2.235$ in. and $y_a = +0.811$ in.; $x_b = +2.130$ in. and $y_b = +3.855$ in.; $x_c = -2.250$ in. and $y_c = -3.124$ in. The ground elevations are: $h_A = 672$ ft, $h_B = 250$ ft, and $h_C = 970$ ft. Compute the ground survey distances AB, BC, and CA. Compute the horizontal angle at C from B to A.

3–12. The elevations of four ground points A, B, C, and D, are 1,452 ft, 1,095 ft, 377 ft, and 395 ft, respectively. The measured photographic coordinates of the images of these four points on a vertical photograph are $x_a = +4.020$ in. and $y_a = -0.851$ in.; $x_b = +3.422$ in. and $y_b = -4.144$ in.; $x_c = -3.831$ in. and $y_c = -0.460$ in.; $x_d = +0.195$ in. and $y_d = +3.722$ in. The flying height for the photograph, taken with a lens having a 6.000 in. focal length is 8,265 ft above sea level. Compute the area, in acres, enclosed by property lines joining the four points.

3–13. The images of two control points A and B appear on a vertical photograph, and their measured coordinates are $x_a = +60.35$ mm and $y_a = +72.04$ mm; $x_b = +64.13$ mm and $y_b = -21.22$ mm. The focal length of the camera lens is 100.20 mm. The elevations of the control points are $h_A = 750$ ft and $h_B = 1,300$ ft. The horizontal distance between the two points is 4,357 ft. Compute the flying height, to the nearest foot, from which the photograph was taken.

3–14. Two points, C and D, whose elevations are 1,455 ft and 2,252 ft, appear as images on a vertical photograph taken with a lens having a 6.040 in. focal length. The ground distance between the two points is 10,466 ft. The measured photographic coordinates of the two points are $x_c = +1.005$ in. and $y_c = -3.762$ in.; $x_d = +0.892$ in. and $y_d = +4.044$ in. Compute the flying height for the photograph.

3–15. If the azimuth of the line CD in Prob. 3–14 is 124° 30′ what is the azimuth of the positive photographic x-axis?

3–16. The coordinate values measured on a vertical photograph taken with a lens having a 152.58-mm focal length are as follows:

Point	x (in.)	y (in.)
r	+2.162	−4.276
s	−1.380	+2.744

The ground-survey coordinates and the elevations of the points are

Point	X (ft)	Y (ft)	Elevation (ft)
R	534,562	1,615,861	727
S	540,612	1,624,843	1,076

Compute the flying height of the aircraft above sea level.

3–17. What is the ground-survey azimuth of the positive photographic y-axis of Prob. 3–16?

3–18. The datum scale of a vertical photograph taken with a lens having a 6-in. focal length is 1:12,000. A hilltop lies at an elevation of 1,600 ft above sea level, and the image of the hilltop is 2.822 in. from the principal point of the photograph. Compute the relief displacement of the hilltop.

3–19. The flying height for a vertical photograph above the downtown area of a city is 6,500 ft. The focal length of the camera lens is 8.25 in. The distance measured from the center of the photograph to the image of the bottom of a radio tower is 2.824 in., and the distance to the image of the top of the tower is 3.144 in. Compute the tower height.

3–20. A point a on a vertical photograph lies on the $+x$-axis at a distance of 3.500 in. from the principal point, and a point b lies on the $+y$-axis at a distance of 3.500 in. from the principal point. The elevation of A is 1,200 ft above sea level, and that of B is 175 ft below sea level. The flying height above sea level is 6,500 ft. After correcting both points for relief displacement, compute the acute angle formed between the line $a'b'$ and the x-axis.

3–21. Solve Prob. 3–20 by means of Eqs. 3–5 and 3–6.

3–22. A vertical photograph taken with a lens having a 152.0-mm focal length has a scale of 1:16,000 at an elevation of 200 ft. The image of the top of an 80-ft flag pole located on a hill whose elevation is 560 ft appears on the photograph at a distance of 2.670 in. from the principal point. What is the ground distance, in feet, from the ground principal point to the base of the flag pole?

3–23. Solve Prob. 3–11, assuming that the photograph, instead of being vertical, was taken with a tilt of 2° 15′ and a swing of 220°.

3–24. Solve Prob. 3–13, assuming that the photograph, instead of being vertical, was taken with a tilt of 3° 40′ and a swing of 320°.

3–25. Compute the tilt displacements of the three points in Prob. 3–23.

3–26. When a photograph was taken with a lens having a 6.000-in. focal length, there was a tilt of 3° 45′ and a swing of 170°. The flying height above sea level was 10,000 ft. A point A whose elevation is 950 ft appears on the photograph, and the measured photographic coordinates of the point are $x_a = -1.515$ in. and $y_a = +2.454$ in. Compute the scale of the photograph at the point.

3–27. On the photograph of Prob. 3–26, the photographic coordinates of the image of a point B at sea level are $x_b = +0.262$ in. and $y_b = -3.132$ in. What is the scale of the photograph at that point?

3–28. Compute the tilt displacement of point a in Prob. 3–26.

3–29. Compute the tilt displacement of point b in Prob. 3–27.

3–30. For a photograph taken with a lens having an 8.25 in. focal length, the tilt was 2° 15′ and the swing was 20°. Compute the photographic coordinates of the nadir point and the isocenter with respect to the axes defined by the fiducial marks.

3–31. Assume that the photograph of Prob. 3–16 is tilted 2° 44′ and has a swing of 270°. Compute the flying height and the azimuth of the principal plane.

3–32. Prepare an orientation matrix for the photograph of Prob. 3–23, by applying Eq. 3–44 and assuming that $\alpha_{x0} = 0$.

3–33. Compute the direction cosines of the lines aL, bL, and cL of points a, b, and c of Prob. 3–23, with respect to the photographic coordinate axes.

3–34. Compute the direction cosines of the lines AL, BL, and CL of points A, B, and C of Prob. 3–23, based on the data computed in Probs. 3–32 and 3–33.

3–35. Using the results obtained in Prob. 3–34, and assuming that the ground-survey coordinates of the exposure station are $X_L = 0$ and $Y_L = 0$, compute the ground coordinates of A, B, and C by Eq. 3–70.

3–36. The following orientation matrix $\mathbf{M}^T$ for a tilted photograph is as follows:

Axis	cos m	cos n	cos k
X	-0.99824	$+0.05919$	0
Y	-0.05917	-0.99794	-0.02482
Z	-0.00147	-0.02477	$+0.99969$

Compute the tilt, the swing, and the azimuth of the principal plane of the photograph.

3–37. The coordinates measured on a photograph taken with a camera whose focal length is 153.10 mm are as follows:

Point	x mm	y mm
a	$+34.25$	-80.10
b	$+50.18$	$+ 4.50$
c	-69.92	-18.46

By using Eq. 3–63, compute the angles at the exposure station between a and b, between b and c, and between c and a.

3–38. The ground-survey coordinates and the elevations of three control points are as follows:

Point	X (ft)	Y (ft)	Elevation (ft)
A	1,805,425	403,860	1,920
B	1,802.318	400,866	2,354
C	1,801.102	404,727	2,422

The ground-survey coordinates of the exposure station of a photograph are $X_L=1,802,051$ ft and $Y_L=402,991$ ft. The flying height is 6,358 ft above sea level. By means of Eq. 3–63, determine the angles at the exposure station between A and B, between B and C, and between C and A.

3–39. The elements of exterior orientation of a photograph are $\omega=+0°\ 21'\ 10''$; $\phi=+2°\ 46'\ 20''$; $\kappa=+25°\ 15'\ 00''$. The flying height above sea level is 18,500 ft. The coordinates of the exposure station are $X_L=224,454$ ft, and $Y_L=18,565$ ft. Focal length of the camera lens is 151.65 mm. Compute the orientation matrix **M** given by Eq. 3–51 and 3–52.

3–40. By means of Eq. 3–77, compute the photographic x- and y-coordinates of a point (in mm) appearing on the photograph of Prob. 3–39 whose ground coordinates are $X=233,621$ ft, $Y=17,905$ ft, and $Z=725$ ft above sea level.

3–41. A point appearing on the photograph of Prob. 3–39 has photographic coordinates $x=-94.622$ mm and $y=+20.626$ mm. The elevation of the point is 1,462 ft. Compute the ground X- and Y-coordinates of the point by Eqs. 3–54, 3–68, 3–71, and 3–72.

Factors in Flight Planning for Aerial Photography 4

4–1. Basic Elements

Before aerial photography is executed to provide photographs suitable for subsequent photogrammetric processes or operations, careful consideration must be given to several factors which will affect the design of the flight plan to be used. The basic elements in flight planning are the flying height above a datum, usually sea level; the ground distance between successive exposures; and the ground spacing between the flight lines. In certain projects where the photographs are to be used in the preparation of maps or mosaics of a relatively narrow strip of terrain, one flight line along the center of the strip will suffice for proper photo-

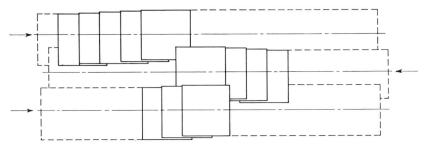

Fig. 4–1. Photographic flight lines.

graphic coverage. This condition is especially common in photography for highway design maps. When the elements have been established, based on the factors to be discussed in this chapter, the flight lines are carefully laid out on the best available map of the area to be photographed. The map then becomes the flight-line map or the flight map. In an instance where no map is available which will allow an aircraft pilot to identify a flight line on the ground as drawn on the map, a map substitute in the form of an uncontrolled mosaic may be constructed from high-altitude, small-scale photography.

The general systematic arrangement of exposing successive photographs for photogrammetric purposes is shown in Fig. 4–1. Three adjacent flight lines are shown. Along a given flight line, photographs are taken at such frequency as to cause successive photographs to overlap each other by about 55 to 65 per cent, the amount depending on several factors to be discussed. This percentage is referred to as forward overlap, or simply *overlap*. Since the overlap is greater than 50 per cent, alternate photographs will overlap one another by about 10 to 30 per cent. It is necessary to have an area common to three consecutive photographs for extending horizontal and vertical control by photogrammetric methods. In Fig. 4–2 is represented a vertical section containing the flight line and

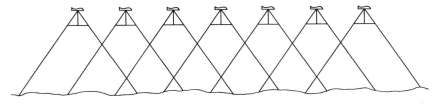

Fig. 4–2. Overlap in direction of flight.

showing the terrain which is common to the successive photographs. Overlap is required in order to provide two viewpoints of the same terrain area necessary for stereoscopic viewing of the photographs and for stereoscopic plotting in the instruments discussed in Chapter 12.

The vertical section represented in Fig. 4–3 is taken normal to three flight lines and, together with the plan in Fig. 4–1, shows the overlap

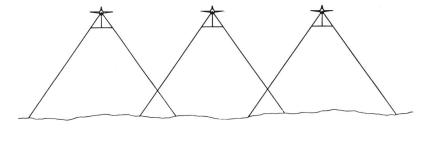

Fig. 4–3. Sidelap between flight lines.

between adjacent flight lines. This overlap amounts to about 15 to 35 per cent and is necessary for proper coverage of the ground. The overlap between flight lines is called *sidelap*. Factors affecting sidelap are to be discussed.

4–2. Purpose of the Photography

Generally speaking, aerial photographs are taken for two purposes: 1) for use in the compilation of topographic maps; 2) for their pictorial qualities. In many instances both of these purposes are considered when the photography is planned. Photography for use in compiling topographic maps must be taken with a precision camera which has been calibrated in the manner described in Chapter 2. Furthermore, in order to increase the angle formed between a set of rays going from a point on the ground to two successive exposure stations, use is made of a lens with a rather short focal length. This should between 3½ and 8.25 in. Such a lens gives a relatively wide angle of coverage. It insures strong intersections of rays in the stereoscopic plotting instruments, and increases the accuracy of the map. For a given flying height, a wider angle of coverage or a shorter focal length will increase the permissible ground distance between exposures.

Good pictorial quality is important in photo interpretation and in making mosaics or composite pictures of the ground. Photo interpretation demands certain photographic scales, and when the flying height is limited to high altitudes to insure safety of the aircraft personnel (for example, in flying over hostile terrain), the camera focal length must be selected accordingly. For larger scales at high altitudes, the focal length of the camera must be longer. Since mosaics are composites of individual photographs assembled into one continuous picture, they are affected to a great extent by tilt displacements, relief displacements, and scale variations due to variation in the flying height. The effects of these factors can be lessened considerably by rectification of the photographs (see Chapter 10). But, if more allowance is made for these factors when planning the photography, the resulting product will be more satisfactory. Flying at a higher altitude and using a camera with a longer focal length to obtain a given photographic scale will decrease tilt displacements, relief displacements, and scale variations due to variations in the flying height.

4–3. Photographic Scale

Scale is a factor in planning aerial photography. Equation 3–1 or Eq. 3–2 shows that, with a given focal length, the scale establishes the flying height. Quite often the desired average scale is the only factor which is considered in the planning. This is true, however, only when photographs are to be used for their pictorial qualities.

4–4. Scale Variation

Scale variation in a photograph or between successive photographs is caused by variation in the terrain elevation, by variation in flying heights, or by both. In Fig. 4–4(a) and (b) are indicated two photographs taken over terrain having an average elevation of 400 ft above the datum and a range in elevation from 175 ft to 600 ft. In each case the average scale is to be 1 in. = 200 ft. With a 6-in. focal length, the required flying height computed by Eq. 3–3 is 1,600 ft above the datum. At an elevation of 175 ft, the scale is

$$S_{175} = \frac{6 \text{ in.}}{(1,600 - 175) \text{ ft}} \qquad \text{or} \qquad 1 \text{ in.} = 238 \text{ ft}$$

At an elevation of 600 ft, the scale is

$$S_{600} = \frac{6 \text{ in.}}{(1,600 - 600) \text{ ft}} \qquad \text{or} \qquad 1 \text{ in.} = 167 \text{ ft}$$

The variation from the high elevation to the low elevation is about 30 per cent, and that from the low elevation to the high elevation is about 42 per cent.

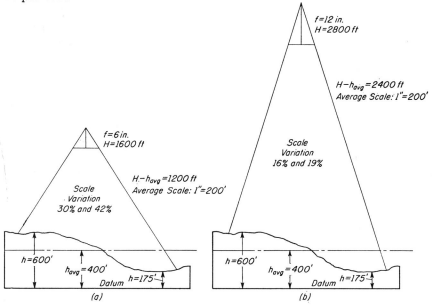

Fig. 4–4. Scale variation.

This large variation in scale can be reduced by using a greater focal length. If a 12-in. focal length is used, the flying height above the datum required to obtain the desired scale of 1 in. = 200 ft is 2,800 ft. At an elevation of 175 ft, the scale is

$$S_{175} = \frac{12 \text{ in.}}{(2,800 - 175) \text{ ft}} \qquad \text{or} \qquad 1 \text{ in.} = 219 \text{ ft}$$

At an elevation of 600 ft, the scale is

$$S_{600} = \frac{12 \text{ in.}}{(2,800 - 600) \text{ ft}} \qquad \text{or} \qquad 1 \text{ in.} = 183 \text{ ft}$$

The variation from the high elevation to the low elevation is about 16 per cent, and that from the low elevation to the high elevation is about 19 per cent. Thus the scale variation for a certain average scale has been considerably decreased by an increase in the focal length and the flying height.

EXAMPLE 4-1. An area to be photographed for mosaic work lies at an average elevation of 450 ft above sea level. The terrain elevation varies from 250 ft to 1,200 ft. A camera with a 12-in. focal length is the only camera available. The average scale of the photographs is to be 1 in.=800 ft, and the variation in scale is not to exceed 10 per cent of the scale at the low elevation. Determine whether the restriction can be met by using this camera.

Solution: By Eq. 3-3,

$$S_{\text{avg}} = \frac{1 \text{ in.}}{800 \text{ ft}} = \frac{12 \text{ in.}}{(H - 450) \text{ ft}}$$

Hence, $H = 10,050$ ft above sea level. Then, by Eq. 3-1,

$$S_{250} = \frac{12 \text{ in.}}{(10,050 - 250) \text{ ft}} \qquad \text{or} \qquad 1 \text{ in.} = 817 \text{ ft}$$

and

$$S_{1,200} = \frac{12 \text{ in.}}{(10,050 - 1,200) \text{ ft}} \qquad \text{or} \qquad 1 \text{ in.} = 738 \text{ ft}$$

$$\text{Scale variation} = \frac{(1/738) - (1/817)}{(1/817)} = 10.7 \text{ per cent}$$

So the restriction cannot be met. To circumvent this difficulty, a flying height of about 10,800 ft above sea level could be used to bring the scale variation within 10 per cent, even though the average photographic scale would be 1 in.=863 ft. Each photograph could then be enlarged by an enlargement factor of 863/800, or 1.08, and the mosaic constructed from these enlarged photographs. This procedure in effect changes the principal distance of the photographs to $12 \times 1.08 = 12.96$ in. (See Fig. 3-1.)

Scale variation also affects photographic coverage because of a rising or falling of the terrain with respect to the flying height, and is an important factor to be considered when relatively low-altitude photography is taken for mapping purposes. In Fig. 4-5, the flying height is seen to be held constant, while the terrain rises steadily from left to right. Two effects are apparent: 1) The overlap between successive photographs continually decreases if the photographs are taken with a constant time interval between exposures. 2) The width of terrain covered by the photographs becomes narrower as the terrain elevation increases. The first effect can be taken into account by using the viewfinder of the camera to obtain the proper overlap. The second effect must be allowed for by basing the spacing between flight lines on minimum allowable sidelap as it is affected by the higher terrain. Otherwise, gaps between the flight strips may occur in the high areas. Although the conditions have been exaggerated in Fig. 4-5, and although a varying flying height can over-

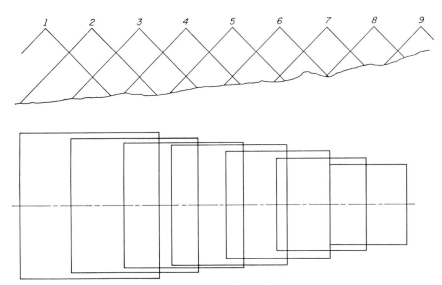

Fig. 4-5. Scale variation from change in terrain elevation.

come these effects, nevertheless a rising and falling terrain remains a factor to be considered in flight planning.

4-5. Relief Displacement

In Sec. 4-2 the desired purpose of the photography is discussed as a factor in planning the flight, and it is pointed out that relief displacement affects the construction of mosaics. Since mosaicking consists of piecing adjacent photographs together to form one composite picture, large relief displacement on successive photographs will make it difficult or even impossible to form a continuous uninterrupted picture. Relief displacements on any pair of adjacent photographs always occur in opposing directions, because the relief displacement on each photograph radiates outward from a point near the center of the photograph.

A study of Eq. 3-7 shows that relief displacement will decrease as the flying height is increased. It is also evident that to maintain a certain scale as the flying height is increased, the focal length must be increased. These principles are taken into account when the flight plan is designed.

In general, relief displacement has no adverse effect upon map compilation in a stereoscopic plotting instrument. In fact, as the relief displacement increases, the more positively can elevations be measured in the instrument. Occasionally, the terrain to be mapped contains isolated areas or peaks at a considerable elevation above the average terrain. The possibility then exists that the relief displacement of these isolated areas is so great as to cause their images to fall off the edge of the photograph.

This problem may occur if the flight line is laid down so that these high points fall near the edge of the photographic coverage.

EXAMPLE 4–2. The distance on the flight map from the nearest flight line to a point which lies 1,150 ft above the average elevation of the terrain scales 0.80 in. The map scale is 1 in.=5,000 ft. The average photographic scale, with a 6-in. focal length, is to be 1 in.=1,000 ft. Determine the distance, at the photograph scale, between the flight line and the image of the high point.

Solution: The flying height above the average terrain elevation, which is taken as the datum, is found from Eq. 3–2. Thus,

$$\frac{1 \text{ in.}}{1,000 \text{ ft}} = \frac{6 \text{ in.}}{H \text{ ft}}$$

and $H = 6,000$ ft above the average datum.

At the scale of the photograph, the distance from the flight line to the datum photograph position of the high point can be found from Eq. 3–4. Thus,

$$\frac{1 \text{ in.}/1,000 \text{ ft}}{1 \text{ in.}/5,000 \text{ ft}} = \frac{\text{photo distance}}{0.80 \text{ in.}}$$

and the photo distance from the flight line is 4.00 in.

The relief displacement of the point with respect to its datum photograph position is, by Eq. 3–8,

$$d = \frac{4.00 \text{ in.} \times 1,150 \text{ ft}}{(6,000 - 1,150) \text{ ft}} = 0.95 \text{ in.}$$

The distance between the flight line and the image of the high point is, therefore, 4.00+0.95=4.95 in. This point would fall off the edge of a 9- by 9-in. photograph.

To allow for irregularities as presented in Example 4–2, the flight line should be adjusted to pass closer to the high points to insure proper coverage on the photographs.

4–6. Tilt of the Photographs

The tilt of a photograph may be resolved into two components. One is the amount in the direction of flight, and the other is the amount in the direction normal to the flight line. The first is called y-tilt, or angle ϕ. The second is called x-tilt, or angle ω. When a photograph has undergone a y-tilt, the overlap on one side will be greater than the desired amount of overlap, while the overlap on the opposite side will be smaller than the desired amount. Two successively exposed photographs with opposite y-tilt will cause the increase or decrease in overlap to accumulate, whereas y-tilt in the same direction will, to a great extent, cancel out the increase or decrease in overlap. An x-tilt of a photograph will cause the sidelap to increase on one side of the flight line and to decrease on the opposite side.

The effect of y-tilt on overlap can be taken into account by using the viewfinder to control the overlap. If a fixed interval between exposures is held, as with the use of an intervalometer, the effect of y-tilt on overlap must be allowed for by decreasing the computed exposure interval slightly to produce a slight increase in the theoretically desired overlap.

The effect of x-tilt on sidelap must be allowed for by decreasing the computed spacing between flight lines slightly to produce a slight increase in the desired sidelap. This adjustment helps to insure proper coverage, and at the same time allows for certain abnormal relief displacements.

4–7. Crab and Drift

Crab is the term given to designate the angle formed between the flight line and the edges of the photograph in the direction of flight. It is caused by not having the focal plane of the camera squared with the direction of flight at the instant of exposure. In Fig. 4–6 are shown a series of consecutively exposed photographs with an extreme amount of crab in each photograph. Under normal flying conditions, the camera

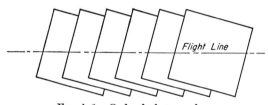

FIG. 4–6. Crab of photographs.

can be corrected to allow for crabbing by a rotation of the camera about the vertical axis of the camera mount. The effect of crab is to reduce the effective width of coverage of the photography. Fortunately the sidelap allowance will in most instances prevent gapping between flight strips caused by crab.

Drift is caused by the failure of the aircraft to stay on the predetermined flight line. If, for example, the aircraft drifts 200 ft to one side or the other of the flight line, and the average scale of the photography is 1:10,000, the drift amounts to about ¼ in. at the photography scale. This amount represents a loss of about 3 per cent in the sidelap on the side opposite the direction of drift. Drifting from the predetermined flight line is the most common cause for requiring re-flights to be made because of serious gapping between adjacent flight lines. Gapping may be due to a poor flight-line map, even though the pilot actually keeps the aircraft on the flight line as drawn on the map.

4–8. Effective Coverage of the Photograph

The factor which contributes most directly to the determination of the amount of overlap and sidelap to be used in flight planning is the effective coverage of each photograph. The coverage depends on the size of the focal-plane opening, or format, on the focal length, and on the angular coverage of the lens. The flying height, of course, determines the actual terrain area covered on a single photograph when the other factors affecting coverage have been established. In Fig. 4–7 are shown three focal lengths associated with a 9- by 9-in. format size, together with representative angular coverage of the lenses. The effective angular coverage of the lens with the 12-in. focal length is represented by a cone the apex of which lies at the front nodal point and the apex angle of which

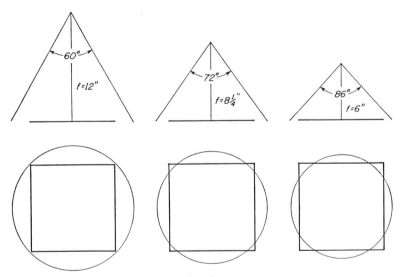

Fig. 4–7. Angular coverage.

is about 60°. It is presumed that all images falling within this cone will be acceptable within tolerance with respect to resolution, lens distortion, and general photographic quality. In general, the effective coverage with a 12-in. lens will embrace more than the 9- by 9-in. format size, and hence the entire photograph is usable.

The effective angular coverage of the lens with an 8.25-in. focal length is a cone whose apex angle is about 72°. All but the extreme corners of the 9- by 9-in. format is usable for photogrammetric purposes.

The wide-angle lens associated with topographic mapping, because of the strong intersection angle it provides, includes an effective cone of rays the apex of which is about 90° or slightly less. The angle of 86° shown in Fig. 4–7 is fairly representative of the lenses with a 6-in. focal length that are used in mapping cameras. A sizable portion of the corners of the 9- by 9-in. format is not usable for three primary reasons: 1) The lens distortion is beyond tolerance and also beyond compensation. 2) The resolution is usually too poor for accurate interpretation of the images. 3) Since the corners are at such a relatively great distance from the lens diaphragm relative to the central portion of the photograph, the negative has not received an exposure sufficient to provide satisfactory definition and contrast in the photograph.

The effective angular coverage of the wide-angle lens is used as a basis to establish the overlap and sidelap for flight planning. In Fig. 4–8, two 9- by 9-in. photographs overlap as shown. The effective area of

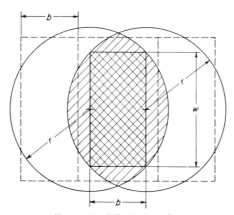

Fɪɢ. 4–8. Effective overlap.

overlap between the two photographs is that bounded by the overlapping circles representing the effective coverages of the photographs. The value of r is equal to $f \tan (\alpha/2)$, where f is the focal length and $\alpha/2$ is one-half the angular coverage. For the 6-in. lens of Fig. 4–7, r equals 5.60 in.

The maximum rectangular area of overlap that can be obtained is the rectangle for which the dimension in the direction of flight is one-half the dimension normal to the direction of flight. The distance b is therefore equal to the distance $w/2$. Note that the two longer sides of this rectangular area pass through the principal points of the photographs. The distance b is equal to $r \sin 45°$. When $r = 5.60$ in., the value of b is 3.96 in. This represents the distance, at the scale of the photograph, between exposures. So the overlap, in terms of inches on the photograph, is $9.00 - 3.96 = 5.04$ in. This represents an overlap of 5.04/9, or 56 per cent in the direction of flight.

The distance w in Fig. 4–8 represents the photographic distance between successive flight lines, as shown in Fig. 4–9. This is the maximum allowable distance when the principal points of the photographs fall directly opposite one another on the two flight lines. For the photograph of Fig. 4–7 having the 6-in. focal length, $w = 2 \times 3.96 = 7.92$ in. The side-lap between flight lines, in terms of inches on the photograph, is $9.00 - 7.92 = 1.08$ in. This represents a sidelap of 1.08/9, or 12 per cent.

The foregoing analysis of effective coverage as a factor in flight planning presumes ideal conditions. These are level terrain; vertical, crab-free photographs; a constant flying height; and no drifting of the aircraft from the line of flight. Such an analysis should be made, however, for it establishes a minimum overlap and sidelap for a given effective cone of coverage. It therefore establishes a basis for the final adopted values of overlap and sidelap, even though the values first selected may be later modified to accommodate the other factors.

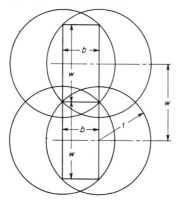

FIG. 4–9. Spacing between flight lines.

An assignment of allowances to be made, in the way of an increase in overlap or sidelap or both, in planning photography is considered to be outside the scope of this book. This phase of photogrammetry requires personal experience and judgment on the part of the person who designs the flight plan. Under a given set of circumstances, however, the student should be able to establish some rational basis for allowances from the foregoing sections in this chapter, together with the subject matter of previous chapters.

4–9. Selection of Flying Height

After the overlap and sidelap to be used for the photography have been established, the final element necessary to design the flight plan is the flying height from which the photographs are to be taken. Several interrelated factors which affect the selection of flying height, such as desired scale, relief displacement, and tilt, have already been discussed. Other factors to be considered are the precision of the photogrammetric equipment used to compile topographic maps from the photography, physical limitations of the stereoscopic plotting instrument to be used in the map compilation, and factors peculiar to some forms of large-scale mapping.

Various types of photogrammetric equipment used in the process of map compilation contain a certain inherent precision, but it is different for each type. In general, the greater the precision in the system, the greater may be the flying height. This relationship is advantageous, because doubling the flying height increases the ground coverage per photograph four times, and considerably reduces the necessary amount of ground control. Since vertical accuracy in a topographic map is the limiting factor in the photogrammetric process, the flying height is quite often related to the contour interval of the finished map. The relationship is expressed as a precision factor, and is designated as the C-factor of the photogrammetric equipment. Thus,

$$C\text{-factor} = \frac{\text{flying height}}{\text{contour interval}}$$

from which

$$\text{Flying height} = (\text{contour interval}) \times (C\text{-factor})$$

The C-factor is understood to be that value, used to compute the flying height, which will produce photography satisfactory to obtain the desired vertical accuracy in the map. The flying height in the preceding relationship is measured above the terrain. A C-factor can be assigned to a photogrammetric system only after sufficient mapping has been produced by the system to permit an analysis of the vertical accuracy that is obtained. In photogrammetric systems presently in operation, C-factors take on values anywhere from 500 to 1,500. For a given system, the factor will depend on the conditions surrounding the entire map-compilation operation.

Stereoscopic plotting instruments are physically limited in the amount of vertical displacement of the measuring device. This limitation is imposed either by depth of focus or by moving parts. Although these causes of limited displacement will be discussed more fully in Chapter 12, they are taken up here as factors controlling the selection of the flying height. The physical limitation of an instrument can be expressed as a percentage of the flying height. For example, an instrument limited in the vertical direction to 20 per cent of the flying height can accommodate a difference in terrain elevation of 2,000 ft where the flying height is 10,000 ft above a particular datum. Conversely, if the relief in the terrain is 1,200 ft, the flying height above a particular datum may not be less than 6,000 ft.

Large-scale topographic mapping to a small contour interval demands more from the photogrammetric process than does small-scale mapping to a large contour interval. Quite often, a maximum permissible flying height is specified in order to insure the required accuracy in the finished map, although this may not always be construed to represent the flying height above the average ground elevation. In Fig. 4–10, the average elevation is very well represented by the arithmetic mean between the high point and the low point. If the flying height measured above the average terrain elevation is equal to the maximum specified value, then the height measured over the valley portion of the terrain will exceed the allowable maximum by 350 ft. Consequently, the map will not be so accurate as desired in the low area, and this inaccuracy may render the map useless for the purpose for which it is intended. Therefore, the flying height should be measured from the lowest elevation of the area. This practice will also insure greater accuracy in the higher elevations.

In the situation illustrated by Fig. 4–10, measuring the flying height above the lowest elevation may cause the relief to extend beyond the upward vertical range of the plotting instrument. Such a condition presents a problem encountered occasionally in large-scale mapping, and the problem must be solved by photographing the area from two different flying heights.

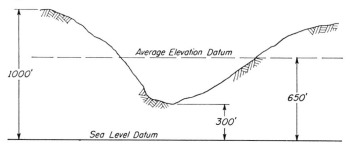

Average Elevation Datum

1000'

650'

300'

Sea Level Datum

Fig. 4–10.   Average elevation.

4–10. Computation of Flight Plan

The data required to compute the quantities for delineating the flight-map lines, to determine the time interval between exposures (if an intervalometer is to be used), and to determine the amount of film which will be needed to complete the photography are: 1) focal length of the camera lens; 2) flying height above a stated datum, or photograph scale for a particular elevation; 3) size of photograph; 4) size of area to be photographed (if area is irregular in shape, its shape must be taken into account in determining the best direction for the flight lines); 5) position of the outer flight lines with respect to the boundary of the area; 6) overlap; 7) sidelap; 8) scale of flight map; 9) ground speed of aircraft (if an intervalometer is to be used).

The method of making the computations necessary for flight planning will be illustrated by the following two examples.

EXAMPLE 4-3. An area that is 25 miles long in the north-south direction and 18.5 miles wide in the east-west direction is to be photographed with a lens having a 12-in. focal length for the purpose of constructing a mosaic. The photograph size is 9 by 9 in. The average scale is to be 1:12,000 effective at an average elevation of 700 ft above sea level. Overlap is to be at least 60 per cent, and sidelap is to be at least 35 per cent. An intervalometer will be used to control the interval between exposures. The ground speed of the aircraft will be maintained at 150 mph. The flight lines are to be laid out in a north-south direction on an existing map having a scale of 1:62,500. The two outer flight lines are to coincide with the east and west boundaries of the area. Determine the data for the flight plan.

Solution:

Flying height. By Eq. 3–2,

$$\frac{1 \text{ ft}}{H \text{ ft}} = \frac{1}{12,000}$$

So $H = 12,000$ ft above the 700-ft elevation, or $H = 12,700$ ft above sea level.

Ground distance between flight lines. Since the minimum sidelap is 35 per cent, the photographic distance between flight lines is 65 per cent of 9 in., or 5.85 in. The ground spacing is

$$W = \frac{5.85 \text{ in.} \times 12,000}{12 \text{ in./ft}} = 5,850 \text{ ft}$$

Number of flight lines. The total width of the area is 18.5 mi × 5,280 ft/mi = 97,680 ft. So the required number of flight lines is

$$\frac{97,680 \text{ ft}}{5,850 \text{ ft}} + 1 = 18$$

Adjusted ground distance between flight lines. With an integral number of flight lines, the original computed spacing W is slightly too large. The actual spacing of flight lines will be

$$W_A = \frac{97,680 \text{ ft}}{18 - 1} = 5,746 \text{ ft}$$

The sidelap will be slightly greater than 35 per cent.

Spacing of flight lines on flight map. The distance on the map corresponding to a ground distance of 5,746 ft is

$$W_M = \frac{5,746 \text{ ft}}{62,500} \times 12 \text{ in./ft} = 1.10 \text{ in.}$$

Ground distance between exposures. Since the overlap is 60 per cent, the net gain per photograph is 40 per cent of the width of the photograph, or 0.40 × 9 in. = 3.60 in. The corresponding ground distance is

$$B = \frac{3.60 \times 12,000}{12 \text{ in./ft}} = 3,600 \text{ ft}$$

Exposure interval. The time interval between exposures is usually an integral number of seconds. The aircraft speed is

$$150 \text{ mph} = \left(\frac{150 \times 5,280}{60 \times 60}\right) \text{ft/sec} = 220 \text{ ft/sec}$$

The required exposure interval is

$$I = \frac{3,600 \text{ ft}}{220 \text{ ft/sec}} = 16.4 \text{ sec or } 16 \text{ sec}$$

Adjusted ground distance between exposures. For the adjusted exposure interval, the ground distance is

$$B_A = 220 \text{ ft/sec} \times 16 \text{ sec} = 3,520 \text{ ft}$$

Number of photographs per flight line. The total length of a flight line is $25 \text{ mi} \times 5,280 \text{ ft/mi} = 132,000 \text{ ft}$. If allowance is made for two extra exposures at each end of each strip, the number of photographs per flight line is

$$\frac{132,000}{3,520} + 4 = 41.5 \text{ or } 42$$

The entire photography will require $18 \times 42 = 756$ photographs. The flight lines are carefully drawn on the flight map at a spacing of 1.10 in. The intervalometer will be set for an exposure interval of 16 sec, which will insure the required overlap of at least 60 per cent.

EXAMPLE 4-4. An area of terrain 2,400 ft wide and 7.2 mi long with very little relief is to be photographed in one strip for use in compiling a topographic map. The photograph size is 9 by 9 in. The focal length is 5.80 in., and the effective angular coverage is 90°. A viewfinder will be used to obtain the proper overlap. Two exposures are to be provided at each end of the flight line. The approximate photograph centers are to be marked on a flight map whose scale is 1 in.=1,000 ft. Compute the data for the flight plan.

Solution:

Photographic distance between photograph centers. In Fig. 4-8,

$$r = 5.80 \tan 45° = 5.80 \text{ in.}$$
$$b = 5.80 \sin 45° = 4.10 \text{ in.}$$

Effective width of coverage on photograph. In Fig. 4-8,

$$w = 2b = 2 \times 4.10 = 8.20 \text{ in.}$$

Flying height above average elevation. The average elevation will be taken as the datum. By Eq. 3-2,

$$\frac{5.80 \text{ in.}}{H \text{ ft}} = \frac{8.20 \text{ in.}}{2,400 \text{ ft}}$$

So $H = 1,700$ ft above the average elevation.

Ground distance between exposures. The following relationship exists:

$$\frac{B \text{ ft}}{4.10 \text{ in.}} = \frac{1,700 \text{ ft}}{5.80 \text{ in.}}$$

Hence, $B = 1,200$ ft.

Flight-map distance between exposures. The map distance corresponding to a ground distance of 1,200 ft is

$$b_M = \frac{1,200 \text{ ft}}{1,000 \text{ ft/in.}} = 1.20 \text{ in.}$$

Number of photographs. The length of the strip is

$$7.2 \text{ mi} \times 5,280 \text{ ft/mi} = 38,020 \text{ ft}$$

The required number of photographs is

$$\frac{38,020 \text{ ft}}{1,200 \text{ ft}} + 4 = 35.7 \text{ or } 36$$

Bibliography

AMERICAN SOCIETY OF PHOTOGRAMMETRY. *Manual of Photogrammetry* (Menasha, Wisc.: George Banta Co., 1952), Chapters 4 and 17.

————. *Manual of Photogrammetry* (Menasha, Wisc.: George Banta Co., 1966), Chapters 5 and 7.

————. *Manual of Photographic Interpretation* (Menasha, Wisc.: George Banta Co., 1960), Chapter 2.

HALLERT, B. *Photogrammetry* (New York: McGraw-Hill Book Co., 1960), Chapter 3.

HEIDELAUF, U. K. "Aircraft Control for Photogrammetric Purposes," *Photogrammetric Engineering*, Vol. XX (1954), p. 87.

LÖSCHER, W. "Optimum Field Angle for Aerial Cameras," *Photogrammetric Engineering*, Vol. XXX (1964), p. 613.

PRYOR, W. T. "Specifications for Aerial Photography and Mapping by Photogrammetric Methods for Highway Engineering Purposes," *Photogrammetric Engineering*, Vol. XVI (1950), p. 439.

RICHARDSON, R. C., and WARNER, J. "Straight Flight of Aircraft Equipped with Radar-Operated Pilot's Indicator," *Photogrammetric Engineering*, Vol. XVI (1950), p. 544.

THOMPSON, M. M. "A New Approach to Flight Planning," *Photogrammetric Engineering*, Vol. XVI (1950), p. 49.

TROREY, LYLE G. "Factors Affecting Specification of Overlap and their Economic Significance," *Photogrammetric Engineering*, Vol. XIII (1947), p. 241.

U. S. COAST and GEODETIC SURVEY. "Topographic Manual," Part II, *Special Publication* No. 249. Washington, D.C.: Government Printing Office, 1949.

Problems

4–1. What is the per cent of scale variation in a photograph taken from an altitude of 5,000 ft, if a lens with a 6-in. focal length is used and the terrain elevation varies from 600 to 1,400 ft?

4–2. The lateral ground coverage of a 9- by 9-in. photograph is 3,000 ft over terrain lying at an elevation of 350 ft. The focal length is 6 in. If the flying height remains constant, what will be the lateral coverage when the terrain elevations is 950 ft?

4–3. If the overlap in the line of flight of Prob. 4–2 is 60 per cent over the 350 ft terrain, and if the exposure interval remains constant, what is the overlap over the 950 ft terrain?

4–4. On a map at a scale of 1:24,000, the position of a peak whose elevation is 3,900 ft lies 1.50 in. from the flight line drawn on the map. The 9- by 9-in. photography at an average scale of 1:10,000 is to be obtained with an 8.25-in. lens. The average elevation of the terrain is 800 ft. Will the image of the peak appear on any photograph of the flight strip, if the pilot holds to the flight line?

4–5. With a nominal 60-per cent overlap, what is the reduction in lateral coverage, in per cent, if all the aerial photographs of a strip contain a crab of 15°?

4–6. An aircraft is flying at an altitude of 10,000 ft above the terrain and contains a 6-in. camera. How closely must the aircraft conform to the flight line, if the lateral drift is to be held to ± 5 per cent of the width of a 9-in. photograph?

4–7. A lens with a 6-in. focal length has a 90° angular coverage. If the dimension b in Fig. 4–8 is established by a given overlap of 60 per cent and 9- by 9-in. photographs are to be taken, what should be the theoretical ground spacing of the flight lines, in feet, for a photographic scale of 12,000?

4–8. A lens having an 8.23-in. focal length and a 70° angular coverage is used with a 9- by 9-in. format. What must be the overlap if the ratio b/w is to be ½?

4–9. Assuming that the C-factor of a plotting instrument is 800, compute the flying height above the average elevation of Fig. 4–10 required for mapping on a 2-ft contour interval. At this flying height, what will be the C-factor based on the lowest elevation? On the highest elevation?

4–10. A rectangular area 11 miles in the east-west direction and 14 miles in the north-south direction is to be photographed with a lens having an 8¼-in. focal length and with a 9- by 9-in. format for the purpose of preparing an aerial mosaic. The flight lines are to be an east-west direction. The two outer flight lines are to coincide with the north and south project boundaries. Overlap is to be 65 per cent, and sidelap is to be least 35 per cent. The average photographic scale is to be 1 in. =1,000 ft. How many exposures will be necessary to complete the photography?

4–11. A highway design map is to be prepared at a scale of 1 in.=50 ft from photography obtained at one-fifth the scale of the design map. The photography is to be taken in one strip by using a camera lens having a 6-in. focal length. The average terrain elevation is 725 ft, the highest elevation is 1,150 ft, and the lowest elevation is 635 ft. If the overlap over the average terrain is 58 per cent, what is the effective overlap over the high elevation? Over the low elevation?

4–12. The effective angular coverage of the camera lens of Prob. 4–11 is 82°. What is the effective ground width covered by the photography over the average terrain elevation? Over the high elevation? Over the low elevation?

4–13. Approximately how many photographs are required to photograph a strip of ground 14 miles long from an altitude of 4,200 ft above the terrain by using 7- by 7-in. photography and a lens with a 5-in. focal length, first when the overlap is 55 per cent, and then when the overlap is 60 per cent?

4–14. Photography is to be taken from a flying height of 40,000 ft above sea level with a lens having a 12-in. focal length. What is the scale variation, in per cent, if the terrain varies in elevation from 500 ft to 5,000 ft?

4–15. Solve Prob. 4–14 for a lens with a focal length of 6 in.

4–16. An area 24,000 ft long in the north-south direction and 61,000 ft wide in the east-west direction is to be photographed for compiling a highway reconnaissance map with a 5-ft contour interval. The average terrain elevation is 1,450 ft. The focal length of the camera is 6 in., and the format is 9 by 9 in. The ground speed of the aircraft is assumed to be 150 mph. The flight lines are to be in the east-west direction, and the positions of the two outer flight lines are to lie inside the north and south boundaries a photographic distance of 2.5 in. at the average photographic scale. Overlap is to be 60 per cent, and sidelap is to be no less than 25 per cent. Assuming a C-factor of 800, determine the optimum flying height above sea level from which the photographs should be taken.

4-17. Compute the number of flight lines necessary to satisfactorily cover the area described in Prob. 4-16. Compute the ground spacing, in feet, between flight lines.

4-18. At what interval, to the nearest second, should the photographs in Prob. 4-16 be exposed in order to insure not less than the specified overlap?

4-19. If allowance is made for two extra exposures at each end of each flight line in Prob. 4-16, how many photographs must be taken to cover the area?

4-20. A flight map is to be prepared for the photography of Prob. 4-16 to a scale of 1:24,000. Compute the map spacing of the flight lines. Compute the map distance between exposures.

Ground Control for Photogrammetry 5

5–1. Types of Control

The objective of ground control is to locate the ground positions of points which can be identified on aerial photographs. The ground position of a point may be defined by its horizontal position with respect to a horizontal datum, or by its elevation with respect to a level datum, or both. Ground control is necessary in order to establish the position and orientation of each photograph in space relative to the ground, and thereby enable the photographs to be used in the compilation of planimetric and topographic maps and mosaics. Ground control also enables the photogrammetrist to determine the elements of exterior orientation of photographs, analytically or instrumentally, and to establish a basis for extending control photogrammetrically.

The field survey operations necessary to establish ground control for photogrammetry are divided into two phases. The first phase, called *basic control*, establishes a basic network of monuments which include triangulation and traverse stations, azimuth marks, and bench marks; the second phase, called *photo control*, establishes the horizontal positions or elevations of points, whose images can be identified on the photographs, with respect to the basic control monuments.

Photo control necessary for photogrammetric operations requires accuracies compatable with the type of map that is to be produced and also with the use to which the map is put. The production of small-scale, large-contour-interval maps does not, for example, require the horizontal or vertical photo control accuracy that is necessary for highway design mapping. In the latter case, the map may have a scale as large as 1 in. equals 20 ft, and contain a one-foot contour interval, with spot elevations shown to a tenth of a foot. Photogrammetry applied to cadastral surveying requires very accurate photo control of at least second-order accuracy.

The science of photogrammetry has advanced to such an extent, because of improved optics, photographic material, and photogrammetric instrumentation, that the limiting accuracy is imposed by the accuracy of the ground control. It is not infrequent that photogrammetric measurements are superior to ground measurements, especially in terrain that does not lend itself to easy ground surveying. Thus, a photogrammetrically determined ground profile or cross-section can be more accurate than an equivalent ground determination. This points up the necessity for accurate ground control.

5–2. Basic Horizontal Control

The horizontal datum of the United States is known as the North American Datum of 1927 and is defined by a network of triangulation and traverse stations whose positions have been located and adjusted most accurately with respect to a fixed point in Kansas, this station being known as Meade's Ranch. The positions of all the triangulation and traverse stations in this network throughout the country have been computed on one single mathematical reference surface having the shape of an ellipsoid which would closely conform to the mean sea level surface if this latter surface could be extended over the country. The mathematical surface itself is known as the Clarke Spheroid of 1866.

The positions of the triangulation and traverse stations have been established primarily by the U. S. Coast and Geodetic Survey, the field surveys being conducted according to specifications for first-order and second-order surveys. It is not the intent of this chapter to discuss these field procedures, since they are set forth in various surveying textbooks and in publications of the U. S. Coast and Geodetic Survey.

The network of first-order and second-order horizontal-control stations is broken down and filled in by third-order triangulation and traversing when the need arises. Many of the third-order stations throughout the country have been established by field operations of the U. S. Geological Survey, for the purpose of providing the basic control for its topographic-mapping program. Most of these third-order stations are well monumented and well described, so that they are available to other users of horizontal control.

5–3. State Plane Coordinate Systems

The first-order and second-order horizontal control established by the U. S. Coast and Geodetic Survey, together with the fill-in control established by the U. S. Geological Survey, establishes the basic horizontal control for all surveying and mapping operations conducted throughout the country. Since the positions of the stations in this network are defined by their geographic positions (latitude and longitude), their use in the past has been limited because of the reluctance on the part of engineers and surveyors to handle geodetic computations. To rectify this difficulty, the U. S. Coast and Geodetic Survey has established the state plane coordinate systems, by which a point whose latitude and longitude are known can also be defined by its X- and Y-coordinates in a specific zone of a specific state plane coordinate system. By means of tables prepared by the U. S. Coast and Geodetic Survey, latitude and longitude can be transformed to plane rectangular coordinates in a given zone with great facility. So the basic control network can be incorporated into a survey network which is computed by plane-surveying methods. In fact, both the U. S. Coast and Geodetic Survey and the U. S. Geological Survey now publish the results of their control surveys in both geographic positions and state plane coordinates.

The student is referred to *Special Publication* No. 193 of the U. S. Coast and Geodetic Survey, titled "Manual of Plane Coordinate Computation," and to textbooks on surveying for a complete discussion of the state plane coordinate systems and their uses.

5–4. Basic Vertical Control

The vertical control datum of the United States is the Sea Level Datum of 1929. It is defined by a network of bench marks whose elevations have been precisely measured and adjusted to about twenty tidal bench marks located on the Atlantic, Gulf, and Pacific coasts of the country. The elevations of the bench marks in this network have been established primarily by the U. S. Coast and Geodetic Survey, the field surveys being conducted according to specifications for first-order and second-order spirit leveling. Because of the nature of spirit leveling, the bench marks are established along railroads and highways and are thus made easily accessible to users of this vertical control.

The network of first-order and second-order bench marks is broken down and filled in by second-order and third-order spirit leveling conducted by various organizations such as those engaged in inland navigation, flood control, water-power development, irrigation, and highway or railroad location, as well as by the U. S. Geological Survey in its mapping operations.

5–5. Photo Control

Photo control is the network of points on the ground whose images can be identified on the photographs taken for a particular photogrammetric operation. Their horizontal positions or elevations are determined by second-, third-, or fourth-order surveying operations and are incorporated directly into the basic control network. A horizontal photo control point can be located by running a traverse from a basic horizontal control monument to the point, and then closing the traverse on a second basic control monument. If the photo control point lies relatively close to a basic monument, the traverse may be carried from the monument to the photo control point and then back to the same monument, forming a loop traverse. The photo control point must be included as a part of the traverse itself, and a line to it should not be treated as a spur line from the traverse. This procedure allows the position of the point to be tested by determining the error of closure of the traverse. Traversing for photo control is discussed in Sec. 5–9. A horizontal photo control point can also be located by the methods of triangulation, intersection and resection.

The elevation of a vertical photo control point is determined by carrying a line of levels from a basic control bench mark to the point, and then carrying the levels to the original bench mark or to a second bench mark. The photo control point itself must be included as a turning point in the level line, and the rod reading on it must not be observed as a side shot. This procedure allows the elevation of the point to be tested by determining the error of closure of the level line. Leveling for photo control is discussed in Sec. 5–10. Vertical photo control can also be established by trigonometric and barometric leveling, depending on the required accuracy of the project.

5–6. Pre-Marking Photo Control Points

Most photo control points are selected after the aerial photography is completed and the contact-print photographs have been made available to office and field personnel. The distinct advantage of selecting the points directly from the photographs is in positive identification and favorable location of the points. In certain instances, however, it becomes necessary to mark points on the ground before the photography is taken, so that these marked points can be identified on the subsequent photographs. When a control traverse is to be incorporated into the photo control network, the traverse stations can be marked with distinctive light-colored flagging, painted panels of wood, lime, whitewash, or white paint. This marking renders the basic control visible on the photographs. What is true for traverse stations applies equally well to triangulation stations and to bench marks.

When there is a possibility that identification of natural features on the photography may be impossible, enough pre-marked points must be established prior to the photography to ensure a photo control network. Wide expanses of sand, grass, certain cereal crops, and the like do not, in every instance, provide natural objects whose images can be identified on photographs. Similarly, dense timber stands with solid cover do not, in some instances, provide identifiable images. These types of areas must be pre-marked prior to the photography.

To reduce the possibility of pre-marked points being accidentally moved, the photography should in point of time closely follow the photo control surveys which establish the positions or elevations of the points.

The rigid requirements for precision photo control for analytic control extension, for cadastral surveys, and for certain types of highway design mapping, make it necessary to pre-mark a great deal of the control points. This has led to much investigation into the proper design of pre-marked targets. The configuration most commonly used is the cross shown in Fig. 5–1. The cross is usually light-colored or white on a naturally or artificially dark background, and dark-colored on a naturally light background such as desert sand. The center target of the cross is separated from the legs in order to prevent bleeding or halation of the image of the intersection due to high target contrast.

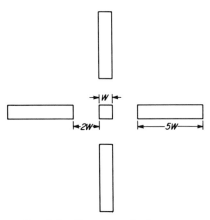

Fig. 5–1. Target used for pre-marking photo control point.

The dimension of the center mark should be such that its dimensions on the negative and subsequent photographs range from 0.01 mm to 0.10 mm square. This variation allows for the size of the measuring mark in the photogrammetric instrument to be used for making the measurements. If, for example, a center mark 0.03 mm square at the photo scale is desired, and the average flying height is to be 4,000 ft, then assuming a focal length of 6 in. the ground center target should be approximately 240 mm or about $9\frac{1}{2}$ in. square. A separation of twice the width of the center target should be allowed between the center target and the legs. The width of the legs can be made the same as the width of the center mark. The length of each leg should be at least five times its width. The function of the legs is to enable one to find the control point on the photograph and to distinguish the point from all other features.

One disadvantage of pre-marking or paneling photo control points is the possibility that the points may not appear on the photograph in the most advantageous position, or that a point may not appear on the photograph at all. In flying for some types of photogrammetric projects for which premarking has been performed, the position of each ground principal point must appear on the flight map. Furthermore, the photographer must be able to identify this point in the viewfinder in order to pinpoint each exposure.

In the event that both natural and pre-marked points are lacking in certain critical areas of a project, resort can be made to *post-marking*. In post-marking, the point is panelled after the photography has been flown, processed, and examined. An auxiliary camera, usually of small format such as a 35 mm camera, is carried over the area in an airplane flying at a height compatible with the scale of the aerial photography and the focal length of the lens of the smaller camera. Each post-marked point is then photographed, with the camera held vertical. After the film has been processed, the post-marked point can be transferred to the aerial photography by means of a point-transfer instrument discussed in Sec. 1–5. If the scale of the auxiliary photography is quite different from that of the aerial photography, transfer can be performed under a stereoscope in which each eyepiece can be given different magnification. (See Sec. 7–4.)

5–7. Characteristics of a Photo Control Point

The control phase of photogrammetry, in general, accounts for as much as 50 per cent of the total cost of an entire operation. Consequently, each photo control point must definitely control its share of the operation. To insure its dependability and usefulness, the photo control point has to meet certain requisites.

The point must lie in its correct position on the photograph, in order that it may accomplish its purpose most effectively. Planning for photo control should be carried out in the office by a person who understands the problems of the photogrammetrist, as well as those of the field party. The person responsible for planning the photo control indicates on the photographs, within limits, the desirable placement of horizontal and vertical photo control points. It is the responsibility of the field party to stay within these limits when picking the actual point in the field. In the infrequent case where pre-marking is necessary, the locations on the photographs of the images of the pre-marked points are left to chance, and many of these points do no fall in useful positions on the photographs.

The photo control point selected must be positively identifiable between the photograph and the ground. The field party should be furnished with stereoscopic coverage of the area, together with a pocket stereoscope (see Chapter 7), in order to properly identify the photo image of a ground point. The person responsible for picking the point must verify that he is, in fact, picking the correct point. He does this by correlating directions and distances to other image features in the vicinity of the point, as seen both on the photograph and on the ground. Misidentification of a photo control point is extremely costly, because the mistake is not generally discovered until the photogrammetric operation involving the point is well advanced.

The image of the point, especially that of a point for horizontal photo control, must be sharp and well defined when seen through the stereoscope. Measurements involving the point in the photogrammetric process can then be made accurately. A point for vertical control need not be so well defined as one for horizontal control, but it must be a distinguishable mark that is easily identifiable.

For reasons of economy, the point should be fairly accessible on the ground. This requisite quite often dictates which of two or three choices the office man will select in picking a photo control point. Accessibility can be judged to a great extent by a stereoscopic examination of the photographs.

The photo control point must be properly marked and documented in the field. Good practice requires that the field man make a pin prick through the emulsion of the photograph at the exact point, that he give the point a number for identification, and that he draw a sketch of the area on the back of the photograph showing the position of the point with respect to the area. In most instances, a word description, such as "Inside corner of sidewalk" or "Intersection of fence rows," will help to identify the point more positively.

A point for vertical photo control should lie in a limited area of no elevation change. The intersection of two road center lines, the base of a lone tree standing in a flat field, or a sand bar in a stream bed provides a good location for a point for vertical photo control. If the point is not so located, it may be difficult to use in a stereoscopic plotting instrument where its function is to establish a vertical datum.

5—8. Photo Control Requirements

The requirements for photo control points depend on the purpose for which the photographs will be used. Since many of the photogrammetric processes have not yet been discussed in this book, a general treatment is given here to indicate the variety of the requirements. Specific needs will become obvious when each process is discussed in its own place.

When a controlled mosaic is being constructed, a group of photo images whose horizontal positions are known is required for each photograph. The positions of nearly all of these points are obtained photogrammetrically. Consequently, only a limited number of points for horizontal photo control are required to control an entire mosaic, and generally no vertical control at all is needed.

To determine the elements of exterior orientation of a single photograph, as well as the space coordinates of the exposure station, it is necessary to include on the photograph at least three photo control points whose horizontal positions and elevations have been established. These three points should be located at the vertexes of a strong triangle.

The determination of the flying height for a vertical photograph requires the length of one line, together with the elevations of the two ends of the line. This requirement is discussed in Sec. 3–6. To determine the X- and Y-coordinates of the exposure station, as well as the flying height for a vertical photograph, requires that the horizontal positions of the two ends of the control line be known.

Topographic mapping by photogrammetry requires that at least two points for horizontal control and four or more points for vertical control appear in the overlap area of each successive pair of photographs. The two points for horizontal control fix the scale of the map, while the four points for vertical control establish the datum above which elevations are measured. These points are located as shown in Fig. 5–2. The points for horizontal and vertical control have been located by photo control field surveys; the horizontal pass points have been located photogrammetrically. It is to be noted that the vertical control points are placed at the corners of the neat area of overlap. They are therefore used to control adjacent flight lines, as well as adjacent areas of overlap. The corner location also provides the strongest determination of the vertical datum. The horizontal pass points are located at the edges of the neat area of overlap so that they can be used also to control adjacent flight lines and to tie the flight lines together.

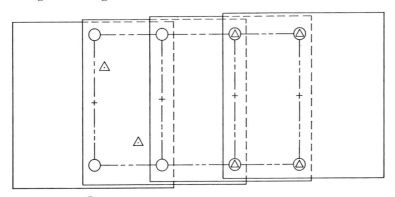

○ *Vertical Control Point*   △ *Horizontal Pass Point*
△ *Horizontal Control Point* + *Principal Point*

Fɪɢ. 5–2. Photo control placement.

Cadastral surveying by photogrammetric methods allows the position and elevation of each boundary corner to be measured and established. The control consists of a minimum of three horizontal control points and four vertical control points in each overlap area. All the boundary markers and photo control points are usually pre-marked for positive identification and for precision measurement. The control is located with methods which will insure second-order accuracy.

In order to compute the elements of exterior orientation of each of a pair of overlapping photographs, four photo points for vertical control appearing in the area of overlap are required. If the space position of each exposure station is to be determined, then two photo points for horizontal control are also required. These requirements are identical with those which must be satisfied for topographic mapping.

The foregoing examples are but a few of the photo control requirements for photogrammetric processes. As the student becomes more familiar with the science of photogrammetry and its applications, he will be in a better position to judge for himself the control requirements for a specific assignment.

5–9. Methods of Establishing Horizontal Photo Control

Photo control points are located with respect to the basic control by second-, third- or fourth-order triangulation, second- or third-order traversing, stadia traversing, trigonometric traversing, subtense-bar traversing, intersection, or resection. The best method depends on the accuracy required.

When horizontal photo control is to be used for mapping purposes, the position of each point should be located with such accuracy that it can be plotted within $\frac{1}{200}$ in. of its theoretically correct position on the map sheet. Thus, to control a map at a scale of 1 in. = 50 ft, each point should be located to within 0.25 ft. For a scale of 1:24,000, the points should be located to within 10 ft.

In triangulation, the basic control and the photo control are connected by a triangle or a network of triangles or quadrilaterals. Work of fourth-order accuracy may be carried out by using a 30-second or a 1-minute transit and measuring each angle six times, three times with the telescope direct and three times with it reversed. For small-scale mapping, satisfactory fourth-order triangulation results can be obtained by plane-table triangulation, if the work is conducted with care and stable, metal-inserted plane-table sheets are used. In triangulation all points, including the basic control monuments and the photo control points, are occupied with the transit or plane table.

Second- and third-order traversing is accomplished by means of steel tapes or electronic distance-measuring instruments together with a transit or theodolite for measuring the angles and controlling directions in the traverse by azimuth observations on the sun or stars. Because the electronic distance-measuring instruments are practically independent of difficult terrain, and because photogrammetric projects usually involve relatively large areas, these instruments are now used for the majority of horizontal photo-control field surveys.

When a stadia traverse is run for photo control, the instrument to be used should be calibrated to determine the stadia constants. The stadia traverse should be run between two basic control points so that the systematic errors introduced by the equipment and the atmospheric conditions are rendered as small as possible by adjustment. A loop traverse beginning and closing on the same point will not reveal any of the systematic errors, because all these errors will be compensating. Thus, at the far end of the loop, uncompensated systematic errors of unknown size will exist, and it is more than likely that the photo control point will be located at this weak point in the traverse.

A trigonometric traverse, or trig traverse, is a degenerate form of triangulation. To obtain the required accuracy, a theodolite reading directly to 1 second must be used. In trig traversing, angles are measured about the traverse stations in the usual manner. However, the distances are measured indirectly by laying out a base at, or nearly at, right angles to the general direction of the traversing and measuring the angle between the two ends of the base from adjacent traverse stations.

In Fig. 5–3, M, P, and R are three consecutive traverse stations. At P, the base line PB is laid out by using a calibrated tape, and a target is set at B. With the theodolite at P, the directions to M, B, and R

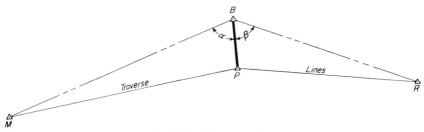

Fig. 5–3. Trig traversing.

are observed. With the theodolite at M and R, respectively, the angle BMP and PRB are measured. The angle $\alpha = 180° - (\angle MPB + \angle BMP)$, and $\beta = 180° - (\angle BPR + \angle PRB)$. Then, by the law of sines, $MP = BP$ sin α/sin $\angle BMP$, and $PR = BP$ sin β/sin $\angle PRB$.

A base is established at every second traverse station, unless greater accuracy is required. Tapes from 100 ft to 500 ft long are used, the choice depending on the lengths of the traverse lines involved, the topography, and the desired accuracy. In much trig-traverse work the results have met the accuracy requirements for third-order triangulation. In fact, this method has been used successfully to obtain basic third-order control. A little thought indicates that the trig method of traversing is applicable only for relatively long traverse lines because the inconvenience of establishing a base line at every second station of a short-sided traverse would nullify the advantage of the trig method. Vertical angles are read at the same time the horizontal angles are measured, thereby furnishing the data needed for computing elevations.

In subtense-bar traversing, the length of the base line is established by orienting a bar on a tripod in a horizontal position normal to the direction of the traverse line. The bar is equipped with three targets. A target is located at each end, and the separation between these two targets is accurately known. Also, an azimuth target is located at the middle point of the bar. The subtense bar can have any convenient length, but the standard lengths are 1, 2, and 3 meters. As shown in Fig. 5–4, the

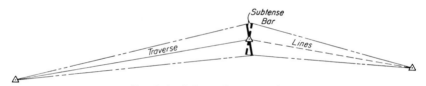

FIG. 5–4. Subtense-bar traversing.

bar is placed at one end of a traverse line and is oriented normal to the line, while the subtended angle is measured at the other end of the line. The length of the traverse line equals one-half the bar length times the cotangent of one-half the subtended angle. With traverse sides between 100 ft and 600 ft in length, the use of a 2-meter bar and twelve direct positions of a 1-second theodolite will limit the probable error of the mean angle to about ±0.30″. Thus, for a measurement up to 600 ft, a well-calibrated bar can produce an accuracy of a little better than ± 1 ft per mile. The accuracy falls off rapidly beyond 600 ft, because the subtended angle changes very little for an appreciable increase in length.

For long traverse lines, the subtense bar can be combined with the principle of trig traverse, as shown in Fig. 5–5. The base line PB is laid out with the instrument at P. Point B is chosen somewhat at random, and S is set somewhere on the line PB. The angles are measured between the traverse lines through P and the base line. The subtense bar is set up at S, and the subtense angles are turned both at P and at B. The

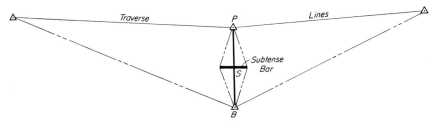

Fig. 5–5. Combined trig and subtense-bar traversing.

subtended distances PS and SB are added to give the trig base PB. If each of the distances PS and SB is held to 300 ft or less, the trig base can be established to within 1 part in 10,000.

Intersection is simply the unconditioned measurement of a triangle formed by the photo control point and two points for basic horizontal control. Any two angles can be measured, but measuring those at the two basic control stations is preferable. The angle formed at the photo control point should lie between 60° and 120°, in order to provide a strong intersection. Because there is no check on the triangle closure, the photo control point should be observed from a third basic control point. Thus, two independent intersections can be computed and the accuracy of the field work can be tested.

Resection is the determination of the position of a point by occupying the point and measuring the directions to three or more fixed basic control points. In this instance, the photo control point is occupied. Since any three points will always give a mathematically perfect solution, there is no check on mistakes or errors in the field observations unless a fourth point is observed to provide the proper checks. When a resection observation comprises the measurement of directions to four or more points with a 1-second direction theodolite, the accuracy of the results will be equivalent to, and quite often better than, that specified for third-order accuracy. This method is used to great advantage in areas containing man-made structures, such as towers and stacks, on which positions have been obtained by intersection from first-order and second-order triangulation stations. The observations are easily made, and there is no necessity for visiting the known points to erect signals.

The U.S. Geological Survey has developed an airborne system of control surveying for controlling topographic mapping in fairly inaccessible areas. The system, which is called Airborne Control, and more commonly known as ABC, employs a helicopter with a stabilized vertical sighting device called the hoversight. The helicopter carries a flashing beacon target, and a plumb line on a drum. It also carries an electronic distance-measuring instrument. As the pilot hovers directly over a point, indicated by the hoversight, he sends a radio signal to two or more ground parties who occupy fixed basic control points with theodolites and electronic instruments. The field parties sight the beacon, read the horizontal and vertical circles on the theodolite, and record the distance to the helicopter as indicated by the electronic instrument. The pilot lowers the plumb line to the ground to measure the height of the beacon above the control point. The position of the control point is determined by an intersection of the theodolite rays, or by an intersection of distance arcs, or by a combination of these measurements according to which geometric conditions will give the strongest solution. The elevation of the point is determined by the vertical angles measured to the beacon together with the measured height of the beacon above the ground point.

5–10. Methods of Establishing Vertical Photo Control

Vertical photo control may be established by second- and third-order leveling, fly leveling, transit-stadia leveling, plane-table leveling, trig leveling, or precision barometric altimetry. The selection of the method depends largely on the desired accuracy. Also, since vertical photo control for the most part is used to control topographic mapping, the method depends on the contour interval of the map. When vertical photo control is used to control topographic mapping, the method selected should be such as to limit the error in elevation to one-tenth of the contour interval. Other factors influencing the selection of the method to be used are the type of terrain, the kind of equipment available, and the accessibility of the terrain.

Third-order leveling must be used to obtain satisfactory vertical photo control for mapping at a contour interval of 2 ft or less. Highway design mapping for determining earthwork quantities is a good example of mapping to a very small contour interval. In some instances, ground cross-sections are measured directly in the model of a stereoscopic plotting instrument. (See Chapter 12.) The vertical control for this type of measurement is located at each station along the route survey. These stations are usually pre-marked for identification. An engineer's dumpy level, a tilting level, or a self-leveling level, if in good adjustment, can be used to carry the level lines. Backsight and foresight distances are balanced, turning points are carefully chosen or set, and the points for vertical photo control are included as turning points in the line of levels. This line begins and closes on a basic control bench mark. Where lines of levels are necessary to maintain accuracy over great distances, second order field methods should be employed. The lines should cross one another to form a net, and should not just be connected end to end. The formation of a net allows the accuracy near the middle points of the lines to be tested, and it establishes a basis for adjustment of the resultant elevations.

Fly leveling is a form of differential leveling where the line of sight is always horizontal but long sights are taken. Fly levels are adaptable to gently rolling terrain where the grades are easy enough to permit long level sights. The instruments used for third-order leveling are also used in fly leveling. The length of sights are stretched out to as much as 1,000 ft. Backsight and foresight distances are not particularly balanced, although the improvement in the results justifies some attempt at balanced sights. A target is used on the leveling rod, being set by the rodman on the line of sight in accordance with signals from the instrumentman. The rod is read to the nearest 0.01 ft. When the party consists of two rodmen and the instrumentman, three sets of notes are kept, one by the instrumentman for both rod readings and one by each rodman for his own target settings. As the personnel pass one another, they verify the recorded rod readings. A fly-leveling circuit should begin and end on a bench mark of third-order accuracy or better. The accuracy of the results is satisfactory for contour intervals between 2 and 5 ft. Backsight and foresight distances must be balanced when this method is used for obtaining vertical control for mapping at a 2-ft contour interval.

Transit-stadia leveling is suited to heavy topography because the line of sight may be inclined at any angle. It is suitable for mapping at contour intervals as small as 5 ft, if the work is done with care. The method of stadia leveling is described in any good surveying text-book. Mention is made here, however, of a technique commonly used to prevent mistakes in reading the vertical circle and to improve the accuracy of the computed differences in elevation.

Assume that a transit whose stadia interval factor is near 100 is to be used to perform the stadia leveling. When the line of sight is directed at the stadia rod, the telescope bubble is centered and the vertical circle is read to determine the index error. With the three cross hairs brought on the rod, all three hairs are read, and the corresponding reading of the vertical circle is recorded. The readings of the upper and lower cross hairs give the rod interval. Finally, either the upper cross hair is lowered or the lower cross hair is raised to the previous position of the center cross hair, and the vertical circle is again read. With a stadia interval factor of 100, the angle subtended by the upper and middle cross hairs or by the middle and lower cross hairs equals $\sin^{-1}(1/200) = 17$ minutes, approximately. Therefore the difference between the two vertical-circle readings obtained as just described should be about 17 minutes. The second reading is algebraically greater if the line of sight was raised for that reading, or is algebraically less if the line of sight was lowered. Two differences in elevation can then be computed, and the value of the interval can thus be checked. Stadia levels are carried between bench marks of third-order or better accuracy and are adjusted as is any line of levels.

Leveling with the plane table and an alidade is similar to transit-stadia leveling. However, the results will usually be inferior because the control bubble of the Beaman arc is less sensitive than that of the transit telescope, and because the Beaman arc itself is read less accurately than the vertical circle on the transit. To eliminate the dependence on the Beaman arc and the control bubble, level sights should be taken so that the more sensitive striding level can be used. Also the method of stepping described in most surveying textbooks can be used where inclined lines are necessary. When a well-adjusted alidade is used with a reasonable amount of care and the lengths of sights are under 800 ft, this method can prove satisfactory for establishing vertical photo control for a contour interval as small as 5 ft.

Trig leveling consists in measuring a vertical angle V and a horizontal distance D. Differences in elevation are then computed by finding the values of $D \tan V$ and making allowances for curvature and refraction. The horizontal distances may be obtained by triangulation, traverse, trig traverse, intersection, or resection. The vertical angles may be measured with an engineer's transit, provided that the distances are less than 1,000 ft or provided that the vertical control is to be used for large contour intervals. Otherwise, the vertical angles should be measured with a 1-second theodolite. For greater accuracy, the vertical angles should be measured from both ends of the line with as short an interval of time between measurements as possible. This procedure tends to eliminate the uncertainty in the refraction correction. Under favorable circumstances, trig leveling produces results comparable to or better than those obtainable by third-order differential leveling. Trig leveling is used most advantageously where the horizontal positions of photo control points have been established by triangulation, intersection, or resection. The lengths of the lines are obtained directly from the computations. The vertical angles are measured coincidentally with the horizontal angles.

The U.S. Geological Survey employs an ingeneous instrument, called the elevation meter, for measuring elevations over large areas in which a good network of roads has been developed. The elevation meter contains a pendulum which lies parallel with an electromagnetic field when the instrument is level. As the instrument becomes inclined when going up or down a hill, an electrical current is set up, the strength of which is proportional to the slope (actually to the sine of the slope angle). The slope distance travelled is measured by a carefully calibrated wheel which is drawn along over the roadway. The slope angle and the slope distance are integrated electrically to give a continous record of the difference in elevation from the starting point. The entire instrument is housed in a panel truck. To begin a circuit, the truck stops at a bench mark and readings are made. The truck then proceeds along the road, stopping at all vertical photo control points and all bench marks. Each control point is identified on the appropriate control photograph. Readings taken at the bench marks allow the accumulated error to be distributed back through the intervening distance. The adjusted readings at the vertical photo control points are then used to compute their elevations. If conditions are favorable, accuracies of the order of ± 2 ft can be obtained. This accuracy, however, is usually not expected of the elevation meter.

Aneroid barometers are used to establish the elevations of photo control points for small-scale mapping with a large contour interval. This method is suited to rugged terrain which is difficult of access. Bench marks on which barometric altimetry is based are usually established by a network of trig leveling because of the nature of the terrain. Barometric altimetry is performed by the two-base method, the three-base method, or the leapfrog method.

In the two-base method of using aneroid barometers, two bench marks are established in the vicinity of the mapping, one at a low elevation and the second at a high elevation. Three altimeters basically are used, one at the low bench mark, or base, a second at the high base, and a third in the field. This last one is referred to as the field, or roving, altimeter. Before any field work is performed, all three altimeters are set to read the same when all three are at the same elevation. At regular time intervals, the altimeters at the low and high bases are read. The roving altimeter is taken to various photo control points, and the altimeter readings and the times are recorded. From the high-base reading, the low-base reading, and the roving-altimeter reading for a given time, the elevation of the photo control point can be determined. The two-base method eliminates to a great extent the effects of temperature and humidity on the altimeter readings. In order to maintain accuracy, limitations must be imposed on the elevation difference between the low and high bases, on the distance between the two bases, and on the area covered by the roving altimeter.

In the accompanying tabulation, the roving-altimeter readings on three photo control points are shown, together with the times and the corresponding readings at the two bases. The difference in elevation between the low base and the high base is 435 ft. At 4:10 P.M. the difference in readings at the two bases is 420 ft. At the same time, the difference between the low-base reading and the photo-control reading is 71 ft. By straight proportion, the difference in elevation between the low base and the photo control point is (71) (435)/420 = 74 ft. Similarly, the differences in elevation between the low base and the other two points are (10) (435)/415 = 10 ft and (236) (435)/(422) = 243 ft.

Two-Base Altimeter Readings

Time	Low-Base Reading (ft)	Low-Base Elevation (ft)	High-Base Reading (ft)	High-Base Elevation (ft)	Roving-Altimeter Reading (ft)
4:10 P.M.	982	615	1,402	1,050	1,053
4:25 P.M.	980	615	1,395	1,050	990
4:55 P.M.	971	615	1,393	1,050	1,207

In the three-base method, three altimeters are indexed at the same point and then taken to three bench marks located at the vertexes of a well-conditioned triangle. The three altimeters are read periodically, and one or more roving altimeters are used to take readings on photo control points. The positions of the photo control points must be determined, usually by spotting them on a map with the aid of the aerial photographs. The readings at the three bases give not only the variation of atmospheric pressure throughout the day, but also the slope and the direction of slope of an assumed plane of equal pressure. The positions of the photo control points with respect to the three bases allow the effect of the sloping plane of equal pressure to be taken into consideration when the elevations of the photo control points are computed.

The leapfrog method has been developed to eliminate the errors caused by the control point being too far from the established base or bases. In this method, two altimeters are indexed at a bench mark. One is then moved to a photo control point, and the time and the altimeter reading are recorded. The temperature and the humidity are measured, and corrections are applied to the difference between the readings of the two altimeters to give a tentative elevation of the photo control point. The altimeter at the bench mark is then taken past the other altimeter to a second photo control point. Based on the time, the altimeter readings, and the temperature and humidity, the tentative elevation of the second point is computed. Finally, the rear altimeter is brought forward to the forward altimeter, and the readings of the two are compared to make refinements to the tentative elevations thus far obtained. The entire process is then repeated at points 3 and 4, 5 and 6, and other pairs until a closure is made on another bench mark. The closing error is then distributed back through the altimeter circuit.

The leapfrog method limits the distance between successive altimeter readings so that unknown atmospheric conditions are less able to affect the results. Each new elevation established along the line becomes, in effect, a new base. This procedure is analogous to carrying a line of differential levels in that each turning point becomes a new base for the forward setup.

5-11. Planning for Photo Control

The first step in planning photo control is to obtain the available basic horizontal and vertical control for the area. This basic control can be obtained from the nearest offices of the U. S. Coast and Geodetic Survey, the U. S. Geological Survey, the U. S. Army Corps of Engineers, state highway agencies, state water-resources agencies, various county, city, and municipal agencies, or public utilities.

A map of the area is used to locate the basic control points. These points are plotted directly on the map. The need for additional basic control of second-order or third-order accuracy is determined from an examination of the density and placement of the existing basic control. Tentative positions for additional triangulation and traverse stations and bench marks should be plotted on the map. When the aerial photographs have been taken, processed, and delivered to the personnel responsible for planning the photo control, the basic control points, together with the tentative control, are located on a set of the photographs with the aid of the map.

A careful stereoscopic study of the aerial photographs, with reference made to the map if necessary, will aid in selecting the areas on the photographs in which the photo control points should fall. The ease of access, the closeness to basic control, the type of equipment, the most effective positions for the photo control, and the availability of identifiable points are all factors which help to limit the selected areas on the photographs. These areas are then marked as discussed in Sec. 5-7.

The field personnel should make a study of the photographs to plan the necessary additional basic control and the photo control. This preliminary study quite often decides the methods to be used, the routes to be taken, and the type and amount of equipment necessary to complete the control work, and is also an effective aid in scheduling the work. Questions arising at this stage are settled between the office and the field personnel.

After the office study by the field personnel has been made, the field work is accomplished, the photo control points are marked and identified, the information for control is computed, and this information is then made available for the particular photogrammetric project at hand.

Bibliography

AMERICAN SOCIETY OF PHOTOGRAMMETRY. *Manual of Photogrammetry* (Menasha, Wisc.: George Banta Co., 1952), Chapter 7.

————. *Manual of Photogrammetry* (Menasha, Wisc.: George Banta Co., 1966), Chapter 8.

BAKER, W. O. "The Use of the Tellurometer for Photogrammetric Mapping," *Surveying and Mapping*, Vol. XIX (1959), p. 50.

BARTHOLD, E. "Supplemental Vertical Control Methods," *Surveying and Mapping*, Vol. XII (1952), p. 123.

BORRELL, S. M. "Terrestrial Photography for Establishing Supplemental Control," *Photogrammetric Engineering*, Vol. XXIII (1957), p. 58.

BOYLE, J. "Geodimeter NASM4," *Surveying and Mapping*, Vol. XX (1960), p. 49.

BURGER, T. D. "Use of the Elevation Meter in Topographic Mapping," *Surveying and Mapping*, Vol. XXI (1961), p. 481.

CHICKERING, H. G., JR. "A Proposed Method of Reconnaissance for Coordinated Aerial and Field Surveys," *Photogrammetric Engineering*, Vol. XIV (1948), p. 551.

"Classification and Standards of Accuracy of Geodetic Control Surveys," *Surveying and Mapping*, Vol. XIX (1959), p. 219.

COCKING, A. V. "A Year with the Tellurometer," *Surveying and Mapping*, Vol. XIX (1959), p. 233.

COMPTON, M. B. "Accuracy Over Short Distances with the Model 4 Geodimeter," *Surveying and Mapping*, Vol. XVII (1957), p. 425.

————. "Distance Measurements, One Million a Second," *Surveying and Mapping*, Vol. XVII (1957), p. 25.

COON, E. J. "Map Control by Photo-Trig and Subtense Bar," *Surveying and Mapping*, Vol. XII (1952), p. 54.

DAMESON, L. G. "New Microwave Distance-Measuring Equipment," *Surveying and Mapping*, Vol. XXIV (1964), p. 579.

EARNEST, G. B. "Cleveland's City Survey," *Surveying and Mapping*, Vol. XII (1952), p. 67.

ECKHARDT, C. V. "Airborne Control for Topographic Mapping," *Surveying and Mapping*, Vol. XXVI (1966), p. 49.

————. "Field Mapping in Yemen," *Surveying and Mapping*, Vol. XXII (1962), p. 259.

EDEN, J. A. "Point Identification on Air Photographs," *Photogrammetric Engineering*, Vol. XVI (1950), p. 185.

GAMBLE, S. G. "Our Experience with the Tellurometer," *Surveying and Mapping*, Vol. XIX (1959), p. 53.

GIGAS, E. "The Electronic Distance Meter for Precision Traverse Surveying," *Surveying and Mapping*, Vol. XV (1955), p. 315.

GRAVAT, H. R. "Leapfrog Barometric Leveling," *Photogrammetric Engineering*, Vol. XXIII (1957), p. 328.

HALLIDAY, J. "The Vital Communications Link—Photoidenification of Horizontal Control," *Photogrammetric Engineering*, Vol. XXIX (1963), p. 804.

HARING, W. F. "Improving the Accuracy of Altimetry," *Surveying and Mapping*, Vol. XV (1955), p. 336.

HARTMAN, P. "Temperature Compensation of the Subtense Bar," *Surveying and Mapping*, Vol. XIX (1959), p. 475.

HEAPE, R. E. "Electrotape: Electronic Distance-Measuring Equipment," *Surveying and Mapping*, Vol. XXII (1962), p. 265.

HEMPEL, C. B. "Electrotape—A Surveyor's Electronic Eyes," *Surveying and Mapping*, Vol. XXI (1961), p. 85.

HICKS, W. R. "A Pressure Transducer for Barometric Surveying," *Surveying and Mapping*, Vol. XXIII (1963), p. 413.

HOPKINS, P. F. "Establishing Control for Aerial Mapping Test Area in Southern Arizona," *Surveying and Mapping*, Vol. XI (1951), p. 288.

HOUGH, F. W. "New Developments in Electron Distance Measuring Equipment," *Photogrammetric Engineering*, Vol. XXVI No. 1 (March 1960), p. 95.

———. "The Tellurometer—Some Uses and Advantages," *Surveying and Mapping*, Vol. XVII (1957), p. 276.

JACKSON, C. D., and LINT, L. B. "Experiments in the Use of Subtense Tachometry for Establishing Fourth Order Horizontal Control," *Photogrammetric Engineering*, Vol. XIV (1948), p. 297.

KING, J. E. "Advantages of Photogrammetry in Cadastral Surveying," *Surveying and Mapping*, Vol. XXII (1962), p. 97.

LARKIN, M. F. "Ground Control for Topographic Mapping in Chilean Disaster Region," *Surveying and Mapping*, Vol. XXIII (1963), p. 437.

LOVING, H. G. "Airborne Control System," *Surveying and Mapping*, Vol. XXIII (1963), p. 91.

LYON, DUANE. "Methods of Supplementing Geodetic Control," *Photogrammetric Engineering*, Vol. XIII (1947), p. 481.

MALCHOW, S. "Cadastral Survey and Its Geodetic Foundation in Swiss Practice," *Surveying and Mapping*, Vol. XXIII (1963), p. 248.

MEARS, A. H. "Multiple Base Altimetry," *Photogrammetric Engineering*, Vol. XX (1954), p. 814.

MILLER, E. W. "Errors in the Three-Point Problem," *Surveying and Mapping*, Vol. XXIII (1963), p. 429.

NAGY, A. "Triangle Chains for Densification of Supplementary Control," *Surveying and Mapping*, Vol. XXII (1962), p. 73.

ROBERTSON, R. R. "Altimeters as Used by the 30th Engineers for Mapping," *Photogrammetric Engineering*, Vol. XVIII (1952), p. 839.

SLAMA, C. C. "Evaluation of an APR System for Photogrammetric Triangulation of Long Flights," *Photogrammetric Engineering*, Vol. XXVII (1961), p. 572.

SMIRNOFF, M. V. "The Use of the Subtense Bar," *Surveying and Mapping*, Vol. XII (1952), p. 390.

TANNER, H. P. "Use of the Subtense Bar," *Surveying and Mapping*," Vol. XV (1955), p. 336.

THEURER, C. "Control for Photogrammetric Mapping," *Photogrammetric Engineering*, Vol. XXIII (1957), p. 318.

TURPIN, R. D. "A Study of the Use of the Wild Telemeter DM1 for a Closed Traverse," *Surveying and Mapping*, Vol. XIV (1954), p. 471.

"Use of the Altimeter and Helicopter for Establishing Vertical Control for Photogrammetric Mapping," *Photogrammetric Engineering*, Vol. XVI (1950), p. 528.

WALKER, H. D. "Third-Order Surveys at Reasonable Cost," *Surveying and Mapping*, Vol. XII (1952), p. 253.

WOODCOCK, L. F., and LAMPTON, B. F. "Measurement of Crustal Movements by Photogrammetric Methods," *Photogrammetric Engineering*, Vol. XXX (1964), p. 912.

Problems

5–1. Outline the specifications for first-order and second-order triangulation, traverses, and levels, as adopted by the U.S. Coast and Geodetic Survey.

5–2. Outline the specifications and procedures for third-order triangulation, traverses, and levels, as adopted by the U.S. Geological Survey.

5–3. Obtain from the nearest regional office of the U.S. Coast and Geodetic Survey a complete description of a first-order or second-order triangulation station in your vicinity, including its location, physical description, reference marks, latitude and longitude, and state plane coordinates, and the azimuths to adjacent stations and azimuth marks.

5–4. Obtain from the nearest regional office of the U.S. Geological Survey the description of a line of third-order levels in your vicinity.

5–5. The base line BP of Fig. 5–3 measures 102.146 ft; $< MPB = 95°$ 22′ 31.3″; $< BPR = 99°$ 06′ 15.0″; $< BMP = 1°$ 52′ 44.2″; $< PRB = 1°$ 27′ 56.2″. Compute the lengths of traverse lines MP and PR to five significant figures.

5–6. The subtense bar of Fig. 5–4 is 2 meters long between the end targets. The angle subtended at the left traverse station is $0°$ 41′ 44.04″ $\pm 0.30″$, and the angle subtended at the right traverse station is $1°$ 15′ 20.60″ $\pm 0.58″$. Assuming that there is no error in the length of the subtense bar, determine the lengths of the two lines and the standard deviations of those lengths.

5–7. In carrying a line of fly levels to a point for vertical photo control, the average distance between the rod positions was 1,700 ft. The total length of the line to the point was 4.40 miles. Since the line progressed upgrade, the average unbalance between the backsight and foresight distances was 200 ft, the backsight distance being longer in each instance. If the line of sight rose at the rate of 0.0005 ft per ft when the level bubble was centered, as determined by a two-peg test, what is the resulting error in the elevation of the control point because of this condition? Is the measured elevation too high or too low?

5–8. The data resulting from two-base altimetry follow:

Time (ft)	Low-Base Reading (ft)	Low-Base Elevation (ft)	High-Base Reading (ft)	High-Base Elevation (ft)	Roving-Altimeter Reading (ft)
11:05 A.M.	1.126	220	2,780	1,857	1,267
12:30 P.M.	1,120	220	2,778	1,857	1,802
3:20 P.M.	1,139	220	2,800	1,857	1,850
3:30 P.M.	1,141	220	2,800	1,857	2,264
4:05 P.M.	1,153	220	2,804	1,857	1,688

At 10:00 A.M., the three altimeters were compared with each other. The high-base altimeter read 12 ft lower than the low-base altimeter, and the roving altimeter read 39 ft lower than the low-base altimeter. These discrepancies were verified again at 5:00 P.M. and found to be the same. Compute the elevations of the five field points.

5–9. The state plane coordinates of points A and B are $X_A = 1,614,850.2$ and $Y_A = 435,572.6$; $X_B = 1,625,754.7$ and $Y_B = 437,030.0$. The clockwise angle measured at A from B to a photo control point is $73°$ 22′ 16.2″. The counter-clockwise angle measured at B from A to the photo control point is 41° 57′ 25.0″. Compute the state plane coordinates of the photo control point.

5–10. The state plane coordinates of three basic control points are as follows:

Point	X (ft)	Y (ft)
P	623,561.0	1,122,899.0
Q	627,988.6	1,123,242.2
R	632,560.1	1,122,006.3

A photo control point lies south of the basic control points. With a theodolite occupying this point, an angle of 16° 20′ 16″ is turned from P to Q, and an angle of 29° 40′ 36″ is turned from Q to R. Compute the state plane coordinates of the control point.

5–11. What are the dimensions of the photographic image of the intersection of two 6-ft sidewalks if the photograph is taken from an altitude of 12,000 ft above the ground with a lens having a 6-in. focal length?

5–12. How large an image will a size 6.00×16 automobile tire, lying flat on the ground, produce on a photograph taken with a lens having a 12-in. focal length from an altitude of 7,500 ft above the ground?

5–13. Design a panel cross such that the center will measure 0.02 mm square when photographed from 40,000 ft with an 88 mm focal length lens.

5–14. What is the error in a horizontal distance determined by means of a 2-meter subtense bar, if the subtended angle is 1° 00′ 00″ and the error in the angle is 1 sec? If the subtended angle is 0° 30′ 00″, what is the error in the horizontal distance for an error of 1 sec in the angle?

5–15. In Fig. 5-3, the base $BP = 90.004$ ft; $<BMP = 1° 22′ 22.3″$; $<BRP = 1° 24′ 16.0″$; $<BPM = 96° 10′ 20.7″$; $<BPR = 93° 14′ 42.2″$. Determine the lengths of the traverse lines MP and PR to five significant figures.

5–16. Outline the desirable characteristics of a point for horizontal photo control.

5–17. In what respect does a point for vertical photo control differ from a point for horizontal control?

5–18. In order to prepare a topographic map, three overlapping strips of seven photographs per strip are taken from an aircraft. How many vertical control points will be needed to establish the datum for elevations for the mapping?

5–19. In Fig. 5-5, the subtense bar is 2 meters long. The subtense-bar angle at P is 1° 16′ 20.4″, and that at B is 0° 45′ 55.2″. The angle at the left traverse station is 4° 15′ 42.8″, and that at the right traverse station is 3° 45′ 15.5″. Compute the lengths of the traverse sides.

5–20. Two electronic measuring instruments occupy Stations A and B whose coordinates are $X_A = 105,060$ ft, $Y_A = 34,541$ ft, $X_B = 113,104$ ft, $Y_B = 19,980$ ft. A photo control point C lies easterly from A. The distance AC is measured as 11,854 ft, and the distance BC is measured as 12,743 ft. Compute the position of the photo control point.

5–21. Outline the methods used to establish horizontal photo control.

5–22. Outline the methods used to establish vertical photo control.

Principles of Radial-Line Plotting and Planimetric Mapping 6

6-1. Properties of Vertical Photograph

The principles of radial-line plotting are applied to the extension of ground control by graphical methods and to the compilation of planimetric maps from aerial photographs. These principles depend on certain geometric properties of the single aerial photograph. On a truly vertical aerial photograph, the angles measured in the plane of the photograph about the principal point are true horizontal angles, except for the very slight effect of tangential distortion. The vertical photograph in space can be considered as an angle-measuring device similar to a transit. The front nodal point of the lens coincides with the intersection of the horizontal and vertical axes of the transit. The plane of the photograph is analogous to the horizontal circle of the transit. A line directed to the front nodal point from a point on the ground is analogous to a line of sight of the transit when the telescope is set at a large depression angle.

In Fig. 6–1(a) a vertical photograph taken at a flying height H_1 above the datum contains the images a_1, b_1, and o of ground points A, B, and O. The true horizontal angle measured about O is $B'O'A'$, which is measured in the horizontal datum plane. As demonstrated in Sec. 3–7, the radial line ob_1 lies in the same vertical plane as does the line $O'B'$, and the radial line oa_1 lies in the same vertical plane as does the line $O'A'$. Since the plane of the photograph is horizontal, $\angle b_1oa_1$ must equal $\angle B'O'A'$. Thus, the angle measured about the principal point of the vertical photograph between b_1 and a_1 is a true horizontal angle, and is identical to the angle which would be measured with a transit at ground point O from B to A. As seen in Fig. 6–1(a), the elevations of the ground points have no effect on the angle measured on the photograph because the relief displacement takes place along the radial lines ob_1 and oa_1.

In Fig. 6–1(b), the same ground points are photographed from a flying height H_2 above the datum. Ground point O appears at the principal point, as in Fig. 6–1(a). By the analysis just given, it is obvious that $\angle b_2oa_2 = \angle B'O'A'$. Therefore, $\angle b_2oa_2$ in view (b) is equal to $\angle b_1oa_1$ in view (a). This equality indicates the significant fact that the angles measured about the principal point of a vertical photograph are

144

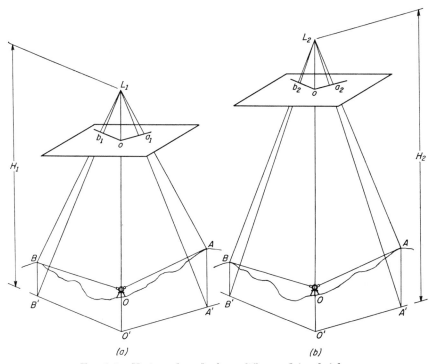

FIG. 6–1. Horizontal angle from different flying heights.

horizontal angles, regardless of the flying height. Another explanation for this fact is that a scale change at a given horizontal position of the exposure station resulting from a change in flying height causes the images of ground points to be displaced along lines radially from the principal point.

Any radial lens distortion, no matter of what magnitude, has no effect on the angles measured about the principal point of a photograph because the distortions take place along radial lines. Tangential distortion does have an effect on the angles, but the effect is absolutely negligible insofar as the operations discussed in this chapter are concerned.

6–2. Map Position of Principal Point of a Vertical Photograph

The map position of a point means the true horizontal position of the point as plotted to the map scale. Assume that a truly vertical photograph contains the images of three photo control points whose horizontal positions have been established by field surveys. In Fig. 6–2 these three points are a, b, and c. Their map positions are plotted on the map at A, B, and C, as shown. If rays are drawn on the photograph

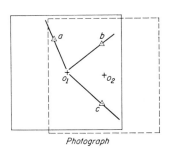

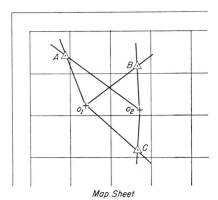

FIG. 6–2.   Location of principal points by 3-point resection.

from o_1 through a, b, and c, the two angles ao_1b and bo_1c are true horizontal angles. If these rays are now transferred to the map sheet by means of tracing paper or a three-armed protractor, and the three rays are caused to pass through the plotted points A, B, and C, the vertex of the angles is the true map position of the principal point. This is a graphical solution of the three-point problem and is called *resection*. (See Sec. 5–9.)

If the next successive photograph (shown by dashed lines) overlaps the first photograph and also contains the images of the three ground points, the map position of the principal point o_2 of this photograph can also be located by resection.

The principal points of two overlapping photographs may be located on the map if only two photo control points, properly placed, appear in the area of overlap. In Fig. 6–3, photo control points d and e appear on both photographs. The position of principal point o_1 is located on photograph *2*, and the position of principal point o_2, is located on photograph *1*. Rays are drawn from o_1 through d, o_2, and e on the left photograph, forming the horizontal angles do_1o_2 and o_2o_1e. Rays are drawn from o_2 through d, o_1, and e on the right photograph, forming the

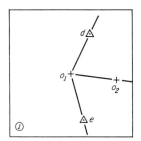

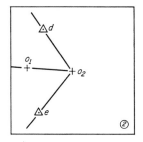

FIG. 6–3.   Tracing-paper rays through two control points.

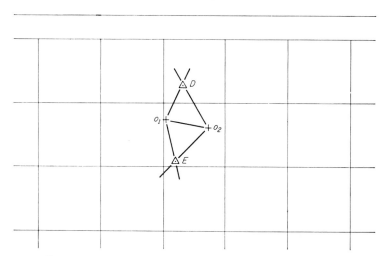

FIG. 6-4. Location of principal points by 2-point resection.

horizontal angles do_2o_1 and o_1o_2e. The two sets of rays are transferred to two sheets of tracing paper and are laid together on the map sheet. Since o_1o_2 is the same line as o_2o_1, these two lines on the two pieces of tracing paper must coincide when one is placed over the other. With the pieces in these positions, the lines o_1d and o_2d intersect, and the lines o_1e and o_2e also intersect. As shown in Fig. 6-4, these intersections are made to coincide with the plotted positions of D and E, thus determining the map positions of o_1 and o_2. Reference to tracing paper is made to help you visualize the transference of rays from the photographs to the map. The line o_1o_2 as located on the map sheet constitutes a base line, and the points o_1 and o_2 represent instrument stations, which they really are.

6–3. Map Positions of Image Points

The map position of a point whose image appears in the area of overlap of a pair of vertical photographs may be located, provided that the principal points of the two photographs have been located on the map sheet. Assume that the map positions of o_1 and o_2 in Fig. 6–5 have been established, and that the map position of a photo point p appearing in the area of overlap is to be determined. Rays o_1p and o_1o_2 are drawn on photograph *1*, forming the horizontal angle po_1o_2. Rays o_2p and o_2o_1 are then drawn on photograph *2*, forming the horizontal angle po_2o_1. The scale of photograph *2* is purposely made considerably larger to emphasize the fact that a difference in the flying heights for the two photographs has no effect on the solution.

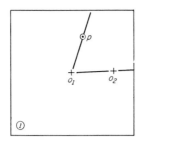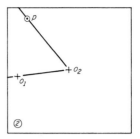

FIG. 6–5. Tracing-paper rays for intersection.

By means of tracing paper, the two sets of rays are transferred to the map sheet which contains the map positions of o_1 and o_2, and the respective vertexes of the angles are made to coincide with these map positions. The base rays are oriented to coincide with the line o_1o_2 on the map, as shown in Fig. 6–6. The intersection of the rays o_1p and o_2p defines the true map position P of the image point p. This is the principle of *intersection*. (See Sec. 5–9.) By combining two sets of rays to several image points appearing in the area of overlap of the two photographs, the map positions of these points can be located. An extension of this procedure will ultimately result in the compilation of a true planimetric map of the overlap area. The scale of the map is fixed by the scale at which the positions of photo control points are plotted. Note that the radial-line method of plotting planimetry requires that each ray center appear on adjacent photographs. Otherwise, it is not possible to establish the base line from which intersections are made. This is one of the reasons why the overlap must be more than 50 per cent when aerial photographs are taken for photogrammetric purposes.

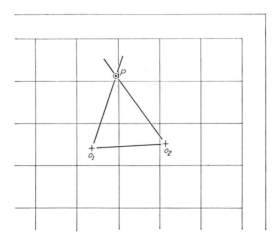

FIG. 6–6. Intersection.

6–4. Extension of Control by Radial-Line Plotting

By applying the principles already developed, horizontal control can be extended graphically between photo control points. The additional control points thus obtained are called *pass points*. In Fig. 6–7(a) five photographs are shown to overlap by about 60 per cent. The principal points o_1 through o_5 are indicated by small crosses. The positions of three photo control points a, b, and c are indicated by small triangles. Points a and b appear in the area of overlap of the first and second photographs; point c appears in the area of overlap of the fourth and fifth photographs. Arbitrary points d through m, which are indicated by small circles, are the pass points.

Pass points are chosen to meet the following requirements: 1) They must be sharp, well-defined points, easily identifiable on successive photographs. 2) They must fall near the edges of the photographs, preferably from $\frac{1}{2}$ to 1 in. from the edges. 3) They should fall as nearly as possible opposite the respective principal points. 4) They must appear on three consecutive photographs in the direction of flight, except for those pass points at the extreme ends of the flight line. 5) When more than one flight line is involved, they must appear also on the adjacent flight lines. These requirements are necessary to insure proper identification of pass points, to make the control extension as strong as possible, and to tie together adjacent flight strips. When pass points that are common to two flight strips are selected, their positions should be chosen so as to lie at about the middle of the sidelap.

In Fig. 6–7(b), the photographs are shown separated from one another. On them the principal points, the photo control points, and the pass points are marked for identification. Five sheets of tracing paper are used, one for each photograph. On each sheet, rays are drawn from the principal point of the photograph to all the other principal points, the photo control points, and the pass points appearing on the photograph. Each ray is identified systematically by reference to the point through which it passes. The tracing paper containing the principal point and all the identified rays is called a *tracing-paper templet* for the photograph. Thus, there are five separate templets, as shown in Fig. 6–7(b).

The horizontal positions of the photo control points A, B, and C are plotted on a map sheet at the selected map scale, as shown in Fig. 6–7(c). This map sheet serves as the base for the radial-line plot. On it will be located the map positions of all the principal points and all the pass points.

The templets for the first and second photographs are brought together over the map sheet, and the bases o_1o_2 and o_2o_1 are made to coincide. The two templets are resected on points A and B, as described

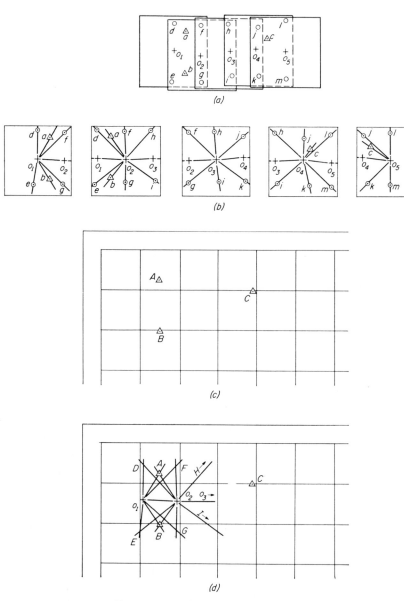

FIG. 6–7. Graphical control extension.

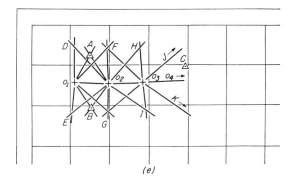

(e)

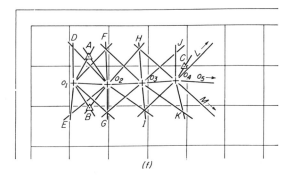

(f)

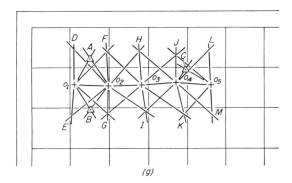

(g)

FIG. 6-7. (*Continued.*)

in Sec. 6–2. This resection fixes the map positions of o_1 and o_2 and establishes the base o_1o_2 on the map. By the principle of intersection discussed in Sec. 6–3, the map positions of the pass points D, E, F, and G are established at the intersections of the four pairs of rays o_1D and o_2D, o_1E and o_2E, o_1F and o_2F, and o_1G and o_2G, as shown in Fig. 6–7(d). Note that the directions of the rays from o_2 to points H, o_3, and I have also been established on the map sheet, because these three rays are included on the templet for the second photograph.

The map positions of F, o_2 and G furnish three points for locating the map position of the principal point of the third photograph, because these three points appear on the third photograph. Furthermore, the base o_2o_3 must coincide with the base o_3o_2 on the map. In Fig. 6–7(e) the third templet has been brought over and placed on the map sheet, so that the base ray o_3o_2 coincides with the base ray o_2o_3. The templet is moved along this line until the ray o_3F passes through F and the ray o_3G passes through G on the map. If the base is held in coincidence, it may not be possible to cause both of these rays to pass through their respective points. A small triangle of error may exist at one point or another. If this be the case, the third templet is shifted along the base o_2o_3 until two small triangles of equal size are obtained. This shifting then fixes the map position of o_3. The small discrepancies exist because of small unavoidable graphical errors in the process. The map positions of H and I are now established by the principle of intersection at the intersection of rays o_2H and o_3H and at the intersection of o_2I and o_3I.

The map positions of the principal point of the fourth photograph and the pass points J and K are located, by means of the templet for the fourth photograph, in a manner identical to that described for locating the third templet position. This position is shown in Fig. 6–7(f). Since the fourth photograph contains photo control point c, the ray o_4C in Fig. 6–7(f) should pass through the map position of this control point as shown. If it does not, then the graphical location of C will be in error, as determined by an intersection with a ray from the principal point of the fifth photograph.

Finally the templet for the fifth photograph is brought over and located in a manner identical to that described for the third and fourth templets. This procedure establishes the map positions of the pass points L and M, the principal point o_5, and the graphical position of the photo control point C. If graphic errors have canceled one another, the intersection of rays o_4C and o_5C shown in Fig. 6–7(g) will coincide with the plotted position of control point C. If an error exists, an adjustment must be made back through the entire strip. This adjustment will cause a slight shift of all the intermediate principal points and pass points.

The end result of a radial-line plot constructed in accordance with the process outlined in this section is a network of graphical control supplementing the existing photo control. The graphical control consists of all the principal points and pass points located in their correct horizontal positions on the map sheet. Ground distances between these points can be determined by measuring the map distances between the points and applying the map scale. In problems involving the determination of elevations from parallax measurements, discussed in Chapter 8, the ground distances between successive exposure stations must be known. These may be scaled between principal-point positions on a radial-line plot prepared from the photographs.

Each photograph used in a radial-line plot, except those at the ends of the strips, will contain at least nine images whose horizontal positions have been established as a result of the plot. For example, the third photograph of Fig. 6–7 contains points o_2, o_3, o_4, f, g, h, i, j, and k, whose horizontal positions have been established. The accuracy of the positions of these points, however, is not equal to that of the photo control points a, b, and c, whose positions have been established by ground surveys.

6–5. Errors in Radial-Line Plotting Due to Tilt

The principles of radial-line plotting are based on the assumption that all the photographs involved are truly vertical. Relief displacement, radial lens distortion, and differences in flying heights between successive exposures are shown to have no effect on the principle that angles measured about the principal point on a vertical photograph are true horizontal angles. If tilt exists in the photograph, then this principle no longer applies. Sections 3–11 and 3–12 show that points on a tilted photograph are displaced because of both relief and tilt. Furthermore, it has been explained that relief displacement on a tilted photograph radiates from the nadir point, and that tilt displacement radiates from the isocenter. The result of combining the displacements due to both the tilt and the relief is shown in Fig. 3–15. It should be observed that under usual conditions there is no one true center of rays on a tilted photograph about which horizontal angles can be measured. When the terrain is perfectly flat, however, angles measured about the isocenter would be true horizontal angles.

When the basic assumption applies, several factors act to reduce the tilt effects to a relatively insignificant amount. On the average, tilts very seldom exceed 1°, and maximum tilts rarely exceed 3°. Even in rough terrain, tilt displacements caused by a 1° tilt do not cause a measurable difference between angles measured about the principal point, the nadir point, or the isocenter. The fact that the direction of tilt is perfectly random tends to cancel out some effects of tilt upon the accuracy of the radial-line plot. Enough photo control is usually available to limit the major errors, especially after the plot has been adjusted to the photo control points.

Since control extension by means of a radial-line plot is more or less a graphical solution, and since it is employed only when the limitations of the process can be tolerated, the assumption that the photographs are truly vertical is reasonable.

6–6. Azimuth Point as Center of Rays

Although the principal point of a photograph can be easily located by drawing lines connecting opposite fiducial marks, the intersection of the lines very rarely occurs at an identifiable point. So, without special mechanical aids, the position of a principal point cannot be transferred to its exact location on the adjacent photographs. Since the transfer of the principal points is necessary, as indicated in Sec. 6–2, a point lying within 1 or 2 mm of the true principal point is selected as the center of rays used to draw the templet. This substitute center is referred to as an *azimuth point*.

The azimuth point must be a well-defined image which can be identified not only on one photograph but also on the two photographs on either side. This azimuth point is transferred visually to the two adjacent photographs. An azimuth point is selected on each photograph, this point lying as close to the principal point as possible. The line segments joining successive azimuth points then constitute the bases on the map sheet. The amount of error introduced by using a substitute ray center depends on the distance from the azimuth point to the principal point, the amount and direction of tilt, and the amount of relief. Errors introduced by this substitution are somewhat random and have a canceling effect on one another. Residual errors are small enough to be masked by other graphical errors in the method.

Where the positions of the principal points must be located on the map sheet, then either one of two methods may be used. In the first method, the principal points are used as ray centers and are transferred stereoscopically to adjacent photographs as described in Sec. 8–4. The subsequent templet assembly then locates the map positions of the principal points directly.

In the second method, the azimuth points are used as ray centers and are transferred to adjacent photographs visually by image identification. The subsequent templet assembly then locates the map positions of the azimuth points. A T-square and a triangle are used to orient each photograph in turn with the map sheet. A ray is drawn on the map sheet through the azimuth point parallel with the direction of the line on the photograph from the azimuth point to the principal point. A pair of proportional dividers, set to the ratio of the average photograph scale to the map scale, is then used to transfer this small photographic distance to the map, thus locating the map position of the principal point. This procedure is shown for two consecutive photographs in Fig. 6–8. In the figure the small distances have been exaggerated considerably. Only rarely will the occasion arise when the principal points themselves must be located on the map sheet, especially if the radial-line plot is assembled for the sole purpose of obtaining additional control.

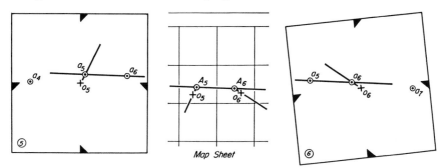

Fig. 6–8. Principal points transferred to map sheet with reference to azimuth points.

6–7. Slotted Templets

In the preceding sections, reference has been consistently made to the use of tracing paper with which to transfer a set of rays from the photograph to the map sheet. As mentioned previously, the purpose was to help convey to the student the principles underlying the radial-line method. For some specialized radial-line plotting, stable-base transparent or translucent acetate sheets are used in a manner similar to that described with tracing paper. For most extension by radial-line control, however, this method proves unsatisfactory because it is difficult to make an adjustment to fit the plotted photo control points. The difficulty can be better appreciated when it is realized that some radial-line plots involve in excess of 2,500 photographs arranged in several strips. To simplify the construction, assembly, and adjustment of the radial-line plot, *slotted templets* are used.

A templet made of cardboard or very thin sheet aluminum is constructed for each photograph by punching a hole in the center of the sheet to define the principal point (or the azimuth point), and then punching slots in the sheet to correspond to the rays through the different points on the photograph. Such a slotted templet is shown in Fig. 6–9 alongside a corresponding tracing-paper templet. The center of the center hole corresponds to the center of rays, and the center lines of the slots correspond to the rays themselves. The slots are elongated to allow for excessive relief displacements and for the difference in scale between the photographs and the radial-line plot.

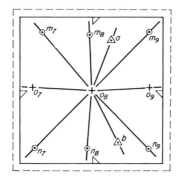 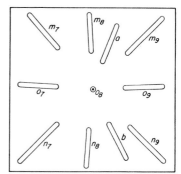

FIG. 6–9. Slotted templet.

The slotted templet is prepared by marking all control points, pass points, ray centers, and transferred ray centers on the photograph, and pricking the positions through the photograph to the templet material underneath.. The center hole is then punched, and the slots are cut by means of a templet cutter, the pricked points being used as guides. The templet is numbered to correspond to the number of the photograph, and the slots are identified to correspond to the points on the photograph.

Before the slotted templets are assembled to form the radial-line plot, a stud is secured at each plotted control point on the map sheet by means of a pin inserted through the stud as shown in Fig. 6–10. The outside diameter of the stud is identical with the diameter of the center hole and within close tolerance is the same as the width of the slots in the slotted templets.

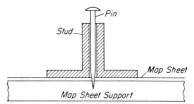

FIG. 6–10.   Center stud.

The method of assembling the slotted templets is shown in Fig. 6–11. It is analogous to that of assembling tracing-paper templets. The photo control points *a* and *b* are plotted on the map sheet at *A* and *B*. Studs are secured at these two points. A separate stud is inserted up through the center hole of the left-hand templet and through each of the slots except those representing rays to *a* and *b*. The templet is then laid down so that the fixed studs at *A* and *B* protrude up through their respective slots. At this stage, the templet may be moved about freely. The right-hand templet is then laid down with its center hole slipped over the stud marked o_9, and with the slot marked o_8 fitted over the stud at the center of the left-hand templet. The assembly is then rotated and shifted until the slots marked A and B on the right-hand templet fall in place over their respective studs. (A moment's study will convince the student that this is identical with the way in which two tracing-paper templets are located with respect to two control points.) The intersection of the pairs of slots at m_8, at m_9, at n_8, and at n_9 fix the map positions (before adjustment) of the four studs representing these pass points.

Studs are slipped up through the slots of the right-hand templet at m_{10}, n_{10}, and o_{10}, as shown in Fig. 6–11. These, together with the studs at m_9, n_9, and o_9, are used to fix the position of the next templet (not shown). Each succeeding templet is laid down and intersections are located at the pass points, until a new control point is reached. The slight

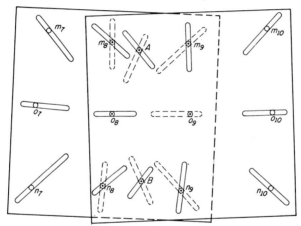

Fig. 6–11. Assembly of slotted templets.

clearances between the studs and the sides of the slots allow the entire assembly to be forced into place in order to fit the new control point. Thus, an automatic adjustment of all intervening intersections will have taken place.

When all the templets for all the flight strips have been laid down and adjusted to the fixed control, there will be a stud at each of the intersections representing pass points and also at each principal point (or azimuth point). The centers of the studs then represent the map positions of the pass points and the principal points (or azimuth points). Each point is identified on the map sheet by dropping a pin through the stud and pressing slightly to make a pin prick in the map sheet.

As the templets are removed one by one, the points on the map sheet are identified by the numbers appearing on the templets. This completes the control extension by means of slotted templets.

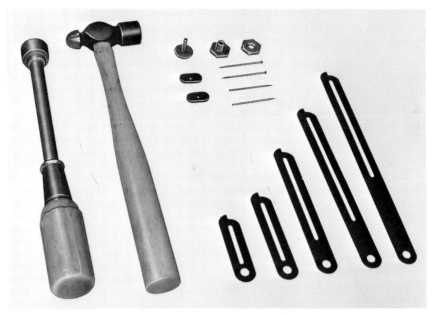

Fig. 6–12. Slotted metal arms.

6–8. Metal-Arm Templets

A radial-line plot may be assembled by preparing templets composed of flat, metal slotted arms fastened together at the center of the rays. In Fig. 6–12 is shown a series of these metal arms of various lengths, together with the studs, pins, and hardware necessary to fasten the arms together.   The steps involved in assembling slotted-arm templets are shown in Fig. 6–13.   The principal point, transferred principal points, pass points, and control points are marked and identified on the photograph.   A headless pin is driven through each of the marked points on the photograph down into a softwood drawing board or some other base

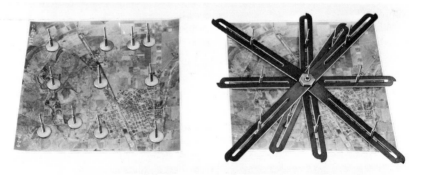

Fig. 6–13. Preparation of a slotted-arm templet.

which will hold the pin securely. While the pin is being driven, it is kept perpendicular to the surface of the board by means of the stud, the bottom flange of which is held flat against the photograph.

A specially designed hexagonal bolt is slipped over the central stud, the outside diameter of the threads of the bolt being the same as the diameter of the holes in the ends of the metal arms. The arms are selected so that when the hole is dropped over the center bolt, the stud is located at about the middle point of the slot. When all the arms are placed over the center bolt and the respective studs, a hexagonal nut is threaded onto the center bolt and tightened by means of the socket wrench. In the tightening process, the metal arms should not be allowed to twist about the center. Otherwise, they will spring out of alignment when removed from the studs. Before the metal-arm templet is removed, the arms are identified to correspond to the points on the photograph.

In Fig. 6–14 is shown the assembly of ten metal-arm templets to fit

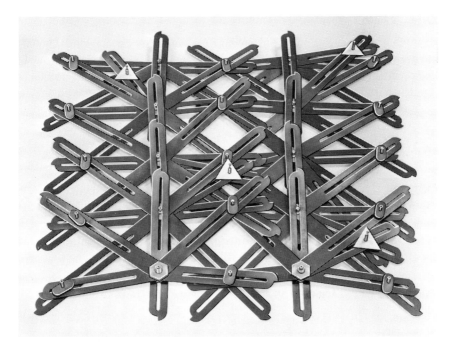

Fig. 6–14. Assembly of slotted-arm templets.

the plotted positions of four photo control points. This assembly represents two flight strips of five photographs each. The control points are marked by the white triangles. The elongated rubber washers fastened over the studs prevent the arms from slipping off the studs. Before the templets are disassembled, the positions of the points represented by the studs are marked by pin pricking, as discussed in Sec. 6–7. As each templet is removed, the pin-pricked points are identified on the map sheet. The method of assembling the metal-arm, or "spider-arm," templets is identical with that described for the slotted arms in Sec. 6–7.

Because of the slight flexibility of the metal arms and because of a tendency of the metal arms to slip about the center of the rays when subjected to undue twist, an assembly of metal-arm templets is not considered to be so rigid as a well-constructed assembly of slotted cardboard templets. Consequently, the map positions of the ray centers and the pass points will not, in general, be so accurate in a metal-arm assembly. The advantage of using the metal-arm templets lies in the fact that the metal arms can be used over and over in different assemblies, while the cardboard templets are of no further use after one assembly. Also the use of the metal arms eliminates the need for a center punch and a templet cutter.

6–9. Photo Control Requirements for Radial-Line Plotting

The ground control requirements for constructing a radial-line plot depend on the number of photographs involved and on the allowable error in the map positions of the pass points and the principal points (or azimuth points). Mr. Lyle G. Trorey, of London, has established an empirical equation for finding the control density required to properly control a radial-line plot constructed from slotted templets. This empirical equation is

$$e = k\left(\frac{t}{c}\right)^{\frac{1}{2}} \tag{6-1}$$

in which e is the average error in the position of a graphical control point, in millimeters; t is the number of the photographs involved in the plot; c is the number of photo control points; and k is a constant. Tests indicate that this equation proves adequate and provides a suitable safety factor if the constant k is about 0.16.

EXAMPLE 6–1. An area was photographed in 12 flight strips with 30 photographs per strip. A mosaic at publication scale of 1/12,000 is to be controlled by means of a radial-line plot constructed by using these photographs. The photographs were taken at an average scale of 1/20,000. If four photo control points are reasonably placed, what will be the expected average position error, at the publication scale, of the points obtained by the plot?

Solution: By Eq. 6–1,

$$e = 0.16\left(\frac{12 \times 30}{4}\right)^{\frac{1}{2}} = 1.52 \text{ mm}$$

At the average photographic scale, therefore, the average position error of the points obtained by the radial-line plot will be 1.52 mm. At the mosaic publication scale, this error will, by Eq. 3–4, be enlarged to (1.52) (20.000) / (12,000) = 2.5 mm.

EXAMPLE 6-2. An area is photographed at an average scale of 1:20,000 for planimetric mapping at a publication scale of 1:62,500. The area requires a total of 2,200 photographs arranged in 23 flight lines. The average error of position of the radial-line points is not to exceed 1/200 in. at publication scale. Determine the number of photo control points needed to meet this requirement.

Solution: Since the photography scale is larger than the publication scale, the average allowable error at the photo scale is, by Eq. 3-4,

$$e = \frac{1/200 \text{ in.} \times 62,500 \times 25.4 \text{ mm/in.}}{20,000} = 0.40 \text{ mm}$$

By Eq. 6-1, the number of photo control points needed to control the mapping is

$$c = 2,200 \times (0.16/0.40)^2 = 352$$

This number allows one control point for every six photographs, or about fifteen control points per flight line.

The actual placement of the ground control influences the effectiveness of the control. The ideal location is obtained if the control density is uniform throughout the area. This distribution is not practical, however, unless the area is easily accessible and lends itself to triangulation. A large area is usually traversed along its outer boundaries, and one or two cross traverses are added. Photo control is therefore located along both the outer traverses and the cross traverses. For a more comprehensive discussion of ground-control placement, the student is referred to the bibliography at the end of this chapter.

6-10. Map Revision by Radial-Line Principle

Quite often there arises the need for revising certain portions of an existing map, chiefly because of the construction of works of man. These works may be industrial developments, subdivisions and additions, buildings, and other structures. Aerial photographs may be used to locate the new planimetric features on the map which is to be brought up to date, usually without any additional ground control.

Assume that a pair of overlapping photographs covering a portion of an existing map contains new features which did not exist at the time the map was compiled. The map position of the principal point of each photograph can be located by carefully selecting three or more image points on each photograph which can be identified also on the map. In general, the center-line intersections of streets and roads or the positions of streams as they cross a street or road are reliable map points whose images can be identified on the photographs.

A piece of translucent or transparent acetate-base material is used as a templet on which rays from the principal point (or azimuth point) of one photograph are drawn to intersect the three or more selected images. The templet is then placed on the map and oriented so that all the rays pass through the respective map points. The center of rays then defines the map position of the principal point (or azimuth point) by the principle of resection. A templet is prepared also for a second photograph, and its principal point (or azimuth point) is similarly located on the map. The use of more than three points for each photograph is advised because of the susceptibility of the process to errors in the map positions of the selected points.

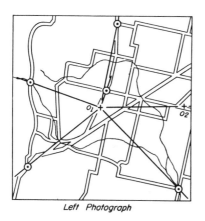

Left Photograph

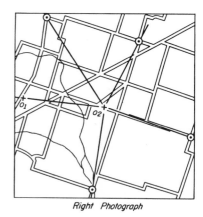

Right Photograph

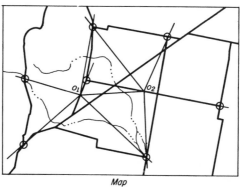

Map

Fig. 6–15. Map revision.

In Fig. 6–15, the map position of the principal point of the left-hand photograph is located by means of rays drawn through five image points, and that of the right-hand photograph by four image points. In preparing the templets, the base rays o_1o_2 and o_2o_1 are drawn. When each templet has been located on the map, these two rays must coincide. They are made to coincide by adjusting the templets to obtain the best average fit through the resected points.

The map positions of both principal points constitute a base line on the map, from which the positions of points appearing in the overlap area of the two photographs may be located by the principle of intersection described in Sec. 6–3. At the time each templet is initially prepared, rays are drawn not only to the points used to locate the principal point but also to all other points whose map positions are to be located. Then, when each templet has been properly located by resection, the intersections of the different pairs of rays define the map positions of the different points. The accuracy of the location of points decreases as the points approach the base line itself, because the intersection angle approaches 180°. It does, in fact, equal 180° when a point lies on the base line.

The radial-line principle must be applied in map revision when the effects of topographic relief prevent the direct tracing of features from the photograph itself or from an enlarged or reduced projection of the photograph. When the topographic relief is so slight that relief displacement would normally be masked by drafting errors, the method described in this section is not appropriate because it proves more tedious than direct tracing.

6–11. Vertical Photograph Versus Planimetric Map

A truly vertical photograph taken over terrain with absolutely no relief would be a planimetric map with a scale of $f/(H-h)$, where h is the elevation of the perfectly flat terrain. As such, the photograph could be enlarged or reduced in some type of projector, and the essential features on the photograph could then be traced in conventional map symbols. Succeeding photographs could be similarly brought to the desired map scale, and the images could be traced as a map. Finally all the individual compilations could be pieced together to form one continuous map.

Since the conditions just mentioned are seldom, if ever, realized, the simple procedure outlined will not produce an accurate planimetric map from a group of near-vertical photographs.

In order to construct a planimetric map, the area to be mapped must contain a minimum amount of photo control. This is provided by ground surveys, as discussed in Chapter 5. The photo control in turn establishes a basic network, to which a radial-line plot is tied and adjusted. The result of the radial-line plot is a network of graphical control in which the true map positions of at least nine identifiable points per photograph have been located to the desired scale. Beyond this stage in the construction of a planimetric map, the final accuracy of the map is dependent on the manner in which map details are transferred from the photographs to the map, on the nature of the topography, on the difference between the average photography scale and the map scale, and on certain refinements made to enhance the accuracy of the map.

6–12. Planimetric Features by Direct Tracing

Perhaps the simplest method of transferring details from the photographs to the map is to select the map compilation scale so that it is equal to the over-all average photograph scale. Then lay a translucent map base containing the radial-line control over each photograph, and orient and position the map sheet to fit each control point in turn. Finally, trace off the features in the neighborhood of each control point. This method is satisfactory when the topography is gentle and when the flying height is fairly constant throughout the photography. The discrepancies existing in the map are localized around each control point, and the over-

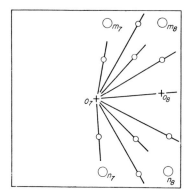
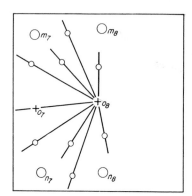

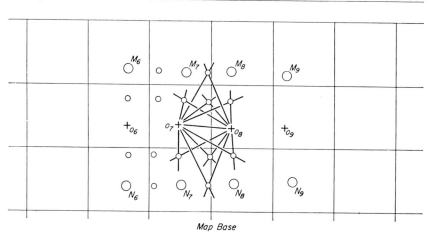

Map Base

Fig. 6–16. Supplementary intersection points.

all map accuracy is fair. Mismatching of features from one control point to the next must be minimized and rectified by the draftsman.

The mismatching of map features may be minimized by obtaining additional pass points by the method of intersection. In Fig. 6–16, the principal point, the transferred principal point, and four pass points which have been located on a map base by means of a radial-line plot are shown on two overlapping photographs. A tracing-paper templet is prepared for each of the two photographs, with rays passing through eight additional points shown by the small circles as well as through the transferred principal points. These templets are brought down and oriented to the map by means of the principal points. The intersections of the eight pairs of rays locate the map positions of these eight points. These additional control points are used to trace off map features surrounding the points, and tend to reduce the mismatching of features caused by relief displacement and difference in scale between successive photographs. The required density of these additional points depends to a great extent on the amount of relief and also on the accuracy desired.

6–13. Planimetric Features by Camera Lucida

The camera lucida is a simple optical device which allows one eye to view a photograph and a map sheet at the same time. The use of this device allows the indirect tracing of photographic features onto the map sheet without the necessity for a translucent medium. The principle of the camera lucida is shown in Fig. 6–17. The map sheet is located

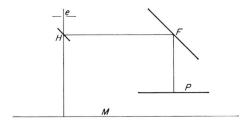

FIG. 6–17. Camera lucida.

at *M*, and the photograph is located at *P*. A small half-silvered mirror is located at *H*, and a larger mirror is located at *F*. The eye is placed at *e*, above a small aperture in a diaphragm. When sighting down through the aperture, the draftsman sees the map through the half-silvered mirror. By reflection at *F* and at *H*, he sees also the image of the photograph, which appears to coincide with the map. The diaphragm prevents the eye from moving back and forth, since such movement would cause the photograph image to move with respect to the map.

The draftsman adjusts the distance from the mirror at F to the photograph so that the images of as many control points as possible fall in their correct positions on the map sheet. This adjustment brings the image of the photograph to the correct scale and orients the photograph with respect to the map sheet. The draftsman then traces the detail

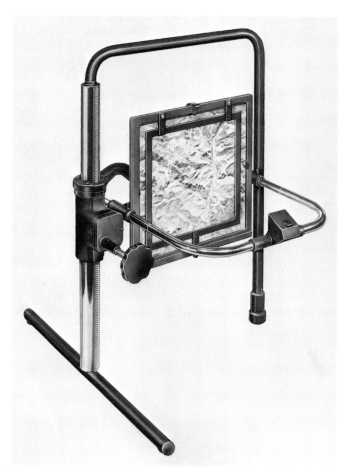

Fig. 6–18.   Rectoplanograph.   (Courtesy of Fairchild Camera and Instrument Corp.)

about each control point by moving the pencil on the map sheet along the apparent image of the photograph.

Refined instruments based on the camera-lucida principle, such as the Rectoplanograph of Fig. 6–18 and the Vertical Sketchmaster of Fig. 6–19, are used in the process of compiling a planimetric map from near-vertical photographs. Provisions for changing the distance from the eye to the photograph or the distance from the eye to the map allow a change in scale to be effected. This change compensates for differences in flying heights. Rotation of the photograph about the x-axis and the y-axis in either of these instruments allows the effect of both tilt and relief displacement to be overcome to a great extent, thus producing a more satisfactory map.

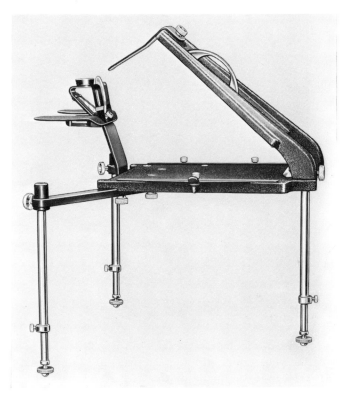

Fig. 6–19. Vertical Sketchmaster.
(Courtesy of Harrison Ryker, Inc.)

6–14. Planimetric Features by Projection of Photograph

The main drawback to the direct-tracing technique discussed in Sec. 6–12 is the limitation of the scale to that of the photograph. The use of an opaque projector, which projects the image of the photograph down onto the map sheet, allows the draftsman to change the scale of the photographic image at will. Such a projector is shown in Fig. 6–20. The main feature of this instrument is its ability to maintain sharp focus of the image automatically, regardless of the enlargement or reduction. Automatic focus is accomplished by means of a device called a *Peaucellier*

Fig. 6–20. Autofocus projector. (Courtesy of
Reed Research, Inc.)

inversor, which is shown diagrammatically in Fig. 6–21. The positions of
the plane of the photograph at *o* and the plane of the map sheet at *i* are
shown with respect to the plane of the lens at *L.* The distance *oL* is
denoted by *p,* and the distance *Li* by *q.* By the basic lens equation,

$$\frac{1}{p}+\frac{1}{q}=\frac{1}{F} \tag{6-2}$$

in which *p* is the distance from the object plane to the lens, *q* is the
distance from lens to the image plane, and *F* is the focal length of the lens.
All distances must be expressed in the same units.

In Fig. 6–21,

$$F+x = p \qquad \text{and} \qquad F + x' = q$$

Therefore,

$$\frac{1}{F+x}+\frac{1}{F+x'}=\frac{1}{F}$$

Multiplying through by F gives

$$\frac{F}{F+x}+\frac{F}{F+x'}=1$$

Reducing to a common denominator on the left side and then cross multiplying gives

$$F^2+Fx'+F^2+Fx=F^2+Fx'+Fx+xx'$$

or

$$F^2=xx' \tag{6-3}$$

In Fig. 6–21, the distance oT between the plane of the photograph and point T is fixed, since it is equal to F. Also, the distance Bi between the plane of the map and point B is F. A mechanical linkage composed of members RT, TR', RB, BR', RL, and LR' is so arranged that point B is fixed on the line oi. The points R, R', T, L, and B are hinges about

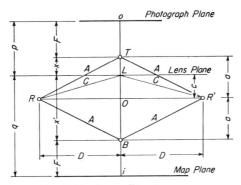

Fig. 6–21. Peaucellier inversor.

which the members rotate. As point T moves in the vertical direction, the photograph plane is also moved by the same vertical amount, in order to maintain the distance F. The lens, represented at L, is forced to move vertically so as to maintain the relationship given in Eq. 6–2 or Eq. 6–3. To produce such motion, the linkage is so designed that the relationship between the dimension A of the four outside members and the dimension C of the two inside members is as follows:

$$A^2-C^2=F^2 \tag{6-4}$$

In triangle RTO,

$$a^2=A^2-D^2 \tag{6-5}$$

Also in triangle RLO,

$$c^2=C^2-D^2 \tag{6-6}$$

Subtracting Eq. 6–6 from Eq. 6–5 gives

$$a^2 - c^2 = A^2 - C^2$$

from which

$$(a-c)(a+c) = xx' = F^2 = A^2 - C^2 \qquad (6\text{--}7)$$

Equations 6–4 and 6–7 are identical. Note that when the lens is located at the middle point of the inversor, the distances x and x' are equal. To satisfy Eq. 6–3, each is then equal to F. This middle position of the lens makes the photograph scale and the map scale the same.

To use the projector, the map is oriented in the map plane under the lens, and the projector is raised or lowered, by means of a hand crank, until the images of as many control points as possible fit their map positions. Detail is then traced off around each of the control points. If control points have been obtained in addition to the radial-line control, as discussed in Sec. 6–12, the scale of the photograph may be varied throughout the area to fit this denser network, and the resulting map will be highly accurate.

A fairly large difference between photograph scale and map scale may be accommodated in an opaque projector. With the autofocus projector of Fig. 6–20, a variation in scale ratio from $\frac{1}{3}$ to 2 may be realized. Thus, if the photography is at an average scale of 1:12,000, the map can be compiled at any scale ranging from 1:36,000 to 1:6,000.

6–15. Planimetric Features by Using Radial Plotter

One of the most positive methods of transferring map features to their correct map positions is the use of a plotting instrument which solves the intersection problem continuously. This instrument, shown in Fig. 6–22, consists of the following parts: a mirror stereoscope, for viewing the photographs in three dimensions (see Chapter 7); two photo tables, on which the photographs are mounted; a pair of transparent arms, which pass above and below the photo tables and rotate about the centers of the photo tables; a parallel bar, which moves parallel with the photo base and the ends of which connect to the lower part of each radial arm by means of a pin fitted into a slot in the arm; a linkage, connecting the parallel bar to a pencil chuck; and the pencil chuck, which holds the drawing pencil. These parts may be identified in Fig. 6–22.

The operating principle is that of continuous intersection. It is shown by the schematic drawing in Fig. 6–23. The overlapping pair of photographs are placed on the photo tables and are oriented by making the lines o_1o_2 on the two photographs coincide with each other when the photographs are viewed through the mirror stereoscope. The positions of the principal points of the photographs are fixed on the tables by pins,

Fig. 6-22. Radial planimetric plotter. (Courtesy of Phillip Kail & Associates.)

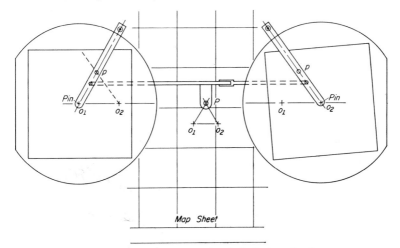

Fig. 6-23. Schematic diagram of radial planimetric plotter.

which also pass through the radial arms, as shown in Fig. 6-23 and Fig. 6-24. Orientation takes place by rotating the photographs about these pins. A map sheet lying underneath the plotter and containing radial-line control is used to fix the plotting scale. As shown, the lower parts of the radial arms are connected by the parallel bar, which may be lengthened or shortened. Pins in the ends of the parallel bar slide freely in slots in the lower parts of the radial arm. A slot is shown in Fig. 6-24.

As the operator views the two photographs as one stereoscopic image, the radial lines etched on the radial arms appear to cross at point p, as

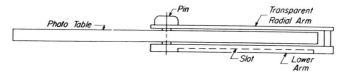

Fig. 6-24. Section of radial arm of radial plotter.

shown by the solid radial line and the dashed radial line on the left-hand photograph. If point p is a control point, the map sheet is shifted so that the pencil falls directly on the map position P of the point. A second control point is located at the intersection of the proper two radial lines as seen through the stereoscope. Note that the radial arms are moved by moving the pencil. The map is then rotated about point P until the second control point is brought under the pencil. If the plotting scale is not the same as the map scale, the pencil will not fall on the control point, and the length of the parallel bar must be adjusted. By going back and forth between two control points, the plotting scale is adjusted and the map sheet is oriented at the same time. Other control points in the area of overlap should be checked, and any discrepancies must be eliminated by a slight scale change and shift of the map sheet.

When the map sheet and the scale have been satisfactorily adjusted to fit the control, the operator can then trace the planimetric features. As he moves the pencil, so does the apparent intersection of radial lines move. He therefore moves the pencil in such a direction as to keep the intersection on the feature being traced. Thus, the feature is located in its correct map position by a continuous intersection.

The three-dimensional image seen through the stereoscope greatly enhances the operator's ability to interpret planimetric features, thus making the plotting operation most satisfactory. The scale range in the plotter shown in Fig. 6–22 is from slightly over the photograph scale to one-third of the photograph scale.

Bibliography

American Society of Photogrammetry. *Manual of Photogrammetry* (Menasha, Wisc.: George Banta Co., 1952), Chapter 8.

———. *Manual of Photogrammetry* (Menasha, Wisc.: George Banta Co., 1966), Chapters 9 and 12.

———. *Manual of Photographic Interpretation* (Menasha, Wisc.: George Banta Co., 1960), Chapter 3.

Hallert, B. *Photogrammetry* (New York: McGraw-Hill Book Co., 1960), Chapter 3.

Houghton, D. E. "Portable Autofocussing Reflecting Projector," *Photogrammetric Engineering*, Vol. XV (1949), p. 439.

Kail, Philip V. "The Radial Planimetric Plotter," *Photogrammetric Engineering*, Vol. XV (1949), p. 402.

McComas, H. O. "Improved Mechanical Slotted Template Equipment," *Photogrammetric Engineering,* Vol. XV (1949), p. 446.

Meyer, D. "A Reflecting Projector You Can Build," *Photogrammetric Engineering,* Vol. XXVII (1961), p. 76.

Podeyn, G. J., Jr. "The Fairchild Rectoplanograph," *Photogrammetric Engineering,* Vol. XV (1949), p. 383.

Schwidefsky, K. *An Outline of Photogrammetry* (New York: Pitman Publishing Corp., 1959). Chapter 7.

Trorey, Lyle, G. "Slotted Template Error," *Photogrammetric Engineering,* Vol. XIII (1947), p. 227.

U. S. Coast and Geodetic Survey. "Topographic Manual," Part II, *Special Publication* No. 249 (Washington, D.C.: Government Printing Office, 1949), Chapter 4.

Problems

6–1. A pass point k falls on the $+y$-axis at a distance of 3.200 in. from the principal point, and a transferred principal point o_t falls on the $+x$-axis at a distance of 3.200 in. from the principal point. If the photograph were truly vertical, the horizontal angle measured at the principal point between k and o_t would be 90°. Assume that the terrain is perfectly flat, but the photograph is tilted. What is the true horizontal angle between k and o_t measured about the isocenter, if $t=2°$, $s=180°$, and $f=6$ in.?

6–2. A radial-line plot is to be constructed by means of photographs at an average scale of 1/15,000. The scale of the map to be controlled by this plot is 1/31,680. A total of 1,500 photographs are involved in the project. If the maximum allowable position error of any pass point is 1/40 in. at the map scale, how many ground control points will be necessary?

6–3. Thirty photographs are used to compile a radial-line plot at the average photographic scale. If three well-placed points for horizontal control are used to establish the plot, what will be the expected position accuracy of the pass points?

6–4. If the value of the empirical constant k is adopted as 0.18 for the plot of Fig. 6–14, what is the expected positional error of the pass points?

6–5. Two control points are used to control a radial-line plot involving a strip of 20 photographs containing 60 per cent overlap. The control points are located in the center of the first and last overlap area. Pass points are picked to lie 1 in. from the edges of the 9- by 9-in. photographs. The two control points are plotted on a map to scale of 1:6000, giving a control line 56.18 in. long. Compute the approximate scale of the photographs.

6–6. In Prob. 6–5, what is the approximate map distance, in inches, between opposite pairs of pass points?

6–7. In Prob. 6–5, what is the approximate map spacing between the principal points?

6–8. In Prob. 6–5, assume that the plotted length of the control line is in error by 0.35 in. What is the error in the map distance between opposite pairs of pass points?

6–9. The focal length of the lens in an opaque projector is 6.75 in. If the enlargement factor is q/p (these distances are shown in Fig. 6–21), compute the distances p and q for enlargement factors of ⅓, ½, ⅔, ¾, 1, 1½, 2, 2½, and 3.

Stereoscopy and Parallax 7

7–1. Stereoscopy

Stereoscopy, or solid vision, is the term given to the following natural phenomenon: When a person looks simultaneously at two photographs which have been taken of the same scene from two viewpoints, viewing one photograph with each eye, he can see an image of the scene in three dimensions. Stereoscopic, or binocular, vision is the facility which makes stereoscopy possible. The perception of depth is made possible in several ways. A person viewing the objects in a room, for example, can gain an impression of depth by evaluating the apparent sizes of familiar objects. This appreciation of depth can be obtained by one eye only. In gazing at several objects at close range, a person realizes that some objects are closer than others because the lens in his eye must change its focus for the varying distances. Thus, in this way, depth can also be appreciated by one eye only. Perspective in a scene gives an impression of depth, and the perception of depth because of perspective also can be realized with one eye only. The apparent movement of one stationary object with respect to another stationary object when one eye is moved back and forth is still another way of perceiving the third dimension. These are but a few ways in which a person gains an impression of depth by the use of only one eye. Some of these impressions may be treated quantitatively in order to determine actual distances between objects, but in a roundabout fashion.

Normal two-eyed vision is required for realizing and measuring depth by stereoscopy. Two primary clues are involved in stereoscopic vision. The first clue is the double-image phenomenon. A simple demonstration indicates what is meant by double vision. If a pencil is held 12 to 15 in. in front of the eyes and the gaze is fixed on a spot on a far wall, there will be two images of the pencil. The left image is formed by the right eye, and the right image is formed by the left eye. When the gaze is now concentrated on the pencil, two images of an object on the wall will be formed. The right image is formed by the right eye, and the left image is formed by the left eye. If, while the eyes are gazing at the wall, the pencil were to be moved away from the eyes and toward the wall, there would be a position of the pencil somewhere in front of the wall where the double image would disappear. In other words, even though the pencil and the wall were at different distances from the eyes, both the pencil and the object on the wall would be seen as single images. This is the depth of clear single binocular vision and is very important in stereoscopy and stereoscopic measurement. The double-image phenomenon can be treated quantitatively to determine the amount of depth.

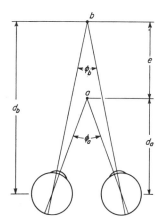

Fig. 7–1. Parallactic angles of optical axes.

The second clue involved in stereoscopy is the relative convergence of the optical axes of the two eyes when viewing points at varying distances from the eyes. In Fig. 7–1, the convergence of the axes of the eyes when gazing at point a is ϕ_a, and when gazing at b it is ϕ_b. Thus, the angle ϕ_a tells the mind that a is at a distance d_a; the angle ϕ_b tells the mind that b is at a distance d_b; and the angle $(\phi_a - \phi_b)$ tells the mind that the distance between the two points is e. The angles ϕ_a and ϕ_b are called the parallactic angles for the two points. For average separation of the eyes and for a distance of distinct vision of about 10 in., the limiting upper value of ϕ is about 16°. The lower limiting value of ϕ ranges from 10 to 20 seconds of arc and represents a distance of somewhere between 1,700 and 2,400 ft for average eye separation.

Stereoscopic vision is not possible at distances closer than about 10 in., unless the eyes are aided by lenses, because the normal eye cannot comfortably focus any closer. The perception of depth by stereoscopic vision is not possible beyond about 2,000 ft, because the parallactic angle is too small beyond that distance. In order to be able to perceive depth beyond 2,000 ft, the eye separation must be increased, as with a rangefinder or a pair of binoculars; or else a pair of photographs must be taken at widely separated camera stations, and each photograph must be presented to the eyes for viewing. This is the phenomenon called stereoscopy.

7–2. Parallax

The term parallax is applied to the movement of the image of one stationary object with respect to the image of another stationary object when the eye is moved sideways. When a person sights on a target with an engineer's transit and the image of the target formed by the telescope objective does not lie in the plane of the cross hairs, parallax is said to exist. It is detected by moving the eye back and forth slightly behind the eyepiece. If the images of the target and the vertical cross hair move relative to one another, there is parallax.

Another example of parallax, which carries over into photogrammetry, is the movement of objects across a window pane of a train coach when the train is moving at a high speed. A person gazing out of the train window sees the telegraph poles near the track go by quite rapidly with respect to the frame of the window. If he lets his gaze rest on a row of fence posts about 1,000 ft in the distance, he sees the fence posts move past the window frame, although not quite so rapidly as do the telegraph poles. Gazing still farther away at a group of buildings about 3 miles away, the person sees the buildings move past the window, although much more slowly than do the fence posts or the telegraph poles. The relative movement of these objects with respect to the window frame is parallax. In a given interval of time, the closer objects will have appeared to move farther than will the distant objects. Thus, the closer objects have indicated a greater parallax than have the distant objects.

The viewfinder of an aerial camera presents an image of the terrain on the ground glass. The photographer thus can view the constantly changing terrain directly on the ground-glass frame. He can perceive that images of the highest points in the terrain will move across the ground glass more rapidly than will the images of the lowest points in the valley. Thus, the points at higher elevations have indicated a greater parallax than have those at lower elevations.

The aerial camera does not take a continuous picture, but rather a series of exposures at regular intervals of time. Suppose, for example, that an aircraft is flying at a speed of 150 mph, and that the camera is making an exposure every 20 seconds. Suppose also that between exposures the image of a high point has moved across the focal plane of the camera a distance of 3.25 in., and the image of a low point has moved a distance of only 3.05 in. Thus, the parallax of the high point is 3.25 in., and that of the low point is 3.05 in. On a straight, level flight, the relative movement of the two points must have taken place parallel with the flight line. This movement is shown in Fig. 7–2. The image of the high point A appears at a on the left photograph and at a' on the right photograph. The image of point B appears at b on the left photograph and at b' on the right photograph. Point a has moved a total distance aa', which is 3.25 in. as shown on the left photograph, and point b has moved a total distance bb', which is 3.05 in. Note that the movement of both points took place parallel with the flight line.

From the foregoing discussion the student may conclude that the image of each point on the terrain has moved through a certain distance (which is dependent on the elevation of the point) between two successive exposures, and that each image in a changing terrain elevation has a slightly different parallax from that of a neighboring image. This point-to-point difference in parallax exhibited between points on a pair

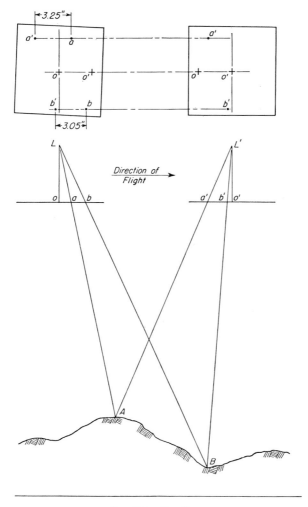

Fig. 7-2. Parallax.

of overlapping photographs is what makes possible the viewing of the photographs stereoscopically to gain an impression of a continuous three-dimensional image of the terrain. The student may conclude also that, in order to gain a stereoscopic impression of the entire area covered by the photography, the minimum overlap of successive exposures must be 50 per cent.

7-3. Stereoscopic Viewing

To gain an understanding of the way a person can see stereoscopically by viewing a pair of photographs taken from two viewpoints, refer to

Fig. 7–3. In Fig. 7–3 (a), two dots of similar size and shape have been drawn on a sheet of paper about 2 in. apart. The sheet of paper is placed on a table or desk, and the viewer looks downward from a height above the table between 12 and 15 in. If he can make the left eye concentrate on the left dot and the right eye on the right dot, he forms a single image of the two dots at some abstract distance d_1 from the eyes. The conjugate images to the right and left are not seen distinctly, since they are out of range of critical resolution of the eyes. The impression of the distance d_1 is gained because of the parallactic angle ϕ_1.

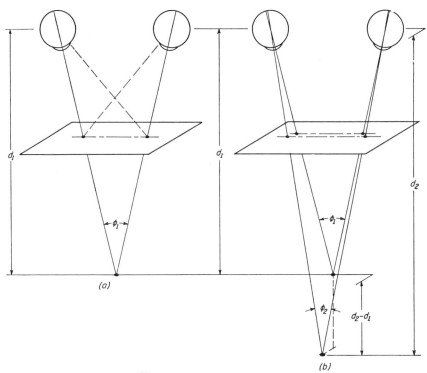

FIG. 7–3. Stereoscopic vision.

In Fig. 7–3 (b), a second pair of dots, slightly more than 2 in. apart, are also drawn on the sheet of paper, the lines joining the two pairs of dots being parallel with one another. On viewing these two pairs stereoscopically, the viewer gains the impression that the second pair of dots form an image at some abstract distance d_2 from the eyes. The increase in distance is caused by a corresponding decrease in the parallactic angle which, for the second pair of dots, is ϕ_2. The impression of the distance $(d_2 - d_1)$ is caused by a difference in parallactic angle $(\phi_1 - \phi_2)$. If the difference in the separation of the two pairs of dots on the sheet of paper is too great, then the viewer will no longer be able to hold the single image of each dot simultaneously, but will see a double image of one set or the other.

The foregoing demonstration of stereoscopic viewing will now be applied to the stereoscopic viewing of a pair of overlapping vertical photographs. In Fig. 7–4, two vertical photographs of the terrain are taken at the two exposure stations L and L' to give an overlap of about 60 per cent. The images of the top and the bottom of a prominent tower appear on the two photographs as shown. The image of the top of the tower has moved farther across the focal plane between exposures than has the image of the bottom of the tower. The positions of the principal

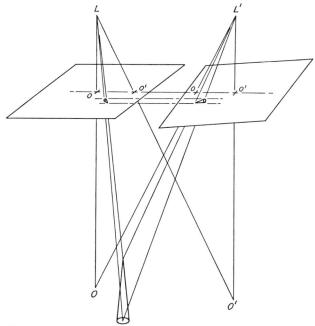

Fig. 7–4. Photographing a tower from two exposure stations.

points are shown. Notice that the relief displacement of the top of the tower with respect to the bottom is exhibited on both photographs. Notice also that the two images of the top lie at the same distance from the flight line, as defined by the line joining the principal points, and that the two images of the bottom likewise lie at the same distance from the flight line.

In Fig. 7–5, the two photographs of Fig. 7–4 have been laid flat on the table with the lines oo' and oo' lined up, and with the two images of the top of the tower about 2 in. apart. If the viewer now fixes his left eye on the left photograph and his right eye on the right photograph, he gains an impression that the tower stands up to a height h, because of the difference in the parallactic angles ϕ_T and ϕ_B. The parallactic angle of each point is a direct result of the parallax of the point. The greater the parallax, the greater will be the parallactic angle subtended by the optical axes of the two eyes.

When viewing the area of overlap of two vertical photographs stereoscopically as just described, the viewer shifts his gaze from point to point. When the topographic relief is changing, he therefore perceives a continuously varying parallactic angle. This variation allows him to gain a continuous, uninterrupted stereoscopic image of the terrain. If a high, nearly vertical cliff appears in the overlap area, the viewer will have difficulty in retaining the stereoscopic impression for the top and the bottom simultaneously, because the great difference in parallax will exceed his depth of clear single binocular vision. He will then see a double image of the top or the bottom of the cliff.

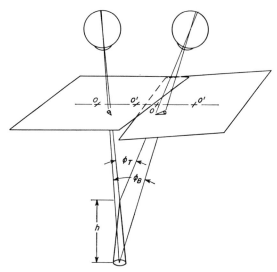

Fig. 7–5. Stereoscopic viewing of tower.

Viewing a pair of photographs stereoscopically in the manner just suggested is not practical for two reasons. First there exists a physiological contradiction. In normal eyesight, a person associates a short focus of the eyes with a rather large parallactic angle, and conversely he associates an infinite focus of the eyes with an extremely small parallactic angle. In fact, when a person views a distant scene, the optical axes of his eyes can be considered parallel with each other. When viewing a pair of photographs with the unaided eye in the manner described in this section, the viewer must focus for objects 12 to 15 in. away and at the same time must maintain a small parallactic angle. To do this is difficult, although quite possible, and such viewing causes a certain amount of eye strain. Secondly, the stereoscopic viewing of photographs in the manner indicated in Fig. 7–5 restricts the amount of overlap area which can be seen at one time. In order to be seen stereoscopically, the photographs must be held one on top of the other and in such positions that conjugate images are not more than about 2 in. apart. The difficulties of stereoscopic viewing are obviated by optical devices, known as stereoscopes, which allow the simultaneous viewing of a pair of photographs.

7–4. Stereoscopes

There are two basic types of stereoscopes for stereoscopic viewing of photographs, namely, the lens stereoscope and the mirror stereoscope. Each has advantages and disadvantages. The lens stereoscope, shown in Fig. 7–6, consists of two simple magnifying lenses mounted with a separation equal to the average interpupillary distance of the human eyes, but provision is made for changing this separation to suit the individual user. The lenses are mounted in a frame so that they are supported at a fixed distance above the table top. The distance between the nodal point of the lens and the plane of the table top, or photograph, depends on the focal length of the lens. If this distance is equal to the focal length of the lenses, the images of points on the photographs will appear to come from infinity. The separation of conjugate images on the photographs will

FIG. 7–6. Lens stereoscope.

then be about equal to the interpupillary distance of the individual viewer for the most comfortable viewing. This condition is shown in Fig. 7–7(a). Conjugate images p and p', lying in the plane of focus of the lenses, appear to the eye to come from infinity, as indicated by the bundle of parallel dashed rays. Thus, the optical axes of the eyes remain parallel, except for convergence due to differences in parallax between the different sets of conjugate images.

If the photographs are placed inside the focal plane of the lenses, the images will appear to come from a finite distance. To produce a parallactic angle compatible with the distance, the separation of conjugate images on the photographs will then have to be slightly less than the

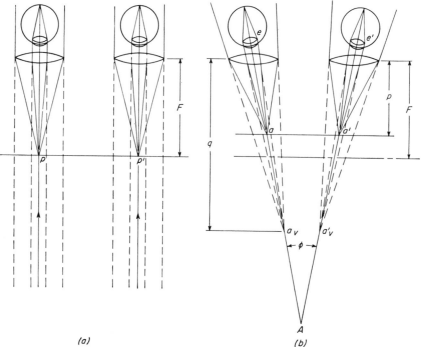

(a)   (b)

Fig. 7–7. Optical principle of lens stereoscope.

interpupillary distance of the individual viewer for the most comfortable viewing. In Fig. 7–7(b), conjugate images a and a' lie in a plane at a distance p from the plane of the lenses. In this case, the distance p is less than the focal length F. Each point, singly, appears to come from a distance q from the lenses; that is, virtual images of points a and a' are formed at a_V and a'_V. The distance q is compatible with the parallactic angle ϕ, provided that points a and a' have been separated for comfortable viewing. The stereoscope permits the eyes to fuse the two virtual images

a_V and a'_V so that they appear to come from point A. The lines eA and $e'A$ can be considered as two chief rays representing the two bundles of rays, and subsequent ray diagrams are to be considered in the same way.

Most lens stereoscopes are quite small and can be slipped in one's pocket, this type being called a pocket stereoscope. If the legs are shorter than the focal length, the lens stereoscope provides a magnification ratio of the images of the photograph equal to q/p, where these distances are as shown in Fig. 7–7(b). Magnification is an advantage when interpreting photographs and when selecting photo control points in the office and in the field. Since the photographs must be brought together under the stereoscope in such positions that the distance between conjugate images is equal to or slightly less than the interpupillary distance of the individual viewer, the photographs must lie one on top of the other to a certain extent. Some of the overlap area is thus obscured. The photographs must then be flipped in order to examine the entire overlap area under the stereoscope. To allow a greater separation, some lens stereoscopes contain prism lenses which bend the chief rays outward below the lenses as shown in Fig. 7–8.

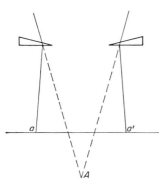

Fig. 7–8. Prism-lens stereoscope.

The mirror stereoscope, pictured in Fig. 7–9 and shown diagrammatically in Fig. 7–10, consists of a pair of small eyepiece mirrors, m and m', and a pair of larger wing mirrors, M and M', each of which is oriented at 45° with the plane of the photographs. The total distance, $emMp$ or $e'm'M'p'$, from the eyes to the plane of the photographs varies from 12 to 18 in., in order that the unaided eye may comfortably view the photographs. The angle ϕ, determined by the separation of the photographs that gives the most eye comfort, is compatible with the distance $emMp$. If this distance is to be reduced, a pair of magnifying lenses are placed at e and e'. Each magnifier has a focal length slightly smaller than the distance $emMp$. Thus, the magnifiers allow comfortable viewing even though the distance from the photographs to the eyes is less than the limit of distinct vision, or about 10 in. Some types of mirror stereoscopes have a set of removable binoculars which are placed at the eye positions e and e' (see Fig. 7-9). The binoculars produce an enlargement of a limited portion of the stereoscopic image for detailed study, as in interpretation or in the selection and identification of photo control points.

The greatest single advantage of the mirror stereoscope is the fact that the photographs may be completely separated for viewing, and the

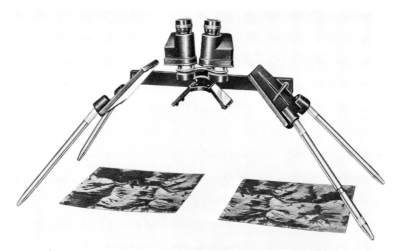

FIG. 7–9. Mirror stereoscope. (Courtesy of Harrison Ryker, Inc.)

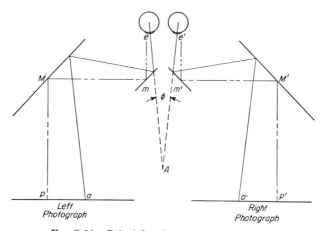

FIG. 7–10. Principle of mirror stereoscope.

entire overlap area may therefore be seen stereoscopically without having
to flip the photographs. Without the aid of binoculars, however, the
scale of the stereoscopic image is small compared with the scale as seen
through the lens stereoscope. Because of its size, the mirror stereoscope
is not so portable as is the pocket stereoscope, and its use in the field is
somewhat awkward.

The stereoscope shown in Fig. 7–11 combines some of the advantages
of both the lens stereoscope and the mirror stereoscope. Each eyepiece
of the binoculars may be individually focused, and the eyepieces themselves may be spread apart or pulled together to suit the individual
viewer. Each photograph is viewed through a highly corrected optical

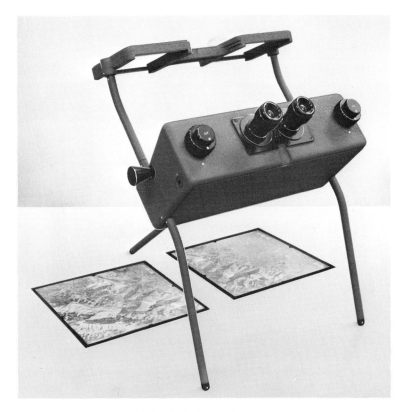

Fɪɢ. 7–11. Optical scanning stereoscope.

train of lenses and prisms, and the resulting stereoscopic image is very clear. A rotation of the outer knob on the left side causes the two optical trains to scan the stereoscopic image in the direction of the line of flight (the X-direction) without the necessity of moving the stereoscope. The outer knob on the right side is used to scan the stereoscopic image in a direction normal to the line of flight (the Y-direction). The smaller inner knob on the left allows one optical train to move in the X-direction relative to the other. This ΔX-movement facilitates viewing when great parallax differences exist in different areas of the stereoscopic image. The smaller inner knob on the right allows one optical train to move in the Y-direction relative to the other. This ΔY-movement eliminates any displacement of conjugate images in the Y-direction caused by tilted photographs, unequal scale between the two photographs, and misalignment of the flight line. (See Sec. 7–6 and Sec. 8–10.) A lever on the side of the stereoscope changes the magnification ratio of the stereoscopic image from 1.5 to 4.5. No intermediate magnification is possible.

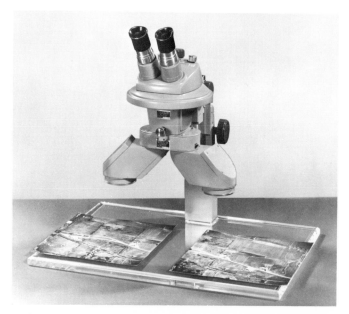

Fig. 7–12. Zoom 95 stereoscope. (Courtesy of Bausch and
Lomb Optical Co.)

The binocular stereoscope shown in Fig. 7–12 has provision for continuous change in magnification accomplished by the Zoom system of
focussing. It also provides for a variation of magnification *between* eyepieces by a factor of four. In other words, one photograph can be at scale
1:10,000 and the other at scale 1:2,500 and the two photographs can still
be viewed stereoscopically by means of this latter provision. The Zoom
stereoscope also permits the rotation of the field of view without physically
rotating either of the photographs. This facilitates viewing when alignment is faulty. It also permits a complete 360° rotation of each view,
desirable in some operations.

7–5. Orienting a Pair of Photographs for Stereoscopic Viewing

Before the stereoscopic, or three-dimensional, impression of the terrain
may be realized, the photographs must be properly oriented under the
stereoscope. This orientation is performed as follows:

1. Make certain that the photographs are consecutively numbered and in the
   same flight line. When aerial photographic negatives have been processed,
   they are numbered consecutively to show the flight number and the photograph number before photographs are printed. This numbering enables a
   person to identify a pair of adjacent overlapping photographs. See Fig.
   7–13(a).

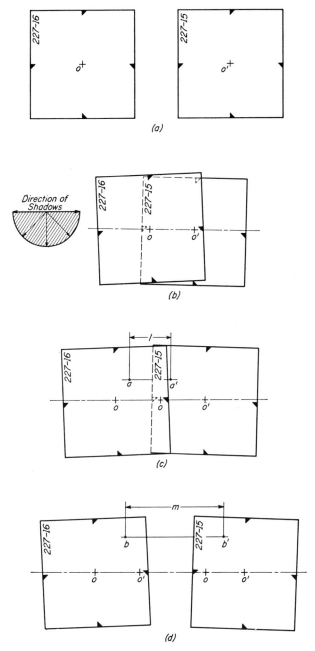

FIG. 7–13. Orienting photographs for viewing
under stereoscope.

2. Lay one photograph down on the other so that their overlap areas coincide, as shown in Fig. 7–13(*b*).

3. Observe the direction in which shadows appearing on the photographs are pointing. The shadows should point generally in the direction of the observer. See Fig. 7–13(*b*). If they do not, the photographs should be picked up together and turned 180°, thus reversing the direction of the flight line. The overlap area should be checked for coincidence. Note that the lines joining the principal points on the two photographs are coincident, and that this coincident line is parallel with the observer's eye base.

4. a) *When using a lens stereoscope,* separate the two photographs in the direction of the flight line until conjugate images, such as *a* and *a'* of Fig. 7–13(*c*), are separated by about the same distance as are the centers of the lenses. This is the distance *l* in Fig. 7–13(*c*). b) *When using a mirror stereoscope,* separate the two photographs in the direction of the flight line until conjugate images, such as *b* and *b'* of Fig. 7–13(*d*), are about the same distance apart as are the centers of the large wing mirrors. This is the distance *m* in Fig. 7–13(*d*).

5. Place the stereoscope over the pair of photographs so that the line joining the lens or eyepiece centers is parallel with the direction of flight.

6. While looking through the stereoscope, make any necessary adjustments to permit you to see a stereoscopic image comfortably. For this purpose, change the separation of the photographs slightly, rotate either photograph, or rotate the stereoscope, or carry out a combination of these slight adjustments. At the first attempt at seeing stereoscopically, the adjustment may prove a bit difficult. But, once it has been mastered, this adjustment becomes easy.

7–6. Factors Affecting Stereoscopic Viewing

If a pair of overlapping photographs are truly vertical, if each of the two photographs has been taken from exactly the same flying height, and if the photographs and the stereoscope are oriented as described in Sec. 7–5, then a person with normal binocular vision should see a clear stereoscopic image throughout the area of overlap of the two photographs. Under practical conditions, several factors affecting the photography and the orientation will tend to make stereoscopic vision quite difficult, if not impossible. These factors are: 1) unequal flying heights; 2) photographic tilt; 3) misalignment of the flight line; 4) misalignment of the stereoscope; 5) great difference in parallax between adjacent images.

Unequal flying heights cause a difference in scale between two overlapping photographs. Even when there is no tilt in either of the photographs and the flight line has been aligned properly, the difference in the scales of the photographs will cause the distance between one conjugate image and the flight line to differ from the distance between the corresponding image and the flight line. This difference is shown in Fig. 7–14(*a*). The left-hand photograph is at a smaller scale than the right-

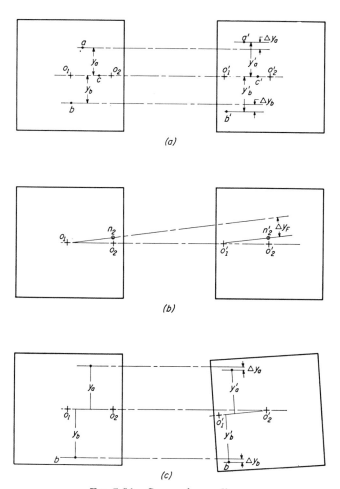

Fic. 7–14. Causes of y-parallax.

hand photograph, because of a greater flying height. If the flight line is taken as the x-axis, the y-coordinate of a is smaller than the y-coordinate of a' by an amount equal to Δy_a. Similarly, y_b is smaller than y'_b by an amount equal to Δy_b. The discrepancy Δy_a or Δy_b is termed the y-parallax of the point. Notice that variation in scale causes no y-parallax at point c, which is on the line of flight.

In normal vision, the optical axes of the two eyes lie in a plane containing the eye base. That is to say, for example, a person with normal vision does not look upward with the left eye and downward with the right eye. The slightest departure of one or the other optical axis from this plane causes serious eye strain. To correct for the situation shown in Fig. 7–14(a), one photograph must be moved slightly in a direction normal to the flight line when viewing different areas of the overlap area, or else the stereoscope base must be rotated until it lies parallel with a line through conjugate images in different portions of the overlap area. The scanning stereoscope of Fig. 7–11 eliminates the y-parallax at various points by means of the ΔY-movement. So, neither the photographs nor the stereoscope need be moved.

Relative tilt between the two photographs in any direction will cause y-parallax to exist in different portions of the area of overlap. Furthermore, the flight line is not truly defined by a line joining the principal points, but is defined by a line joining the nadir points. In Fig. 7–14(b) are shown a pair of photographs aligned according to the principal points. When there is no tilt in the left photograph, but the right photograph is tilted in the direction of the observer, the true flight line is indicated by the two segments o_1n_2 and $o'_1n'_2$. If the stereoscope base were to be rotated parallel with these segments, the amount of the over-all y-parallax would be Δy_F. Added to this is the y-parallax caused by tilt displacement of points on the right-hand photograph. Thus, tilted photographs will cause a certain amount of eye strain unless the tilt is corrected for by shifting the photographs and rotating the stereoscope slightly when moving from one point to another in the area of overlap, or by using the ΔY-motion on the scanning stereoscope.

When the flight line as defined by two principal points on a photograph is not properly aligned with the flight line on an overlapping photograph, the effect is shown in Fig. 7–14(c). Here it is assumed that both photographs are vertical and at the same scale. The y-coordinate of a is equal to the y-coordinate of a', but y-parallax exists in the amount Δy_a. Similarly, $y_b = y'_b$, but parallax Δy_b exists. The greatest difficulty in seeing the stereoscopic image because of misalignment of the flight line occurs along the flight line itself and away from the center of the right-hand photograph. Misalignment can be checked if the principal points have been transferred to their conjugate positions as described in Sec. 8–4 and the segments of the flight line have been drawn on the photographs. When the photographs are properly aligned, the two segments of the flight line should appear as one line in the stereoscopic image.

Misalignment of the stereoscope in such manner that the stereoscope base is not parallel with the flight line has much the same effect as has misalignment of the flight line. This misalignment becomes an impediment to comfortable stereoscopic viewing only when the stereoscope and the photographs remain fixed during the entire viewing period. Generally, the viewer detects and corrects stereoscope misalignment in the process of viewing.

Where terrain with very rugged and precipitous topography is photographed to a fairly large scale, and in some cases where the ground distance between exposures approaches or exceeds the flying height, the difference in the parallax between adjacent points is so great that the viewer has difficulty in maintaining the stereoscopic image. Photography taken with a camera having an extremely wide angle, convergent photography, and photography taken with the U. S. Coast and Geodetic Survey's 9-lens camera cause great parallax differences in the resulting overlapping photographs. The difficulty in viewing such photography is due more or less to the limited depth of clear single binocular vision of the viewer's eyes. This difficulty is experienced to a much greater extent when using the lens stereoscope than when using the mirror stereoscope.

7–7. Vertical Exaggeration in Stereoscopic Image

When a person examines stereoscopically a pair of overlapping vertical photographs which have been taken with a lens having a 6-in. focal length and which include about 60 per cent overlap, he senses a certain amount of relief exaggeration in the stereoscopic image. That is, he is conscious of a disparity between the horizontal scale and the vertical scale, even though he is not at all familiar with the terrain depicted in the image. The viewer perceives depth in the image because of the differences in parallactic angles at the various points, and these differences in parallactic angles are a direct result of the differences in parallax at the various points. Vertical exaggeration is caused by real or apparent changes in the parallax differences between points on the photographs.

The primary factor which contributes to vertical exaggeration in the stereoscopic image is the ratio of the ground distance between exposure stations to the flying height above the average elevation of the terrain. The ground distance between exposure stations is called the air base, and is designated by the symbol B. The ratio of air base to flying height is called the base-height ratio, and it is designated as B/H, where H is understood to mean the flying height of the aircraft above the average terrain elevation. All other factors remaining constant, an increase in B/H will cause a corresponding increase in vertical exaggeration.

In Fig. 7–15(a), assume that exposures at L and L' are taken on a 9- by 9-in. format with a lens having a 6-in. focal length, and that the overlap is about 60 per cent. Then the base-height ratio is found to be 0.60. The images of the idealized topographic shape (a building, for example) appear on the two photographs as shown. In Fig. 7–15(b), these two photographs have been placed under a lens stereoscope and overlapped so that the average separation of the conjugate images is

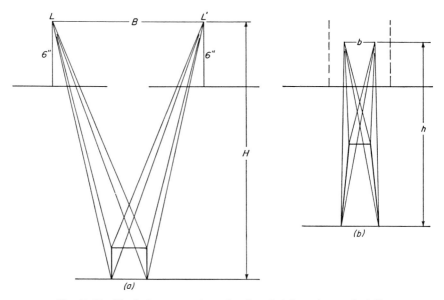

Fɪɢ. 7–15. Vertical exaggeration when base-height ratio equals 0.60.

roughly equal to the interpupillary distance of the viewer's eyes. The ratio between the eye base b and its height h above the image datum is much smaller than the ratio B/H of the photography. Since the difference in parallax, as measured on the photographs, between the low point and the high point has remained constant for the two diagrams, the difference in the parallactic angles between the low point and the high point now represents a larger elevation difference, to the scale of the stereoscopic image. If it were possible to view the photographs stereoscopically in such manner that the ratio B/H is the same as the ratio b/h, then no apparent vertical exaggeration would be observed.

In Fig. 7–16(a), assume that exposures at L and L' are taken on a 9- by 9-in. format with a lens having a 6-in. focal length, and that the overlap is about 80 per cent. The base-height ratio is then 0.30. When the photographs are placed under a lens stereoscope, as shown in Fig. 7–16(b), and brought together for comfortable stereoscopic viewing, the ratio b/h is somewhat near the ratio B/H. Here the horizontal scale at the image datum and the vertical scale are compatible.

In Fig. 7–15 and Fig. 7–16, the distance b represents the interpupillary distance of the viewer. The distance h, from the image datum to the eye base, is not a fixed distance because the datum itself is a virtual image. This distance is simply an impression on the mind, and can be anywhere between 10 and 20 in. It depends on the physical features of the stereoscope and the separation of the photographs. If the separation of the

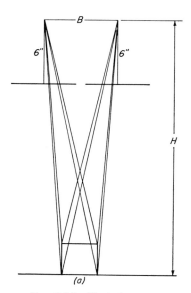

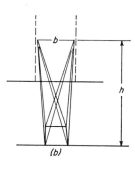

FIG. 7–16. **Vertical exaggeration when base-height ratio equals 0.30.**

photographs under the stereoscope is changed, the parallactic angle between the eye axes is also changed, causing a momentary apparent change in the distance h. The natural distance h however is restored to its original impression on continued viewing. The difference in the parallactic angles formed by two points of different parallax remains unchanged no matter what the photo separation is. Thus, the observer sees the same vertical exaggeration at all times.

The student is cautioned not to treat Figs. 7–15 and 7–16 from a geometric standpoint. They are pseudo-geometric representations of a physiological phenomenon which occurs in stereoscopic viewing of pairs of photographs, and which cannot be rigorously diagrammed. In fact, the stereoscopic impression is considered by some investigators to be gained by the disparity of image *shapes* presented to the two eyes from the two photographs. This disparity of shapes is of course a direct result of difference in parallax between different image points.

Bibliography

AMBROSE, W. R. "Stereoscopes with High Preformance," *Photogrammetric Engineering*, Vol. XXXI (1965), p. 822.

AMERICAN SOCIETY OF PHOTOGRAMMETRY. *Manual of Photogrammetry* (Menasha, Wisc.: George Banta Co., 1952), Chapter 11.

———. *Manual of Photogrammetry* (Menasha, Wisc.: George Banta Co., 1966), Chapter 11.

———. *Manual of Photographic Interpretation* (Menasha, Wisc.: George Banta Co., 1960), Chapter 3.

ASCHENBRENNER, C. M. "A Review of Facts and Terms Concerning the Stereoscopic Effect," *Photogrammetric Engineering*, Vol. XVIII (1952), p. 818.

————. "High Altitude Stereo Techniques," *Photogrammetric Engineering*, Vol. XVI (1950), p. 712.

CALBICK, C. J. "The Study of Size and Shape by Means of Stereoscopic Electron Micrography," *Photogrammetric Engineering*, Vol. XVI (1950), p. 695.

FISCHER, W. A. "Photogeologic Instruments Used by the U. S. Geological Survey," *Photogrammetric Engineering*, Vol. XXI (1955), p. 32.

GOODALE, E. R. "An Equation for Approximating the Vertical Exaggeration Ratio of a Stereoscopic View," *Photogrammetric Engineering*, Vol. XIX (1953), p. 607.

GUMBEL, E. J. "The Effect of the Pocket Stereoscope on Refractive Anomalies of the Eyes," *Photogrammetric Engineering*," Vol. XXX (1964), p. 795.

HALLERT, B. *Photogrammetry* (New York: McGraw-Hill Book Co., 1960), Chapter 1.

KISTLER, PHILIP S. "Viewing Photographs in Three Dimension," *Photogrammetric Engineering*, Vol. XIII (1947), p. 127.

MILLER, C. I. "Vertical Exaggeration in the Stereo Space-Image and Its Use," *Photogrammetric Engineering*, Vol. XXVI, No. 5 (Dec. 1960), p. 815.

MILLER, V. C. "Some Factors Causing Vertical Exaggeration and Slope Distortion on Aerial Photographs," *Photogrammetric Engineering*, Vol. XIX (1953), p. 592.

MOESSNER, K. E. "A Simple Test for Stereoscopic Perception," *Photogrammetric Engineering*, Vol. XXI (1955), p. 303.

PALMER, D. A. "Stereoscopy and Photogrammetry," *Photogrammetric Record*, Vol. IV (1964), p. 391.

RAASVELDT, H. C. "The Stereomodel, How It is Formed and Deformed," *Photogrammetric Engineering*, Vol. XXII (1956), p. 708.

RYKER, H. C. "Notes on Stereoscopy," *Photogrammetric Engineering*, Vol. XIII (1947), p. 115.

SALZMAN, M. H. "Notes on Stereoscopy," *Photogrammetric Engineering*, Vol. XVI (1950), p. 475.

————. "The Factors in Human Vision Applicable to Photogrammetry," *ibid.*, Vol. XV (1949), p. 637.

————. "The Place for Vision Testing in Photogrammetry," *ibid.*, Vol. XVI (1950), p. 637.

SCHWARTZ, A. I., and ZEIDNER, J. "Comparison of Photo Interpreter Performance Under Stereo and Non-Stereo Viewing Conditions," *Photogrammetric Engineering*, Vol. XXVII (1961), p. 720.

SCHWIDEFSKY, K. *An Outline of Photogrammetry* (New York: Pitman Publishing Corp., 1959), Chapter 2.

SINGLETON, R. "Vertical Exaggeration and Perceptual Models," *Photogrammetric Engineering*, Vol. XXII (1956), p. 175.

THURRELL, R. F. "Vertical Exaggeration in Stereoscopic Models," *Photogrammetric Engineering*, Vol. XIX (1953), p. 579.

VERES. S. A. "The Effect of the Fixation Disparity on Photogrammetric Processes," *Photogrammetric Engineering*, Vol. XXX (1964), p. 148.

VON GRUBER, O. *Photogrammetry* (Boston: American Photographic Publishing Co., 1942), Chapter 10.

ZELLER, M. *Textbook of Photogrammetry* (London: H. K. Lewis and Co., Ltd., 1952), Chapter 1.

Geometry of Overlapping Vertical Photographs $\quad 8$

8–1. Remarks

In Chapter 3, the geometry of a single aerial photograph was discussed, and the items taken up included photographic scale, ground coordinates from photographic coordinate measurements, relief displacement on vertical and tilted photographs, displacements caused by tilts, and the relationship between the photographic and ground coordinate axes. The principle of horizontal angles measured about the principal point of a vertical photograph was developed in Chapter 6. In the same chapter was discussed the use of two overlapping photographs to obtain the true planimetric positions of points based on intersection. In Chapter 7, the student was introduced to the principles of stereoscopy and was shown how a pair of overlapping vertical photographs can be viewed under a stereoscope to form a three-dimensional image. The impression of depth is made possible because the images of points lying at different elevations have been displaced in the focal plane by different amounts on successive exposures. In stereoscopy the displacement of the image of a point on two successive exposures is called the parallax of the point, and the difference between the displacements of the images of two points on successive exposures is called the difference in parallax between the two points.

The present chapter will deal with the measurement of parallax and its application to the determination of elevations and ground coordinates of ground points, the determination of differences in elevation between ground points, and the map locations of contour lines.

8–2. Algebraic Definition of Parallax

The parallax of a point measured on a pair of overlapping vertical photographs is equal to the x-coordinate of the point measured on the left-hand photograph minus the x-coordinate of the point measured on the right-hand photograph. In this definition, the x-axis passes through the principal point and is parallel with the flight line, and the y-axis passes through the principal point and is perpendicular to the flight line. Then,

$$p = x - x' \qquad (8\text{-}1)$$

in which p is the parallax of the point; x is the x-coordinate of the point with respect to the axes of the left-hand photograph, and x' is the x-coordinate with respect to the axes of the right-hand photograph. All distances are measured in the same units. In Fig. 8–1 are shown a pair of overlapping photographs which were exposed at L and L' and on which the parallax of point a is equal to $x_a - x'_a$ and the parallax of point b is equal to $x_b - x'_b$.

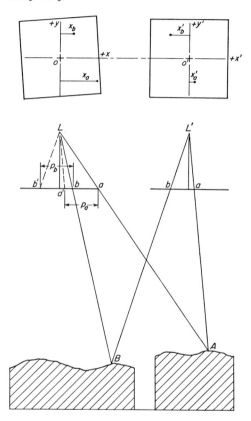

Fɪɢ. 8–1. Algebraic parallax.

Since the x-axis of each photograph of an overlapping pair must be parallel with the flight line, then a single photograph may have two sets of axes from which parallaxes are obtained. One set is associated with the flight line to the left, and the other set is associated with the flight line to the right. In Fig. 8–2, where the effective flight line changes direction at exposure *5*, photograph *5* will have two sets of axes; one set is located as shown at the lower left, and the other set as shown at the lower right. The only way in which the axes defined by the flight

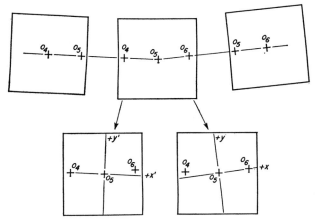

Fɪɢ. 8–2. Parallax axes.

line are associated with the photographic coordinate axes as defined by lines joining opposite fiducial marks is by the fact that the principal point is the origin of both sets. In general, however, the flight-line x-axis is usually very close to the fiducial-mark x-axis, because of the effort made to eliminate drift and crab at the time of photography.

8–3. Elevation and Ground Coordinates of Point Based on Parallax

In Fig. 8–3, two overlapping vertical photographs are taken from the same flying height H above the datum. The distance between exposure stations L and L' is the air base B. Both H and B are expressed in feet. The image of ground point P appears on the left-hand photograph at point p, whose coordinates as defined by the flight-line axes are (x, y). The image of P appears on the right-hand photograph at point p', whose coordinates as defined by the flight-line axes are (x', y'). The elevation of point P, in feet above the datum, is h. The focal length Lo or $L'o$ is denoted by f, and the principal points are at o and o'. Point w on the left-hand photograph is the projection of p on the x-axis, and point w' on the right-hand photograph is the projection of p' on the x'-axis. The line $L'w'$ for the right-hand photograph is imagined to be moved parallel to itself to the position Lw' for the left-hand photograph, as shown.

A pair of ground coordinate axes are established in such positions that the origin is at the ground position of the left-hand principal point O, and the X-axis and Y-axis are parallel, respectively, to the x-axis and y-axis of the photographs as defined by the flight line. The ground coordinates of point P are (X, Y) as shown. In triangles LOW and Low,

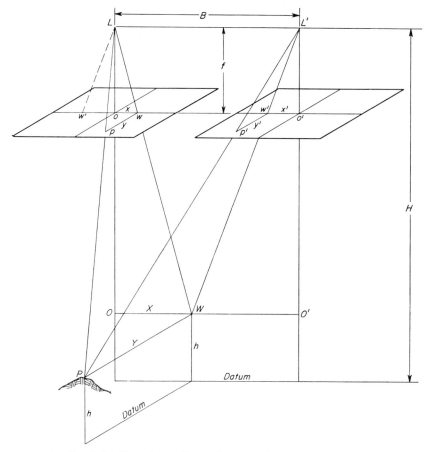

Fɪɢ. 8-3. Ground coordinates from parallax measurements.

$$\frac{Lo}{LO} = \frac{Lw}{LW} = \frac{ow}{OW} \quad \text{or} \quad \frac{f}{H-h} = \frac{x}{X} \qquad (8\text{-}2)$$

In the triangles Lwp and LWP,

$$\frac{Lw}{LW} = \frac{wp}{WP} \qquad (8\text{-}3)$$

From Eq. 8-2,

$$\frac{Lw}{LW} = \frac{f}{H-h}$$

Therefore, from Eqs. 8-2 and 8-3,

$$\frac{wp}{WP} = \frac{y}{Y} = \frac{f}{H-h} \qquad (8\text{-}4)$$

In triangles $L'O'W$ and $L'o'w'$, and in triangles $L'w'p'$ and $L'WP$,

$$\frac{L'o'}{L'O'} = \frac{L'w'}{L'W} = \frac{w'p'}{WP} = \frac{y'}{Y} \quad \text{or} \quad \frac{y'}{Y} = \frac{f}{H-h} \qquad (8\text{-}5)$$

By Eqs. 8–4 and 8–5,

$$\frac{y}{Y}=\frac{f}{H-h} \quad \text{and} \quad \frac{y'}{Y}=\frac{f}{H-h}$$

Therefore,

$$y = y' \tag{8–6}$$

Equation 8–6 indicates that on a pair of overlapping vertical photographs taken from the same flying height, the distance from the flight line to a point on the left-hand photograph is equal to the distance from the flight line to its conjugate, or corresponding, point on the right-hand photograph. In other words, under the assumptions made, there is no y-parallax. This is simply a restatement of some principles discussed in Secs. 7–2, 7–3, and 7–6.

In triangles LWL' and Lww' (for the left-hand photograph), LL' is parallel to ww'; LW coincides with, and is therefore parallel to, Lw; $L'W$ is parallel to Lw'. Therefore, the two triangles are similar triangles. Their corresponding altitudes are $(H-h)$ and f. Then, by similar triangles,

$$\frac{f}{H-h}=\frac{ww'}{B}$$

Since $ww' = x - x' = p$,

$$\frac{f}{H-h}=\frac{p}{B} \tag{8–7}$$

From Eqs. 8–2, 8–4, and 8–7, the following parallax equations result:

$$H-h=\frac{B}{p}f \tag{8–8}$$

$$X=\frac{B}{p}x \tag{8–9}$$

$$Y=\frac{B}{p}y \tag{8–10}$$

in which the quantities are as defined previously. The distances H, h, B, X, and Y are expressed in feet; x, y, p, and f are expressed in the same units, either inches or millimeters. Equations 8–8, 8–9, and 8–10 are valid only for a pair of truly vertical photographs which are taken from the same flying height and on which the photographic x-axes are coincident with the flight line. These equations can be used to solve any ground-surveying problems involving lengths, areas, angles, and elevations from measurements made on vertical photographs, provided that the air base and the constant flying height are known.

8–4. Defining Flight Line on Pair of Photographs

When both photographs of a pair are truly vertical, the photographic position of the exposure station for each is at the principal point. The flight line is defined on a photograph by transferring the principal point of the adjacent photograph to that photograph. The transferred principal point is called the *conjugate principal point*. A photograph thus contains its own principal point and two conjugate principal points, unless the photograph lies at the end of the flight line.

For determining the precise location of a conjugate principal point, the transfer must be done under a stereoscope for two reasons. First, stereoscopic vision enhances the precision of measurement, especially when under magnification; second, the principal point to be transferred may not fall on an identifiable point. The use of the azimuth point discussed in Sec. 6–6 is not applicable here. Even though azimuth points are satisfactory for ray centers as used in radial-line plotting, they will not define the flight line.

The principle of the *floating mark* and its application to the stereoscopic transfer of principal points will now be demonstrated. Assume that a pair of photographs have been oriented under a stereoscope for comfortable stereoscopic viewing. Such orientation is shown in Fig. 8–4,

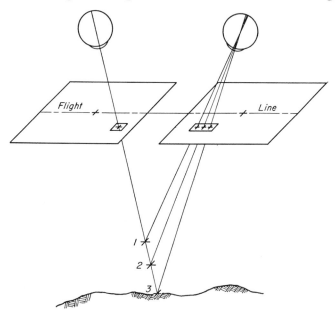

Fig. 8–4. Principle of floating mark.

with the stereoscope eliminated from the diagram for clarity. Two small pieces of acetate or other translucent material, each about 1 in. square, are prepared by placing directly in the center of each piece an identical mark, such as a dot, a cross, a V, or a small circle. One piece is placed on the left-hand photograph, as shown in Fig. 8–4. The mark on this piece will be called the left mark. The second piece is placed on the right-hand photograph and is adjusted so that the left mark as seen by the left eye and the right mark (or the mark on this second piece) as seen by the right eye fuse together at the apparent position *1*, shown in the figure. The viewer will experience the sensation that the image of the mark lies in space above the terrain.

If the right-hand mark is moved slightly to the right and the marks are again fused together, the image will appear to have been lowered to position *2* in space. If the right-hand mark is moved still farther to the right until the apparent position of the fused mark coincides with the stereoscopic image of the terrain, in position *3*, then the left mark and the right mark on the two photographs define the exact position of a pair of conjugate points, even though the two points cannot be identified by images. The floating mark appears to move vertically in the stereoscopic image because the parallax of the mark has been changed. Notice that the x-coordinate of the mark as measured on the left-hand photograph has remained fixed, while the x'-coordinate of the mark as measured on the right-hand photograph has increased in a positive direction when the mark has been moved from left to right. Thus, $(x-x')$ is reduced as the two marks are separated, and the fused mark is caused to appear to fall.

In Fig. 8–5, the two principal points o_1 and o'_2 have been located by lines joining fiducial marks, and they have been identified by small fine crosses drawn on the photographs. The legs of the crosses are $\frac{1}{16}$ in. long or less. The photographs have been oriented under a

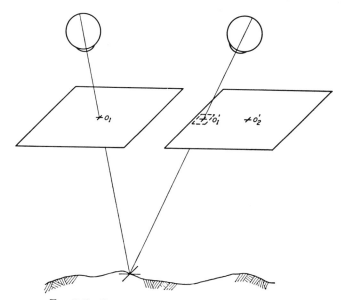

FIG. 8–5. Stereoscopic transfer of principal point.

stereoscope. A cross identical with those at the two principal points has been drawn on a piece of frosted acetate, which is placed on the right-hand photograph in the vicinity of the position of the left-hand principal point (as yet unidentified). The acetate is shifted around until there is stereoscopic fusion of the cross at o_1 and the movable cross. The movable cross is then moved to the left or right in the direction of the flight line so as to cause the floating mark to just touch the stereoscopic image of the terrain. At this point, a fine needle is pricked through the intersection of the legs of the movable cross, thus precisely locating the position o'_1 of the transferred principal point.

The piece of acetate is now placed on the left-hand photograph in the vicinity of the right-hand principal point, and the floating mark is made to touch the stereoscopic image at the right-hand principal point. This transferred principal point is marked by a pin prick. The flight line as defined on both photographs may now be drawn by joining each principal point and conjugate point with a line on the face of the photograph. This line should be made with the needle. A line at right angles to the flight line and passing through the principal point defines the y-axis for parallax measurement.

The method just described for transferring principal points stereoscopically is very positive. However, the student will find out that, with practice, he can mark the principal points with pin pricks, and then locate the transferred principal points by observing under the stereoscope coincidence of the pinhole on one photograph and the tip of the needle on the other photograph. After the position of the transferred principal point has been pricked in this manner, the two pinholes should form a single image appearing to touch the stereoscopic image; otherwise, the point has not been transferred properly.

The point transfer devices discussed in Chapter 1 are ideal for the stereoscopic transfer of the principal points of a pair of photographs. Each principal point must first be identified by intersecting the lines joining the fiducial marks. The appropriate measuring or floating mark of the transfer instrument is then centered on this intersection. The other mark, is then brought into stereoscopic fusion with the former, by a movement of either the mark or the photograph, depending on the type of instrument. Finally, the conjugate principal point is identified by means of the mechanical device built into the instrument. After the points have been transferred, they should be observed under the stereoscope to establish the accuracy of the transfer.

8–5. Measurement of Parallax

The parallax of a point may be determined in any one of several ways. After the flight line has been identified on each photograph by the stereoscopic transfer of conjugate principal points, a fine line carefully drawn at right angles to the flight line and passing through the principal point defines the y-axis. The x- and x'-coordinates of a point can then be measured by means of a precise scale. The parallax is then obtained by applying Eq. 8–1.

These measurements may be refined considerably in a comparator if the principal points have been identified and transferred. The photographs are oriented in turn in the comparator so that the flight line is parallel to the x-direction of the comparator. An x-reading on the principal point together with an x-reading on the desired point will give the value of the x-coordinate of the point. When the parallaxes of several points are to be determined, the reading for the principal point need be taken only once (unless several readings are to be taken on each point) for the purpose of obtaining the x-coordinates of all the points. The parallaxes are then obtained from the results of both photographs by applying Eq. 8–1.

A highly satisfactory method for making simple parallax measurements is the use of a device called a *parallax bar*. There are two advantages to using the bar: 1) The parallax measurement is performed by stereoscopic vision, as opposed to monocular vision in using a scale. 2) A movement of one of the measuring marks is recorded to the nearest 0.01 mm, with a probable accuracy of the resulting parallax on the order of ± 0.03 mm, provided that enough readings are made.

Two types of parallax bars are shown in Fig. 8–6(a) and (b). Both devices contain the bar proper, which holds a fixed piece of transparent material (clear plastic or glass) near the left end and a movable piece toward the right end. A reference mark, or measuring mark, is located at the center of each piece and on the underneath surface as shown. Each measuring mark is called a *half-mark*, because when they are viewed under a stereoscope, the two fuse together to constitute the floating mark. The movable half-mark of the parallax bar in Fig. 8–6(a) is moved by means of a micrometer screw, the total movement being about 25 mm. to 40 mm, depending on the manufacture of the instrument. The micrometer is read to the nearest 0.01 mm. The movable half-mark of the bar in Fig. 8–6(b) is moved by means of a knurled knob. The movement is recorded by means of a dial gage fastened to the bar as shown, the total movement being about 8 mm. The dial is graduated to 0.01 mm and can be indexed to read zero for any position of the right-hand mark.

In Fig. 8–6(c), a fine straight line has been drawn on a sheet of heavy drafting paper, and the left-hand photograph has been oriented on the paper so that the flight line, defined by the principal point and the conjugate principal point, is in exact coincidence with the line on the paper. This orientation may be obtained by laying a straightedge over

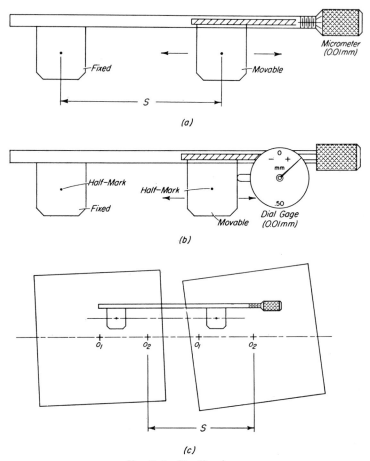

Fɪɢ. 8–6. Parallax bars.

the photograph and orienting it to the line. The micrometer of the parallax bar has been set to the middle reading, and the separation between the two half-marks has been measured to within $\frac{1}{2}$ mm. This separation is the distance S. The right-hand photograph is oriented by means of the flight line and is so placed as to cause a separation S between the principal point on one photograph and its corresponding position on the other photograph, as shown. Positioning in this manner will allow increasing and decreasing parallaxes to be measured without exceeding the travel of the movable mark. The photographs are now properly oriented for stereoscopic parallax measurement.

When the parallax bar is used, it is laid on the photographs, thus bringing the measuring marks in contact with the photographs. A stereoscope is then placed over the photographs. The viewer will gain an impression of the stereoscopic image, together with an impression of the floating mark according to the principle developed in Sec. 8–4. If the two half-marks appear to be separated in a direction perpendicular to the flight line, a slight rotation of the bar in the plane of the photographs will bring them together. If, while the viewer has a comfortable view of the stereoscopic image of the terrain, the two marks appear to be separated in a direction parallel with the direction of the flight line, the half-marks contain either too much parallax or too little parallax, or the observer's eyes have a limited depth of clear single binocular vision. The marks are made to fuse by moving the movable mark either to the right or to the left. After they have fused, a slight movement of the movable mark will give the viewer the impression that the floating mark is moving up or down relative to the stereoscopic image.

There is a wide variation between individuals as to the proper spacing of the photographs under the stereoscope which will give the most natural and most comfortable stereoscopic viewing. Consequently, provision is made on most parallax bars for moving the so-called fixed mark to allow for this variation. To take advantage of this flexibility, the photographs are first placed beneath the stereoscope and adjusted for comfortable stereoscopic vision. Next, the moveable mark is set to its mid-position, and the parallax bar is then placed on the photographs. The fixed mark is shifted to a point along the bar which will allow the viewer to see the floating mark in approximate contact with the stereoscopic image. Finally, the fixed mark is clamped in this position where it remains for all subsequent measurements.

The student should note that if the movable mark is moved to the left, the fused mark will appear to rise; and if it is moved to the right, the fused mark will appear to fall. These statements follow from the facts that a movement to the left increases the parallax of the marks, whereas a movement to the right decreases the parallax of the marks. Unfortunately, some parallax bars record an increasing micrometer or dial reading when the movable mark is moved to the right. For the purpose of discussion, such a numbering system will be referred to as a backward graduation. On the other hand, if the micrometer or dial reading increases when the mark is moved to the left, the numbering system will be referred to as a direct graduation.

Assume that the parallax of a point is known (see Sec. 8–6). In Fig. 8–7, let it be known that the parallax of point a is 73.22 mm. The parallax bar of Fig. 8–6(a) is placed over the photographs at a and a' and is rotated so that no y-parallax exists in the measuring mark. The micrometer is turned and the floating mark is brought into apparent contact with point a in the stereoscopic image. A micrometer reading

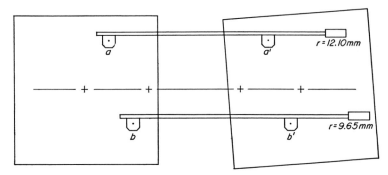

FIG. 8-7. Micrometer readings of parallax bar.

of 12.10 mm is taken. Assume a direct graduation. Now subtracting the reading r from the parallax p gives a constant, denoted by C_D, for this particular photograph setup and parallax bar. Thus,

$$C_D = p - r \qquad (8\text{–}11)$$

in which C_D is the constant for a parallax bar with direct graduation. In the preceding situation, $C_D = 73.22 - 12.10 = 61.12$ mm.

The parallax of point b is obtained by setting the floating mark in apparent contact with the stereoscopic image at b, reading the micrometer, and combining the reading 9.65 mm shown in Fig. 8–7 with the constant in accordance with the following relationship:

$$p = C_D + r \qquad (8\text{–}12)$$

For point b, $p_b = 61.12 + 9.65 = 70.77$ mm. The student will observe that in going from point a to point b, the half-marks were separated farther. So the parallax of b is less than that of a.

Equations 8–11 and 8–12 apply also to the dial-type parallax bar, but for convenience the dial is indexed to zero when the measuring mark has been set on the point of known parallax. In Fig. 8–8, the reading

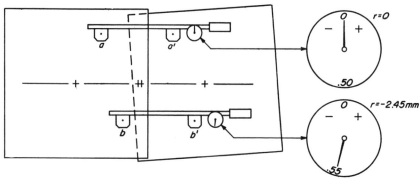

FIG. 8-8. Dial readings of parallax bar.

on the dial is made 0 for the setting at point a. In the movement from a to point b, the dial indicator has gone through two complete negative rotations and down to 0.55 mm. Since each rotation of the indicator represents a movement of 1 mm, the value of r at point b is -2.45 mm. By Eq. 8–11, $C_D = 73.22 - 0 = 73.22$ mm. By Eq. 8–12, $p_b = 73.22 + (-2.45) = 70.77$ mm, as before.

If the parallax bar contains a backward graduation, the value of the constant C_B is given by the relationship

$$C_B = p + r \qquad (8\text{–}13)$$

Also the parallax of any point is determined by the relationship

$$p = C_B - r \qquad (8\text{–}14)$$

It should be noted that the value of C_D or C_B will remain fixed for a given positioning of the photographs, a given parallax bar, and a given position of the fixed mark along the bar. If any of these is changed, a new value of C_D or C_B must be determined, as just discussed. Once the constant is obtained, the parallaxes of all points to be measured are then determined by either Eq. 8–12 or Eq. 8–14.

8–6. Parallax of the Principal Points

The direct determination of the parallax of a point by means of a parallax bar requires that the parallax of one point be known, as explained in Sec. 8–5. The parallaxes of two points, namely, the two principal points, may be determined quite readily. In Fig. 8–9, for example, the parallax of the left principal point o_1 is the x-coordinate of o_1 minus the x'-coordinate of o'_1. Since the x-coordinate of o_1 is 0 and the x'-coordinate of o'_1 is $-b'$, the parallax of o_1 is $0 - (-b') = b'$. That is, the parallax of the left principal point is measured on the right-hand photograph between the two principal points. Similarly, the parallax of the right principal point o'_2 is the x-coordinate of o_2 minus the x'-coordinate of o'_2, or $b - 0 = b$. That is, the parallax of the right principal point is measured on the left-hand photograph between the two principal points. Note that b is larger than b' because the ground point O_2 lies at a greater elevation than does O_1.

Before the parallax bar is used, the distances b and b' should be measured carefully. Two values of C_D or C_B may then be based on the known parallaxes of the two principal points. Because of tilts of the photographs, unequal flying heights, differential paper shrinkage, and scaling errors, the two values of the constant will rarely be the same. Unless otherwise justified, an average value of the constant should be used in Eq. 8–12 or Eq. 8–14. Use of the average value is justified, because the errors in the parallaxes of all measured points resulting from

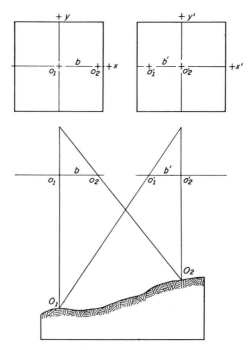

Fɪɢ. 8–9. Parallaxes of principal points.

the use of an erroneous value of C_D or C_B will have the same magnitude and the same algebraic sign, and the effects of an error in the constant will tend to cancel.

Another device which is used to measure parallaxes is called the *parallax ladder* or *parallax wedge*. This device shown in Fig. 8–10 oriented to an overlapping pair of photographs can be prepared from a negative of a large-scale drawing of the ladder. The type of stereoscope and spacing of the photographs, together with the reduction in the copying process must be taken into account when preparing the drawing. Assume that the stereoscope to be used allows a separation of approximately 12 in. between conjugate points such as a and a' of Fig. 8–10. Also, assume that a total parallax difference of 20 mm is to be accomodated by the parallax ladder. A drawing is very carefully prepared in which the distance between the centers of the legs is say 36 in. The drawing will thus ultimately be reduced to ⅓ its original size to reduce the distance between the centers of the legs to 12 in. The difference in the separation between the upper ends and the lower ends must be 20 mm on the reduction. Therefore, this difference must be 60 mm at the scale of the drawing. The upper spacing is thus 36 in. minus 30 mm, and the lower spacing is 36 in. plus the 30 mm on the drawing.

The length of each leg is arbitrary; however, the sensitivity increases

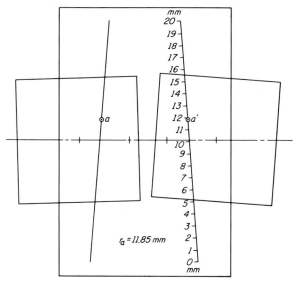

FIG. 8–10. Parallax ladder.

as the length of the legs is increased. Assume that each leg is drawn 60 in. long, and subdivided by 20 divisions. Each such 3-in. division then represents 1 mm of parallax. If each division is then subdivided say 20 times, then each of these divisions represents 0.05 mm. The numbering should increase up the ladder. The drawing is then inked and copied in a copy camera to $\frac{1}{3}$ size onto high-contrast negative material. Contact prints of the negative can then be made on positive transparency material. This results in the parallax ladder as shown in Fig. 8–10.

The constant for the parallax ladder is obtained by shifting the ladder under the stereoscope until the two legs, which now constitute a line in space inclined to and piercing the stereoscopic image, appear to intersect the image at a point of known parallax. The ladder reading at this point is then used in Eq. 8–11 to obtain C_D. The parallax at any other point is then obtained by piercing the image with the floating line at the point in question, reading the ladder, and applying Eq. 8–12.

8–7. Elevations from Known Air Base and One Control Point

Assume that a pair of overlapping, vertical photographs, the air base of which is known, have been oriented for parallax-bar measurements. Also the constant C_D has been taken as the average of the two values determined from the readings on the two principal points. The elevation of a control point designated as V-17 has been determined by field surveys. The elevations of ten points are to be determined from their parallax measurements. The accompanying tabulation gives the parallax-bar readings on the points, together with other pertinent data.

DATA FOR COMPUTING ELEVATIONS FROM PARALLAX MEASUREMENTS

Point	Parallax-Bar Reading, r (mm)	Parallax, p (mm)
V-17	12.62	90.82
1	14.04	92.24
2	10.91	89.11
3	11.02	89.22
4	13.56	91.76
5	15.15	93.35
6	16.11	94.31
7	14.25	92.45
8	12.33	90.53
9	9.76	87.96
10	10.52	88.72

Focal length f = 6.000 in. = 152.4 mm
Air base B = 1,730 ft
Elevation of V-17 = 735 ft
Constant C_D = 78.20 mm

The parallaxes of the points are determined by substituting the constant and the readings in Eq. 8–12. These results are shown in the right-hand column along with the data for the problem.

By using the parallax and known elevation of the control point, together with the air base and the focal length of the camera, the flying height above the datum (sea level) is determined by Eq. 8–8. Thus,

$$H - 735 \text{ ft} = \frac{1,730 \text{ ft}}{90.82 \text{ mm}} \times 152.4 \text{ mm}$$

and $H = 3,638$ ft above sea level.

By applying Eq. 8–8 to the parallax of each point, the elevations of the points are obtained. Thus,

$$h = H - \frac{B}{p} f$$

The intermediate values and the results are arranged in tabular form as shown.

COMPUTATION OF ELEVATIONS FROM PARALLAXES

Point	p (mm)	$\frac{B}{p} f$ (ft)	$h = H - \frac{B}{p} f$ (ft)
1	92.24	2,858	780
2	89.11	2,959	679
3	89.22	2,955	683
4	91.76	2,873	765
5	93.35	2,824	814
6	94.31	2,796	842
7	92.45	2,852	786
8	90.53	2,912	726
9	87.96	2,997	641
10	88.72	2,972	666

At the given flying height, the elevations of the points determined in this problem may be in error by 30 ft or more just because of tilts and unequal flying heights. An error in the air base, together with observational errors and differential paper shrinkage, will also affect the computed elevations, either favorably or unfavorably. Note that the flying-height computation is based on the elevation of only one control point. The farther the other points lie from this one control point, the greater are the chances for elevation errors.

8–8. Parallax Correction Based on More Than One Control Point

To render parallax measurements more reliable for determining the elevations of ground points appearing in the overlap area of a pair of near-vertical photographs, there should be additional well-placed vertical control points in the overlap area. In Fig. 8–11 is represented the overlap area discussed in Sec. 8–7, with five vertical control points located as shown. By using the value of C_D given in Sec. 8–7 and parallax measurements for these points, their parallaxes are determined. Then, a flying height is determined from the parallax and elevation of each point by applying Eq. 8–8, and five separate flying heights are thus obtained. The data and computations for the flying heights are shown in the tabulation on page 212. The average flying height, which is 3,631 ft, is used to compute the theoretical parallaxes of the five control points.

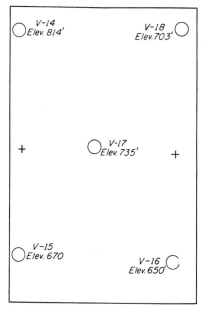

Fig. 8–11. Locations of
vertical control points.

These are shown as corrected parallaxes. For each point the difference between the corrected parallax and the measured parallax represents the amount by which the parallax-bar reading would have to be corrected in order to arrive at the corrected parallax. (If the parallax bar contains a backward graduation, the corrections to the readings would have algebraic signs opposite to those shown.)

AVERAGE FLYING HEIGHT AND CORRECTED PARALLAXES
FOR FIVE CONTROL POINTS

Point	Elev. (ft)	Meas. Parallax (mm)	$\frac{B}{p}f$ (ft)	$H = \frac{B}{p}f + h$ (ft)	Corr. $\frac{B}{p}f$ (ft)	Corrected Parallax (mm)	Correction to Parallax-Bar Reading (mm)
V-14	814	93.63	2,816	3,630	2,817	93.59	-0.04
V-15	670	88.12	2,992	3,662	2,961	89.04	$+0.92$
V-16	650	88.59	2,976	3,626	2,981	88.44	-0.15
V-17	735	90.82	2,903	3,638	2,896	91.04	$+0.22$
V-18	703	90.98	2,898	3,601	2,928	90.05	-0.93

Avg. 3,631

A transparent overlay is placed over the overlap area, as shown in Fig. 8–12, and the values of the corrections are entered at the five points. The overlay may be referenced to the two principal points, as shown. By interpolating between the control points, lines of equal correction may be drawn, the method being similar to that used for locating contour lines

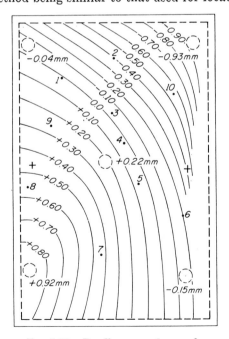

FIG. 8–12. Parallax-correction graph.

on a plane-table sheet. This overlay containing the lines of equal correction is called a *parallax-correction graph*. When the graph is superimposed on one of the photographs, it indicates the correction to be applied to each micrometer reading to obtain the corrected parallax of the point whose elevation is to be determined. In the accompanying tabulation, the readings for the ten points of Sec. 8–7 are shown, together with the corrected parallaxes and elevations. Here, $C_D = 78.20$ mm; $B = 1,730$ ft; $H = 3,631$ ft; $f = 152.4$ mm.

CORRECTED ELEVATIONS BASED ON PARALLAX CORRECTION GRAPH

Point	Parallax-Bar Reading (mm)	Correction from Graph (mm)	Corrected Reading (mm)	Corrected Parallax (mm)	$\dfrac{B}{p}f$ (ft)	$h = H - \dfrac{B}{p}f$ (ft)
1	14.04	+0.02	14.06	92.26	2,858	773
2	10.91	−0.40	10.51	88.71	2,972	659
3	11.02	−0.03	10.99	89.19	2,956	675
4	13.56	+0.02	13.58	91.78	2,873	758
5	15.15	+0.07	15.22	93.42	2,822	809
6	16.11	−0.20	15.91	94.11	2,802	829
7	14.25	+0.44	14.69	92.89	2,838	793
8	12.33	+0.56	12.89	91.09	2,894	737
9	9.76	+0.27	10.03	88.23	2,988	643
10	10.52	−0.56	9.96	88.16	2,991	640

As the density of vertical control becomes greater, the closer will the parallax-correction graph represent the true corrections to measured parallaxes. With five vertical control points distributed as shown in Fig. 8–11, the error in the elevation of a point computed from simple parallax measurements should not exceed 1/200 to 1/400 times the flying height above average terrain, provided that sufficient readings are taken on each point and that the points are not near the very edges of the overlap area.

8–9. Determination of Air Base

The air base of a pair of overlapping vertical photographs may be determined in either of two ways, both depending on horizontal ground control. Chapter 6 discusses the method of locating the correct map positions of the principal points or azimuth points of a series of overlapping vertical photographs by a radial-line plot. The accuracy with which these points may be located depends on the density of photo control points. This accuracy, however, is of an absolute nature. Errors in a given area of a radial-line plot tend to be generally of the same magnitude and in the same general direction. Therefore, even though the error in the absolute map positions of two consecutive principal points may be considerable, the error in the relative map positions of the two points will tend to be small. This means that the map distance between consecutive principal points is highly reliable, provided of course that the plot has been executed with care, and that it has been adequately fixed by photo control. The air base of any overlapping pair of photographs included in the plot is obtained by scaling the map distance between the two principal points and applying the scale of the plot to this scaled distance. For example, assume that the photo control of a radial-line plot has been plotted on a map grid to a scale of 1 in.$=800$ ft and the distance between two consecutive principal points scales 3.842 in. The air base B of this pair of photographs is then $3.842\times800=3{,}074$ ft. If azimuth points have been used as ray centers in constructing the radial-line plot, the principal points may be located on the map sheet as described in Sec. 6–6.

The air base may be computed if the images of the end points of a line of known ground length appear in the area of overlap of the two photographs. The flight line is drawn on each photograph as described in Sec. 8–4, and the y-axis is constructed at right angles to the flight line at each principal point. The coordinate axes are thus established for parallax measurements. The parallax of each point defining an end of the ground control line is determined as outlined in Sec. 8–5, preferably by means of the parallax bar. The x- and y-coordinates of the two points are then carefully measured on the left-hand photograph. Let the two points be designated as a and b. Then, by Eqs. 8–9 and 8–10,

$$X_A = \frac{B}{p_a} x_a \qquad Y_A = \frac{B}{p_a} y_a$$

$$X_B = \frac{B}{p_b} x_b \qquad Y_B = \frac{B}{p_b} y_b$$

Also, by the distance formula,

$$D_{AB} = \sqrt{(X_A - X_B)^2 + (Y_A - Y_B)^2}$$

or

$$D_{AB} = \sqrt{\left(\frac{B}{p_a} x_a - \frac{B}{p_b} x_b\right)^2 + \left(\frac{B}{p_a} y_a - \frac{B}{p_b} y_b\right)^2}$$

Since the distance, the photographic coordinates, and the parallaxes are all known, the air base B may be computed by solving the preceding equation for B. Thus,

$$B = \left[\frac{D_{AB}^{~2}}{\left(\dfrac{x_a}{p_a} - \dfrac{x_b}{p_b}\right)^2 + \left(\dfrac{y_a}{p_a} - \dfrac{y_b}{p_b}\right)^2}\right]^{\frac{1}{2}} \qquad (8\text{–}15)$$

In Eq. 8–15, the fractions in the denominator must be carried out to the fifth or sixth decimal place because they involve differences. To verify the value of B, ground coordinates of the two points are computed by Eqs. 8–9 and 8–10, and the distance formula is applied by using the ground coordinates in order to compute the ground length of the control line. The computed length must agree with the known length.

EXAMPLE 8–1. A pair of overlapping vertical photographs contain the images of the ends of a ground control line AB whose length is 8,452 ft. The focal length of the camera lens is 150.00 mm. The measured parallax of point a is 86.16 mm, and that of point b is 88.04 mm. The coordinates of the two points measured on the left-hand photograph, with the flight line as the x-axis, are $x_a = +28.22$ mm and $y_a = +66.05$ mm; $x_b = +18.70$ mm and $y_b = -71.70$ mm. Compute and verify the length of the air base.

Solution: By Eq. 8–15,

$$B = \left[\frac{8,452^2}{\left(\dfrac{28.22}{86.16} - \dfrac{18.70}{88.04}\right)^2 + \left(\dfrac{66.05}{86.16} - \dfrac{-71.70}{88.04}\right)^2} \right]^{\frac{1}{2}} = 5,332 \text{ ft}$$

By Eqs. 8–9 and 8–10,

$$X_A = \frac{5,332}{86.16} \times 28.22 = +1,746 \text{ ft} \quad \text{and} \quad X_B = \frac{5,332}{88.04} \times 18.70 = +1,133 \text{ ft}$$

$$Y_A = \frac{5,332}{86.16} \times 66.05 = +4,087 \text{ ft} \quad \text{and} \quad Y_B = \frac{5,332}{88.04} \times (-71.70) = -4,342 \text{ ft}$$

By the distance formula,

$$D_{AB} = \sqrt{(1,746 - 1,133)^2 + (4,087 + 4,342)^2}$$

$$= \sqrt{613^2 + 8,429^2} = 8,451 \text{ ft}$$

The 1-ft discrepancy between the computed value of the length and the known value is the result of rounding off values in the computation, and is not due to errors in measuring.

The air base may be computed also by assuming the length of an air base, computing the ground coordinates of the ends of the control line by use of this assumed value of B, computing the length of the control line by using the assumed coordinates, and comparing this computed length with the known length. The comparison then gives the correct air base by the following equation:

$$\frac{\text{Correct } B}{\text{Assumed } B} = \frac{\text{known } D}{\text{computed } D} \tag{8–16}$$

The value of B thus obtained should be verified by using it in Eqs. 8–9 and 8–10 and then computing the ground length. Since B and D are directly proportional, the first solution of Eq. 8–16 will be correct, unless mistakes have been made in the computations.

EXAMPLE 8–2. Using the data of Example 8–1, first assume that the value of B is 10,000 ft. Then, compute the correct value of the air base.

Solution: By Eqs. 8–9 and 8–10,

$$X_A = \frac{10,000}{86.16} \times 28.22 = +3,275 \text{ ft} \quad \text{and} \quad X_B = \frac{10,000}{88.04} \times 18.70 = +2,124 \text{ ft}$$

$$Y_A = \frac{10,000}{86.16} \times 66.05 = +7,666 \text{ ft} \quad \text{and} \quad Y_B = \frac{10,000}{88.04} \times (-71.70) = -8,144 \text{ ft}$$

By the distance formula,

$$\text{Computed } D_{AB} = \sqrt{(3,275 - 2,124)^2 + (7,666 + 8,144)^2}$$
$$= \sqrt{1,151^2 + 15,810^2} = 15,852 \text{ ft}$$

By Eq. 8–16,

$$\frac{\text{Correct } B}{10,000 \text{ ft}} = \frac{8,452 \text{ ft}}{15,852 \text{ ft}}$$

or correct $B = 5,332$ ft.

This value of the air base was verified in Example 8–1, and the computation will not be repeated here. It should be made, however, in order to detect any mistakes in the computations.

8–10. Plotting Contour Lines in Perspective Projection

The principles established thus far in this chapter concerning parallax measurements and the determination of elevations can be applied to the plotting of contour lines. Contour lines may be plotted by determining the elevations of discrete points in the area of overlap of a pair of vertical photographs and interpolating between these points to determine the positions of the contour lines, or they may be plotted continuously in the stereoscopic image by means of a movable combination of a stereoscope and a parallax bar, to which is attached a drawing arm.

Contour Lines by Interpolation. In this method, a pair of overlapping photographs are oriented for parallax measurement, and with the aid of a radial-line plot or a ground control line, the air base for the pair is determined. An average flying height is computed by considering all the available vertical control points in the overlap area, and a parallax-correction graph is constructed as outlined in Sec. 8–8.

The elevations of a set of well-selected points are determined from their corrected parallaxes. The positions of the points are marked on one photograph or the other. These points should be chosen along ridges, along drainage ways, and at points where the slope of the terrain exhibits a definite break as seen in the stereoscopic image. The computed elevations of the points are entered either directly on one photograph or on a translucent overlay which has been oriented to the photograph by means of the principal points. By viewing the photographs under the stereoscope and using the elevations of the points as guides, the viewer can sketch the positions of the contour lines either directly on the one photograph or on the overlay. The stereoscopic image affords a complete view of the shapes of the terrain features being contoured, and enables the viewer to give the contour lines their proper forms.

The contour lines drawn as just described, together with the planimetric features shown on the photograph, now constitute a perspective projection of the terrain. The result cannot be considered as a true topographic map. In Fig. 8–13, an area of terrain containing imaginary contour lines as shown is photographed from L and L' to form a stereoscopic pair. The contour lines would appear on the left-hand photograph in a perspective projection as shown. Beneath the terrain, an orthographic projection or map projection of the contour lines is shown in solid lines. The perspective projection of the left-hand photograph has been enlarged so that the lowest contour line is at the scale of the map projection, and the higher contour lines are shown as dashed lines, superimposed over the map projection. Two things are apparent in this superposition. First, the scale of the dashed contour lines increases from the bottom contour line to the top contour line. In other words, each contour line is at a different scale, determined by Eq. 3–1. Secondly, each closed contour line has been displaced outward from the center of the photograph. This relief displacement is in accordance with Eq. 3–7.

The perspective projection may be reduced to an orthographic projection by means of an opaque projector. A point representing the principal point is marked on the map sheet beneath the projector, and a line is drawn on the map sheet through the principal-point mark to represent the flight line. The principal-point mark and the line are used to adjust the projected image to the map sheet. Each contour line on the perspective projection is then projected down onto the map sheet, the proper enlargement or reduction being made to bring the contour line to the common map scale. To carry out this work, the first step is to make the projected image of the principal point coincide with the mark on the map sheet (provided by a radial-line plot or in some other suitable way), and to orient the map sheet so that the projected flight line coincides with the flight line on the map sheet. The contour line on the perspective projection that is at the map scale and the planimetric features adjacent to this contour line are traced onto the map sheet. This procedure places the contour line and the planimetric features in their correct map positions and at the proper scale. The next contour line is then brought to scale by an enlargement or a reduction, the principal point and the flight line are oriented to the map sheet, and the tracing process is repeated.

Suppose that the map sheet is at a scale of 1 in. $=1,000$ ft, and that the photograph was taken with a lens having a 6-in. focal length from a height of 5,500 ft above sea level. Assume that the 650-ft contour line is to be traced. Then, by Eq. 3–1, the scale at the 650-ft elevation is 6 in./(5,500−650) ft, or 1 in. $=808$ ft, and the reduction factor will be $808/1,000=0.808$. For the 1,000-ft contour line, the photo scale is

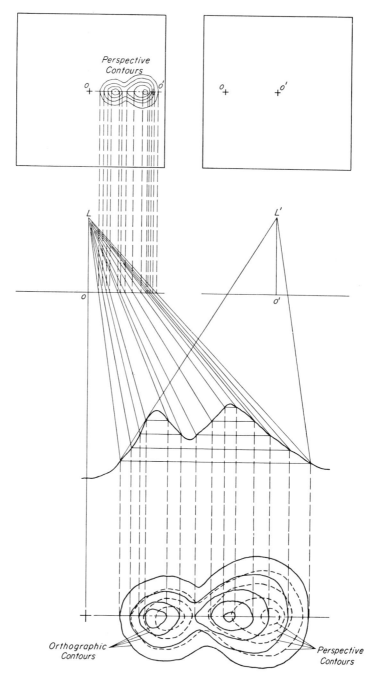

Fig. 8-13. Perspective projection and orthographic projection.

6 in./(5,500−1,000) ft, or 1 in.=750 ft, and the reduction factor will be 0.750.

Some of the older types of precise stereoscopic plotting instruments embody this principle of converting the perspective projection to an orthographic projection by computation and projection in the manner just described. Other instruments incorporate a shifting mechanism to compensate for the relief displacement, and also a variable-scale pantograph to effect the proper scale change. The Brock process of photogrammetric mapping is an example of the former type, while the Reading plotter of the U. S. Coast and Geodetic Survey, which is used to compile topographic maps from photographs taken with the 9-lens camera, is an example of the latter type. Either of these methods is far more precise than is the simple parallax-bar method, but the principle embodied in all three methods is the same.

Contour Lines by Continuous Tracing. In this method of plotting contour lines, a simple stereoscopic plotting instrument is used. The instrument is composed of a stereoscope and an attached parallax bar, which together form a movable assembly. The assembly is attached to a drafting machine to provide the motion and to keep the stereoscope base and the parallax bar parallel to the flight line of the photographs. Attached to the assembly is a pencil arm which supports a pencil chuck. As the stereoscope is moved about, the drawing pencil traces the desired features onto the map sheet.

In Fig. 8–14 is shown a plotting instrument of the mirror-stereoscope type. The parallax bar attached to the stereoscope contains a micrometer similar to that shown in Fig. 8–6(a). This type of instrument is called a *stereocomparagraph.* The drafting machine, pencil arm, and map sheet are clearly visible in the picture, along with the stereoscope and the parallax bar. In Fig. 8–15 is shown a plotting instrument of the lens-stereoscope type, with an attached parallax bar similar to that shown in Fig. 8–6(b). The dial gage and the other components are plainly visible in the picture. A distinct disadvantage of this instrument, called a *contour finder,* is that the photographs must be overlapped when they are oriented for stereoscopic plotting. A contour finder of more recent design incorporates a mirror stereoscope and a correspondingly longer parallax bar which allows complete separation of the photographs when they are oriented for parallax measurements.

The stereocomparagraph and the contour finder are used in the same way. A pair of overlapping photographs is oriented for parallax measurement by defining the flight line of the photographs and determining the average spacing of the measuring marks as described in Secs. 8–4 and 8–5. The parallax of each principal point is measured in order that an

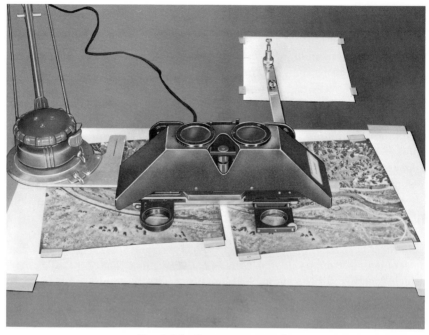

FIG. 8–14.   Stereocomparagraph.

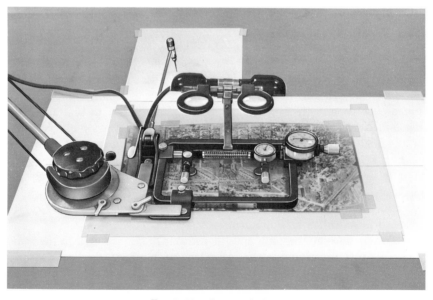

FIG. 8–15.   Contour finder.

average value of C_D or C_B may be determined for the setup later. The drafting paper containing the photographs is fastened to the drafting table. A large sheet of transparent acetate is placed over the photographs so as to extend beyond the photographs about 3 in. on all sides. The extra coverage prevents the photographs from being damaged when the assembly is moved about. The photographs are now ready for stereoscopic measurement.

Since the plotting instrument must move parallel to the flight line at all times, the y-parallax occuring in different portions of the overlap area cannot be removed by rotating the parallax bar, as can be done with a separate parallax bar. Therefore, the parallax bar of the plotting instrument is provided with an adjustment for moving one or the other (or both) of the measuring marks in a direction normal to the flight line, that is, in the y-direction. Before the assembly is set over the photographs, the mark (or marks) must be placed in the middle position of the y-movement. This setting makes the line joining the two half-marks parallel to the eye base of the stereoscope.

The assembly is now set over the photographs, and the operator rotates the assembly in a horizontal plane until stereoscopic vision is achieved. For perfect alignment, the flight line of the left-hand photograph as seen by the left eye must coincide precisely with the flight line of the right-hand photograph as seen by the right eye. When this coincidence occurs, the assembly is locked in position by the lever or knob on the drafting machine. The assembly is now ready for parallax measurements.

The parallax-bar readings for the right-hand and left-hand principal points are taken, and these readings, together with the parallaxes of the principal points previously measured, are used to determine an average value of C_D or C_B. The air base is determined either from a radial-line plot or else from parallax measurements on the two ends of a ground control line, as outlined in Sec. 8-9. Next, readings are taken on all the available vertical control points, and an average flying height is computed from these readings. Then a parallax-correction graph is prepared, as explained in Sec. 8-8.

Assume for the moment that no correction graph is required, and that the air base, the flying height, and the focal length are all known. A reading taken for a point, after the floating mark has been placed in apparent contact with the point as seen in the stereoscopic image, is added to C_D (or subtracted from C_B) to determine the parallax of the point. Then the elevation of the point may be determined by applying Eq. 8-8.

Suppose, instead, that it is desired to find the reading of the parallax bar which will cause the floating mark to come in contact with the stereo-scopic image at a certain elevation. To obtain this reading, the first step is to compute the parallax representing the given elevation by apply-ing Eq. 8–8. Thus,

$$p = \frac{Bf}{H-h}$$

Then the desired parallax-bar reading is computed by using either Eq. 8–12 or Eq. 8–14, the proper one depending on whether the graduation is direct or backward. Thus, from Eq. 8–12,

$$r = p - C_D$$

or from Eq. 8–14,

$$r = C_B - p$$

If the parallax-bar screw is turned to give the computed reading, the operator will see the floating mark lying in space at the desired elevation when he views the stereoscopic image. If he now moves the stereoscope assembly until the floating mark comes in apparent contact with the stereoscopic image of the terrain, the point of contact lies at the desired elevation. Finally, if the operator lowers the pencil to the map sheet and then moves the assembly around so as to cause the floating mark to appear in continuous contact with the stereoscopic image of the terrain, he is now tracing out a line of constant elevation, or a contour line, on the map sheet.

The procedure just outlined is that applied for plotting a continuous contour line by means of a simple stereoscopic plotting instrument, such as the stereocomparagraph or the contour finder. During the tracing process, the half-marks will separate in the y-direction if there is y-parallax because of tilts or unequal flying heights, or for any other reason. When such separation occurs, the operator must correct for the y-parallax by adjusting one of the measuring marks in the y-direction by the means provided.

Since the parallax-correction graph (assumed to be unnecessary in the preceding discussion) indicates that the two photographs contain parallax errors, a contour that is traced will be in error unless the graph is used to make corrections to the parallax-bar readings. In some areas the contour line will be too high, while in other areas it will be too low. A correction graph was used in the problem of Sec. 8–8 for correcting the readings to compute a true parallax. In plotting contours, however, the correction is made in the reverse manner. The true parallax repre-senting the elevation of a contour line is known, and a reading containing the actual errors must be obtained. Therefore, when a contour line is being traced out, the computed value of r must be continuously corrected by an amount equal to that shown on the correction graph for the area, but of opposite sign. If changing the sign of the correction is found to be inconvenient, the algebraic signs on the correction graph can simply be reversed, and the values applied directly.

EXAMPLE 8–3. A pair of overlapping photographs are taken with a lens having a 150-mm focal length. The air base is determined from a radial-line plot to be 4,246 ft, and an average value of the flying height computed from parallax measurements of six points for vertical control is 7,090 ft. The photographs are oriented for contouring by using a stereocomparagraph, and the value of C_D is determined to be 80.50 mm. Determine the values of r, for a contour interval of 40 ft, from elevation 500 ft to elevation 900 ft.

Solution: The results are shown in the accompanying tabulation.

MICROMETER READINGS FOR STEREOCOMPARAGRAPH

Elevation (ft)	$H-h$ (ft)	$p=\dfrac{Bf}{H-h}$ (mm)	$r=p-C_D$ (mm)
500	6,590	96.65	16.15
540	6,550	97.24	16.74
580	6,510	97.83	17.33
620	6,470	98.44	17.94
660	6,430	99.05	18.55
700	6,390	99.67	19.17
740	6,350	100.30	19.80
780	6,310	100.94	20.44
820	6,270	101.58	21.08
860	6,230	102.23	21.73
900	6,190	102.89	22.39

As the floating mark is moved along in apparent contact with the terrain, the value of r must be corrected each time a correction line on the correction graph is crossed. Theoretically, the result would be a zigzag line similar to that drawn to depict a stroke of lightning, but the operator will tend to smooth this line out as it is drawn.

When the contour finder is used, the computations for the various values of r representing contour settings must be arrived at in a manner different from that explained in Example 8–3. Because of the cyclic nature of the dial reading, and because of the indexing features, the dial readings for contour lines must be referred to one point in the stereoscopic image. The contour finder shown in Fig. 8–15 does not permit the complete delineation of the overlap area of 9- by 9-in. photographs taken with the normal overlap of 55 to 65 per cent. When 7- by 7-in. or 7- by 9-in. photography is used, the photographs must be so spaced that one will overlap the other by about 1½ to 2 in., because of the short base of the lens-type stereoscope. The photographs must therefore be flipped during the process of compilation. The reference point must be located near the middle of the overlap area, in order that it may be seen stereo-scopically no matter which of the two photographs lies on top. This point should be a vertical control point. If no control point can be seen in both positions of the photographs, then it is necessary to select a point which can be easily located with the floating mark and is as close to a control point as possible.

In Fig. 8–16, a pair of photographs are oriented for measuring with a contour finder. With the left-hand photograph on top, the distance between the right principal point and its position on the left-hand photo-graph is then S. Suppose that the parallax of the right principal point, determined as described in Sec. 8–6, is 72.00 mm. Also assume that the floating mark is set on the right principal point and the dial gage is indexed to zero. If the floating mark is then set on point a and a full positive sweep of the dial indicator plus an additional 0.23 mm takes place, the parallax of a is $72.00 + 1.23 = 73.23$ mm. The parallax of a should be established by going back and forth between o_2 and a several times, say 5, to obtain an average value.

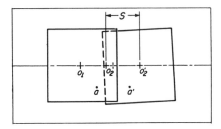 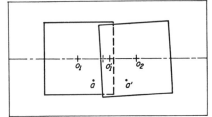

Fig. 8–16. Photographs oriented for contour-finder measurements, with left photo on top.

Fig. 8–17. Photographs oriented for contour-finder measurements, with right photo on top.

The photographs are now flipped, so that the right-hand photograph is on top, as shown in Fig. 8–17. Suppose that the parallax of the left principal point, determined as described in Sec. 8–6, is 74.50 mm; and that the floating mark is indexed on the left principal point. If the floating mark is then set on point a and a full negative sweep of the dial indicator and an additional 0.09 mm in the negative direction (dial reading = 0.91 mm) takes place, the parallax of a is $74.50 - 1.09 = 73.41$ mm. The aver-age parallax for point a, based on the readings obtained from both prin-cipal points, is 73.32 mm. The value of C_D may now be related to this one point a, which can be seen in the stereoscopic image no matter which photograph lies on top. The parallaxes of all the vertical control points can then be determined, and from them an average flying height and a parallax-correction graph can be obtained.

When dial readings are computed to represent contour settings, the dial readings are actually referred to the reading at the reference point, which is zero.

EXAMPLE 8–4. A pair of overlapping vertical photographs are oriented for contour-finder measurements. The air base is 2,300 ft; the flying height is 5,020 ft above sea level; the focal length is 150 mm; the parallax of a reference point in the middle position of the overlap area is 73.32 mm, based on an average determined from the two principal points. Compute the dial readings, for a contour interval of 40 ft, from elevation 200 ft to elevation 480 ft.

Solution: Since the dial will be set to read zero when the floating mark is on the reference point, the value of C_D is 73.32 mm. The computations for this example are shown in the accompanying tabulation.

DIAL READINGS FOR CONTOUR FINDER

Elevation (ft)	$H-h$ (ft)	$p = \dfrac{Bf}{H-h}$	$r = p - C_D$
200	4,820	71.58	−1.74
240	4,780	72.18	−1.14
280	4,740	72.78	−0.54
320	4,700	73.40	+0.08
360	4,660	74.03	+0.71
400	4,620	74.68	+1.36
440	4,580	75.33	+2.01
480	4,540	75.99	+2.67

When tracing the contour lines, the operator must correct the dial setting in accordance with the correction lines on the correction graph.

It will be noted that a contour map drawn by means of a stereocomparagraph or a contour finder is a perspective projection of the left-hand photograph, because the left measuring mark is fixed in the x-direction. When the planimetry is drawn in the perspective projection, the right measuring mark should be lifted from the surface of the photograph and out of sight of the right eye. The planimetric features on the left-hand photograph are then traced by means of the left measuring mark. This operation completes the perspective compilation of the pair of photographs. Finally, the perspective projection can be converted to an orthographic projection or map projection by means of an opaque projector, as previously explained. A radial-line plot of the photography usually serves as the map base for this conversion.

8–11. Approximation to the Parallax Equation

The elevation of a point is determined from parallax measurements by applying Eq. 8–8 and using the known quantities p, f, B, and H. The difference in elevation between two points can be obtained by measuring the parallax of each point, then applying Eq. 8–8 to get the elevation for each measured parallax, and finally subtracting one elevation from the other. The difference in elevation between two points can also be determined directly by measuring the difference in parallax between the two points. Then, if the elevation of one of the points is known, the elevation of the second point can be readily obtained.

Difference in parallax is measured by placing the floating mark of the parallax bar on one point, reading the micrometer, and then placing the floating mark on the other point and again reading the micrometer. The difference between the readings is the difference in parallax between the two points. When the contour finder is used, the dial is set to read zero at one point, and the difference in parallax is obtained directly from the second dial reading. It is necessary to take into account the number of full revolutions of the dial indicator and the direction of rotation.

In Fig. 8–18 are shown a pair of overlapping vertical photographs

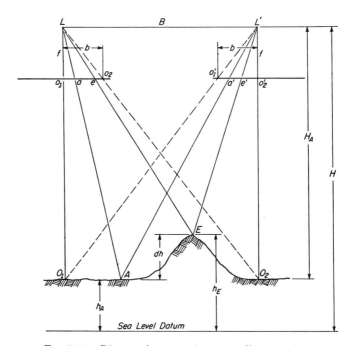

Fig. 8–18. Diagram for approximate parallax equation.

taken at L and L' with an air base B. The elevation of point A above sea level is known to be h_A ft, and it is desired to determine the elevation of point E, which lies h_E ft above sea level. The parallax of A is p_a, and that of E is p_e. By Eq. 8–8,

$$H - h_A = \frac{B}{p_A} f \quad \text{or} \quad h_A = H - \frac{B}{p_A} f$$

Also,

$$H - h_E = \frac{B}{p_E} f \quad \text{or} \quad h_E = H - \frac{B}{p_E} f$$

The difference in elevation between A and E is, therefore,

$$dh = h_E - h_A = \left(H - \frac{B}{p_E} f\right) - \left(H - \frac{B}{p_A} f\right) = \frac{B}{p_A} f - \frac{B}{p_E} f$$

or

$$dh = \frac{B f p_E - B f p_A}{p_A p_E} = \frac{B f (p_E - p_A)}{p_A p_E} \tag{8-17}$$

If the difference in parallax between points A and E is denoted by dp, then $dp = p_E - p_A$ and $p_E = p_A + dp$. Substituting in Eq. 8-17 gives:

$$dh = \frac{B f \, dp}{p_A (p_A + dp)} \tag{8-18}$$

In Fig. 8-18, let the datum pass through control point A. Then the flying height above the datum becomes H_A, and the elevation of point A becomes zero. Since both ground principal points O_1 and O_2 lie on the datum, $o_1 o_2 = o'_1 o'_2 = b$. Furthermore, since O_1, O_2, and A are all at the same elevation, their parallaxes are the same. Therefore,

$$p_A = b \tag{8-19}$$

In Fig. 8-18, triangle LO_1O_2 is similar to triangle Lo_1o_2. So

$$\frac{o_1 o_2}{O_1 O_2} = \frac{Lo_1}{LO_1} \quad \text{or} \quad \frac{b}{B} = \frac{f}{H_A}$$

from which

$$B = \frac{H_A b}{f} \tag{8-20}$$

Substituting the value of p_A from Eq. 8-19 and the value of B from Eq. 8-20 in Eq. 8-18 and clearing the equation of fractions gives

$$dh = \frac{H_A \, dp}{dp + b} \tag{8-21}$$

The student should review the derivation of Eq. 8-21 carefully, in order to have a complete understanding of the assumptions that have been made. These assumptions are: 1) The vertical control point and the two ground principal points all lie at the same elevation; 2) the flying height of the aircraft is measured above the elevation of the control point and not above sea level (unless the control point happens to lie at sea level). For these assumptions, Eq. 8-21 is exact. In the practical application of the equation, the average of the two photo bases $o_1 o_2$ and $o'_1 o'_2$ is adopted as the value of b, and the flying height above the average terrain is adopted as the value of H. The error in the computed difference in elevation between two points is governed by the closeness with which the actual conditions agree with the assumed conditions. If, upon examination of the photographs under the stereoscope, the elevation of the left principal point lies nearer to the elevation of the control point than does the elevation of the right principal point, and if the elevation of the control point lies somewhere near the average terrain elevation, then the value of b should be measured on the right-hand photograph. If the elevation of the right principal point is nearer, b should be measured on the left-hand photograph. If both principal points appear to lie somewhere near the average terrain elevation, and if the flying height is measured from the average elevation, then b is obtained by averaging o_1o_2 and $o'_1o'_2$. The error in a computed difference in elevation thus depends on the amount by which the control point lies above or below the average terrain elevation.

EXAMPLE 8–5. A pair of overlapping vertical photographs were taken with a lens having a 6-in. focal length. The average scale of the photography is 1:12,000. A control point V-21, whose elevation is 725 ft, appears in the overlap area. When the two photographs are oriented for parallax measurement, the distance o_1o_2 is measured to be 3.623 in. and the distance $o'_1o'_2$ is measured to be 3.697 in.

The following parallax-bar readings are taken on the control point and on five additional points in the overlap area: V-21, 13.44 mm; point 1, 10.52 mm; point 2, 9.82 mm; point 3, 16.22 mm; point 4, 14.00 mm; point 5, 16.01 mm. The micrometer screw reads backward. Determine the elevations of points 1 through 5.

Solution: By Eq. 3–2, the flying height above the datum (the datum being the average terrain elevation) is found as follows:

$$\frac{(6/12)\ \text{ft}}{H\ \text{ft}} = \frac{1}{12,000}$$

or $H = 6,000$ ft above the average elevation.

The photo base b, which is taken as average of the two measured distances, is $(3.623+3.697)/2=3.660$ in.$=92.96$ mm.

Since the screw is graduated backward, an increase in the micrometer reading represents a decrease in parallax. This fact must be considered when values of dp are computed. The solution of the example is shown in tabular form.

ELEVATIONS FROM DIFFERENCE IN PARALLAX MEASUREMENTS

Point	r (mm)	dp (mm)	$dp+b$ (mm)	$dh=\dfrac{H\ dp}{dp+b}$ (ft)	Elevation (ft)
V-21	13.44				725 (Known)
1	10.52	+2.92	95.88	+183	908
2	9.82	+3.62	96.58	+225	950
3	16.22	−2.78	90.18	−185	540
4	14.00	−0.56	92.40	− 36	689
5	16.01	−2.57	90.39	−171	554

Because Eq. 8–21 is applied to measured parallax differences where the situation does not generally satisfy the assumptions made in the derivation, it is quite often used in a more abbreviated form as follows:

$$dh = \frac{H\,dp}{b} \qquad (8\text{--}22)$$

The elevations of points 1 through 5 of Example 8–5, when Eq. 8–22 is applied, are 913, 959, 546, 689, and 559 ft, respectively. Thus it is seen that elevations computed by the abbreviated equation are greater than those found by Eq. 8–21.

Bibliography

AMERICAN SOCIETY OF PHOTOGRAMMETRY. *Manual of Photogrammetry* (Menasha, Wisc.: George Banta Co., 1952), Chapter 13.

———. *Manual of Photogrammetry* (Menasha, Wisc.: George Banta Co., 1966), Chapter 12.

CHURCH, E., and QUINN, A. O. *Elements of Photogrammetry*, Syracuse University Press, 1948.

DOYLE, F. J. "Photogrammetric Measurement of Spectrograms," *Photogrammetric Engineering*, Vol. XXI (1955), p. 76.

GOODALE, E. R. "The Measurement of Elevation Differences by Photogrammetry Where No Elevation Data Exists," *Photogrammetric Engineering*, Vol. XXIII (1957), p. 774.

HACKMEN, R. J. "The Isopachometer—A New Type Parallax Bar," *Photogrammetric Engineering*, Vol. XXVI (1960), p. 457.

HALLERT, B. *Photogrammetry* (New York: McGraw-Hill Book Co., 1960), Chapter 1.

JOHNSON, E. W. "The Effect of Tilt on the Measurement of Spot-Heights Using Parallax Methods," *Photogrammetric Engineering*, Vol. XXVIII (1962), p. 492.

———. "The Limit of Parallax Perception," *Photogrammetric Engineering*, Vol. XXIII (1957), p. 933.

———. "A Training Program for Men Measuring Tree Heights with Parallax Instruments," *ibid.*, Vol. XXIV (1958), p. 50.

MOESSNER, K. E. "Comparative Usefulness of Three Parallax Measuring Instruments in the Measurement and Interpretation of Forest Stands," *Photogrammetric Engineering*, Vol. XXVII (1961), p. 705.

ROBBINS, A. R. "Parallax," *Photogrammetric Engineering*, Vol. XV (1949), p. 631.

SCHUT, G. H., and VAN WIJK, M. C. "The Determination of Tree Heights from Parallax Measurements," *Canadian Surveyor*, Vol. XIX (1965), p. 415.

SCHWIDEFSKY. K. *An Outline of Photogrammetry* (New York: Pitman Publishing Corp., 1959), Chapter 5.

SINGLETON, ROBERT. "The Brock Method," *Photogrammetric Engineering*, Vol. XIV (1948), p. 538.

VISSER, J. "The Construction of the Datum-Correction Graph for Map Compilation with Stereometer-Type Instrument," *Photogrammetric Engineering*, Vol. XX (1954), p. 849.

VLCEK, J. "Vertical Control Extension with Mirror Stereoscope and Parallax Bar," *Canadian Surveyor*, Vol. XVI (1962), p. 6.

VON GRUBER. O. *Photogrammetry* (Boston: American Photographic Publishing Co., 1942), Chapter 10.

Problems

8–1. On a pair of overlapping vertical photographs taken with a lens having a 6-in. focal length, there appear the images of five points whose elevations are to be determined. The coordinates measured with respect to the flight line as the x-axis and the x'-axis are as follows:

Point	x (mm)	y (mm)	x' (mm)
a	+15.51	+90.60	−74.65
b	+89.32	+52.32	− 2.38
c	+92.21	−55.21	+ 1.55
d	+ 4.37	−58.36	−85.70
e	− 3.06	+28.90	−96.82

The air base is 5,850 ft, and the flying height is 10,950 ft above sea level. Compute the elevations of the five points.

8–2. Determine the ground distance between points B and C in Prob. 8–1.

8–3. A parallax bar, reading from 0 mm to 25 mm, is graduated so that the reading decreases as the right-hand measuring mark is brought toward the left-hand measuring mark. When the floating mark is brought in contact with the left-hand principal point of a pair of overlapping photographs, the parallax bar reads 18.15 mm. The known parallax of the left-hand principal point is 86.76 mm. Readings are now taken on three points with the following results: $r_a = 18.80$ mm, $r_b = 20.26$ mm, $r_c = 17.54$ mm. What are the values of the absolute parallaxes of a, b, and c?

8–4. The distance between two ground control points A and B is 10,950 ft. The elevation of A is 685 ft. When a pair of overlapping vertical photographs containing the images of the two control points are oriented under a stereoscope, the parallaxes of a and b found by parallax-bar measurements are $p_a = 72.21$ mm and $p_b = 74.16$ mm. The coordinates of a and b, measured on the left-hand photograph with respect to the flight line as the x-axis, are as follows: $x_a = +48.28$ mm and $y_a = +50.60$ mm, $x_b = +67.66$ mm and $y_b = −70.15$ mm. The focal length of the camera was 100.60 mm. Determine the length of the air base, the flying height, and the elevation of point B.

8–5. Five vertical control points, V-4, V-5, V-6, V-7, and V-8, appear in the area of overlap of a pair of vertical photographs. The positions of these points correspond with the positions of V-14, V-15, V-16, V-17, and V-18, respectively, in Fig. 8–11. The air base of the photographs is 5,504 ft. The parallaxes of the five control points are carefully measured, with the following results:

Point	Measured Parallax (mm)	Elevation (ft)
V-4	89.95	497
V-5	87.98	247
V-6	92.34	672
V-7	88.49	297
V-8	88.39	235

The focal length of the aerial camera is 152.10 mm. Prepare a parallax-correction graph for the overlap area, drawing each 0.05-mm correction line.

8–6. Using the average flying height determined in Prob. 8–5 as a basis, compute the uncorrected parallaxes for contour elevations 280, 320, 360, 400, 440, 480, 520, 560, 600, and 640 ft.

8-7. A stereocomparagraph is to be used to plot the contour lines of Prob. 8–6. The readings increase as the right-hand measuring mark is brought toward the left-hand measuring mark. When the floating mark is set on a point whose parallax is 91.10 mm, the reading is 6.05 mm. Compute the uncorrected readings for the parallaxes of Prob. 8–6.

8-8. The distances $b_1 = 70.55$ mm and $b_2 = 71.90$ mm are scaled between the principal point and transferred principal point of each of a pair of overlapping vertical aerial photographs. The distance between the same two principal points on a radial-line plot, which is at a scale of 1:15840, measures 60.80 mm. The focal length of the photography is 101.64 mm. The two photographs are oriented under a contour finder, and the measuring mark is indexed on a control point V, whose elevation is 1.255 ft. The following dial readings are taken on point V and on seven additional points:

Point	Dial Reading (mm)	Point	Dial Reading (mm)
V	0.00	4	−0.02
1	−3.15	5	+2.60
2	−2.00	6	+0.40
3	+3.68	7	+3.40

Compute the approximate elevations of the points by Eq. 8–21 and by Eq. 8–22.

8-9. If the parallax of point 6 in Prob. 8–8 is known to be 73.70 mm, what are the exact elevations of the six points?

8-10. For the photographic coordinates and the focal length of Prob. 8–1, the air base is 1,825 ft and the flying height is 3,530 ft above sea level. Compute the elevations of the five points.

8-11. Compute the ground distance of the line AC in Prob. 8–10.

8-12. Construct a parallax wedge at 4x scale in which the average spacing of conjugate points under the stereoscope is 60 mm, and in which the range of parallax difference is to be 10 mm. The finished length of the legs is to be 6¼ in.

8-13. The difference in parallax between a point lying at sea level and another point on a hill is measured and found to be 2.60 mm. The flying height is 6,850 ft above sea level, the air base is 2,940 ft, and the focal length of the camera lens is 209.50 mm. Determine the elevation of the point on the hill.

8-14. A parallax difference of 0.60 mm is measured between the image of the top of a water tank and the image of a point near the base of the tank. The nominal flying height is 16,000 ft above the ground. The average of the distances between the principal points and the transferred principal points, measured on the photographs is 77.6 mm. What is the approximate height of the tank?

8-15. Readings made with a contour finder on four points appearing in the overlap area of a pair of vertical photographs were as follows:

Point	Dial Reading (mm)
a	0.00
b	+0.90
c	+1.25
d	−2.05

The elevation of A is 965 ft, and the parallax of a is 70.40 mm. The camera focal length is 153.08 mm. The scale of the photographs at the elevation of A is 1:14,000. Compute the flying height above sea level for the photographs.

8–16. Compute the air base of the photographs of Prob. 8–15.

8–17. Compute the elevations of points B, C, and D of Prob. 8–15.

Determination of the Orientation of a Photograph 9

9–1. Factors Affecting Accuracy

The tilts existing in aerial photographs at the times of exposure have an effect on the accuracy of the results of photogrammetric processes which have been discussed thus far. The ground coordinates computed from photographic coordinate measurements will not be exact if it is assumed that no tilt exists. The relief displacement of a point on a photograph computed by Eq. 3–7 will not be correct if the photograph is tilted, because on a tilted photograph the relief displacement radiates from the nadir point, and not the principal point, and because the relief displacement takes place in a tilted plane.

Tilted photographs introduce errors in the map positions of pass points which have been located by radial-line plotting. Furthermore, planimetric features which have been plotted from aerial photographs by the principle of intersection will be in error because of tilts existing in the photographs.

All processes involving parallax measurements on a pair of overlapping photographs are subject to the effects of tilt, because the parallax equations have been developed under the assumption that the photographs are vertical. Consequently, elevations and contour lines determined by the parallax-bar measurements are subject to errors, some of considerable size.

The construction of a controlled or uncontrolled mosaic, to be discussed in Chapter 11, is affected by tilted photographs. The displacements of points due to tilt, together with relief displacements, cause mismatches of the images of points on successive photographs when the individual photographs are assembled into one composite picture.

In the practical applications of photogrammetry to the determination of ground coordinates and elevations, to the construction of mosaics, and to the compilation of planimetric and topographic maps, the effects of tilt may be tolerated to a certain extent. Where these effects would render the resultant product virtually useless, they must be compensated for to an extent that is consistent with the accuracy desired. Any compensation for tilt in photographs is based on adequate ground control, including both horizontal and vertical control.

The accuracy of the map positions of ray centers and pass points resulting from a radial-line plot depends on the density and placement of horizontal photo control points. Regardless of tilt in photographs, pass points lying near the control points will be highly dependable, unless mistakes or blunders have been committed in constructing the plot.

The reliability of elevations and contour lines obtained by simple parallax-bar measurements depends on the accuracy of the correction graph. In turn, the accuracy of the correction graph depends on the density and placement of vertical photo control points in the overlap area. In precise mapping methods based on parallax measurements, where the amount of vertical control necessary to maintain the desired accuracy would be far too costly, the photographs are rectified (see Chapter 10) to eliminate the tilts and at the same time to equalize the scales. The determination of the amount and direction of the tilt in each photograph, however, depends on adequate ground control.

The majority of topographic maps are compiled in precise stereoscopic plotting instruments, wherein each photograph of an overlapping pair can be rotated about three mutually perpendicular axes in order to recover the elements of exterior orientation of each photograph which existed at the time of exposure. The absolute amount and direction of each rotation is established by ground control. Tilts are thus determined instrumentally in these plotters. For accurate extension of horizontal control by means of two-dimensional triangulation, as in radial-line plotting, each individual templet is constructed from a rectified stereoscopic image of the photograph formed by a stereoscopic plotting instrument. These templets are known as stereo-templets. Thus the errors introduced into a radial-line plot because of tilted photographs are eliminated by the stereo-templet triangulation.

Many methods have been devised to determine the exterior orientation of an aerial photograph. Each method depends on adequate control—in general, ground control. Almost every method is based on successive approximations. That is, small corrections are applied to each preceding approximate value, until the corrections become small enough to have no effect on the solution. The methods can be instrumental, analytical, or graphical, or combinations of these methods can be used. The stereoscopic plotting instrument solves for the tilts of the photographs by a process of orientation of the photographs, first relative to each other and then relative to the ground control. This orientation is accomplished by trial and error, supplemented to a certain extent by computations. Tilts can be determined instrumentally in the rectification process by a trial-and-error solution, which may sometimes include a certain amount of graphics.

In this chapter, two methods for the determination of the tilt and swing of a single aerial photograph are presented. Both methods can be easily grasped by the beginning student of photogrammetry, and being familiar with them will add to his understanding of the principles of photogrammetry. The ground-control requirements are identical for both methods. The first method to be discussed is entirely analytical and is based on one of many analytical methods developed by the late Professor Earl Church for determining the scale data of a photograph. The second method, developed originally by the late Ralph O. Anderson, is semi-analytical and semigraphical in nature. This latter method is known as the *scale-point method*.

9–2. Analytical Determination of Tilt, Swing, and Flying Height

The tilt, swing, and azimuth of a photograph, together with the space coordinates of the exposure station (X_L, Y_L, Z_L), may be determined if the photograph contains well-defined images of three ground control points whose horizontal positions and elevations are known. These control points must not lie in a straight line, but rather should form the vertexes of a strong triangle. The tilt, swing, and flying height of a photograph may be determined if the images of the ends of three ground control lines whose lengths are known appear on the photograph, provided that the elevations of the end points of each line are also known. Three control points whose horizontal positions and elevations are known will satisfy this condition.

The solution for tilt and swing to be presented here is based on the fact that the ratio of two ground lengths computed by the equations involving ground coordinates from measurements on a tilted photograph (Sec. 3–9) must be the same as the ratio of the corresponding known ground lengths. Three control lines will form two independent ratios, and since the two ratios formed by the lengths as determined from photographic measurements must be equal to the corresponding two ratios as determined from the known ground lengths, the solution to the problem will allow two unknown quantities to be determined. These unknown quantities are the two components of tilt, one about the photographic y-axis, called t_y, and the other about the photographic x-axis, called t_x.

The solution is carried out by determining the rate of change of the two ratios per minute of t_y and t_x. When this rate of change has been established for each component, the unknown components may then be determined by the two conditions of equal ratios. The swing of the photograph can then be computed from the tilt components.

In Fig. 9–1, the images of ground control points A, B, and C appear at a, b, and c, respectively. The photographic coordinates of the three images are measured with respect to the lines joining opposite fiducial marks, giving (x_a, y_a), (x_b, y_b), and (x_c, y_c). These values are assumed

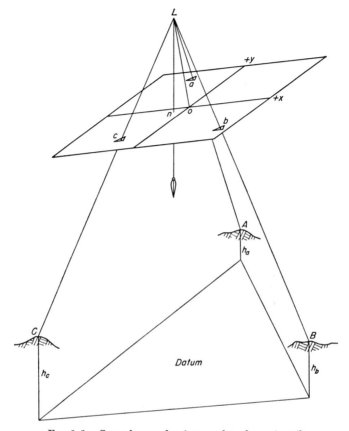

Fɪɢ. 9–1. Ground control points used to determine tilt.

to have been corrected for film shrinkage, for lens distortions based on the camera calibration data, and for other systematic errors. An approximate flying height is determined as outlined in Sec. 3–6 or Sec. 3–10 by scaling a distance such as bc and comparing it with the known ground length BC, the elevations of the ends of the line being taken into account.

Three sets of ground coordinates will now be computed by using the measured photographic coordinates and the approximate flying height. The computations for the first set of ground coordinates are based on the assumption that the photograph is truly vertical. Thus, by Eqs. 3–5 and 3–6,

$$X_A = \frac{H - h_A}{f} x_a \quad \text{and} \quad Y_A = \frac{H - h_A}{f} y_a$$

$$X_B = \frac{H - h_B}{f} x_b \quad \text{and} \quad Y_B = \frac{H - h_B}{f} y_b$$

$$X_C = \frac{H - h_C}{f} x_c \quad \text{and} \quad Y_C = \frac{H - h_C}{f} y_c$$

The second set of ground coordinates, denoted by primes, is computed after the introduction of a tilt of an arbitrary amount about the y-axis of the photograph. The amount of induced tilt is taken as 100 minutes. As shown in Fig. 9–2(a), the swing is 90°, the $+y'$-axis coincides with the $-x$-axis, and the $+x'$-axis is parallel to the $+y$-axis. By Eq. 3–9,

$$\theta = 180° - 90° = 90°$$

$$\sin \theta = +1$$

$$\cos \theta = 0$$

By Eqs. 3–10 and 3–11,

$$x'_a = y_a \qquad y'_a = -x_a + f \tan 100'$$
$$x'_b = y_b \qquad y'_b = -x_b + f \tan 100'$$
$$x'_c = y_c \qquad y'_c = -x_c + f \tan 100'$$

By Eqs. 3–13 and 3–14,

$$X'_A = \frac{H - h_A}{f \sec 100' - y'_a \sin 100'} x'_a$$

$$Y'_A = \frac{H - h_A}{f \sec 100' - y'_a \sin 100'} y'_a \cos 100'$$

Expressions for X'_B, Y'_B, X'_C, and Y'_C are obtained in a similar way.

The third set of ground coordinates, denoted by double primes, is computed after the introduction of 100 minutes of tilt about the x-axis of the photograph. As shown in Fig. 9–2(b), the swing is 0°, the $+y'$-axis coincides with the $-y$-axis, and the $+x'$-axis is parallel to the $-x$-axis.

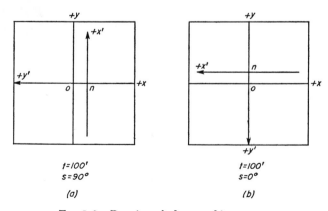

FIG. 9–2. Rotation of photographic axes.

By Eq. 3–9,

$$\theta = 180° - 0° = 180°$$
$$\sin \theta = 0$$
$$\cos \theta = -1$$

By Eqs. 3–10 and 3–11,

$$x'_a = -x_a \qquad y'_a = -y_a + f \tan 100'$$
$$x'_b = -x_b \qquad y'_b = -y_b + f \tan 100'$$
$$x'_c = -x_c \qquad y'_c = -y_c + f \tan 100'$$

By Eqs. 3–13 and 3–14,

$$X''_A = \frac{H - h_A}{f \sec 100' - y' \sin 100'} x'_a$$

$$Y''_A = \frac{H - h_A}{f \sec 100' - y' \sin 100'} y'_a \cos 100'$$

Expressions for X''_B, Y''_B, X''_C, and Y''_C are obtained in a similar manner.

Three sets of ground lengths are computed from the three sets of ground coordinates by the distance formula. For the set based on a vertical photograph,

$$AB = \sqrt{(X_B - X_A)^2 + (Y_B - Y_A)^2}$$

$$AC = \sqrt{(X_C - X_A)^2 + (Y_C - Y_A)^2}$$

$$BC = \sqrt{(X_C - X_B)^2 + (Y_C - Y_B)^2}$$

The set $A'B'$, $A'C'$, and $B'C'$ and the set $A''B''$, $A''C''$, and $B''C''$ are similarly computed for the assumptions that $t_y = 100'$ and $t_x = 100'$.

Let the ratio between the actual ground lengths $A_G B_G$ and $A_G C_G$ equal R_G, and let the ratio between the actual ground lengths $A_G B_G$ and $B_G C_G$ equal S_G. That is,

$$R_G = \frac{A_G B_G}{A_G C_G} \qquad \text{and} \qquad S_G = \frac{A_G B_G}{B_G C_G} \tag{9-1}$$

Let R_V and S_V denote the ratios between the same lines, as determined from photographic measurements under the assumption that the photograph is vertical. Thus,

$$R_V = \frac{AB}{AC} \qquad \text{and} \qquad S_V = \frac{AB}{BC} \tag{9-2}$$

If $R_V = R_G$ and $S_V = S_G$, provided that the approximate value of the flying height is not in error by more than 1 or 2 per cent, then the photograph must be vertical. Note that an erroneous flying height has little or no effect on the ratios, because if one line in a ratio is too long, the other line in the same ratio will also be too long almost proportionately. If $R_V = R_G$ but $S_V \neq S_G$, then the photograph must be tilted. Also, if $R_V \neq R_G$, but $S_V = S_G$, or if $R_V \neq R_G$ and $S_V \neq S_G$, the photograph must be tilted.

Let R' and S' denote the ratios between the lines previously considered, as determined from photographic measurements for an assumed tilt of 100 minutes about the y-axis. Then,

$$R' = \frac{A'B'}{A'C'} \quad \text{and} \quad S' = \frac{A'B'}{B'C'} \tag{9-3}$$

Let the unknown tilt about the y-axis be designated as t_y. The total change in the ratio R_V due to 100' of t_y is $R' - R_V$, and the rate of change in the ratio per minute of t_y is $(R' - R_V)/100$. The *actual* change in the ratio R_V due to an unknown amount of tilt about the y-axis is therefore $t_y (R' - R_V)/100$. Similarly, the actual change in the ratio S_V due to an unknown amount of tilt about the y-axis is $t_y (S' - S_V)/100$.

Let R'' and S'' denote the ratios between the lines, as determined from photographic measurements for an assumed tilt of 100 minutes about the x-axis. Thus,

$$R'' = \frac{A''B''}{A''C''} \quad \text{and} \quad S'' = \frac{A''B''}{B''C''} \tag{9-4}$$

Let the unknown tilt about the x-axis be t_x. The total change in the ratio R_V due to 100' of t_x is $R'' - R_V$, and the rate of change in the ratio per minute of t_x is $(R'' - R_V)/100$. The *actual* change in the ratio R_V due to an unknown amount of tilt about the x-axis is therefore $t_x (R'' - R_V)/100$. Similarly, the actual change in the ratio S_V is $t_x (S'' - S_V)/100$.

The ratios R_G and S_G are the true ratios between the ground lengths. These ratios would be obtained by adding the changes in ratios due to the correct amounts of tilt about the y-axis and the x-axis to the ratios obtained when the photograph is assumed to be vertical. Two condition equations are as follows:

$$R_V + \frac{R' - R_V}{100} t_y + \frac{R'' - R_V}{100} t_z = R_G \tag{9-5}$$

$$S_V + \frac{S' - S_V}{100} t_y + \frac{S'' - S_V}{100} t_z = S_G \tag{9-6}$$

in which t_y and t_x are the unknown components of the tilt of the photograph expressed in minutes. Eqs. 9–5 and 9–6 are now solved simultaneously for t_y and t_x.

The resultant tilt of the photograph is given by the relationship

$$t = \sqrt{t_y^2 + t_z^2} \tag{9-7}$$

Also, the swing of the photograph is given by the relationship

$$\tan s = \frac{t_y}{t_x} \tag{9-8}$$

Due regard must be given to the algebraic signs of t_y and t_x.

The values of the tilt and swing may now be verified by using the computed tilt and swing in Eqs. 3–9, 3–10, 3–11, 3–13, and 3–14, and then determining the lengths of the lines from the computed ground coordinates. These lengths will now form new ratios, R and S, which will be equal to R_G and S_G, respectively, if the computed tilt and swing are correct. If the two sets of ratios differ, corrections must be made to the computed values of t_y and t_x. These corrections, denoted by Δt_y and Δt_x are obtained by forming a second set of condition equations in which the rates of change of ratios previously determined are again used. The results are

$$R + \frac{R' - R_V}{100} \Delta t_y + \frac{R'' - R_V}{100} \Delta t_x = R_G \tag{9-9}$$

$$S + \frac{S' - S_V}{100} \Delta t_y + \frac{S'' - S_V}{100} \Delta t_x = S_G \tag{9-10}$$

The rates of change, which are the coefficients of the unknowns in the condition equations, will be slightly in error because the change in ratio is not directly proportional to a change in tilt. However, the error which is introduced by using the original coefficients is very small, especially if tilts are less than $4°$.

Second values for t_y and t_x are obtained by solving Eqs. 9–9 and 9–10 and adding the values of Δt_y and Δt_x to the previously computed values of t_y and t_x. A new tilt is then computed by Eq. 9–7, and a new swing is computed by Eq. 9–8. These values may be verified in the manner previously described, to obtain still new values for t_y and t_x, but there is not much gain in accuracy after the second solution.

By using the values of the tilt and swing obtained from Eqs. 9–7 and 9–8, the true flying height can now be obtained as outlined in Sec. 3–10. This calculation completes the determination of the scale data for the photograph.

EXAMPLE 9–1. A photograph containing the images of three ground control points, A, B, and C, is taken with a lens having a 150-mm focal length. The ground lengths of the three lines are $AB = 15,811$ ft; $AC = 21,213$ ft; $BC = 20,000$ ft. The elevations are $h_A = 3,500$ ft; $h_B = 1,000$ ft; $h_C = 250$ ft. The photographic coordinates, in millimeters, as measured and corrected for shrinkage and lens distortion, are as follows: $x_a = -51.93$ and $y_a = +49.98$; $x_b = -84.40$ and $y_b = -73.42$; $x_c = +65.61$ and $y_c = -67.51$. A preliminary determination gives an approximate flying height of 20,500 ft. Determine the tilt, swing, and flying height of the photograph.

Solution: Based on the assumption that the photograph is vertical, the ground coordinates of the three points, by Eqs. 3–5 and 3–6, are as follows:

$$X_A = \frac{20{,}500 - 3{,}500}{150} \times (-51.93) = -5{,}885 \text{ ft}$$

$$Y_A = \frac{20{,}500 - 3{,}500}{150} \times (+49.98) = +5{,}664 \text{ ft}$$

$$X_B = \frac{20{,}500 - 1{,}000}{150} \times (-84.40) = -10{,}972 \text{ ft}$$

$$Y_B = \frac{20{,}500 - 1{,}000}{150} \times (-73.42) = -9{,}545 \text{ ft}$$

$$X_C = \frac{20{,}500 - 250}{150} \times (+65.61) = +8{,}857 \text{ ft}$$

$$Y_C = \frac{20{,}500 - 250}{150} \times (-67.51) = -9{,}114 \text{ ft}$$

For an assumed tilt of 100 minutes about the y-axis, the transformed photographic coordinates of the three points are obtained from Eqs. 3–9, 3–10, and 3–11. By Eq. 3–9, $\theta = 90°$. Values needed in Eqs. 3–10 and 3–11 follow:

$\sin \theta = +1$	$t = 1°40'$	$f \tan 1° \, 40' = 4.37 \text{ mm}$
$\cos \theta = 0$	$\sin t = 0.02908$	$f \sec 1° \, 40' = 150.06 \text{ mm}$
	$\cos t = 0.99958$	
	$\tan t = 0.02910$	
	$\sec t = 1.00042$	

By Eqs. 3–10 and 3–11,

$$x'_a = +49.98 \text{ mm} \qquad y'_a = +51.93 + 4.37 = +56.30 \text{ mm}$$

$$x'_b = -73.52 \text{ mm} \qquad y'_b = +84.40 + 4.37 = +88.77 \text{ mm}$$

$$x'_c = -67.51 \text{ mm} \qquad y'_c = -65.61 + 4.37 = -61.24 \text{ mm}$$

For an assumed tilt of 100 minutes about the y-axis, the ground coordinates of the three points are obtained by Eqs. 3–13 and 3–14 as follows:

$$X'_A = \frac{20{,}500 - 3{,}500}{150.06 - (56.30)(0.02908)} \times (+49.98) = +5{,}725 \text{ ft}$$

$$Y'_A = \frac{20{,}500 - 3{,}500}{150.06 - (56.30)(0.02908)} \times (+56.30)(0.99958) = +6{,}446 \text{ ft}$$

$$X'_B = \frac{20{,}500 - 1{,}000}{150.06 - (88.77)(0.02908)} \times (-73.42) = -9{,}708 \text{ ft}$$

$$Y'_B = \frac{20{,}500 - 1{,}000}{150.06 - (88.77)(0.02908)} \times (+88.77)(0.99958) = +11{,}732 \text{ ft}$$

$$X'_C = \frac{20{,}500 - 250}{150.06 - (-61.24)(0.02908)} \times (-67.51) = -9{,}003 \text{ ft}$$

$$Y'_C = \frac{20{,}500 - 250}{150.06 - (-61.24)(0.02908)} \times (-61.24)(0.99958) = -8{,}163 \text{ ft}$$

For an assumed tilt of 100 minutes about the x-axis, the transformed photographic coordinates of the three points are obtained from Eqs. 3–9, 3–10, and 3–11. By Eq. 3–9, $\theta = 180°$. So $\sin \theta = 0$ and $\cos \theta = -1$.

By Eqs. 3–10 and 3–11,

$$x'_a = +51.93 \text{ mm} \qquad y'_a = -49.98 + 4.37 = -45.61 \text{ mm}$$
$$x'_b = +84.40 \text{ mm} \qquad y'_b = +73.42 + 4.37 = +77.79 \text{ mm}$$
$$x'_c = -65.61 \text{ mm} \qquad y'_c = +67.51 + 4.37 = +71.88 \text{ mm}$$

For an assumed tilt of 100 minutes about the x-axis, the ground coordinates of the three points are obtained by Eqs. 3–13 and 3–14 as follows:

$$X''_A = \frac{20,500 - 3,500}{150.06 - (-45.61)(0.02908)} \times (+51.93) = +5,831 \text{ ft}$$

$$Y''_A = \frac{20,500 - 3,500}{150.06 - (-45.61)(0.02908)} \times (-45.61)(0.99958) = -5,119 \text{ ft}$$

$$X''_B = \frac{20,500 - 1,000}{150.06 - (77.79)(0.02908)} \times (+84.40) = +11,135 \text{ ft}$$

$$Y''_B = \frac{20,500 - 1,000}{150.06 - (77.79)(0.02908)} \times (+77.79)(0.99958) = +10,259 \text{ ft}$$

$$X''_C = \frac{20,500 - 250}{150.06 - (71.88)(0.02908)} \times (-65.61) = -8,979 \text{ ft}$$

$$Y''_C = \frac{20,500 - 250}{150.06 - (71.88)(0.02908)} \times (+71.88)(0.99958) = +9,833 \text{ ft}$$

The lengths of the three sets of ground lines based on the three assumptions are computed from the three sets of ground coordinates by means of the distance formula as follows:

$$AB = \sqrt{5,087^2 + 15,209^2} = 16,037 \text{ ft}$$

$$AC = \sqrt{14,742^2 + 14,778^2} = 20,874 \text{ ft}$$

$$BC = \sqrt{19,829^2 + 431^2} = 19,834 \text{ ft}$$

$$A'B' = \sqrt{15,433^2 + 5,286^2} = 16,313 \text{ ft}$$

$$A'C' = \sqrt{14,728^2 + 14,609^2} = 20,745 \text{ ft}$$

$$B'C' = \sqrt{705^2 + 19,895^2} = 19,907 \text{ ft}$$

$$A''B'' = \sqrt{5,304^2 + 15,378^2} = 16,267 \text{ ft}$$

$$A''C'' = \sqrt{14,810^2 + 14,952^2} = 21,045 \text{ ft}$$

$$B''C'' = \sqrt{20,114^2 + 426^2} = 20,119 \text{ ft}$$

Based on the true ground distances and those computed under the three assumptions, four sets of ratios between the ground lengths are formed in accordance with Eqs. 9–1, 9–2, 9–3, and 9–4. These sets are as follows:

$$R_G = \frac{15,811}{21,213} = 0.745\ 345 \qquad \text{and} \qquad S_G = \frac{15,811}{20,000} = 0.790\ 550$$

$$R_V = \frac{16,037}{20,874} = 0.768\ 276 \qquad \text{and} \qquad S_V = \frac{16,037}{19,834} = 0.808\ 561$$

$$R' = \frac{16,313}{20,745} = 0.786\ 358 \qquad \text{and} \qquad S' = \frac{16,313}{19,907} = 0.819\ 460$$

$$R'' = \frac{16,267}{21,045} = 0.772\ 963 \qquad \text{and} \qquad S'' = \frac{16,267}{20,119} = 0.808\ 539$$

Two linear equations are formed from these ratios in accordance with Eqs. 9–5 and 9–6, as follows:

$$0.768\ 276 + \frac{(0.786\ 358 - 0.768\ 276)}{100}t_y + \frac{(0.772\ 963 - 0.768\ 276)}{100}t_x = 0.745\ 345$$

$$0.808\ 561 + \frac{(0.819\ 460 - 0.808\ 561)}{100}t_y + \frac{(0.808\ 539 - 0.808\ 561)}{100}t_x = 0.790\ 550$$

Reducing and multiplying through by 10^8 gives the following results:

$$18{,}082\ t_y + 4{,}687\ t_x = -2{,}293{,}100$$

$$10{,}899\ t_y - 22\ t_x = -1{,}801{,}100$$

From these equations, $t_y = -165.0'$, and $t_x = +147.1'$.

By Eq. 9–7,

$$t = \sqrt{165.0^2 + 147.1^2} = 221' = 3°41'$$

By Eq. 9–8,

$$\tan s = \frac{-165.0}{+147.1} = -1.12169 \ (\text{4th quadrant})$$

So,

$$s = 311°\ 43'$$

The values of the tilt and swing just computed are used to obtain a new set of ground coordinates for points *A, B,* and *C,* and the lengths and ratios are computed again. If the computed tilt and swing are correct, the ratios formed by these lengths will be identical with the fixed ratios formed by the known ground lengths. If these ratios differ from the fixed ratios, another solution of the two simultaneous equations is required.

By Eq. 3–9, $\theta = 180° - 311°43' = -131°\ 43'$. Then,

$$\sin \theta = -0.74644$$
$$\cos \theta = -0.66545$$

$$\begin{array}{ll} \sin\ t = 0.06424 & f \tan 3°\ 41' = 9.66\ \text{mm} \\ \cos\ t = 0.99793 & f \sec 3°\ 41' = 150.31\ \text{mm} \\ \tan\ t = 0.06438 & \\ \sec\ t = 1.00207 & \end{array}$$

By Eqs. 3–10 and 3–11,

$$x'_a = (-51.93)(-0.66545) + (49.98)(-0.74644) = -2.75\ \text{mm}$$
$$y'_a = -(-51.93)(-0.74644) + (49.98)(-0.66545) + 9.66 = -62.36\ \text{mm}$$
$$x'_b = (-84.40)(-0.66545) + (-73.42)(-0.74644) = +110.96\ \text{mm}$$
$$y'_b = -(-84.40)(-0.74644) + (-73.42)(-0.66545) + 9.66 = -4.48\ \text{mm}$$
$$x'_c = (+65.61)(-0.66545) + (-67.51)(-0.74644) = +6.73\ \text{mm}$$
$$y'_c = -(+65.61)(-0.74644) + (-67.51)(-0.66545) + 9.66 = +103.55\ \text{mm}$$

By Eqs. 3–13 and 3–14,

$$X_A = \frac{20{,}500 - 3{,}500}{150.31 - (-62.36)(0.06424)} \times (-2.75) = -303\ \text{ft}$$

$$Y_A = \frac{20{,}500 - 3{,}500}{150.31 - (-62.36)(0.06424)} \times (-62.36)(0.99793) = -6{,}855\ \text{ft}$$

$$X_B = \frac{20{,}500 - 1{,}000}{150.31 - (-4.48)(0.06424)} \times (+110.96) = +14{,}367\ \text{ft}$$

$$Y_B = \frac{20{,}500 - 1{,}000}{150.31 - (-4.48)(0.06424)} \times (-4.48)(0.99793) = -579\ \text{ft}$$

$$X_C = \frac{20,500 - 250}{150.31 - (+103.55)(0.06424)} \times (+6.73) = +949 \text{ ft}$$

$$Y_C = \frac{20,500 - 250}{150.31 - (+103.55)(0.06424)} \times (+103.55)(0.99793) = +14,567 \text{ ft}$$

By the distance formula,

$$AB = \sqrt{14,670^2 + 6,276^2} = 15,956 \text{ ft}$$

$$AC = \sqrt{1,252^2 + 21,422^2} = 21,459 \text{ ft}$$

$$BC = \sqrt{13,418^2 + 15,146^2} = 20,235 \text{ ft}$$

Two ratios are now formed based on $t=3°\,41'$ and $s=311°\,43'$, as follows:

$$R = \frac{15,956}{21,459} = 0.743\,557 \quad \text{and} \quad S = \frac{15,956}{20,235} = 0.788\,535$$

Two linear equations are formed according to Eqs. 9–9 and 9–10 by using these new ratios and the fixed ratios R_G and S_G. It is not necessary to change the previously computed coefficients of t_y and t_x because they represent the rates of change in the ratios per minute of t_y and t_x with sufficient accuracy. The resulting equations are

$$18,082\,\Delta t_y + 4,687\,\Delta t_x = +178,800$$
$$10,899\,\Delta t_y - \quad 22\,\Delta t_x = +201,500$$

Solving these equations for Δt_y and Δt_x gives the amounts to be added to the first values of t_y and t_x. The solution of the equations give $\Delta t_y = +18.4'$, and $\Delta t_x = -32.9'$.

The corrected t_y is $-165.0 + 18.4 = -146.6'$.

The corrected t_x is $+147.1 - 32.9 = +114.2'$.

By Eq. 9–7,

$$t = \sqrt{146.6^2 + 114.2^2} = 185.8' = 3°\,06'$$

By Eq. 9–8,

$$\tan s = \frac{-146.6}{+114.2} = -1.28371 \quad (\text{4th quadrant})$$

Hence,

$$s = 307°\,55'$$

By using these values of the tilt and swing of the photograph, the flying height is now determined by the method outlined in Sec. 3–10. The first step is to select a control line whose end points lie closest in elevation to one another. In the example, this is line BC.

By Eq. 3–9, $\theta = 180° - 307°\,55' = -127°\,55'$. Also,

$\sin \theta = -0.78891$	$\sin t = 0.05408$	$f \tan t = 8.12 \text{ mm}$
$\cos \theta = -0.61451$	$\cos t = 0.99854$	$f \sec t = 150.22 \text{ mm}$
	$\tan t = 0.05416$	
	$\sec t = 1.00146$	

By Eqs. 3–10 and 3–11,

$$x'_b = (-84.40)(-0.61451) + (-73.42)(-0.78891) = +109.78 \text{ mm}$$
$$y'_b = -(-84.40)(-0.78891) + (-73.42)(-0.61451) + 8.12 = -13.34 \text{ mm}$$
$$x'_c = (+65.61)(-0.61451) + (-67.51)(-0.78891) = +12.94 \text{ mm}$$
$$y'_c = -(+65.61)(-0.78891) + (-67.51)(-0.61451) + 8.12 = +101.37 \text{ mm}$$

By Eqs. 3–13 and 3–14,

$$X_B = \frac{20,500 - 1,000}{150.22 - (-13.34)(0.05408)} \times (+109.78) = +14,183 \text{ ft}$$

$$Y_B = \frac{20,500 - 1,000}{150.22 - (-13.34)(0.05408)} \times (-13.34)(0.99854) = -1,721 \text{ ft}$$

$$X_C = \frac{20,500 - 250}{150.22 - (101.37)(0.05408)} \times (+12.94) = +1,810 \text{ ft}$$

$$Y_C = \frac{20,500 - 250}{150.22 - (101.37)(0.05408)} \times (+101.37)(0.99854) = +14,161 \text{ ft}$$

By the distance formula,

$$BC = \sqrt{12,373^2 + 15,882^2} = 20,133 \text{ ft}$$

This distance is based on a flying height of 20,500 ft. A better height is obtained by the following ratio:

$$\frac{H - (1,000 + 250)/2}{20,500 - (1,000 + 250)/2} = \frac{20,000}{20,133}$$

Then $H = 20,369$ ft.

This value is verified by recomputing new ground coordinates and a new distance, and then comparing with the known ground distance, as follows:

$$X_B = \frac{20,369 - 1,000}{150.22 - (-13.34)(0.05408)} \times (+109.78) = +14,087 \text{ ft}$$

$$Y_B = \frac{20,369 - 1,000}{150.22 - (-13.34)(0.05408)} \times (-13.34)(0.99854) = -1,709 \text{ ft}$$

$$X_C = \frac{20,369 - 250}{150.22 - (101.37)(0.05408)} \times (+12.94) = +1,799 \text{ ft}$$

$$Y_C = \frac{20,369 - 250}{150.22 - (101.37)(0.05408)} \times (+101.37)(0.99854) = +14,070 \text{ ft}$$

$$BC = \sqrt{12,288^2 + 15,779^2} = 19,999 \text{ ft}$$

A second solution for the flying height based on the last computed distance gives $H = 20,370$ ft.

The analytical solution for the scale data of a photograph discussed here requires from three to five hours of computation on an ordinary desk computer. The example given has been laid out in detail so that the student may easily follow the solution. In an actual solution, most of the figures recorded in the example would be carried by the desk computer, reducing the amount of recording time needed. Furthermore, a tabular arrangement of the computations will allow common multipliers to be used in the computer. The same type of problem may be solved in a high-speed electronic digital computer in about thirty seconds. If data for several photographs are to be computed, the use of such a computer is practical.

Referring back to the three different orientations of the photograph used to compute the rates of change of ground length ratios, under the first condition, that of a vertical photograph, the orientation matrix is given by Eq. 3–78 as

$$\mathbf{M}^T{}_V = \begin{bmatrix} 1 & 0 & 0 \\ 0 & 1 & 0 \\ 0 & 0 & 1 \end{bmatrix}$$

Under the second condition, that of 100 minutes of tilt about the y-axis, $t = 1° \ 40'$, $s = 90°$, and since we are interested in ground lengths only, the azimuth of the principal plane can be given any value. Let α_{NO} be $0°$. Then the orientation matrix becomes, by Eqs. 3–43 and 3–44

$$\underset{(t_y = 100')}{\mathbf{M}^T =} \begin{bmatrix} 0 & 1 & 0 \\ -0.99958 & 0 & -0.02908 \\ -0.02908 & 0 & +0.99958 \end{bmatrix}$$

Under the third condition, that of 100 minutes of tilt about the x-axis, $t = 1° \ 40'$, $s = 0°$, and α_{NO} can be taken as $0°$. The orientation matrix under this condition becomes

$$\underset{(t_x = 100')}{\mathbf{M}^T =} \begin{bmatrix} -1 & 0 & 0 \\ 0 & -0.99958 & -0.02908 \\ 0 & -0.02908 & +0.99958 \end{bmatrix}$$

The solution given in Example 9–1 is then as follows:

By Eqs. 3–60, 3–61, and 3–62,

$$\cos maL = -x_a/aL \qquad \cos mbL = -x_b/bL \qquad \cos mcL = -x_c/cL$$
$$\cos naL = -y_a/aL \qquad \cos nbL = -y_b/bL \qquad \cos ncL = -y_c/cL$$
$$\cos kaL = +f/aL \qquad \cos kbL = +f/bL \qquad \cos kcL = +f/cL$$

Then, by Eq. 3–68, for each condition, a set of direction cosines for each line can be computed thus,

$$\begin{bmatrix} \cos MAL \\ \cos NAL \\ \cos KAL \end{bmatrix} = \mathbf{M}^T \begin{bmatrix} \cos maL \\ \cos naL \\ \cos kaL \end{bmatrix}$$

$$\begin{bmatrix} \cos MBL \\ \cos NBL \\ \cos KBL \end{bmatrix} = \mathbf{M}^T \begin{bmatrix} \cos mbL \\ \cos nbL \\ \cos kbL \end{bmatrix}$$

$$\begin{bmatrix} \cos MCL \\ \cos NCL \\ \cos KCL \end{bmatrix} = \mathbf{M}^T \begin{bmatrix} \cos mcL \\ \cos ncL \\ \cos kcL \end{bmatrix}$$

Again, since we are concerned only with ground lengths, the ground X- and Y-coordinates of the exposure station are immaterial and can be assumed to be $X_L = 0$ and $Y_L = 0$. Then, by Eqs. 3–71 and 3–72, and for each condition, ground coordinates are computed as

$$X_A = -\frac{\cos MAL}{\cos KAL}(H - h_A) \qquad Y_A = -\frac{\cos NAL}{\cos KAL}(H - h_A)$$

$$X_B = -\frac{\cos MBL}{\cos KBL}(H - h_B) \qquad Y_B = -\frac{\cos NBL}{\cos KBL}(H - h_B)$$

$$X_C = -\frac{\cos MCL}{\cos KCL}(H - h_C) \qquad Y_C = -\frac{\cos NCL}{\cos KCL}(H - h_C)$$

The solution can then be continued as shown in Example 9–1, in which three sets of ground lengths AB, AC, BC, $A'B'$, $A'C'$, $B'C'$, $A''B''$, $A''C''$, and $B''C''$ are computed as shown.

After the tilt and swing have been computed, an orientation matrix is then computed, under the assumption that $\alpha_{NO} = 0°$. The numerical values of the orientation matrix for the values of $t = 3° \ 41'$ and $s = 311° \ 43'$, computed in Example 9–1 are, assuming $\alpha_{NO} = 0°$

$$\mathbf{M}^T = \begin{bmatrix} -0.66545 & -0.74644 & 0 \\ +0.74489 & -0.66407 & -0.06424 \\ +0.04795 & -0.04275 & +0.99793 \end{bmatrix}$$

Application of Eqs. 3–71 and 3–72 will give a set of ground coordinates for the three points which are then used to solve for the corrections to the first solution of t_y and t_x, and the computations are then continued as indicated in Example 9–1.

The use of the orientation matrix for the solution of this problem is somewhat more advantageously programmed for digital computer operation than the approach given in Example 9–1 because of the nature of the repetitive operations of storing the 3 by 3 matrices and of the matrix multiplications involved.

The principles discussed in this section for determining the tilt and swing of a single photograph may be applied to the solution for the tilt and swing of each of a pair of overlapping photographs, provided that the images of four vertical control points, properly located, appear on each of the photographs. An approximate flying height is obtained from altimeter readings or by comparing a distance on the photographs with a corresponding map distance. In Fig. 9–3 are shown a pair of photographs containing the images of vertical control points a, b, c, and d. Ground lengths AB, AC, AD, BC, and BD are computed from measurements on the left-hand photograph for each of the three assumptions, giving three sets of four independent ratios designated as follows: R_{V_1}, S_{V_1}, T_{V_1}, and U_{V_1}; R'_1, S'_1, T'_1, and U'_1; and R''_1, S''_1, T''_1, and

U''_1. For each of the three assumptions,

$$R = \frac{AB}{AC} \qquad S = \frac{AB}{AD}$$

$$T = \frac{AB}{BC} \qquad U = \frac{AB}{BD}$$

Similarly, ratios designated as R_{V_2}, S_{V_2}, T_{V_2}, U_{V_2}, and so on are obtained for the second photograph. Four condition equations may then be

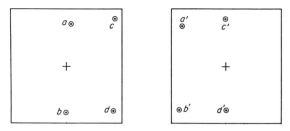

FIG. 9–3. Vertical control points in overlap area.

formed by stating that the ratios computed from the left-hand photograph and the ratios computed from the right-hand photograph must be identical. One of these equations is

$$R_{V_1} + \frac{R'_1 - R_{V_1}}{100} t_{y_1} + \frac{R''_1 - R_{V_1}}{100} t_{x_1} = R_{V_2} + \frac{R'_2 - R_{V_2}}{100} t_{y_2} + \frac{R''_2 - R_{V_2}}{100} t_{x_2}$$

The others have a similar form. The four equations are solved for t_{y_1}, t_{x_1}, t_{y_2}, and t_{x_2}. From these values t_1 and s_1, and t_2 and s_2 are obtained.

This method is described by Professor Earl Church in *Photogrammetry Bulletin* No. 19, published by Syracuse University Press.

9–3. Scale-Point Method for Tilt, Swing, and Flying Height

This method requires three ground lines of known length. Also, the elevations of the ends of the lines must be known. The images of the end points of the lines are corrected on the photograph for relief displacement, to bring all the lines to a common datum. If the photograph is vertical, there should be the same relation between all corrected photographic lengths and the corresponding ground lengths. In other words, the scales of all three lines should be identical, since the lines have been reduced to a common datum. If the photograph is tilted, the three scales will be different. From the three different scales, the rate of change of scale across the photograph in the direction of the principal line can be computed. The direction of constant scale, which is perpendicular to the principal line, can also be determined, and the direction of the tilt axis can then be established. The angle of tilt is computed from the computed rate of change of scale.

In Fig. 9–4, three points p_1, p_2, and p_3, called *scale points*, are located on a tilted photograph. The scale points are not to be confused with photo control points. By the principles discussed in Sec. 3–8, the scale

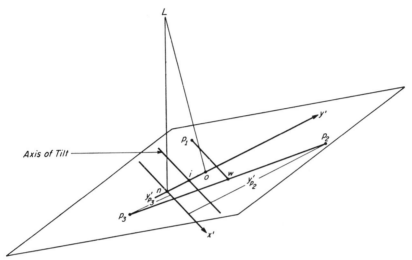

FIG. 9–4. Scale points.

at p_3 is the greatest, since this point is on the downward side of the axis of tilt. The scale at p_2 is the smallest. If these two scales are known, the position of a point w, where the scale is the same as at p_1, can be determined by interpolating along the line p_2p_3. The line wp_1 is a line of constant scale because the scale is the same at two points on the line. The line of constant scale is parallel to the axis of tilt, as shown in the illustration.

The rate of change of scale per inch in the direction of the principal line may be determined by dividing the difference in scale between p_2 and p_3 by the distance between the two points measured parallel to the principal line. This distance is the difference between the y'-coordinates of the two points. Let dS denote the rate of change of scale, and let S_{p_3} and S_{p_2} denote the scales at p_3 and p_2, respectively. Then

$$dS = \frac{S_{p_3} - S_{p_2}}{y'_{p_2} - y'_{p_3}} \tag{9–11}$$

The subscripts in the denominator have been reversed to make dS positive.

Since all lines have been reduced to a common datum, the three scale points are assumed to lie in a common datum, and the elevation of each is therefore zero. By Eq. 3–12,

$$S_{P_2} = \frac{f \sec t - y'_{P_2} \sin t}{H - 0}$$

and

$$S_{P_3} = \frac{f \sec t - y'_{P_3} \sin t}{H - 0}$$

The difference in scale between the two points is

$$S_{P_3} - S_{P_2} = \frac{f \sec t - y'_{P_3} \sin t}{H} - \frac{f \sec t - y'_{P_2} \sin t}{H}$$

or

$$S_{P_3} - S_{P_2} = \frac{y'_{P_2} \sin t - y'_{P_3} \sin t}{H}$$

Hence,

$$\sin t = \frac{H(S_{P_3} - S_{P_2})}{y'_{P_2} - y'_{P_3}} \tag{9-12}$$

Substituting Eq. 9–11 in Eq. 9–12 gives

$$\sin t = H \, dS \tag{9-13}$$

Since the scale along the axis of tilt is the same as the scale of an equivalent vertical photograph, and since all points have been reduced to a common datum, the scale along the axis of tilt, and consequently at the isocenter, can be expressed by Eq. 3–2. Thus,

$$S_i = \frac{f}{H} \tag{9-14}$$

in which S_i is the scale at the isocenter. Substituting the value of H from Eq. 9–14 in Eq. 9–13 gives

$$\sin t = \frac{f \, dS}{S_i} \tag{9-15}$$

in which f is the focal length, in inches or millimeters; dS is the rate of change of scale in the direction of the principal line, in inches per foot per inch or in millimeters per foot per millimeter; and S_i is the scale at the isocenter, in inches per foot or in millimeters per foot.

If the positions of three scale points have been located, the direction of the axis of tilt may be determined by fixing a line of constant scale. This line also fixes the direction of the principal line. The quantity

$y'_{p_2} - y'_{p_3}$ in Eq. 9–11 can be measured directly on the photograph between the two points, this measurement being in the direction of the principal line. The scale at the isocenter cannot be determined as yet, since the position of the isocenter is not known. The scale at the principal point, however, can be determined by interpolation along the principal line between a line of constant scale through the high scale point and a line of constant scale through the low scale point. The scale at the principal point, denoted by S_o, is used in Eq. 9–15 to obtain a first value for sin t.

The scale points which are used to determine the rate of change of scale and the scales S_o or S_i are located empirically as herein described. This method, although not in strict accordance with the geometry of a tilted photograph, is in most cases satisfactory for locating scale points with the necessary degree of accuracy. In Fig. 9–5, points a and b, c and

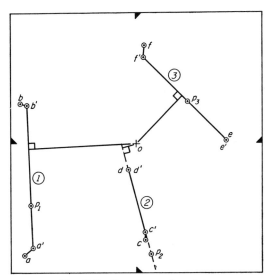

FIG. 9–5. Locating scale points.

d, and e and f are the images of the ends of three ground control lines. The elevations of the corresponding points A through F are known. An approximate flying height above sea level is determined from the approximate scale of the photograph, or of one line on the photograph, as discussed in Sec. 3–6. The elevation of the lowest of the six ground control points is taken as the datum. Hence,

$$H = H_{SL} - h_L \qquad (9\text{--}16)$$

in which H is the flying height above the datum; H_{SL} is the flying height above sea level; and h_L is the elevation of the lowest point.

All images are brought to their datum photograph positions by computing the relief displacements of the points by means of Eq. 3–7, and then laying off these displacements along radial lines inward toward the principal point. The value of h in Eq. 3–7 is the elevation of a point above the lowest point, and not above sea level. Since the tilt of the photograph is as yet unknown, the value of r in Eq. 3–7 must be measured from the principal point, rather than from the nadir point. In Fig. 9–5, all the points have been displaced inward to positions a' through f'. Note that neither d nor e have been corrected. Point e is the lowest point and is, therefore, in its correct datum photograph position. Point d lies so close to the center of the photograph that its relief displacement is unmeasurable.

The scales of the three lines are now obtained by the following relationship:

$$S = \frac{\text{datum photograph length, in inches or millimeters}}{\text{known ground length, in feet}} \quad (9\text{--}17)$$

Let $a'b'$ be line 1, $c'd'$ be line 2, and $e'f'$ be line 3. Then, by Eq. 9–17,

$$S_1 = \frac{a'b'}{AB} \qquad S_2 = \frac{c'd'}{CD} \qquad S_3 = \frac{e'f'}{EF}$$

If the photograph is vertical, the scales S_1, S_2, and S_3 will be identical. If each scale is different, the photograph is tilted. The scale of each line, as determined by Eq. 9–17, is effective only at one point along the line. This point is at the intersection of the line with the line of constant scale having the same scale. The point at which the scale is effective is the scale point.

A scale point is located empirically as follows. Drop a perpendicular from the isocenter to the datum line. Since the position of the isocenter is at first unknown, the perpendicular is dropped from the principal point as a first approximation, as shown in Fig. 9–5. Next, measure the distance from the foot of the perpendicular to the nearer end of the datum line. Lay off this distance from the other end of the datum line to a point, which is the scale point p. Notice that the foot of the perpendicular to datum line *2* falls on an extension of the line. The scale point p_2 then falls on an extension from the other end of the line, as shown.

The student will note that three control points whose horizontal positions and elevations are known will suffice to determine the tilt of a photograph by the scale-point method. All three points are brought to the datum of the lowest of the three points by laying off the relief displacements of the two higher points. The sides of a triangle whose vertexes are the three datum points then constitute the necessary three scale lines on which scale points are located as just described.

After the tilt of the photograph has been determined by Eq. 9–15, the nadir point is located on the downward side of the principal line at a distance f tan t from the principal point. The downward side is in the direction of increasing scale. The isocenter is located on the principal line at a distance f tan $(t/2)$ from the principal point toward the nadir point. The swing is determined by measuring the angle, with a protractor, from the $+y$-axis defined by fiducial marks clockwise to the principal line on the side of the nadir point.

If a tilt greater than about 2° is obtained on the first solution, a second solution should be made. In the second solution, the nadir point determined from the first solution is used to measure the radial distances for computing relief displacements. The isocenter is used to determine the positions of the scale points. The second value of the tilt is determined by Eq. 9–15, using the scale at the isocenter.

When satisfactory values for the tilt and the swing have been obtained, the flying height is determined by the relationship given in Eq. 9–14. This value of H represents the flying height above the elevation of the lowest point. The flying height above sea level is then computed by Eq. 9–16.

The use of the scale-point method for determining the tilt and swing of a photograph is demonstrated by the following example.

EXAMPLE 9–2. The photograph of Fig. 9–6 contains the images a, b, and c of ground control points A, B, and C. The elevations of the three points are $h_A=674$ ft; $h_B=321$ ft; $h_C=775$ ft. The ground lengths are $AB=6,904.6$ ft; $BC=5,263.7$ ft; $CA=4,983.7$ ft. The focal length of the camera is 4.060 in. A preliminary flying height is computed by scaling the line ac and comparing it with the ground length AC; it is necessary to take into consideration the elevations of the end points of the line. This preliminary value of H is 5,420 ft above sea level. Determine the tilt, the swing, and the exact flying height above sea level for the photograph.

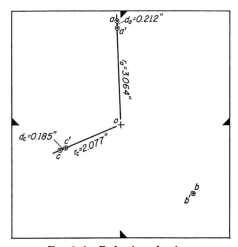

Fig. 9–6. Reduction of points to common datum.

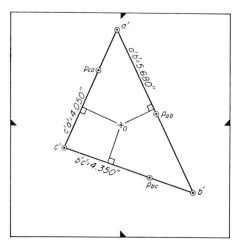

FIG. 9–7. Scale lines and scale points.

Solution: The first step in the solution is to determine the flying height and the elevations of the three control points above the selected datum. Since B lies at the lowest elevation, the selected datum is at elevation 321 ft. Then,

$$H_{321} = 5,420 - 321 = 5,099 \text{ ft}$$
$$h'_A = 674 - 321 = 353 \text{ ft}$$
$$h'_B = 321 - 321 = 0 \text{ ft}$$
$$h'_C = 775 - 321 = 454 \text{ ft}$$

The radial distances to points a and c, measured from the principal point, are $r_a = 3.064$ in. and $r_c = 2.077$ in. The relief displacements d_a and d_c of the two points are, by Eq. 3–7,

$$d_a = \frac{3.064 \times 353}{5,099} = 0.212 \text{ in.} \quad \text{and} \quad d_c = \frac{2.077 \times 454}{5,099} = 0.185 \text{ in.}$$

The two points are brought to their datum photograph positions as shown in Fig. 9–6.

The datum points a', b', and c' are joined by lines, as shown in Fig. 9–7. A perpendicular is dropped from the principal point to each of the datum lines, and the scale point of each line is located as previously explained. This procedure locates scale points p_{ab}, p_{bc}, and p_{ca}. The lengths of the datum lines, as measured on the photograph, are $a'b' = 5.680$ in.; $b'c' = 4.350$ in.; and $c'a' = 4.050$ in. The values of the scales at the three scale points are determined by Eq. 9–17, as follows:

$$S_{ab} = \frac{5.680 \text{ in.}}{6,904.6 \text{ ft}} = 0.000\ 8226 \text{ in. per ft}$$

$$S_{bc} = \frac{4.350 \text{ in.}}{5,263.7 \text{ft}} = 0.000\ 8264 \text{ in. per ft}$$

$$S_{ca} = \frac{4.050 \text{ in.}}{4,983.7 \text{ ft}} = 0.000\ 8126 \text{ in. per ft}$$

For convenience, the decimal point is moved 7 places to the right and the units are dropped. The results are

$$S_{ab} = 8226 \qquad S_{bc} = 8264 \qquad S_{ca} = 8126$$

These values are shown alongside the scale points in Fig. 9–8.

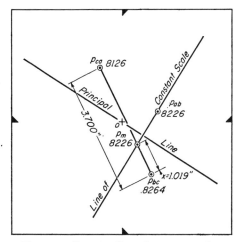

FIG. 9–8.   Locating line of constant scale.

A line of constant scale is now located   A line is drawn joining the point of highest scale with that of lowest scale. This is the line $p_{ca}\ p_{bc}$ in Fig. 9–8. The length of this line is measured and found to be 3.700 in. The difference between the two scales is $8264-8126=138$. The difference between the highest scale at p_{bc} and the middle scale at p_{ab} is $8264-8226=38$. The next step is to compute the distance x from p_{bc} to a point p_m on the line $p_{ca}\ p_{bc}$ at which the scale is the same as at p_{ab}. Thus,

$$x = \frac{38}{138} \times 3.700 = 1.019 \text{ in.}$$

The line joining p_m and p_{ab} is a line of constant scale, because the scale is the same at both points. A line drawn through the principal point and perpendicular to $p_m p_{ab}$ is the principal line of the photograph. This line is shown in Fig. 9–8.

In Fig. 9–9, lines of constant scale are drawn through the scale points of high and low scale. These lines intersect the principal line at points h and l. The distance hl, as measured, is 3.154 in. The rate of change of scale can be determined by Eq. 9–11, since hl is, in fact, the difference in y'-coordinates between p_{ca} and p_{bc}. Therefore,

$$dS = \frac{8264 - 8126}{3.154} = \frac{138}{3.154} = 43.75 \text{ units per in.}$$

The scale at the principal point is found by interpolation along the principal line between points h and l. The distance y scales 1.514 in., and the scale at the principal point is

$$S_o = 8126 + (1.514)(43.75) = 8192$$

The tilt of the photograph is found by Eq. 9–15. Thus,

$$\sin t = \frac{4.060 \times 43.75}{8192} = 0.02168$$

and

$$t = 1° \ 15'$$

The nadir point lies on the downward side of the photograph at a distance $f \tan t = 0.088$ in. from the principal point. The isocenter lies at a distance

f tan $(t/2)=0.044$ in. from the principal point toward the nadir point. The positions of the nadir point and the isocenter are shown in Fig. 9–9.

The swing s is measured with a protractor as shown in Fig. 9–9, and is found to be **122°35′.**

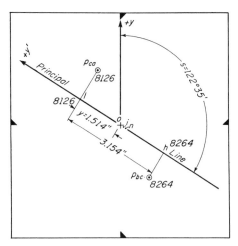

Fig. 9–9. Rate of change of scale
along principal line.

The scale at the isocenter is found by interpolation along the principal line. The distance li is $1.514+0.044=1.558$ in. Therefore,

$$S_i = 8126 + (1.558)(43.75) = 8194$$

The actual scale obtained is 0.000 8194 in. per ft, because the decimal point was moved 7 places to the right in the scales originally determined. The exact flying height above the 321-ft datum is given by Eq. 9–14. Thus,

$$H_{321} = \frac{4.060 \text{ in.}}{0.000\ 8194 \text{ in./ft}} = 4{,}955 \text{ ft}$$

The flying height above sea level is, by Eq. 9–16,

$$H_{SL} = 4{,}955 + 321 = 5{,}316 \text{ ft}$$

A second solution for the tilt of the photograph would give only a slight improvement over the first solution, because the tilt is relatively small. No measurable difference in relief displacements would be obtained by using the nadir point from which to measure radial distances. Using the isocenter from which to drop perpendiculars to determine the positions of the scale points will affect the locations of the scale points to a slight extent. Substituting S_i for S_o will not change the tilt by any meaningful amount.

The scale-point method for determining tilt, swing, and flying height is seen to be a combination of graphics and arithmetic. If the photographs have been printed on paper with a stable base and low shrinkage, and if the drafting and measuring have been done with care, the scale-point method will give highly reliable results. Each solution requires from ½ to 1 hour of time, which is considered reasonable.

9–4. Determination of Azimuth of Photograph

According to the definitions given in Chapter 3, the azimuth of the principal plane of a photograph, or simply the azimuth of the photograph, is the ground-survey direction of the principal plane. The horizontal positions of at least two points appearing on the photograph must be known before the azimuth of the photograph may be computed. These two points are usually the end points of one of the control lines used to compute the tilt, swing, and flying height. From the ground-survey coordinates of the ends of the control line, the ground-survey azimuth from north is obtained by the relationship

$$\tan \alpha_G = \frac{X_{G_2} - X_{G_1}}{Y_{G_2} - Y_{G_1}} \tag{9–18}$$

in which α_G is the ground-survey azimuth, and points 1 and 2 are the end points of the control line. If a set of ground coordinates are computed by Eqs. 3–9, 3–10, 3–11, 3–13, and 3–14, or by Eqs. 3–71 and 3–72, in which the measured photographic coordinates of the images of the two ends of the control line are used, the azimuth of this line is obtained by the relationship

$$\tan \alpha_P = \frac{X_2 - X_1}{Y_2 - Y_1} \tag{9–19}$$

in which α_P is the azimuth of the control line based on a set of ground coordinates whose origin is at the ground nadir point of the photograph and whose Y-axis lies in the principal plane of the photograph. This assumes that $X_L = 0$, $Y_L = 0$, and $\alpha_{NO} = 0°$.

In Fig. 9–10, X_G and Y_G are the ground-survey coordinate axes, and X and Y are the ground coordinate axes based on the ground nadir point N and the principal plane of the photograph. The angle formed between Y_G and Y is the azimuth of the principal plane or α_{NO}. The ground-survey azimuth of the control line AB, as determined from Eq. 9–18, is α_G. Its ground azimuth, based on photographic measurements and determined from Eq. 9–19, is α_P. From the illustration it is obvious that

$$\alpha_{NO} = \alpha_G - \alpha_P \tag{9–20}$$

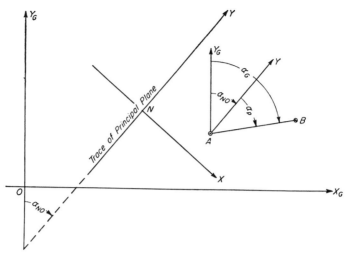

FIG. 9–10. Azimuth of photograph from ground control line.

EXAMPLE 9–3. The ground-survey coordinates of points C and B of Example 9–1 are as follows:

$$X_{G_C} = 35,000 \text{ ft} \qquad \text{and} \qquad Y_{G_C} = 25,000 \text{ ft}$$

$$X_{G_B} = 15,000 \text{ ft} \qquad \text{and} \qquad Y_{G_B} = 25,000 \text{ ft}$$

Using the tilt, swing, and flying height computed in Example 9–1, compute the azimuth of the photograph.

Solution: The ground survey azimuth of CB is obtained by Eq. 9–18, as follows:

$$\tan \alpha_{G_{CB}} = \frac{15,000 - 35,000}{25,000 - 25,000} = -\text{infinity}$$

$$\alpha_{G_{CB}} = 270°$$

Based on the final solution of the flying height in Example 9–1, the ground coordinates of C and B are as follows:

$$X_C = 1,799 \text{ ft} \qquad \text{and} \qquad Y_C = 14,070 \text{ ft}$$

$$X_B = 14,087 \text{ ft} \qquad \text{and} \qquad Y_B = -1,709 \text{ ft}$$

By Eq. 9–19,

$$\tan \alpha'_{P_{CB}} = \frac{14,087 - 1,799}{-1,709 - 14,070} = -0.77876 \text{ (2nd quadrant)}$$

and

$$\alpha_{P_{CB}} = 142° \, 05'$$

By Eq. 9–20,

$$\alpha_{NO} = 270° - 142° \, 05' = 127° \, 55'$$

9–5. Ground-Survey Coordinates of Exposure Station

The ground-survey coordinates of the exposure station, X_L and Y_L, may be determined from one control point, provided that the azimuth of the photograph is known. In Fig. 9–11, X_G and Y_G are the ground-survey axes, and X and Y are the ground axes based on the nadir point N and the principal plane. The ground-survey coordinates of point A are (X_{G_A}, Y_{G_A}), and its ground coordinates, based on Eqs. 3–13 and 3–14,

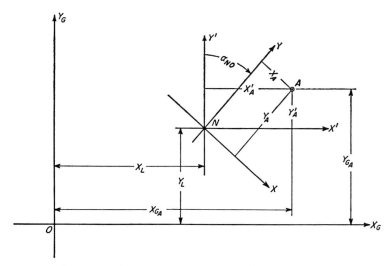

FIG. 9–11. Ground-survey coordinates of exposure station.

are (X_A, Y_A). The ground-survey coordinates of N are (X_L, Y_L). If the X- and Y-coordinate axes are rotated through a positive angle α_{NO}, the transformed coordinates of A are (X'_A, Y'_A). This transformation is performed by the following rotation equations:

$$X' = X \cos \alpha_{NO} + Y \sin \alpha_{NO} \qquad (9\text{--}21)$$

$$Y' = -X \sin \alpha_{NO} + Y \cos \alpha_{NO} \qquad (9\text{--}22)$$

Or in matrix notation

$$\begin{bmatrix} X' \\ Y' \end{bmatrix} = \begin{bmatrix} \cos \alpha_{NO} & \sin \alpha_{NO} \\ -\sin \alpha_{NO} & \cos \alpha_{NO} \end{bmatrix} \begin{bmatrix} X \\ Y \end{bmatrix} \qquad (9\text{--}23)$$

Expressions for the ground-survey coordinates of the exposure station are then as follows (refer to Fig. 9–11):

$$X_L = X_{G_A} - X'_A \qquad (9\text{--}24)$$

$$Y_L = Y_{G_A} - Y'_A \qquad (9\text{--}25)$$

EXAMPLE 9–4. Determine the ground-survey coordinates of the exposure station of the photograph of Examples 9–1 and 9–3, based on both point B and point C.

Solution: From Example 9–3, $\alpha_{NO} = 127° 55'$. Then $\sin \alpha_{NO} = +0.78891$ and $\cos \alpha_{NO} = -0.61451$.

By Eqs. 9–21 and 9–22,

$$X'_B = (14,087)(-0.61451) + (-1,709)(+0.78891) = -10,005 \text{ ft}$$
$$Y'_B = -(14,087)(+0.78891) + (-1,709)(-0.61451) = -10,063 \text{ ft}$$
$$X'_C = (1,799)(-0.61451) + (14,070)(+0.78891) = +9,994 \text{ ft}$$
$$Y'_C = -(1,799)(+0.78891) + (14,070)(-0.61451) = -10,065 \text{ ft}$$

By Eqs. 9–23 and 9–24, based on point B,

$$X_L = 15,000 - (-10,005) = 25,005 \text{ ft}$$
$$Y_L = 25,000 - (-10,063) = 35,063 \text{ ft}$$

Based on point C,

$$X_L = 35,000 - 9,994 = 25,006 \text{ ft}$$
$$Y_L = 25,000 - (-10,065) = 35,065 \text{ ft}$$

The agreement between the two sets of results would doubtless be slightly improved if the exact flying height from a second solution were to be used in computing X_B, Y_B, X_C, and Y_C. However, this agreement is sufficiently close for the rather large flying height.

9–6.   Resection by Collinearity Conditions

The term resection is used to define the process of locating the space coordinates X_L, Y_L, Z_L of the exposure station together with the exterior orientation elements t, s, α_{NO} or ω, ϕ, κ. In fact, the operations conducted in Secs. 9–2, 9–4, and 9–5 constitute a resection inasmuch as they establish the above-mentioned six quantities. The requirements for solving a space resection problem are, as mentioned in Sec. 9–1, three ground control points whose coordinates and elevations are known, together with the camera focal length.

Assume that the photographic coordinates of three ground control points have been measured and corrected for various systematic errors of lens distortion, film distortion, atmospheric refraction, and so on. Then, by Eq. 3–77,

$$\left. \begin{aligned} x &= \frac{z\left[(X_P - X_L)m_{11} + (Y_P - Y_L)m_{12} + (Z_P - Z_L)m_{13} \right]}{(X_P - X_L)m_{31} + (Y_P - Y_L)m_{32} + (Z_P - Z_L)m_{33}} \\[2mm] y &= \frac{z\left[(X_P - X_L)m_{21} + (Y_P - Y_L)m_{22} + (Z_P - Z_L)m_{23} \right]}{(X_P - X_L)m_{31} + (Y_P - Y_L)m_{32} + (Z_P - Z_L)m_{33}} \end{aligned} \right\} \quad (9\text{–}26)$$

In these equations, x and y are the measured photographic coordinates of a control point, corrected for systematic errors; z is the camera focal length with a minus sign $(-f)$; X_P, Y_P, and Z_P are the known ground coordinates and elevations of the control point. These are all known quantities. In this discussion, they will be considered as fixed quantities, not subject to variation. The remaining terms are the exposure station coordinates

X_L, Y_L, and Z_L; and the elements of the **M**-matrix defined in Secs. 3–13 and 3–14. These elements are defined by three quantities, either t, s, and α_{NO} or ω, ϕ, and κ. Thus, it is seen that there are six unknown quantities in Eq. 9–26.

If the photographic coordinates of three ground control points have been measured and corrected, then six equations can be formed, containing six unknown quantities. A direct simultaneous solution of the six equations is not feasible, however, because they contain transcendental functions.

The most practical solution is to assume a set of values for the unknown quantities, formulate six linear equations containing corrections to these initial set of values, and iterate the solution of these equations until they satisfy the collinearity equations. An initial value for Z_L can be obtained from altimeter readings or by the method given in Sec. 3–6 or Sec. 3–10. An initial value for X_L and Y_L can be obtained from a radial line plot. Initial values of the exterior orientation elements are obtained by assuming the photograph to be vertical. This initial assumption forces the selection of the ω, ϕ, κ system, since in the t, s, α_{NO} system, the swing and azimuth are undefined if the photograph is vertical. Thus both ω and ϕ are initially assumed to be zero.

The angle kappa is taken as the angle measured counterclockwise from the photographic position of the ground X-axis (x_T) to the photographic x-axis as shown in Fig. 9–12. If the flight line is due east or west, the value of κ is near $0°$ or $180°$. If the flight line is due north or south,

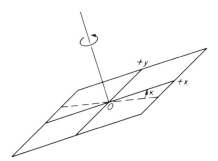

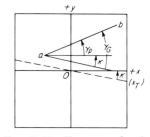

Fig. 9–12. Definition of kappa angle.   Fig. 9–13. Kappa angle determined by direction of a line.

κ is near $90°$ or $270°$. An initial value can be obtained by computing the slope of one of the control lines on the ground with respect to the ground X-axis, then computing the slope of the same line in the photographic system, and finally computing the difference in the slopes. Thus, from Fig. 9–13,

$$\tan \gamma_P = \frac{y_b - y_a}{x_b - x_a} \qquad \tan \gamma_G = \frac{Y_B - Y_A}{X_B - X_A}$$

and

$$\kappa = \gamma_G - \gamma_P$$

Eq. 9–26 can be stated as

$$\left. \begin{array}{l} x = F_x(X_L, Y_L, Z_L, \omega, \phi, \kappa) \\ y = F_y(X_L, Y_L, Z_L, \omega, \phi, \kappa) \end{array} \right\} \qquad (9\text{--}27)$$

Initial values of F_x and F_y can be computed by substituting the initially assumed values of X_L, Y_L, Z_L, ω, ϕ, κ, which are designated X_{L_0}, Y_{L_0}, Z_{L_0}, ω_0, ϕ_0, κ_0, into Eq. 9–26. This operation evaluates F_{x_0} and F_{y_0}.
But

$$\left. \begin{array}{l} x = F_x = F_{x_0} + dF_x \\ y = F_y = F_{y_0} + dF_y \end{array} \right\} \qquad (9\text{--}28)$$

and, by the calculus,

$$\left. \begin{array}{l} dF_x = dx = \dfrac{\partial x}{\partial X_L} dX_L + \dfrac{\partial x}{\partial Y_L} dY_L + \dfrac{\partial x}{\partial Z_L} dZ_L + \dfrac{\partial x}{\partial \omega} d\omega + \dfrac{\partial x}{\partial \phi} d\phi + \dfrac{\partial x}{\partial \kappa} d\kappa \\[2ex] dF_y = dy = \dfrac{\partial y}{\partial X_L} dX_L + \dfrac{\partial y}{\partial Y_L} dY_L + \dfrac{\partial y}{\partial Z_L} dZ_L + \dfrac{\partial y}{\partial \omega} d\omega + \dfrac{\partial y}{\partial \phi} d\phi + \dfrac{\partial y}{\partial \kappa} d\kappa \end{array} \right\}$$
$$(9\text{--}29)$$

Thus,

$$\left. \begin{array}{l} x = F_{x_0} + A_1 dX_L + A_2 dY_L + A_3 dZ_L + A_4 d\omega + A_5 d\phi + A_6 d\kappa \\ y = F_{x_0} + B_1 dX_L + B_2 dY_L + B_3 dZ_L + B_4 d\omega + B_5 d\phi + B_6 d\kappa \end{array} \right\} \quad (9\text{--}30)$$

in which x and y are the measured and corrected photographic coordinates; F_{x_0} and F_{y_0} are the values of the right-hand side of Eq. 9–26 obtained by substituting the initially assumed values of the six unknown parameters X_{L_0}, Y_{L_0}, Z_{L_0}, ω_0, ϕ_0, and κ_0; dX_L, dY_L, dZ_L, $d\omega$, $d\phi$, and $d\kappa$ are as yet unknown corrections to the initially assumed values; and the A's and the B's are the partial differential coefficients obtained by differentiation of Eq. 9–26. These partial differential coefficients are evaluated using the initially assumed values of the unknown parameters.

With three given control points, six linear equations can be formed, two for each point, by which the six unknown quantities, dX_L, dY_L, dZ_L, $d\omega$, $d\phi$, and $d\kappa$ can be solved. These quantities are then added to the initial values, the values of F_{x_0} and F_{y_0} are again computed, the partial differential coefficients are again evaluated, and the six equations are again solved. Each time the process is iterated, the corrections become smaller. The process is stopped when the corrections are considered small enough to have no effect.

The method of resection discussed in this section is best handled by matrix manipulation. A breakdown of the entire process is considered to be outside the scope of this textbook The student is referred to the literature cited in the bibliography for an exhaustive treatment of this and other analytical methods of determining the orientation of a photograph.

Bibliography

AMERICAN SOCIETY OF PHOTOGRAMMETRY. *Manual of Photogrammetry* (Menasha, Wisc.: George Banta Co., 1952), Chapter 6.

————. *Manual of Photogrammetry* (Menasha, Wisc.: George Banta Co., 1966), Chapters 2 and 10.

ANDERSON, R. O. "Scale Point Method of Tilt Determination," *Photogrammetric Engineering,* Vol. XV (1949), p. 311.

BOGE, W. E. "Resection Using Iterative Least Squares," *Photogrammetric Engineering,* Vol. XXXI (1965), p. 701.

BRUBAKER, L. N. "Recovering Precise Tilts and Azimuths of Aerial Mapping Photographs," *Photogrammetric Engineering,* Vol. XXI (1955), p. 439.

CHURCH, EARL. "Theory of Photogrammetry," *Photogrammetry Bulletin* No. 19, Syracuse University Press, 1948.

————. "Tilt Analysis Based Upon Vertical Control Data," *Photogrammetric Engineering,* Vol. XIII (1947), p. 463.

HALLERT, B. "Quality of Exterior Orientation," *Photogrammetric Engineering,* Vol. XXXII (1966), p. 464.

LEHMAN, E. H., JR. "Determining Exposure Point, Tilt, and Direction of Photograph From Three Known Ground Positions and Focal Length," *Photogrammetric Engineering,* Vol. XXIX (1963), p. 702.

McNEIL, G. T. "Tilt by the Graphical Pyramid Method," *Photogrammetric Engineering,* Vol. XIII (1947), p. 403.

MILLER, O. M. "An Approach to Exterior Orientation," *Photogrammetric Engineering,* Vol. XIV (1948), p. 155.

MORSE, M. "Projective Methods," *Photogrammetric Engineering,* Vol. XXXII (1966), p. 849.

UNDERWOOD, P. H. "The Determination of Tilt from Scale Check Lines," *Photogrammtric Engineering,* Vol. XIII (1947), p. 143.

Problems

9–1. The images of three ground control points appear on an aerial photograph taken with a lens having a 150-mm focal length from a flying height of approximately 20,000 ft above sea level. The measured photographic coordinates, together with the control data, are as follows:

Point	Photographic Coordinates (mm)		Elevation (ft)	Ground Coordinates (ft)	
	x	y		X	Y
51A	−83.25	+77.97	200	33,560	46,120
51B	+71.98	0.00	700	53,560	36,120
51C	−44.09	−77.66	300	38,560	26,120

Compute the tilt and swing of the photograph.

9–2. Compute the true flying height of the photograph of Prob. 9–1.

9–3. Compute the azimuth of the principal plane of the photograph of Prob. 9–1.

9–4. Compute the X- and Y-coordinates of the exposure station of the photograph of Prob. 9–1, based on the ground coordinates of both point 51B and point 51C.

9–5. Carefully construct a set of rectangular coordinates on a sheet of stable drafting material, and plot the photographic coordinates of points 51A, 51B, and 51C of Prob. 9–1. Using the plotted photographic positions of the three points, solve for tilt, swing, and flying height of the photograph by the scale-point method.

9–6. What is the datum scale, in the form of a representative fraction, of the photograph of Prob. 9–5 at a point on the photograph whose coordinates are $x = +70.00$ mm and $y = +70.00$ mm?

9–7. A pair of overlapping aerial photographs were taken with a lens having a 150-mm focal length from a flying height of approximately 20,000 ft above sea level. The images of four points for vertical control appear in the overlap area of the two photographs. The measured photographic coordinates, together with the elevations of the four points, are as follows:

Point	Elevation (ft)	Measured Photographic Coordinates (mm)			
		Left Photograph		Right Photograph	
		x	y	x	y
V-10	1050	+20.39	+77.05	−55.46	+113.11
V-11	50	−11.87	−74.76	−85.87	− 40.12
V-12	600	+97.35	+59.89	+24.04	+ 89.73
V-13	1200	+75.01	−57.54	− 7.12	− 26.58

Compute the tilt and swing of both photographs.

Rectification of Tilted Photographs 10

10-1. Rectification and Magnification

The rectification of a tilted photograph taken from a given exposure station in space transforms the photograph into an equivalent vertical photograph taken from the same exposure station. The equivalent vertical photograph may then be enlarged or reduced by a desired magnification. This changes the principal distance of the photograph, as discussed in Sec. 3-1. If the magnification is denoted by m, the focal length of the camera lens by f, and the principal distance of the rectified photograph by p, the principal distance is given by the equation

$$p = mf \qquad (10\text{-}1)$$

A magnification less than unity signifies an actual reduction of the photograph. A unit magnification gives the photograph a principal distance equal to the focal length of the camera lens. In the process of rectification, the transformation and magnification are usually, but not always, carried out simultaneously.

The purpose of magnification is to bring a series of photographs taken at different flying heights to the same scale *at a particular elevation.* This may be the datum elevation, or the average elevation of the area. In Fig. 10-1 are represented three photographs (assumed vertical) which

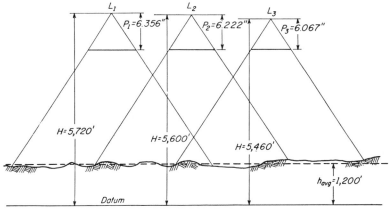

Fig. 10-1. Photographs taken at different flying heights.

265

have been taken at exposure stations L_1, L_2, and L_3, respectively, from flying heights $H_1 = 5{,}720$ ft, $H_2 = 5{,}600$ ft, and $H_3 = 5{,}460$ ft, respectively. In order to bring all the photographs to the same datum scale, say 1 in. $= 900$ ft, the required principal distances may be found by Eq. 3–2, in which p is substituted for f. The results follow:

$$p_1 = \frac{5{,}720 \text{ ft}}{900 \text{ ft/in.}} = 6.356 \text{ in.}$$

$$p_2 = \frac{5{,}600 \text{ ft}}{900 \text{ ft/in.}} = 6.222 \text{ in.}$$

$$p_3 = \frac{5{,}460 \text{ ft}}{900 \text{ ft/in.}} = 6.067 \text{ in.}$$

If the focal length of the taking camera lens is 6.000 in., the magnification factors must be, by Eq. 10–1, as follows:

$$m_1 = \frac{6.356 \text{ in.}}{6.000 \text{ in.}} = 1.059$$

$$m_2 = \frac{6.222 \text{ in.}}{6.000 \text{ in.}} = 1.037$$

$$m_3 = \frac{6.067 \text{ in.}}{6.000 \text{ in.}} = 1.011$$

If these photographs were enlarged according to the magnification factors just computed, all the datum scales would be the same. Suppose that the average elevation of the terrain is 1,200 ft, as shown in Fig. 10–1. The scales of the three enlarged photographs at this elevation are obtained by Eq. 3–3, in which the principal distances are substituted for the focal length. Thus,

$$S_1 = \frac{6.356 \text{ in.}}{(5{,}720 - 1{,}200) \text{ ft}} \qquad \text{or} \qquad 1 \text{ in.} = 711 \text{ ft}$$

$$S_2 = \frac{6.222 \text{ in.}}{(5{,}600 - 1{,}200) \text{ ft}} \qquad \text{or} \qquad 1 \text{ in.} = 707 \text{ ft}$$

$$S_3 = \frac{6.067 \text{ in.}}{(5{,}460 - 1{,}200) \text{ ft}} \qquad \text{or} \qquad 1 \text{ in.} = 702 \text{ ft}$$

On the other hand, if the scale at the average elevation is to be uniform throughout the photographs, say 1 in. $= 700$ ft, the principal distances must be, by Eq. 3–3, as follows:

$$p_1 = \frac{(5{,}720 - 1{,}200) \text{ ft}}{700 \text{ ft/in.}} = 6.457 \text{ in.}$$

$$p_2 = \frac{(5{,}600 - 1{,}200) \text{ ft}}{700 \text{ ft/in.}} = 6.286 \text{ in.}$$

$$p_3 = \frac{(5,460 - 1,200) \text{ ft}}{700 \text{ ft/in.}} = 6.086 \text{ in.}$$

The corresponding magnification factors are

$$m_1 = \frac{6.457 \text{ in.}}{6.000 \text{ in.}} = 1.076$$

$$m_2 = \frac{6.286 \text{ in.}}{6.000 \text{ in.}} = 1.048$$

$$m_3 = \frac{6.086 \text{ in.}}{6.000 \text{ in.}} = 1.014$$

It is thus seen that magnification of the photograph in no way affects the value of the flying height or the positions of the exposure stations, but it does determine the required principal distance. For practical reasons the magnification factors are generally computed for a uniform scale at or near the average elevation of the terrain.

As indicated in Fig. 10–2, a photograph with a tilt t is taken at ex-

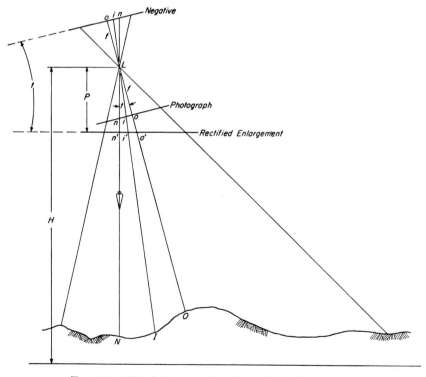

FIG. 10–2. Tilted photograph and rectified enlargement.

posure station L from a flying height H and with a camera having a focal length f. The tilted negative and the resulting tilted photograph are shown in their correct positions. If the negative is transformed into an equivalent vertical photograph taken from the same exposure station and then enlarged by a magnification factor m, the principal distance of the resulting vertical photograph will be $p=mf$. This rectification and enlargement could be accomplished, although not satisfactorily, by placing the negative in a tilted plane, a sheet of enlarging paper in a horizontal plane called the easel plane, and a pinhole opening between the two planes, in such positions that the pinhole lies at a distance f from the negative plane and at a distance p from the easel plane, as shown in Fig. 10–3. A source of light over the negative would produce

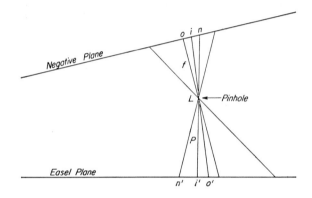

Fig. 10–3.   Pinhole rectification.

a point-to-point projection of the negative images onto the enlarging paper, thus effecting the desired transformation. The pinhole projection is unsatisfactory, however, for the following reason. In order to maintain definition in the enlargement, the pinhole must be extremely small and the exposure must therefore be unreasonably long.

If a lens with a focal length f is placed at the position of the pinhole, it will project the images from the negative in the proper direction. But, since the distance from the lens to the negative is equal to the focal length of the lens, the projected bundles of rays would be parallel with one another. Consequently, they would never come to focus as points on the enlarging paper. In order to form a rectified image at a finite distance in the easel plane, the entire negative must lie behind the focal plane of the lens used in the rectifier.

In Fig. 10–4 these principles are illustrated for a simple enlarger wherein a magnification only is to take place. The tilt of the negative is zero. In Fig. 10–4(a), a magnification m requires a principal distance *p*. Point *L* is a pinhole, through which images *a*, *o*, and *b* are projected to *a'*, *o'*, and *b'*. In Fig. 10–4(*b*), a lens having a focal length *f* is placed at *L* and images of the three points *a*, *o*, and *b* are formed at an infinite

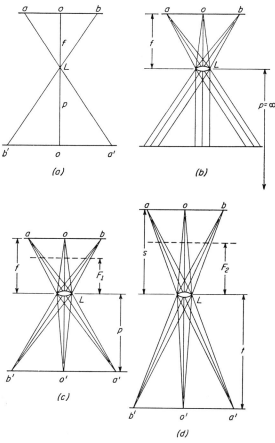

FIG. 10–4. Photographic enlargement.

distance in the directions shown. In Fig. 10–4(*c*), a lens having a focal length F_1, which satisfies Eq. 6–2, is placed at *L* at a distance *f* from the negative. Thus,

$$\frac{1}{f}+\frac{1}{p}=\frac{1}{F_1}$$

With this focal length, the images of *a*, *o*, and *b* will be formed at the proper distance *p* from the lens, and the proper magnification will be obtained.

In Fig. 10–4(*d*) a lens having a focal length F_2 is placed at *L* at a distance s from the negative. The distance s is selected to give a distance t to the easel plane such that $t/s = p/f = m$. The distance s is computed by applying Eqs. 6–2 and 10–1 and solving the following equations simultaneously:

$$\frac{1}{s} + \frac{1}{t} = \frac{1}{F_2}$$

$$\frac{t}{s} = m$$

The situation illustrated in Fig. 10–4(d) exists in an enlarger or in a rectifier, simply because the lens has a focal length F_2 which is independent of the focal length of any particular aerial-camera lens.

10–2. Scheimpflug Condition

The lens law stated by Eq. 6–2, which relates object and image distances to the focal length of a projector lens for projection between parallel planes, applies equally well to projection between nonparallel planes. The Scheimpflug condition, which must exist in order to produce sharp focus between the negative plane and the easel plane when these planes are not parallel, states that the negative plane, the plane of the lens, and the easel plane must intersect along one line. The plane of the lens is the plane perpendicular to the optical axis of the lens and passing through the optical center of the lens.

In Fig. 10–5, which is a section of a rectifier, the negative plane makes an angle α with the lens plane. The focal length of the projector lens is designated as F. The distance F measured along the optical axis upward along Ld from L defines the position of point k. The line kL in turn fixes the direction of the easel plane in the following way. Since k lies at a distance F from the lens at L, measured along the optical axis, it is in the focal plane of the lens, and its image is formed at infinity. Therefore, the easel plane must be parallel with the line kL, forming the angle β with the lens plane. Otherwise, a bundle of rays from k will form an image at a finite distance in the easel plane. Furthermore, by the Scheimpflug condition, the easel plane must intersect the negative plane along the line formed by the intersection of the negative plane and the lens plane. The point trace of this line in the plane of Fig. 10–5 is at V.

Point r is defined by the distance F below the lens. Since r lies in the focal plane of the lens, it represents the point where a bundle of rays lying in the plane of Fig. 10–5 and coming from infinity will be brought to focus in the easel plane. The line rL must therefore be parallel with the negative plane.

With the positions of the negative plane, the lens plane, and the

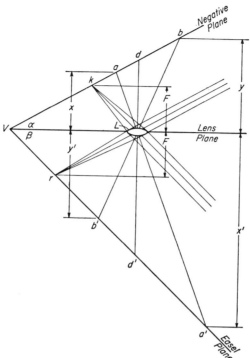

FIG. 10-5. Scheimpflug condition.

easel plane fixed as just explained, a bundle of rays from point a will come to focus at a' and rays from point b will come to focus at b'. The points a' and b' are so located that

$$\frac{1}{x}+\frac{1}{x'}=\frac{1}{F} \quad \text{and} \quad \frac{1}{y}+\frac{1}{y'}=\frac{1}{F}$$

10-3. Rectifier Equations

In order to allow for a continuous range of tilt angles and magnifications, a rectifying camera must be designed to permit changes in angles α and β of Fig. 10-5, and also to permit changes in the distances dL and $d'L$. The rectifier must also allow the negative to be rotated about the principal point. This freedom of rotation allows the principal plane of the photograph to be brought into coincidence with a plane which contains the optical axis and which is normal to the line of intersection of the negative, lens, and easel planes. The rotation of the negative is determined by the angle of swing of the photograph.

In Fig. 10-6, the negative of the tilted photograph has been placed in the negative plane and rotated, or swung, about the principal point o which remained on the optical axis during rotation. The nadir point of the negative lies upward from the principal point. This brings the principal plane into the plane of Fig. 10–6. In order to preserve the proper perspective geometry in the rectification, the negative must then be shifted in the direction of the principal line a distance do so that the axial point d comes on the optical axis. This distance is considered positive in the direction away from the intersection of the negative, lens, and easel planes (point V in Fig. 10–5). After this shift has been made, the negative plane is rotated about a line in the negative, represented as a point trace at d, so as to form the angle α with the lens plane. The easel plane is then rotated about a line in the easel plane, represented as a point trace at d', so as to form the angle β with the lens plane. Finally, the distances D and D' are set off. The negative is then ready for an exposure.

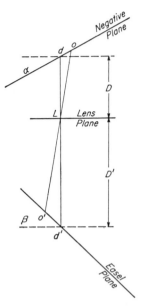

Fig. 10–6. Principal plane of fixed-lens rectifier.

The five settings, α, β, D, D', and do, depend on the tilt of the photograph, the focal length of the aerial camera lens, the focal length of the rectifier lens, and the desired magnification. The following relationships are given here without geometric proof:

$$\sin \alpha = \frac{F \sin t}{mf} \qquad (10\text{–}2)$$

$$\sin \beta = \frac{F \sin t}{f} \qquad (10\text{–}3)$$

$$D = F \left(1 + \frac{\tan \alpha}{\tan \beta} \right) \qquad (10\text{–}4)$$

$$D' = F \left(1 + \frac{\tan \beta}{\tan \alpha} \right) \qquad (10\text{–}5)$$

$$do = \frac{f}{\sin t} \left(\cos t - \frac{\cos \beta}{\cos \alpha} \right) \qquad (10\text{–}6)$$

In these equations, f is the focal length of the aerial camera lens; F is the focal length of the rectifier lens; m is the magnification; t is the tilt of the negative; α is the angle formed by the negative plane and the lens plane; β is the angle formed by the lens plane and the easel plane; D is the distance from the optical center of the lens to the point where the optical axis intersects the negative plane; D' is the distance from the optical center of the lens to the point where the optical axis intersects the easel plane; and do is the amount by which the principal point must be moved along the principal line in the negative plane away from the optical axis. The quantities f, F, D, D', and do are all expressed in the same units, either inches or millimeters. Because of a physical separation of the nodal points, as shown in Fig. 2–3, the values of both D and D' must be increased by a constant amount equal to one-half the separation of the nodal points.

The student is referred to the publications listed in the bibliography at the end of this chapter for a geometric proof of the rectifier equations just given. These equations are based on a fixed, or nontilting, lens plane, and the settings can be made only after the tilt and swing of the photograph are known and the desired magnification has been established.

EXAMPLE 10–1. The three photographs of Fig. 10–1 are to be rectified and brought to a common scale of 1 in.=700 ft at the 1,200-ft elevation. The three tilts are $t_1=0°\,40'$; $t_2=3°\,00'$; $t_3=2°\,05'$. The focal length of the aerial camera lens is 6.000 in., and the focal length of the rectifier lens is 7.500 in. Compute the necessary settings in a nontilting lens rectifier, neglecting the nodal separation.

Solution: The magnifications needed to give the required scale were computed in Sec. 10–1, and are as follows: $m_1=1.076$; $m_2=1.048$; $m_3=1.014$.

By Eq. 10–2,

$$\sin \alpha_1 = \frac{7.500 \sin 0°\,40'}{(1.076)(6.000)} = \frac{(7.500)(0.011635)}{(1.076)(6.000)} = 0.013516$$

$$\sin \alpha_2 = \frac{7.500 \sin 3°\,00'}{(1.048)(6.000)} = \frac{(7.500)(0.052336)}{(1.048)(6.000)} = 0.062424$$

$$\sin \alpha_3 = \frac{7.500 \sin 2°\,05'}{(1.014)(6.000)} = \frac{(7.500)(0.036353)}{(1.014)(6.000)} = 0.044814$$

Hence, $\alpha_1 = 0°\,47'$; $\alpha_2 = 3°\,35'$; $\alpha_3 = 2°\,34'$.

By Eq. 10–3,

$$\sin \beta_1 = \frac{(7.500)(0.011635)}{6.000} = 0.014544$$

$$\sin \beta_2 = \frac{(7.500)(0.052336)}{6.000} = 0.065420$$

$$\sin \beta_3 = \frac{(7.500)(0.036353)}{6.000} = 0.045441$$

So $\beta_1 = 0°\,50'$; $\beta_2 = 3°\,45'$; $\beta_3 = 2°\,36'$.

By Eqs. 10–4 and 10–5,

$$D_1 = 7.500\left(1 + \frac{\tan 0°\,47'}{\tan 0°\,50'}\right) = 7.500\left(1 + \frac{0.01367}{0.01455}\right) = 14.546 \text{ in.}$$

$$D_2 = 7.500\left(1 + \frac{\tan 3°\,35'}{\tan 3°\,45'}\right) = 7.500\left(1 + \frac{0.06262}{0.06554}\right) = 14.666 \text{ in.}$$

$$D_3 = 7.500\left(1 + \frac{\tan 2°\,34'}{\tan 2°\,36'}\right) = 7.500\left(1 + \frac{0.04483}{0.04541}\right) = 14.904 \text{ in.}$$

$$D'_1 = 7.500\left(1 + \frac{0.01455}{0.01367}\right) = 15.483 \text{ in.}$$

$$D'_2 = 7.500\left(1 + \frac{0.06554}{0.06262}\right) = 15.350 \text{ in.}$$

$$D'_3 = 7.500\left(1 + \frac{0.04541}{0.04483}\right) = 15.097 \text{ in.}$$

By Eq. 10–6,

$$(do)_1 = \frac{6.000}{\sin 0° \, 40'}\left(\cos 0° \, 40' - \frac{\cos 0° \, 50'}{\cos 0° \, 47'}\right)$$

$$= \frac{6.000}{0.01164}\left(0.99993 - \frac{0.99989}{0.99991}\right) = -0.026 \text{ in.}$$

$$(do)_2 = \frac{6.000}{\sin 3° \, 00'}\left(\cos 3° \, 00' - \frac{\cos 3° \, 45'}{\cos 3° \, 35'}\right)$$

$$= \frac{6.000}{0.05234}\left(0.99863 - \frac{0.99786}{0.99805}\right) = -0.135 \text{ in.}$$

$$(do)_3 = \frac{6.000}{\sin 2° \, 05'}\left(\cos 2° \, 05' - \frac{\cos 2° \, 36'}{\cos 2° \, 34'}\right)$$

$$= \frac{6.000}{0.03635}\left(0.99934 - \frac{0.99897}{0.99900}\right) = -0.104 \text{ in.}$$

The displacement of each negative along the principal line is seen to be in the direction of the intersection of the negative, lens, and easel planes.

EXAMPLE 10–2. Using the rectifier in Example 10–1, determine the settings to obtain an enlargement factor of 2.00 for photograph *1*.

Solution: By the rectifier equations,

$$\sin \alpha = \frac{(7.500)(0.011635)}{(2.000)(6.000)} = 0.00727 \quad \text{and} \quad \alpha = 0° \, 25'$$

$$\sin \beta = \frac{(7.500)(0.011635)}{6.000} = 0.01454 \quad \text{and} \quad \beta = 0° \, 50'$$

$$D = 7.500\left(1 + \frac{\tan 0° \, 25'}{\tan 0° \, 50'}\right) = 7.500\left(1 + \frac{0.00727}{0.01455}\right) = 11.247 \text{ in.}$$

$$D' = 7.500\left(1 + \frac{0.01455}{0.00727}\right) = 22.510 \text{ in.}$$

$$do = \frac{6.000}{\sin 0° \, 40'}\left(\cos 0° \, 40' - \frac{\cos 0° \, 50'}{\cos 0° \, 25'}\right)$$

$$= \frac{6.000}{0.01164}\left(0.99993 - \frac{0.99989}{0.99997}\right) = +0.005 \text{ in.}$$

A diagram of a rectifier with a tilting lens plane is shown in Fig. 10–7. In a rectifier of this type, there is no need for a displacement of the negative along the principal line, because the tilting of the lens through the angle γ brings the optical axis of the rectifier lens on the axial point d. The angles α, β, and γ are computed so that the negative plane, the lens plane, and the easel plane all intersect along one line,

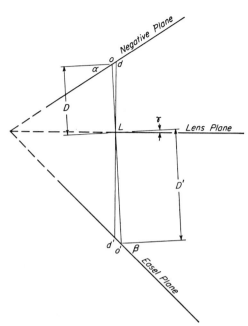

Fɪɢ. 10-7. Principal plane of tilting-lens rectifier.

in order to satisfy the Scheimpflug condition for sharp focus over the easel plane. To be able to carry out the necessary calculations, three auxiliary angles, designated as A, B, and θ, must be introduced. The equations for determining the settings to be made in the tilting-lens rectifier are as follows:

$$\sin A = \frac{F \sin t}{mf} \tag{10-7}$$

$$\sin B = \frac{F \sin t}{f} \tag{10-8}$$

$$\tan \theta = \tan^2 \frac{t}{2} \cot \frac{A+B}{2} \tag{10-9}$$

$$\alpha = \frac{A+B}{2} - \theta \tag{10-10}$$

$$\beta = \frac{A+B}{2} + \theta \tag{10-11}$$

$$\gamma = \alpha - A \tag{10-12}$$

$$D = \frac{f \sin (A+B)}{\sin t \cos \alpha} \tag{10-13}$$

$$D' = \frac{mf \sin (A+B)}{\sin t \cos \beta} \tag{10-14}$$

In these equations, α is the angle between the negative plane and a plane perpendicular to the reference axis of the rectifier; β is the angle between the easel plane and a plane perpendicular to the reference axis; γ is the angle between the optical axis of the lens and the reference axis; D is the distance measured along the reference axis between the optical center of the lens and the negative plane, in inches or millimeters; D' is the distance measured along the reference axis between the optical center of the lens and the easel plane, in inches or millimeters; and the quantities f, t, F, and m are the same as previously defined. The distances D and D' are increased slightly to allow for the separation of the nodal points of the rectifier lens. The correction to D and D' is, for all practical purposes, equal to one-half the nodal separation times cos γ.

When a tilting-lens rectifier is used, the negative is placed in the negative plane and is oriented so as to place the principal point on the reference axis of the rectifier. The negative is then rotated in the negative plane through an angle determined by the swing, so as to place the principal plane of the photograph in the principal plane of the rectifier and to have the nadir point on the upward side of the principal point. The setting for the angles α, β, and γ are made, and the distances D and D' are set off. The exposure is then made. To set off the angle α, the negative plane is rotated about a line in the negative containing the principal point of the negative; and to set off the angle β, the easel plane is rotated about a line in the easel plane containing the easel position o' of the principal point o.

EXAMPLE 10–3. The magnification factor for the photograph of Example 10–2 is to be 2.00. The rectifier is of the tilting-lens type, and the focal length of its lens is 7.500 in. Determine the settings for rectifying the photograph.

Solution: Use Eqs. 10–7 through 10–14. Thus,

$$\sin A = \frac{(7.500)(0.011635)}{(2.00)(6.000)} = 0.00727 \quad \text{and} \quad A = 0°\ 25'$$

$$\sin B = \frac{(7.500)(0.011635)}{6.000} = 0.01454 \quad \text{and} \quad B = 0°\ 50'$$

$$\tan \theta = \tan^2 0°\ 20' \cot 0°\ 37.5' = (0.005817)^2(35.25041) = 0.001193$$

$$\theta = 0°\ 04'$$

$$\alpha = 0°\ 37.5' - 0°\ 04' = 0°\ 33.5'$$

$$\beta = 0°\ 37.5' + 0°\ 04' = 0°\ 41.5'$$

$$\gamma = 0°\ 33.5' - 0°\ 25' = 0°\ 08.5'$$

$$D = \frac{6.000 \sin 1°\ 15'}{(0.011635)(0.999952)} = \frac{(6.000)(0.021815)}{(0.011635)(0.999952)} = 11.250 \text{ in.}$$

$$D' = \frac{(2.000)(6.000)(0.021815)}{(0.011635)(0.999927)} = 22.501 \text{ in.}$$

10–4. Automatic Rectifiers

An automatic rectifier is a rectifier so constructed that it auto-matically maintains the relationship between the object distance and the image distance expressed in Eq. 6–2, and at the same time fulfils the Scheimpflug condition. The object-image relationship is maintained by an inversor, one design of which is described in Sec. 6–14. The Scheimpflug condition is satisfied by means of a *Carpentier inversor,* which causes the negative plane, the easel plane, and the lens plane to intersect along a common line.

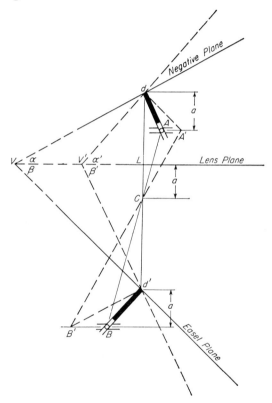

Fɪɢ. 10–8. Carpentier inversor.

A Carpentier inversor is shown schematically in Fig. 10–8. The member dA is fixed perpendicular to the negative plane, and the member Bd' is fixed perpendicular to the easel plane. Point A is located at a dis-tance a from the axis of rotation of the negative plane, this distance being measured parallel to the lens axis dLd'. Point B is located at a distance a from the axis of rotation of the easel plane. The member AB pivots about a fixed point C, which is located at a distance a from the optical center of the lens. Both point A and point B are constrained to move along a horizontal line so as to maintain the distance a. A change of the angle α to α' causes a corresponding change of β to β', and also movement of the common point of intersection V to V'. Coupled with the Carpentier inversor is the inversor which maintains the object-image relationship.

The automatic rectifier is provided with five basic motions and has corresponding dials or graduations for setting off computed or assumed values. These motions provide for the required magnification; the swing of the negative so as to place the principal plane of the negative in the principal plane of the rectifier; the offset motion in the direction of the principal plane; an offset motion normal to the direction of the principal plane; and the rotation of the easel plane with respect to the lens plane.

The automatic rectifier shown in Fig. 10–9 contains a negative

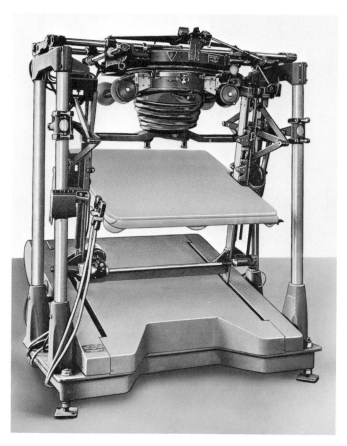

FIG. 10–9. Bausch and Lomb Autofocus Rectifier.
(Courtesy of Bausch and Lomb Optical Co.)

carrier, which is fixed in a horizontal position. Although this arrangement requires the optical axis to be swung in the principal plane of the rectifier, the rectifier itself has a fixed, or nontilting, lens. Critical focus is maintained by means of a combination *Peaucellier-Carpentier* inversor. The Peaucellier inversor can be easily identified in the picture. Scales are provided for setting off the five angles and distances described in the preceding paragraph.

The automatic rectifiers shown in Figs. 10–10 and 10–11 maintain critical focus by means of a combination *Pythagorean-Carpentier* inversor. The Pythagorean inversor performs the same function as does the Peaucellier inversor. The rectifiers are of the fixed-lens type. By means

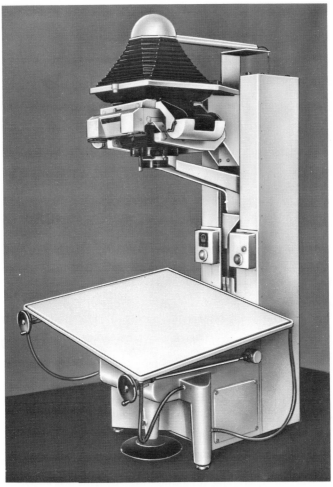

Fig. 10–10. Zeiss SEG V rectifier. (Courtesy of Carl Zeiss, Oberkochen.)

FIG. 10–11. Wild E4 rectifier. (Courtesy
of Wild-Heerbrugg Instruments, Inc.)

of automatic calculators, any three settings of the rectifier establish the
remaining two settings in the instrument. The negative is automatically
displaced in the direction of the principal plane of the photograph, the
displacement corresponding to the distance do of Fig. 10–6.

10–5. Rectifier Operation Based on Scale Data

The results of a solution for tilt, swing, and flying heights can be
used as a basis for rectifier operation. Two methods of obtaining these
results were described in Chapter 9. The values of the tilt, swing, magnification, camera focal length, and rectifier focal length are then used
to compute the settings necessary to properly rectify the photograph.
Typical computations for determining these settings have been given in
Examples 10–1, 10–2, and 10–3 for nonautomatic rectifiers of both the
fixed-lens type and the tilting-lens type. The automatic rectifiers in
present use are of the fixed-lens type. The settings necessary for these
rectifiers are: 1) the swing of the negative carrier based on the computed
swing of the photograph; 2) the offset do along the principal line, computed by Eq. 10–6; 3) the magnification, determined from the flying
height as explained in Sec. 10–1; and 4) the tilt β of the easel plane, com-

puted by Eq. 10–3. The value of α, found by Eq. 10–2, is automatically fixed by the Carpentier inversor. Also, the values of D and D' found by Eqs. 10–4 and 10–5 are automatically established in the rectifier by the action of the magnification motion combined with the inversor used to satisfy Eq. 6–2.

When an automatic rectifier is used, the negative is oriented in the negative carrier by means of the fiducial marks, and the angle of swing is set off. The negative is then displaced a distance do by means of the offset motion in the direction of the principal plane. The desired magnification factor is set off, and finally the easel tilt β is established by the proper setting. Enlarging paper is placed in the easel plane, and an exposure is made. The resulting enlargement is an equivalent vertical photograph, which is ratioed to the desired scale at a definite ground elevation.

10–6. Rectifier Operation by Empirical Orientation

Settings for the automatic rectifier may be arrived at by a trial-and-error method. For the purpose of discussion, such a process is called an empirical orientation of the negative and the rectifier components. The preparation necessary for the empirical orientation depends on the purpose for which the rectified photographs are made. Sometimes the photographs are intended for contour-line delineation in a stereoscopic plotting instrument designed around the parallax equations of Sec. 8–3. It is then necessary to know the elevations of at least four vertical control points on each photograph, in order to properly rectify the negatives. Another possible use for the photographs is in the construction of a controlled mosaic. For this use, vertical control may or may not be available.

Assume that the three photographs of Fig. 10–1 are to be rectified for use in a plotting instrument based on the parallax equations. These photographs are shown in plan view in Fig. 10–12. The pass points shown by small circles are vertical control points. A radial-line plot including these three photographs has been prepared and properly adjusted to fit horizontal control points. The principal points and

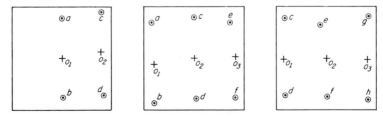

Fig. 10–12. Vertical control pass points.

the vertical control points are thus located with sufficient accuracy in their correct map positions at a fixed map scale. The map scale becomes the datum scale for the determination of a flying height by Eq. 3–2.

In Fig. 10–13, photograph *2* is shown alongside a portion of the radial-line plot. The map scale is seen to be substantially larger than the average scale of the photographs in the illustration. The vertical control points *a* through *f* have been located in their correct map or

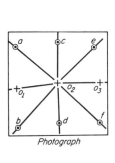 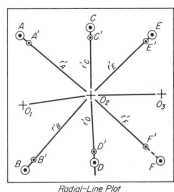

Fɪɢ. 10–13. Photographic and map positions of pass points.

datum positions at points A' through F' on the radial-line plot. If the radial distances r'_A through r'_F are measured, these distances can be used with the flying height above the map datum and the elevations of the points to compute relief displacements of the vertical control points by Eq. 3–8. For instance,

$$d_A = \frac{r'_A h_A}{H - h_A}$$

in which H is obtained by Eq. 3–2. Thus,

$$H = \frac{f}{\text{map scale}}$$

The relief displacements thus computed are laid off on radial lines outward from the map position of the principal point to locate points A through F. With allowances for inaccuracies in the radial-line plot, these six points are the photographic positions of the vertical control points on a vertical photograph whose datum scale is equal to the scale of the map or the radial-line plot. This portion of the radial-line plot may now be placed on the easel of a rectifier, and the negative may be placed in the negative carrier. Then, by a trial-and-error process, the projected images of points *a* through *f* can be made to coincide with the positions of A through F. This process automatically sets off the necessary magnification, the easel tilt β, the offset distance do, and the swing of the negative.

After the foregoing adjustment has been completed, the radial-line plot is removed from the easel, a sheet of enlarging paper is placed on the easel, and an exposure is made. The result is the desired rectified photograph. The process is repeated for each negative to bring all photographs to a uniform scale at the datum elevation. As will be shown, the offset motion of the negative carrier perpendicular to the principal line is necessary in the empirical orientation of the rectifier.

Assume that a series of photographs are to be used for the construction of a controlled mosaic. It is necessary that the photographs be rectified and brought to a common scale at a particular elevation. For practical reasons, the datum selected for the common scale should be the average elevation of the area. The easel control for the rectification can take several forms, three of which will be discussed here. In the first method, where no vertical control exists, a radial-line plot is prepared to the desired scale. The pass points for this plot are selected very carefully by stereoscopic examination because they should lie as near to the average terrain elevation as possible. If some pass points depart considerably from the average elevation but are necessary for the construction of the plot, they are noted. The map positions of the pass points lying near the average elevation are used for the easel control. Since all these points are assumed to lie at nearly the same elevation, the relief displacement of each individual point with respect to the average elevation as a datum will be zero, or nearly so. The rectifier is then oriented empirically by matching the projected images of the pass points to the map positions on the radial-line plot. When an exposure is made, the result is a photograph which has been rectified and brought to the desired scale.

In the second method for rectifying photographs for the construction of a controlled mosaic, the easel control takes the form of a planimetric or topographic map. Such a map should be compiled in a stereoscopic plotting instrument and should be enlarged or reduced to the desired scale at which the mosaic is to be constructed. The negative is placed in the negative carrier of the rectifier, and the map sheet is placed on the easel. The photographic features are matched as well as possible to the map features by orienting the rectifier components. If the terrain varies in elevation, no over-all fit will be obtainable. The features may be made to agree in different portions of the photograph area by using different rectifier orientations and making multiple exposures of one negative. Although all the several portions of a photograph have not been truly rectified, the resulting photographs will be satisfactory for mosaic construction.

In the third method for rectifying photographs to be used in the construction of a controlled mosaic, the map positions of vertical control points are determined in a stereoscopic plotting instrument incidental to the compilation of topographic maps. The easel control is then obtained by displacing the map positions of these points outward from the nadir-point position by the method discussed previously. The photograph is thus rectified, and the datum elevation is brought to the scale of the map.

The effects of the five rectifier motions on the image of a square figure projected from the negative onto the easel are shown in Fig. 10–14. The quadrilateral $ABCD$ is the original figure obtained on the easel when there is a downward slope of the easel as indicated in view (a). The effect of magnification is shown in the same view. The four points A, B, C, and D have been displaced outward to points A', B', C', and D' along radials from the point at which the easel is pierced by the optical axis of the lens. Points A and B on the upward side have not been displaced so much as have points C and D on the downward side. In views (b), (c), (d), and (e), the quadrilateral $A'B'C'D'$ is the net result of each of the four motions after the line $A'B'$ has been made to coincide with the line AB by a change in magnification, a rotation of the sheet on the easel, or a shift of the sheet, or a combination of these three. In this way the effects of the motions are reduced to their effects on points C and D only.

In Fig. 10–14(b), the negative has been rotated about the principal point, this rotation corresponding to a swing motion. Point C has swung from C'' to C', while point D has swung from D'' to D'. After the line $A'B'$ has been made to coincide with AB by swinging the easel sheet and changing the magnification, the net effect of the negative swing motion is seen at points C and D. The side AD has shortened to $A'D'$, while the side BC has lengthened to $B'C'$. The sides $A'D'$ and $B'C'$ do not converge quite so much as do the sides AD and BC. Furthermore, side $C'D'$ is no longer parallel to side $A'B'$.

In Fig. 10–14(c) the tilt of the easel has been increased. So, after $A'B'$ has been made to coincide with AB, points C and D are seen to have moved outward to C' and D'. The entire quadrilateral has been elongated in a direction perpendicular to the tilt axis of the easel, and the convergence of the sides has increased.

In Fig. 10–14(d) the negative has been displaced in a direction parallel to the principal plane of the rectifier and in a direction toward the intersection of the negative plane and the easel plane. This movement is designated as a Y-displacement. The displacements CC' and

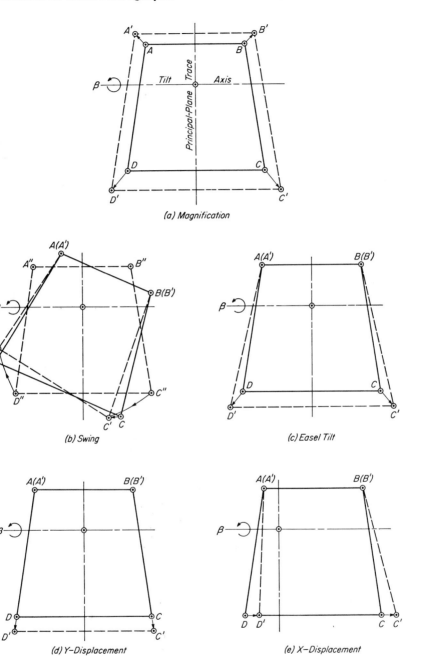

(a) Magnification

(b) Swing

(c) Easel Tilt

(d) Y-Displacement

(e) X-Displacement

FIG. 10–14. Deformation of the easel image. (Altenhofen, *Manual of Photogrammetry*, American Society of Photogrammetry.)

DD' are in a direction opposite to that of the negative, and along the lines BC and AD as shown.

In Fig. 10–14(e) the negative has been displaced to the left in a direction parallel to the tilt axis of the easel. This movement is termed an X-displacement. Such a displacement causes a deformation of the figure similar to a shear deformation. The net displacements of the points are to the right and in a direction parallel to the tilt axis of the easel.

Let it be assumed that a square $abcd$, whose corners represent four control points or pass points on the negative, is projected onto the easel of a rectifier that is set for unit magnification and for zero tilt. With these settings the projection of the image of the square onto the easel will appear as shown in Fig. 10–15(a) at $abcd$. The easel control quadilateral $ABCD$ has been located to the desired datum scale as previously outlined. The problem is to orient the projected image of $abcd$ so that it fits the control quadrilateral.

In Fig. 10–15(a), the image has undergone a magnification that makes side $A'B'$ fit side AB. Note that C' and D' must now be displaced in a direction away from line AB and outward from the center of the format. An analysis of Fig. 10–14 will show that an easel tilt will produce a certain amount of the desired displacement. If at this stage C and D were required to be displaced toward AB and inward toward the center, the entire negative would have to be swung approximately 180°. The line CD would then become the control line.

In Fig. 10–15(b), the easel has been tilted simultaneously with an increase in magnification (to hold the control line). As a result, C has been slightly overcorrected to C', while D has been greatly overcorrected to D'.

In Fig. 10–15(c), a swing and a slight change in magnification have caused line $C'D'$ to lie nearly parallel to CD. If AB were parallel to the tilt axis of the easel at this stage, the swing would be increased until $C'D'$ was, in fact, parallel to CD. The effect of an X-displacement, as shown in Fig. 10–15(d), is to cause lines AD and $A'D'$ and lines BC and $B'C'$ to nearly coincide. If at this stage AB were parallel to the tilt axis of the easel, the X-displacement would be increased until these lines did, in fact, coincide.

In Fig. 10–15(e), a Y-displacement and a change in magnification cause points C' and D' to coincide with the easel control points C and D, respectively. The easel control sheet is now replaced by enlarging paper, and an exposure is made. The result is a rectified photograph brought to the desired scale.

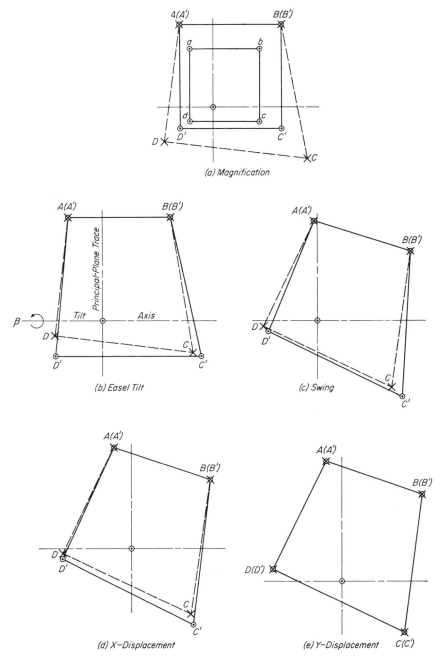

FIG. 10–15. Empirical rectifier orientation. (Altenhofen, *Manual of Photogrammetry*, American Society of Photogrammetry.)

The substance of this section forms the basis for rectification by empirical orientation of the motions of an automatic rectifier. In practice, there are usually more than four control or pass points per photograph on which to orient the rectifier. Since this method is empirical, it is virtually impossible to establish a perfect fit between all the projected images and their easel control positions. Some points, such as those pass points whose elevations depart from the average, may be neglected, and a fit is established at the remaining points.

10–7. Rectifier Operation Based on Plotting-Instrument Readings

In the process of map compilation in a stereoscopic plotting instrument, each photograph is placed in a carrier and is first oriented precisely to ground control. The purpose of this orientation is to recover the elements of exterior orientation of the photograph and the space coordinates (to the map scale) of the exposure station. The photograph carrier in some types of plotting instruments contains scales from which are read the tilt of the oriented carrier (and consequently the photograph) about the flight line, and the tilt of the carrier about a line in the plane of the photograph and normal to the flight line. These components of tilt correspond generally to t_x and t_y of Sec. 9–2 and are designated by the symbols ω and ϕ, respectively. The tilt of the photograph is then the resultant of the components ω and ϕ, as indicated by Eq. 9–7. The position of the nadir point with respect to the principal point can be recovered directly on the map sheet. This process determines the direction of the principal line. The flying height, to the map scale, is determined from the Z-coordinate of the carrier. This height establishes the proper magnification for the rectification of the photograph. The tilt and the direction of the principal line then furnish the remaining scale data necessary to compute the proper settings for the rectifier.

If easel control has been obtained incidental to the mapping operation, the rectifier settings can be tested by noting the coincidence between projected control points and their easel positions. If there is a general disagreement, the motions of the rectifier may be adjusted slightly until agreement is obtained.

Bibliography

American Society of Photogrammetry. *Manual of Photogrammetry* (Menasha, Wisc.: George Banta Co., 1952), Chapter 9.

American Society of Photogrammetry. *Manual of Photogrammetry* (Menasha, Wisc.: George Banta Co., 1966), Chapter 16.

Boughton, O. W., and Sharp, J. V. "Development of Bausch and Lomb Autofocus Rectifier," *Photogrammetric Engineering*, Vol. XIV (1948), p. 349.

CHURCH, EARL. "Notes on the Rectification of Tilted Aerial Photographs," *Bulletin 14*, Syracuse University Press, 1944.

———, and FAULDS, A. H. "Notes on the Rectification of Tilted Aerial Photographs," *Bulletin 1*, Syracuse University Press, 1955.

CLARK, H. W. "The Geometry of Photorectification," *Photogrammetric Engineering*, Vol. XV (1949), p. 288.

ELDIN, H. K. "The Influence of Rectification Upon the Relative Positions of the Features on the Photographic Plate," *Photogrammetric Engineering*, Vol. XVII (1951), p. 511.

GRUNER, H. E. "A Two Stage Rectification System," *Photogrammetric Engineering*, Vol. XXVII (1961), p. 600.

HALLERT, B. *Photogrammetry* (New York: McGraw-Hill Book Co., 1960), Chapter 3.

JONES, A. D. "The Development of the Wild Rectifiers," *Photogrammetric Record*, Vol. V (1966), p. 181.

LEVINE, S. W. "A Slit-Scan Electro Optical Rectifier," *Photogrammetric Engineering*, Vol. XXVII (1961), p. 740.

McFARLAND, F. A. "Rectifying Projection Printer," *Photogrammetric Engineering*, Vol. XV (1949), p. 443.

McHAIL, R. R. "Autofocus Rectifier Modified for Electronic Dodging and Automatic Exposure Control," *Photogrammetric Engineering*, Vol. XXVII (1961), p. 611.

PARENTI, G., and FRIEDMAN, J. "Nistri Telescopic Photoprinter-Rectifier," *Photogrammetric Engineering*, Vol. XXVII (1961), p. 142.

SCHWIDEFSKY, K. *An Outline of Photogrammetry* (New York: Pitman Publishing Corp., 1959), Chapter 6.

SHARP, J. V. "Bausch and Lomb Autofocus Rectifier," *Photogrammetric Engineering*, Vol. XV (1949), p. 436.

TRAENKLE, C. A. "Data, Range and Adjustment of Affinity Transformations in Photogrammetric Rectifiers," *Photogrammetric Engineering*, Vol. XXII (1956), p. 750.

———. "Reduction Process of Resection Problems by Photogrammetric Rectifiers," *Photogrammetric Engineering*, Vol. XXII (1956), p. 741.

U.S. COAST AND GEODETIC SURVEY. "Topographic Manual," Part II, *Special Publication No. 249* (Washington, D.C.: Government Printing Office, 1949), Chapters 3 and 6.

VON GRUBER, O. *Photogrammetry* (Boston: American Photographic Publishing Co., 1942), Chapter 11.

ZELLER, M. *Textbook of Photogrammetry* (London: H. K. Lewis and Co., Ltd., 1952), Chapter 3.

Problems

10–1. The scale data for three photographs taken with a camera whose focal length is 5,800 in. are as follows:

Photograph	Tilt	Swing	Flying Height (ft)
1	2° 53′	205°	14,210
2	1° 22′	10°	15,110
3	3° 20′	136°	15,400

The photographs are to be rectified to bring them to a common scale of 1:24,000 at an elevation of 800 ft. Determine the five settings, given by Eqs. 10–2 through

10–6, which are to be set off in a fixed-lens rectifier whose focal length is 7.600 in., in order to accomplish the proper rectification.

10–2. If the enlargement factor for all three photographs of Prob. 10–1 is arbitrarily selected as 1.5, what is the resulting datum scale of each photograph? What is the scale at the 800 ft elevation?

10–3. Compute the values of α, β, γ, D, and D' to be set off in a tilting-lens rectifier whose focal length is 10.00 in., in order to accomplish the rectification of Prob. 10–1.

10–4. Compute the settings in a fixed-lens rectifier for rectifying a low-oblique photograph whose tilt is 15° 50′. The rectifier lens has an 8.25 in. focal length, and the camera focal length is 6 in. The enlargement factor is to be 2.

Mosaics 11

11–1. Features of Mosaics

A mosaic is a series of overlapping vertical or near-vertical photographs assembled in sequence on a mounting board to form one single picture of the terrain. Although the planning of photography, the preparation of the necessary control, and the photographic rectification required in constructing a mosaic are based on several of the metrical principles discussed thus far in this text, the actual assembly of the photographs is an art requiring a great deal of experience. This chapter is intended to give the student sufficient background to appreciate the advantages and limitations of mosaics, and to be able to compile a simpler mosaic than is usually found in photogrammetric practice. References at the end of this chapter contain descriptions of some of the finer points of the art of mosaic construction, and should be consulted when the assembly of an elaborate mosaic is contemplated.

A mosaic is similar to a planimetric map in certain respects. It is an overhead view of the terrain and, like a map, shows the relative horizontal positions of terrain features. The mosaic has an over-all average scale comparable to the scale of a planimetric map. Once made, it can be reproduced in quantity just as a map is reproduced.

A mosaic differs from a map in many respects. The mosaic is composed of a series of perspective projections of the terrain, whereas a map is a single orthographic projection. A mosaic assembled from nonrectified and nonratioed photographs contains local relief displacements, tilt displacements, and nonuniform scales, but a map theoretically shows each and every map feature in its correct horizontal position at a uniform scale. A mosaic assembled from rectified and ratioed prints will still contain local relief displacements, and these displacements will cause mismatching of images between the lines of contact of adjacent photographs. Map features appear as realistic photographic images on a mosaic, whereas map features must be portrayed by standard symbols on a map.

To varying degrees of accuracy, a mosaic is a map substitute. The sizes of the errors depend on the amount of terrain relief, the exactness of photographic rectification and scale ratioing, and the accuracy and density of control to which the photographs are fitted in the process of assembly. Photographs taken over flat terrain will more nearly resemble a planimetric map, especially when the photographs have been rectified. Photographs taken over mountainous terrain, no matter how precisely they have been rectified and brought to some common datum scale, will always exhibit relief displacement, local variation in scale, and mismatching.

11–2. Advantages of Mosaics

For use as map substitutes, mosaics have an advantage over maps in that they may be compiled more rapidly and more economically than maps. A mosaic shows a vast amount of detail, large and small, and can be used to recognize and interpret terrain features more readily than can a map. No detail of the terrain is omitted on a mosaic, whereas a map portrays a relatively incomplete picture of the terrain. This incompleteness is due to cost considerations involved in map compilation and also to the difficulty of symbolizing an infinite variety of terrain features on a map. To the layman unaccustomed to reading and interpreting maps the mosaic is far more intelligible, because terrain images are presented to him as they would actually look from overhead. Even though the overhead view itself is relatively unfamiliar to the layman, he nevertheless may form a fairly accurate opinion of the terrain features which show on a mosaic.

11–3. Disadvantages of Mosaics

The basic disadvantage of a mosaic, when it is to be used as a map substitute, is the inaccuracy in the horizontal positions of features because of relief, tilt, and unequal scales. On a mosaic used simply in a qualitative manner, the inaccuracies are of no consequence. In such a case, quantitative measurements are made on a map and the mosaic is used for interpretive purposes. Since a mosaic resembles a planimetric map, there is no quantitative method of obtaining elevations or configuration of the terrain in the vertical direction unless contour lines are superimposed over the mosaic before it is reproduced. A qualitative study of the topography is possible to a limited extent, however, because light models and shadows on the mosaic reveal shapes, changes in slopes, gulleys, and other features.

The wealth of terrain detail which appears on a mosaic is often a disadvantage, because it tends to obscure those features which are of primary importance to the user of the mosaic. These features would normally be portrayed on a map by some standard symbol, easily recognizable by the map user. Where features do not appear so prominently as desired, they may be annotated either directly on the mosaic or on a transparent overlay which is oriented to the mosaic.

11–4. Types of Mosaics

A mosaic of the simplest form is one in which each succeeding photograph is laid down untrimmed on a piece of plywood or fiberboard, matched to preceding photographs, and stapled into place. The photographs are laid in such a sequence as to allow the photo number and flight number of each photograph to appear on the finished assembly. This assembly is called an *index mosaic* or a *photo index*. In Fig. 11–1

Fig. 11–1. Assembling an index mosaic.

is shown an index mosaic in the process of being assembled. An effort is made to match images between successive photographs and to control the directions of the flight lines during assembly, but there is no control besides this visual control. An index mosaic is used as a file system for photographs, since an inspection of the index mosaic or a copy thereof will indicate the photo number and flight number of a particular set of photographs which may be desired. The photographs may then be ordered or pulled from the files by their index numbers. If an index mosaic is assembled immediately after photography has been taken and processed, it will reveal any gapping in flight lines or any deviation from the overlap and sidelap required for the particular process for which the photographs were taken. Since the assembly is fairly rapid, re-flights may be made shortly after the original photography has been obtained.

A mosaic which is assembled from a single strip of photography is called a *strip mosaic*. The photographs are prepared, prior to assembly, by trimming and featheredging, as described in Sec. 11–10. Control may be in the form of a single strip radial-line plot, a highway or railroad center line plotted on the mounting board to the scale of the photography, or an azimuth line as described in Sec. 11–7. Care is taken to obtain a good image match along the trimmed edge of the photograph being laid in position. The strip mosaic is an invaluable adjunct to maps when any type of route study is underway, such as for a highway, railroad, transmission line, pipe line, canal, or set of flood-control levees.

A mosaic which is assembled without regard to any plotted control is called an *uncontrolled mosaic*. An index mosaic is a form of uncontrolled mosaic. The photographs used in the assembly of an uncontrolled mosaic are contact prints of the original negatives. No effort is made to rectify the photographs or to bring them to a common datum scale.

Except when used for an index mosaic, the photographs are carefully trimmed and featheredged prior to assembly. During assembly, every effort is made to obtain a good visual match between successive photographs, especially along the trimmed edge of each succeeding top photograph. The middle photograph of the center flight is pasted to the mounting board first, and then the entire center flight is laid down. The adjacent flights are laid in succession, each strip being started with its middle photograph. The cumulative matching errors will appear at the four corners of the completed mosaic.

In order to localize the matching errors and to reduce them as much as possible, matching between photographs is held along features lying at a constant or nearly constant elevation. Railroads and most highways are limited in grade, and a network of roads and railroads in the area will afford some visual control at a nearly constant elevation. Large streams and rivers have gentle gradients, and so the drainage network may afford a certain amount of visual control. Mismatching of images due to tilt and relief displacements and to scale differences between successive photographs cannot be avoided, however, especially as the work progresses out toward the corners.

A mosaic assembled to fit control which has been plotted on the mounting board is called a *controlled mosaic*. This plotted control may be of a very rudimentary form, such as an azimuth line described in Sec. 11–7, or it may be very precise and complete, such as a planimetric or topographic base map brought to the scale of the photographs. The photographs may consist of direct contact prints, of prints which have all been ratioed to a given datum scale in an enlarger, or of prints which have been fully rectified and ratioed in a rectifier. Some photogrammetrists restrict the use of the term controlled mosaic to one assembled from prints that have been fully rectified and ratioed and have been laid to fit control obtained by means of a radial-line plot or a base map. Any other form of controlled mosaic is designated as a semicontrolled mosaic.

11–5. Factors in Flight Planning for Mosaic Photography

The three factors which affect the photography taken for mosaic construction are the focal length, the flying height, and the overlap and sidelap. If the photography is to be taken expressly for mosaics, the longest available focal length should be used. The aerial camera to be used need not meet the requirements of a precision mapping camera. The reconnaissance camera, discussed in Chapter 2, is suitable for mosaic photography. Because of a longer focal length, the flying height may be increased for a given desired photographic scale.

There are three advantages in maintaining as high a flying height as possible. 1) The relief displacement, for a given photographic scale, is reduced as the flying height (and the focal length) is increased. 2) For a given photographic tilt, a given photo size, and a given scale, the displacements due to tilt are reduced as the flying height (and focal length) is increased. 3) The variations in scales between successive photographs are reduced as the flying height increases, provided that the change in the flying height between photographs is the same at higher altitudes than at lower altitudes. The variation in flying height can, in fact, be held smaller at higher altitudes.

The overlap and sidelap have the effect of fixing the total effective amount of each photograph to be used in assembling the mosaic. The full lines in Fig. 11–2(a) represent the edges of a photograph containing 55 per cent overlap and 20 per cent sidelap, and the dashed lines indicate the effective amount of the photograph which will be used in mosaic construction. On a 9- by 9-in. photograph, the radial distance from the center of the photograph to each corner of the effective area is about 4.05 in. In Fig. 11–2(b) are shown the edges of a photograph containing 65 per cent overlap and 40 per cent sidelap and also the effective area which will be used for the mosaic. The radial distance to each corner of that area has been reduced to about 3.15 in. The reduction amounts to almost 25 per cent.

Since both relief displacement and tilt displacement are proportional to the distance out from the center of the photograph (actually from the nadir point and the isocenter, respectively), their effect on mismatching can be reduced by increasing overlap and sidelap. If the photographs are to be rectified, the tilt displacement is of no consequence. Nevertheless, the relief displacement will be present. Where the area to be photographed for mosaic construction is fairly flat, then the overlap and sidelap should be reduced to a practical minimum for the sake of over-all economy, but the reduction in lap must be consistent with the prevention of gapping in the flight line. On the other hand, where the topography is rugged or where the flying height over rolling terrain is limited, the overlap and sidelap should be sufficient to reduce the effect of relief displacement to the allowable limit.

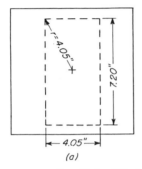
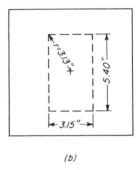

(a)   (b)

Fig. 11–2. Effective portion of photograph
for mosaic construction.

When photography is taken to serve the dual purpose of providing aerial photographs both for the compilation of topographic maps and for the construction of mosaics, the requirements for the mapping photography will control the factors in flight planning. A lens with a short focal length and a wide angle must be used in a precision mapping camera in order to obtain a desirable base-height ratio. The flying height will be dictated by the required vertical accuracy of the map, and the overlap and sidelap will be as small as possible for reasons of economy.

11–6. Preparation of Control

This section pertains only to controlled or semicontrolled mosaics. The control for a strip mosaic is plotted directly on the mounting board, the procedure depending on the type of control. An azimuth line consists of one continuous straight line drawn on the board by means of a pencil and a straightedge. If the control is provided by means of a radial-line plot, the first step is to plot a grid or reference line directly on the mounting board. The control points are then plotted. Finally, the radial-line plot is assembled on the mounting board. If the radial-line plot has been used for rectifying the photographs as discussed in Sec. 10–5, the pass points and principal points may be transferred to the mounting board by scaling from the grid for the radial-line plot or by using a pantograph.

For a series of strips, the azimuth lines are located on the mounting board in succession, as described in Sec. 11–7. If a radial-line plot is to be used to furnish the control for a multiple-strip mosaic, it may be plotted directly on the mounting board, or it may be transferred from the base sheet for the radial-line plot by laying out a grid to the scale of the (rectified) photographs, scaling the coordinates of the pass points and the principal points from the base-sheet grid, and transferring these points to the mounting board by their coordinates.

When a planimetric or topographic map is used for the mosaic control, the map sheet must be fastened to the mounting board with a waterproof paste or glue. The map sheet may then be sized to insure proper adhesion of the photographs.

11–7. Azimuth Line

Where no horizontal photo control is available, or where the accuracy requirements do not demand more precise control, an azimuth line or a series of azimuth lines may be used to afford simple control. The azimuth line is prepared as follows: The photographs are laid on the map table in proper sequence, care being taken to match images between successive photographs. As each photograph is placed, it is held in position along its edges by small weights. A straightedge is laid over the strip so as to pass through the centers of as many photographs as possible. The position of the straightedge is shown in Fig. 11–3(a). A fine line is drawn across the face of the top photograph, as photograph 33 of Fig. 11–3(a). The photographs are now separated. Two points are selected on the line on the first photograph which appear also on the next photograph. These points should be as widely separated as possible. The two points are then carefully marked on the adjacent photograph, as shown at a and b in Fig. 11–3(b). A fine line is drawn across the face of this photograph, and a new pair of points, c and d, are chosen which appear also on the third photograph, as shown in Fig. 11–3(c). A fine line is drawn across the face of this photograph, as shown in Fig. 11–3(d), and the process is continued throughout the remainder of the strip.

Assume that one strip of photographs of a multiple strip mosaic has been trimmed, featheredged, and fastened on the mounting board to conform to the control furnished by an azimuth line, as AA in Fig. 11–4. An adjacent strip is prepared by prolonging an azimuth line across the

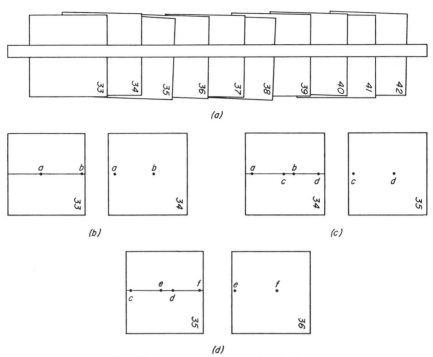

FIG. 11–3. Constructing an azimuth line.

face of each photograph in the strip. At regular intervals of say four or
five photographs in a strip, a photograph of the new strip is laid over its
corresponding photograph in the preceding strip (the first strip in this
example), and details at or near the average elevation are carefully
matched. The photographs are held in place by weights. The distances
between the azimuth line AA and the segments of the azimuth line on
the selected photographs of the next strip, as photos 74, 79, and 83 of
Fig. 11–4, are measured with a beam compass, a pair of dividers, or a
scale, and distances m, n, and p are obtained. The photographs are removed, and the distances m, n, and p are laid off from line AA to locate
several points (three points in the illustration) on the new azimuth line

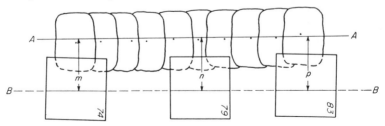

FIG. 11–4. Locating azimuth line for second flight strip.

BB. The line *BB* is drawn by passing the straightedge through the points to obtain the best average fit. The photographs are then trimmed, feather-edged, and mounted to conform to the azimuth line *BB.* This procedure is repeated for each strip.

The azimuth line for control in lieu of horizontal control is very useful in that it prevents the flight strips from swinging off line as the photographs are mounted. It also prevents errors caused by mismatches from accumulating out toward the corners of the mosaic. This type of control is very easy to prepare and is recommended to the student in his first attempts at constructing mosaics.

11–8. Mounting Boards

Mounting boards in actual photogrammetric practice are fairly large, from about 4 by 8 ft to about 6 by 8 ft. Several types of mounting board may be used. A veneer of birch or maple plywood that is smoothly sanded and periodically sealed with a resin sealer is fairly satisfactory. Fir plywood is not satisfactory because the alternating bands of hard and soft wood will cause ridges to appear in the finished mosaic. Open-grained veneers, like walnut, mahogany, and oak, are not recommended. A piece of masonite ¼-in. thick is a very satisfactory mounting board, although its hardness all but precludes the construction of a radial-line plot directly on the board. Inlaid linoleum of a light neutral color cemented to a piece of ¾-in. fir plywood is satisfactory for use with most mosaic adhesives. A mounting board known as Vehosote, which is specially prepared for mosaic construction, is excellent. It presents a firm, smooth surface that is not too porous, and it can be used for constructing a radial-line plot.

11–9. Adhesive

The most convenient adhesive to work with in mounting prints in mosaic construction is gum arabic. It comes in powdered form or in tear-drop form. Although the powdered form is more expensive, it is easier to prepare in small batches. All that is required is first to form a paste by stirring the powder and a small amount of warm water, and then to add more warm water and stir until the mixture attains the consistency of strained honey. Gum arabic in the tear-drop form must be soaked in water for two or three days. The proportions of the mixture should be 5 lb of tears for each gallon of water. To prevent the mixture from becoming sour, 3 or 4 ounces of salicylic acid should be added to each gallon of adhesive. Also, a pint of glycerine added to each gallon of adhesive will prevent the mounted photographs from becoming brittle and from curling at the edges.

11–10. Preparation of the Photographs

If a controlled mosaic is to be constructed, the control points must be marked on the photographs and circled, a grease pencil being used for this purpose. The control points consist of all principal points, conjugate principal points, and pass points, as well as all photo control points obtained from a radial-line plot. If some of the pass points chosen for the rectifying process were excluded from the easel control because their elevations departed considerably from the average elevation, these pass points need not be marked when laying the mosaic.

When more than one photograph has been prepared from a single negative with different rectifier settings or orientations (see Sec. 10–6), only the control points used in the rectifier for each photograph are marked on that photograph. During the rectification process, each photograph must be keyed to certain control points by writing the control-point numbers on the back of the print before it is developed. Fine lines should be drawn on each photograph from the principal point to each of the two conjugate principal points, in order that the flight-line segments may be matched to the radial-line control which has been plotted on the mounting board.

If the control takes the form of an azimuth line, the control line is, of course, located on each photograph as described in Sec. 11–7.

If the control consists of a base map which has been cemented to the mounting board, the photographs need not be marked, because each photograph is fitted to the map control by continuous images appearing both on the photograph and the map.

Whether the mosaic is controlled or uncontrolled, each photograph must be properly trimmed and featheredged before it is pasted into place. When the trim line has been established (see Sec. 11–11), a single-edge razor blade is used to just barely cut through the emulsion of the photograph, as shown in an exaggerated section in Fig. 11–5 and in Fig. 11–6(a).

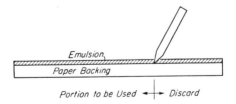

Emulsion

Paper Backing

Portion to be Used ◄─┼─► Discard

FIG. 11–5. Cutting through photograph emulsion.

The photograph is picked up and bent back along the cut to expose the paper backing, as shown in Fig. 11–6(b). The photograph is then placed with the emulsion side down, and the discard portion is torn back toward the portion to be used, as shown in Fig. 11–6(c). This process gives

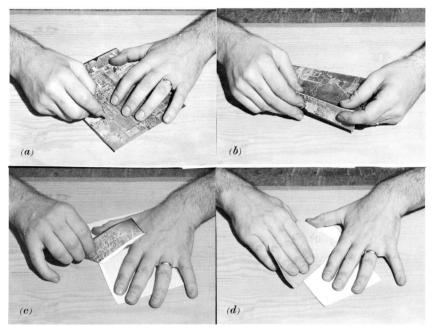

FIG. 11-6. Preparation of photograph for mounting.

the edge of the photograph a feathered appearance. Finally, a fine sand-paper is used to smooth out the featheredge, as shown in Fig. 11-6(d). The strokes of the sandpaper should be out toward and perpendicular to the trimmed edge.

11-11. Mounting the Photographs

The materials necessary for mounting a print, in addition to the adhesive, razor blade, and sandpaper, are a pan or pail of water, two or three cellulose-acetate sponges, a squeegee made from $\frac{1}{16}$- or $\frac{1}{8}$-in. celluloid whose edges have been rounded by sanding and whose corners have been well rounded to prevent their tearing the photographs, and one or more needles or pins. The first photograph to be mounted is trimmed and featheredged on all four sides, about $\frac{1}{2}$ in. in from the edges of the uncut photograph. The adhesive is spread onto the back of the print by hand, and the print is then placed in position on the mounting board.

When an uncontrolled mosaic is laid, all that is required is that the first photograph be placed so as to allow the remaining photographs to fit on the board. When a controlled mosaic is being laid to fit a radial-line plot, a needle is pushed through the print at the principal point, and a second needle is pushed through another control point. The needle passing through the principal point is centered on the mounting-board position of the principal point; the other needle is centered on the corresponding control point on the mounting board. This operation positions and orients the photograph on the mounting board.

Before the print is squeegeed down, the coincidence of other control points may be checked visually by rapidly flipping the edges of the photograph over the mounting board. A slight amount of rotation may be necessary to strike an average coincidence of all points. However, the position of the principal point must be held fixed. When a smaller portion of a multiple-print photograph is laid, all the control points should fit, because that portion of the print has been rectified to fit these control points on the rectifier easel. If the control is an azimuth line, it is sufficient to make the line on the photograph coincide with the line plotted on the board.

The photograph is then secured by means of the squeegee, working from the center outward (on the first photograph). The squeegee should be pressed gently, to prevent undue stretching of the print. All air pockets and surplus adhesive must be removed by means of the squeegee. It is quite often found helpful to bend the squeegee slightly by pressure of the thumb, when forcing out the bubbles from underneath the print. The method of working the squeegee is shown in Fig. 11–7, where a celluloid protractor is used for the purpose.

When the print is securely in place, all surplus adhesive is wiped from the surface of the print with a damp sponge. This is moved outward from the center of the print, in the direction in which the squeegee was worked. Adhesive is then wiped from the board by means of the sponge.

The next print is laid over the mounted print and matched by images. By use of a grease pencil, a trimming line is marked on the photograph along a line located near the middle of the overlap area. The position of this line may be varied slightly, due consideration being given to tone match between the two photographs, to the avoidance of cuts across roads which may show mismatching, and to other requirements. Trimming along the middle of the overlap of each succeeding print exposes only the very center of each photograph in the finished mosaic. This practice tends to reduce mismatching caused by relief displacement.

The photograph is trimmed along the marked trim line and along the remaining three sides about $\frac{1}{2}$ to 1 in. in from the edges. The print is then featheredged and sanded, and the adhesive is applied. The print is matched to the principal point and to the remainder of the control. If an azimuth line is the control, the photograph is oriented on the line and slid back and forth until flipping indicates that images at the average elevation or along roads or streams coincide. If an uncontrolled mosaic

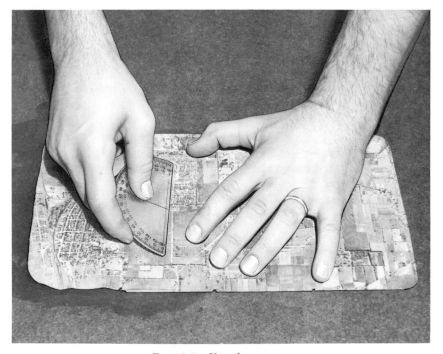

FIG. 11–7. Use of squeegee.

is being constructed, the second and subsequent photographs are oriented by matching image details.

The second print is squeegeed into place, and the excess adhesive is wiped from the face of the print and from the board. The directions in which both the squeegee and the sponge must be worked are shown in Fig. 11–8 for different stages of the assembly. Note that the direction is always toward the edge of the print being mounted.

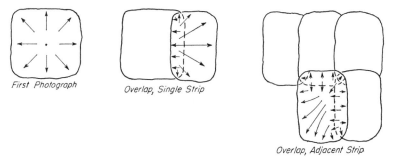

First Photograph

Overlap, Single Strip

Overlap, Adjacent Strip

FIG. 11–8. Stages of assembly, showing directions in which squeegee and sponge are worked.

11–12. Preparation of the Mosaic for Copying

After the assembly of all the photographs has been completed, the grease-pencil marks are removed from the face of the prints with cleaning fluid, care being taken not to brush against the edges of the prints. If a grid is to show on the reproductions, it may be ruled directly on the face of the mosaic by reference to the grid lines on the mounting board extending beyond the limits of the mosaic. The mosaic may be trimmed by mounting a white border along the four edges. It is necessary to prepare a title, which contains a graphic scale. The graphic scale is desirable because it represents the correct scale at any enlargement or reduction.

11–13. Copying and Reproduction

The mosaic is mounted on the easel board of a copy camera. The usual characteristics of a copy camera are a process lens with a high resolution and a flat field, and a large negative carrier up to 40 by 40 in. in size. The mosaic is brought to the desired enlargement or reduction on the ground glass of the copy camera and is then copied, either on one negative or else in sections. The resulting negatives are used for photographic reproduction of the mosaic in quantity, usually by contact printing.

When the mosaic is to be reproduced by dry-process reproduction, such as in an ozalid machine, a halftone screen is placed in the copy camera and a halftone negative is made. A halftone positive can then be made by contact printing, a special type of reproduction material being used. The positive is then used to reproduce the mosaic in quantity by a dry process.

Bibliography

AMERICAN SOCIETY OF PHOTOGRAMMETRY. *Manual of Photogrammetry* (Menasha, Wisc.: George Banta Co., 1952),) Chapter 10.
———. *Manual of Photogrammetry* (Menasha, Wisc.: George Banta Co., 1966), Chapter 17.
HALLERT, B. *Photogrammetry* (New York: McGraw-Hill Book Co., 1960), Chapter 4.
HEATH, G. R. "Improvements in the Stereo-Mosaic," *Photogrammetric Engineering,* Vol. XXIII (1957), p. 536.
———. "The Stereo-Mosaic, A New Mapping Technique," *Photogrammetric Engineering,* Vol. XVI (1950). p. 152.
McNEIL, G. T. "The Wet Process of Laying Mosaics," *Photogrammetric Engineering,* Vol. XV (1949), p. 315.
MEYER, D. "Mosaics You Can Make," *Photogrammetric Engineering,* Vol. XXVIII (1962), p. 167.
MORANDA, P. B. "A Study of the Propagation of Errors in a Simplified Photographic Mosaic," *Photogrammetric Engineering* Vol. XXVI, No. 4 (Sept. 1960), p. 582.
ROSENFIELD, G. H. "The Accuracy of Mosaics," *Photogrammetric Engineering,* Vol. XXI (1955), p. 670.

Stereoscopic Plotting Instruments 12

12–1. Main Components

A stereoscopic plotting instrument is an optical instrument of high precision. To use such an instrument, a pair of overlapping photographs are first placed in a pair of carriers and are oriented to ground control. Then the rays from the two photographs are projected and caused to intersect in the measuring space of the instrument to form a theoretically perfect model of the terrain. The instrument will be referred to simply as a plotter. The photograph carriers are called projectors or cameras. The model of the terrain will be referred to simply as a model.

The model formed by the projection of rays from the two projectors is at a known scale, which is established by the scale used for plotting the ground control. The horizontal scale and the vertical scale are the same. The operator may view the model stereoscopically, that is, in three dimensions. A measuring mark, visible to the operator at all times, is used to measure the model in all three dimensions. When aerial photographs are used, the real or apparent up-and-down motion of the measuring mark is a measure of elevation, to the scale of the model, and the movement of the mark in a horizontal plane is a measure of the change in the X- and Y-coordinates between points, to the scale of the model.

The space position of the measuring mark in the model can be read from graduations, or can be measured by scaling, to give the space position of any point appearing in the model, to the scale of the model. The horizontal movement of the measuring mark throughout the model is transmitted to a plotting pencil, which traces out the map positions of the features appearing in the overlap area of the two photographs forming the model. The plotting pencil may move at the same scale as the model, or it may move at a larger or a smaller scale than the model, the relative movement depending on the type of plotter.

The position of a contour line is traced out by the plotting pencil when the Z-position of the measuring mark is held fixed at the desired elevation of the contour line. In this way the operator locates points of equal elevation in the model by a continuous trace along the surface of the model. The contour lines thus plotted, together with the planimetric features previously mentioned, are plotted in orthographic projection on a map sheet, producing a topographic map at the desired scale.

From the foregoing general remarks, the student will realize that a plotter has four general components: 1) a projection system, 2) a viewing system, 3) a measuring system, and 4) a tracing system. These components are contained in all plotters, but their features vary among different types of instruments.

12–2. Multiplex Instrument

Because the design of the Multiplex instrument is so simple and direct, it lends itself well to a discussion of all the features and operations of a plotting instrument. In Fig. 12–1, a pair of Multiplex projectors are suspended from a horizontal bar, which represents the general direction of the line of flight. A pair of reduced pictures, printed on glass plates, are placed in the two projectors above the projector lenses. These small

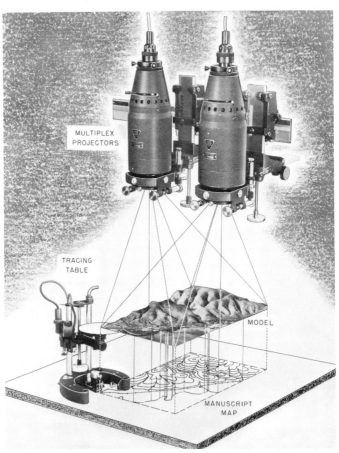

FIG. 12–1. Pair of Multiplex projectors forming a stereoscopic model. (Courtesy of U. S. Geological Survey.)

glass photographs are called *diapositives*. As will be discussed later, the reduction of the original negative from a 9- by 9-in. size down to the size of the diapositive depends on the principal distance of the projector lens, which is about 30 mm, and on the focal length of the aerial camera lens which took the photographs.

Each of the two projectors has six motions, three translational motions and three rotational motions. The three translational motions are shown in Fig. 12–2. Each projector may be moved independently in a direction parallel to the supporting bar, that is, in the direction of the flight line. This motion is referred to as the *X-motion*. Each projector may also be moved independently in a horizontal direction and perpendicu-

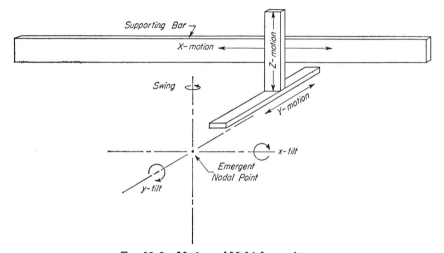

FIG. 12–2. Motions of Multiplex projector.

lar to the supporting bar. This motion is referred to as the *Y-motion*. Moreover, each projector may be moved independently in a vertical direction and perpendicular to the supporting bar. This motion is called the *Z-motion*. The three translation motions are used to establish the air base in the plotting instrument between two projectors. They are thus referred to as base component motions *BX*, *BY*, and *BZ*.

The three rotational motions of each projector are also indicated in Fig. 12–2. A projector may be rotated about a line generally parallel with the supporting bar and passing through the emergent nodal point of the projector lens. This rotation is called the *x-tilt*. The projector may be rotated similarly about a horizontal line which is perpendicular to the supporting bar and which passes through the emergent nodal point of the projector lens. This rotation is called the *y-tilt*. The projector may also be rotated about the optical axis of the projector lens. This rotation is called the *swing* of the projector, but it should not be confused with the swing of a photograph as defined in Chapter 3. It should be noted that the axes of rotation are mutually perpendicular. These rotations correspond to the rotations ω, ϕ, and κ introduced in Sec. 3–14. The ϕ-axis is the primary rotational axis of the Multiplex instrument. Its direction with respect to the supporting bar remains unchanged, whereas both the x-axis (ω-axis) and the optical axis (κ-axis) are rotated during the orientation process.

The six motions of each projector are used to orient the projectors in their correct space positions and attitudes with respect to the map sheet, as described in Secs. 12–4 and 12–6.

Light rays from a lamp located in the upper part of the projector pass through the diapositive. As indicated in Fig. 12–3, the images on

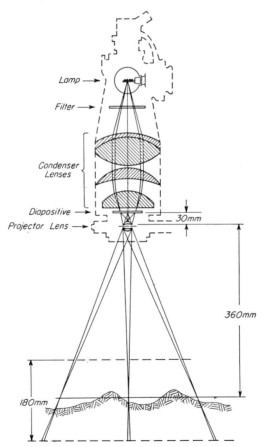

Fig. 12–3. Multiplex-projector optical system. (Pennington, *Manual of Photogrammetry*, 2d ed., American Society of Photogrammetry.)

the diapositive are projected downward into the area underneath the projector, and come to focus in a plane parallel with the plane of the diapositive. Because of the small diaphragm lying between the elements of the projector lens, the focus is maintained within an acceptable tolerance through a vertical distance of about 180 mm; in other words, the depth of focus is about 180 mm. If two projectors are properly oriented in space, the various conjugate rays projected from the two projectors will intersect each other in the space beneath the projectors, and a continuous model will be formed in the measuring space, as shown in Fig. 12–1 Such a projection system is referred to as a direct-optical, double-projection system. It produces a theoretically perfect model of the terrain to the scale of the map.

When studying Fig. 12–1, the student will note that the situation existing at the time of photography is re-created at a small scale in the instrument. The two projectors represent the two positions of the aerial camera, properly oriented to the ground. The distance between the emergent nodal points of the projector lenses represents the air base, to the map scale. The vertical distance from a nodal point down to the model represents the flying height above the terrain.

The intersections of conjugate rays must be viewed by the operator in such a manner that he may see the model created by projection. In the first place, the rays must be intercepted by a diffused reflecting surface. This is the top surface of the small white disc of the tracing table shown in Fig. 12–1. The disc is called the tracing-table platen. If the conjugate images projected by the two projectors are received on the platen surface, and if the operator views the platen, he will see a double image of the terrain features.

In order that the model may be seen stereoscopically, one of the images must be seen with one eye only while the other image is seen with the other eye only. A blue-green filter is placed under the lamp of one projector, say, the left-hand one, giving a blue-green color to the image projected onto the platen by that projector. The position of the filter is shown in Fig. 12–3. A red filter placed under the lamp of the right-hand projector gives a red color to the image projected onto the platen by that projector. The operator now sees a double image of the terrain features on the platen, one being blue-green and the other red. These images may be made to coincide at different points by raising or lowering the platen, as diagrammed for points *a* and *b* in Fig. 12–4.

If the operator puts on a pair of spectacles the left lens of which is blue-green and the right lens of which is red, he no longer sees a double image. Instead, since the left eye now sees only the image projected by the left projector and the right eye now sees only the image projected by the right projector, the operator can see the terrain model stereoscopically.

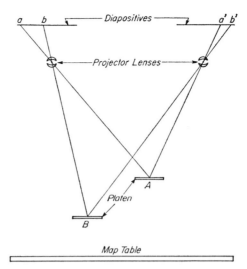

FIG. 12–4.   Coincidence of double images at
different platen heights.

This model, in fact, has three dimensions, and is not to be considered as a virtual stereoscopic image as seen beneath a simple stereoscope.

The method of viewing just discussed is called the *anaglyph system* of viewing reflected light. This viewing system is common to all direct-optical, double-projection instruments that are based on the Multiplex design.

The tracing-table platen contains a small hole about 0.3 mm in diameter directly in the center of the platen. A small source of light is located under the hole, and it forms a small pin point of light as viewed from the top. This pin point of light is the measuring mark of the Multiplex instrument. An up-and-down motion of the tracing-table platen causes an up-and-down motion of the measuring mark. This up-and-down motion is read on a dial or counter on the tracing table, either in millimeters or directly in feet of ground elevation. A reading in millimeters is converted into feet of elevation by applying the scale of the model and adding a constant (see Sec. 12–6).

Directly under the measuring mark is a pencil holder containing a length of pencil lead. The point of the pencil may be adjusted so that it lies directly beneath the measuring mark or, more precisely stated, so that it lies at the foot of a perpendicular dropped from the measuring mark to the map table on which the tracing table rests. The pencil may be raised from or lowered to the map sheet by means of a lever on the tracing table.

Assume that a map sheet containing grid lines is located on the map table in its proper position with respect to the model. If the operator wishes to measure the space coordinates of a point in the model, he first moves the tracing table (with the pencil raised from the map sheet) to the vicinity of the point. He then raises or lowers the platen until the measuring mark is in apparent contact with the stereoscopic model precisely at the desired point. The counter on the tracing table is now read to give the Z-coordinate of the point, either directly in feet of elevation or in millimeters to the scale of the model. The operator lowers the pencil to the map sheet, marking the orthographic or map position of the point on the map sheet. The X- and Y-coordinates may now be scaled by reference to the grid lines. This is the measuring system of the Multiplex instrument. Note that the measuring system is rather indirect, inasmuch as the X- and Y-coordinates must be scaled after the map position of the point has been plotted.

If the manual movement of the tracing table over the map sheet were replaced by a carriage wherein the entire tracing table were moved along mutually perpendicular axes by means of rotations of a set of lead screws, the rotations of the lead screws could be registered on counters, and the X- and Y-coordinates could be read directly from the counters. Such a system of measurement is incorporated in several types of plotting instruments and can be adapted to the Multiplex instrument.

The tracing system or plotting system of the Multiplex consists of the measuring mark, the manual movement of the tracing table over the map sheet, and the plotting pencil. The tracing table rests on three highly polished, flat, agate bearings, or bosses, which glide rather smoothly over the map sheet when guided by the operator.

Assume that the planimetric features in the model are to be plotted in their orthographic positions on the map sheet. With the pencil point in the raised position, the operator moves the tracing table to the vicinity of the feature, raises or lowers the measuring mark until it is in apparent contact with the feature, and then lowers the pencil to the map sheet. As he guides the tracing table along the feature, he must raise the measuring mark if the elevation is increasing or must lower the measuring mark if the elevation is decreasing, in order to keep the mark in apparent contact with the model surface. A continuous orthographic trace is produced by the pencil on the map sheet underneath the model. This idea is shown in a general way in Fig. 12–1.

Suppose that a specific contour line is to be traced on the map sheet. The platen is raised or lowered to give the correct reading on the counter corresponding to the desired elevation of the contour line. This step places the measuring mark at the desired elevation. The operator now moves the tracing table (with the pencil in the raised position) until he finds a point where the measuring mark comes into apparent contact with the model surface, and then lowers the pencil to the map sheet. By examining the stereoscopic view of the model slightly ahead of the measuring mark, he can move the tracing table in such a direction as to keep the measuring mark in contact with the surface of the model at all times. Since the platen is fixed in elevation, the line traced out by the measuring mark, and hence by the plotting pencil, is a line of constant elevation or a contour line.

When one contour line has been traced completely, the operator then moves the tracing-table platen up or down to the next succeeding contour-line elevation, lifts the pencil, moves the tracing table until the measuring mark again coincides with the model, lowers the pencil, and finally traces out this contour line.

12–3. Interior Orientation

The steps in interior orientation include preparing the diapositive to the correct size, eliminating the radial distortion of the aerial camera

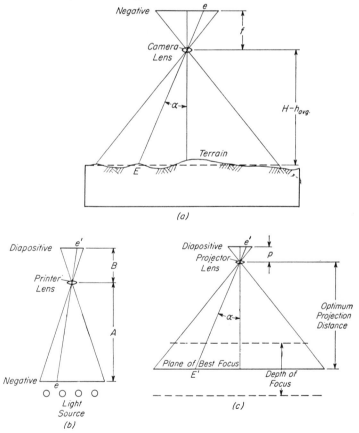

Fɪɢ. 12–5. Relationship between aerial negative and diapositive by proper reduction.

lens, and centering the principal point of the diapositive on the optical axis of the projector lens.

In Fig. 12–5 (a) the camera focal length is f, and in Fig. 12–5 (c) the principal distance of the diapositive is p. As indicated in view (a), a ray of light from ground point E enters the camera lens at an angle α with the optical axis of the camera lens, and appears at e on the negative. As represented in view (b), the negative has been reduced in a reduction printer, two types of which are shown in Fig. 12–6, to make a diapositive containing image e'. As indicated in Fig. 12–5 (c), the diapositive is projected through the projector lens, and the ray from e' is projected to E' in the plane of best focus. The ray $e'E'$ makes the same angle with the optical axis of the projector lens as the ray Ee made with the optical axis of the camera lens at the time of exposure. In order to re-create this true angular relationship, the distances A and B in Fig. 12–5 (b) must bear the following relationship:

$$\frac{A}{B} = \frac{f}{p} \tag{12–1}$$

in which A is the distance in the reduction printer from the plane of the negative to the front nodal point of the reduction-printer lens; B is the distance from the emergent nodal point of the reduction-printer lens to the diapositive plane; f is the focal length of the aerial camera lens; and p is the distance in the Multiplex projector from the diapositive plane to

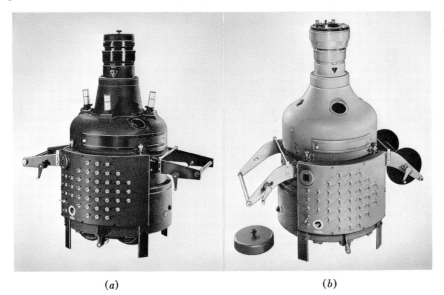

(a)   (b)

Fɪɢ. 12–6. (a) Multiplex reduction printer. (b) Balplex reduction printer. (Courtesy of Bausch and Lomb Optical Co.)

the front (upper) nodal point of the projector lens, called the principal distance of the projector lens. All terms are expressed in the same units.

By this reduction, the rays leaving the projector lens theoretically bear the same angular relationship to one another as did the corresponding rays entering the camera at the time of exposure. Since the projector lens is practically distortion-free, the relationship between the rays is in error by the amount of radial distortion of the aerial camera lens contained in the negative.

Two methods are employed for producing a diapositive in which the aerial camera lens distortion is practically eliminated. The first method employs a reduction printer lens whose distortion characteristics match those of the nominal distortion of a particular type of lens, as for example the Metrogon lens discussed in Sec. 2–11. This correction counteracts to a great degree the effect of the radial distortion of the images contained in the negative, leaving only a slight amount of residual distortion. The second method, which allows for more flexibility, employs a correction plate interposed between the negative and a distortion-free reduction printer lens. The correction plate is ground either flat on both sides or curved on one side, its design and thickness depending on the distortion characteristics of the aerial camera lens. With this method of compensation, plates may be interchanged to fit any particular aerial camera lens.

The settings of the distances A and B are accomplished in the reduction printer by means of a graduated collar which raises and lowers the upper components slightly. The graduations are expressed as focal lengths of camera lenses. When a diapositive is made, the focal length must be modified by any enlargement or reduction of the negative resulting from expansion or shrinkage in processing. The ratio is determined by comparing the dimensions of the negative with the calibrated dimensions of the focal-plane opening (see Sec. 2–11).

On examination of Fig. 12–5 (a) and (c), it is seen that the orientation of the diapositive in the projector must be the same as the orientation of the negative in the camera. That is, the right-to-left and front-to-back relationships must be the same. When using a conventional enlarger, in order to make a photographic enlargement, the photographer places the negative in the negative holder with the emulsion side *facing* the enlarger lens, and the enlarging paper in the easel also with the paper emulsion facing the lens. This is referred to as emulsion-to-emulsion enlarging. The resulting picture is correct in orientation. In preparing a diapositive, which itself will be used to project an image as in Fig. 12–5 (c), the negative is placed in the reduction printer with the emulsion *away* from the printer lens. The emulsion of the diapositive glass is placed to face the lens. This process is referred to as printing through the negative. Then, when the diapositive is placed in the projector, with the emulsion down, the diapositive image is in the same orientation in the projector as the negative was in the aerial camera. When the diapositive is projected this way, the image of the ground will be correct right-to-left and front-to-back.

The negative is held in place in the reduction printer between a bottom glass plate and a pressure plate on the top. The negative is oriented on the optical axis of the reduction-printer lens by matching the fiducial marks on the negative to the scribed marks on the glass plate. A mark is etched into the surface of the glass plate at the intersection of lines joining the scribed marks on the sides. This mark is the principal point of the reduction printer. When the negative is projected onto the diapositive glass, the principal-point mark is also projected. As a result, the position of the principal point of the diapositive is shown directly, rather than having to be found by lines joining opposite fiducial marks on the diapositive.

A pair of diapositives prepared as just outlined are laid, emulsion side down, on the map sheet in their proper order of overlap. They are spread apart, and each diapositive is rotated 180°. The lamp housings of the projectors are removed, and the diapositives are placed in the diapositive stages in the order in which they were laid on the map sheet. The diapositive stage is defined by the upper surfaces of four small bosses very precisely machined to define a plane lying at the principal distance from the front (upper) nodal point of the projector lens and perpendicular to the optical axis of the lens. The diapositive (resting firmly on the four bosses) may be moved in two mutually perpendicular directions in order to bring the principal point of the diapositive precisely on the optical axis of the projector lens. This matching is obtained either by means of a centering microscope or by a built-in centering device. This completes the interior orientation of the diapositives.

12–4. Relative Orientation

Now consider for the time being the exterior orientation of the aerial camera at each of two consecutive exposure stations. The relative positions of the three camera axes for these two orientations can be easily visualized. There are three angles to consider. One is formed between the two positions of the optical axis of the lens. Another is formed between the two positions of the x-axis of the camera. The third is formed between the two positions of the y-axis of the camera. In order to form a perfect stereoscopic model, these three relative angles must be re-created between the two projectors. By this re-creation, which is called relative orientation, the positions of the two projectors relative to one another are made the same as the two positions of the aerial camera relative to one another at the time of exposure. The basis for relative orientation is the fact that any point in a perfect stereoscopic model must lie in a plane containing the air base. An equivalent way of expressing this condition is as follows: A ray representing any point and emerging from the emergent nodal point of one projector, say the left-hand one, must intersect a ray representing the same point and emerging from the emergent nodal point of the right-hand projector. Intersections are shown in Fig. 12–1 for four points lying in the four corners of the model.

All conjugate rays are made to intersect by systematically eliminating the horizontal displacements of conjugate images in a direction perpendicular to the flight line throughout the entire area of overlap. The student will recognize these displacements to be y-parallax as defined in Chapter 8. Relative orientation is accomplished, therefore, by clearing the stereoscopic model of y-parallax. The term *vertical parallax* is commonly, but erroneously, used to define a horizontal displacement in the y-direction. This term is confusing since the vertical direction is perpendicular to the horizontal X-Y plane.

In order to form an understanding of the way in which relative orientation is accomplished, the effect of each of the six motions of the projector on the movement of images must be investigated. In Fig. 12–7, the six patterns represent the traces of images on the map sheet as a projector is moved through its six motions. In Fig. 12–7(a), the projector has been translated by an X-motion, and the images are seen to have moved parallel to the direction of the supporting bar. This movement has no effect on y-parallax if it is assumed that the flight line is parallel to the supporting bar.

In Fig. 12–7(b), the projector has been translated by a Y-motion, in which all the images have moved in a horizontal direction perpendicular to the supporting bar. Thus, the Y-motion introduces an equal amount of y-parallax over the entire area.

In Fig. 12–7(c), the projector has been lowered by the Z-motion. As a result, all the points are seen to have moved inward toward the center of the area. The maximum y-parallax occurs along the far and near side of the area, that is, along the upper and lower edges of Fig. 12–7(c). No y-parallax has been introduced in any of the points lying on a line bb, which passes through the center and is parallel to the supporting bar.

In Fig. 12–7(d), the projector has been given an x-tilt. The result is a movement of images along a set of hyperbolas as shown. The magnitude of the y-parallax introduced by this movement increases in the Y-direction from the center outward to the far side and the near side of the area. The y-parallax is uniform at points lying on a line parallel to the

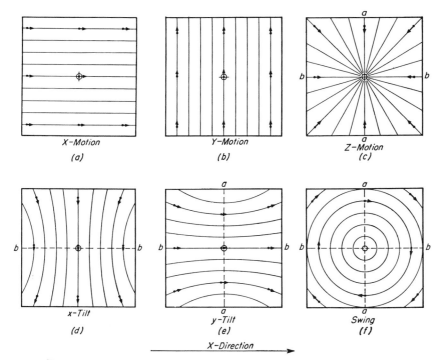

X-Direction

Fig. 12-7. Image movements on map sheet caused by projector motions.

supporting bar. It is a minimum for points lying along a line *bb*, which is parallel to the *X*-direction and passes through the center of the area, because this line lies closest to the projector lens.

In Fig. 12-7(*e*), the projector has been given a *y*-tilt. As a result, there has been a movement of images along a set of hyperbolas as shown. No *y*-parallax has been introduced along the line *bb*, and there has been very little along the line *aa*. The maximum *y*-parallax is introduced in the four corners of the area. This is the most critical motion in the relative-orientation process.

In Fig. 12-7(*f*), the projector has been rotated about its optical axis. This is the swing motion defined in Sec. 12-2. The points have been moved concentrically about the center of the area. If the optical axis is normal to the map sheet, these movements are perfect circles having a common center at the point at which the optical axis intersects the map sheet. The maximum *y*-parallax occurs at points at the outer ends of the line *bb*. No *y*-parallax is introduced at the center of the area, and very little is introduced at points lying on line *aa*.

The overlap area of the projection of two diapositives is shown in Fig. 12-8. Point *1* is the principal point of the left-hand projected

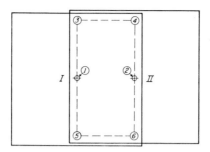

FIG. 12–8. Points for y-parallax
removal.

diapositive. The left projector is designated projector I. Point *2* is
the principal point of the right-hand projected diapositive. The right
projector is designated projector II. Points *3, 4, 5,* and *6* lie at the four
corners of the neat model. If the plotter operator has placed a pair of
diapositives into projectors I and II and has centered them, and he
now turns on the projector lamps, the images from the two projectors
will overlap one another in the measuring space beneath the projectors.

Before any orientation is attempted, both projectors should first
be brought to a vertical position by eye, the x-tilt and y-tilt motions
being used. Then the BY- and BZ-settings should be equalized by
reference to the scales provided, it being assumed that the two photographs
are vertical and that they have been taken from the same flying height.
These settings also make the air base parallel to the supporting bar, this
position being convenient for the orientation process.

The operator brings the tracing table to the vicinity of point *1.*
Without wearing the colored spectacles, he will see a mismatching of
the red image and the blue-green image coming from the two projectors.
It being assumed that he is permitted to move both projectors, he
orients them in the following manner.

The displacement of conjugate images in the X-direction at point
1 is removed by raising or lowering the platen, because x-parallax is a
measure of elevation. This displacement will be called Δx-parallax to
distinguish it from absolute parallax $(x-x')$. The y-parallax between
the conjugate images is removed by swinging projector II. A study of
Fig. 12–7 (*f*) will indicate that a swing of projector II imparts a Y-motion
to the image of point *1* projected from projector II. The necessary
amount of swing is indicated by visual coincidence between the red
and blue-green images of a well-defined image at point *1.*

The tracing table is moved to point *2,* and the Δx-parallax is removed
by raising or lowering the platen. The y-parallax is now removed by
swinging projector I, as indicated by Fig. 12–7 (*f*). This swing does

not, or should not, introduce y-parallax at point *1*, because projector I is swung around that point. The y-parallax is thus cleared at the two principal points.

The tracing table is moved to point *3*, and the Δx-parallax is removed by raising or lowering the platen. If, on analysis, the image of point *3* coming from projector II lies outside its conjugate point the y-parallax is removed by a y-tilt of projector II in a counterclockwise direction. Conversely, if the image of point *3* coming from projector II lies inside its conjugate point, the y-parallax is removed by a y-tilt of projector II in a clockwise direction. As y-tilt is introduced, a considerable amount of Δx-parallax will be introduced at point *3*. This must be removed by raising or lowering the platen simultaneously with the removal of y-parallax by use of the y-tilt motion of projector II. An examination of Fig. 12–7(e) will indicate that this motion should introduce no y-parallax at either of the principal points.

The tracing table is moved to point *4*, and the platen is raised or lowered to eliminate the Δx-parallax at the point. A y-tilt of projector I will move the image coming from projector I in the y-direction as well as in the x-direction. But this motion should introduce no y-parallax at the principal points, and should introduce very little, if any, at point *3*. Therefore, a y-tilt of projector I and a simultaneous raising or lowering of the platen will remove the y-parallax and the Δx-parallax at point *4*. At this stage of orientation, points *1*, *2*, *3*, and *4* have been cleared of y-parallax.

The tracing table is now moved to either point *5* or point *6*, and Δx-parallax is removed by raising or lowering the platen. An x-tilt of either projector will introduce y-parallax at all four of the previously cleared points. If it is assumed that the y-parallax at point *5* has been precisely cleared by tilting projector II, then the y-parallax introduced at points *3* and *4* will be equal in amount to that which had existed at point *5* but will be in the opposite direction. Only about two-thirds of this amount will be introduced at points *1* and *2*, because these two points are not affected quite so much by x-tilt as are points *3* and *4*. A reorientation to clear the y-parallax at points *1* through *4* will again introduce y-parallax at point *5*.

A careful analysis of the effects of the rotational motions indicates that the following procedure will be satisfactory: If point *5* is over-corrected to introduce y-parallax in the opposite direction equal to about one-half of the original y-parallax, then a reorientation to clear the y-parallax at points *1* through *4* should completely clear the y-parallax at point *5*. The effect of the two swing motions in the reorientation of points *1* through *4* is to reduce the y-parallax at the principal points to zero and to reduce the y-parallax at points *3*, *4*, and *5* to about one-third of the original y-parallax, but now the displacements at points 3 and 5 are in opposite directions. Hence, a y-tilt of projector II will eliminate the y-parallax at points 3 and 5 simultaneously. A y-tilt of projector I will eliminate the remaining y-parallax at point 4.

The amount of overcorrection to be introduced by the x-tilt motion depends on the type of photography. It is greatest for normal-angle photography, decreasing for wide-angle and super-wide-angle photography. Overcorrection must be increased as point 5 is selected nearer to the air base. Also, the height of point 5 and the slope of the topography at the point has an effect on the amount of overcorrection to be applied. The experienced operator can judge the proper amount after the first or second iteration through the orientation process.

To recapitulate this orientation process, the steps will be briefly stated in the order of their performance.

1. Clear y-parallax at 1 with swing of projector II.
2. Clear y-parallax at 2 with swing of projector I.
3. Clear y-parallax at 3 with y-tilt of projector II.
4. Clear y-parallax at 4 with y-tilt of projector I.
5. Introduce one-half of the y-parallax existing at point 5 or 6 in the opposite direction with x-tilt of either projector.
6. Repeat steps 1 through 5 until no parallax exists at the five points.

When the adjustment just outlined has been completed, the sixth point should be checked. If it contains y-parallax, then the y-parallax has not really been cleared at all of the original five points.

When the orientation by matching red and blue-green images has been refined until no apparent y-parallax can be detected, the operator puts on the spectacles and checks each point by bringing the measuring mark on the model surface at the five points. If y-parallax exists, he will detect a slight y-displacement of the two images of the measuring mark received by the eyes. In fact, the optical axes of the eyes are not coplanar when y-parallax exists. The images of the terrain are so gross as to receive all the attention of each eye, whereas the measuring mark is relatively insignificant. As a consequence, the eyes eliminate the y-parallax from the terrain by assuming an unnatural position with respect to one another (see Sec. 7–6). The residual y-parallax is cleared by trimming the adjustments slightly until the split image of the measuring mark disappears at all the points. At this stage, the entire model is assumed to be free from y-parallax, and relative orientation is completed.

In the preceding description of the method of relative orientation, both projectors were allowed to be moved. Furthermore, only the three rotational motions were used in the orientation process. Although this condition exists when a pair of projectors are oriented for map compilation, it sometimes becomes necessary to hold one projector fixed (see Sec. 12–8). A different method of orientation must then be used. The method is given here step by step without comment. The student should examine Fig. 12–7 while studying these steps in order to satisfy himself of their logic.

Assume that projector I of Fig. 12–8 is to be held fixed. Assume also that Δx-parallax is removed at each point by raising or lowering the tracing-table platen. The orientation procedure by using the motions of projector II is then as follows:

1. Clear y-parallax at *2* with Y-motion.
2. Clear y-parallax at *1* with swing.
3. Check for y-parallax at *2* and remove with Y-motion.
4. Clear y-parallax at *1* with swing.
5. Clear y-parallax at *4* with Z-motion.
6. Clear y-parallax at *3* with y-tilt.
7. Introduce one-half of the y-parallax existing at *6* in the opposite direction with x-tilt.
8. Repeat steps 1 through 7 until no y-parallax exists at the five points.
9. Check for y-parallax at *5*. If y-parallax exists, then the y-parallax has not really been removed from the original five points.

After this procedure has been carried out, the orientation is touched up by using the spectacles to detect residual y-parallax at the points.

Although these methods of relative orientation are but two of many possible procedures, they will demonstrate the principles underlying all methods. They must therefore be fully understood by the student. The procedures described here are applicable to all the plotting instruments to be discussed in this chapter.

The net result of relative orientation of a pair of diapositives is the creation of a theoretically perfect stereoscopic model which has a definite, but as yet unknown, scale. The entire model as a unit lies tilted with respect to the datum for elevations by an unknown amount and in an unknown direction. Before the model can be measured in the map-compilation process, it must be oriented to ground control in order to bring it to the desired scale and to the correct orientation with respect to the datum for elevations. This is the purpose of the process of absolute orientation to be discussed in Sec. 12–6.

12–5. Plotting Scale

The scale at which a map is to be compiled in a plotter not equipped to change plotting scales is determined by the flying height of the photography above the average terrain elevation. The plotting scale in the Multiplex instrument cannot be varied mechanically. It must be the same as the model scale. In Fig. 12–5(a), the quantity $H-h_{avg}$ is the flying height above the average terrain elevation, and in Fig. 12–5(c) the equivalent distance in the projector is called the optimum projection distance. The optimum projection distance defines the plane of best focus of the projector lens. When the reduction printer has been set correctly, the following relationship is obvious:

$$\text{Optimum model scale} = \frac{\text{optimum projection distance}}{H-h_{avg}} \qquad (12\text{--}2)$$

The optimum projection distance in the Multiplex instrument is 360 mm or 360/304.8 ft. Therefore, if the flying height above average terrain is 7,500 ft, the optimum scale at which the map should be plotted in a Multiplex instrument is, by Eq. 12–2,

$$\text{Optimum scale} = \frac{(360/304.8)\ \text{ft}}{7,500\ \text{ft}} = \frac{1}{6,350}$$

EXAMPLE 12–1. Plotting in a Multiplex instrument is to be done at a scale of 1 in.=800 ft. What should be the flying height above sea level for the photography if the average elevation of the area is 2,700 ft?

Solution: The scale 1 in.=800 ft is equivalent to a scale of 1/9,600. Therefore, by Eq. 12–2,

$$\frac{1}{9,600} = \frac{(360/304.8)\ \text{ft}}{(H-2,700)\ \text{ft}}$$

So $H=14,039$ ft above sea level.

EXAMPLE 12–2. A series of photographs are taken with a lens having a 5.2-in. focal length. The average scale of the photographs is 1:15,000. The photography is to be used to produce disapositives for use in a Multiplex instrument. Determine the optimum scale of the map.

Solution: By Eq. 3–3,

$$\frac{1}{15,000} = \frac{(5.2/12)\ \text{ft}}{H-h_{avg}}$$

Hence, $H-h_{avg}=6,500$ ft.
  By Eq. 12–2,

$$\text{Optimum scale} = \frac{(360/304.8)\ \text{ft}}{6,500\ \text{ft}} = \frac{1}{5,503}$$

In Example 12–2, the actual plotting scale would be selected for convenience of plotting. A scale of 1/5,400 could be adopted, and the average projection distance would be correspondingly increased by applying the factor 5,503/5,400 and getting 367 mm.

A scale of 1/6,000 or 1 in.=500 ft would result in an average projection distance of 330 mm, whereas a scale of 1/4,800 or 1 in.=400 ft would result in an average projection distance of 413 mm. As mentioned in Sec. 12–2, the usable depth of focus in the model is 180 mm. So there is an allowable distance of 90 mm above and below the plane of optimum focus. With a scale of 1/6,000 and an average projection distance of 330 mm, analysis shows that the upper limit of the model is 60 mm above the average model elevation. The high point of the terrain could then be about 1,180 ft above the average terrain elevation. With a scale of 1/4,800 and an average projection distance of 413 mm, the lower limit of the model is only 37 mm below the average model elevation. The low point of the terrain could then be only about 580 ft below the average terrain elevation. The depth of focus must therefore be considered when the plotting scale is selected, in order to allow for the variation in the terrain elevation of the area to be mapped.

With a proper choice of plotting scale, the vertical limit of the Multiplex model is rarely exceeded by the terrain relief. However, in other instruments the depth of focus may be a much smaller fraction of the flying height. This fact must be taken into consideration when the photography is planned. As an example, suppose that an instrument had an optimum projection distance of 30 in. and a depth of focus of 6 in. The range of relief could then be one-fifth of the flying height. If the flying height is 3,000 ft above average terrain, the limiting range of relief would be $3,000/5 = 600$ ft. Thus, points lying more than 300 ft above or below the average elevation could not be mapped reliably. Furthermore, the flying height must be kept quite near the theoretically correct value. A deviation of 100 ft in the flying height in the preceding example would reduce the allowable relief range by one-sixth.

12–6. Absolute Orientation

The purpose of absolute orientation is to bring a stereoscopic model to the desired map scale, and to place the model in its correct orientation with respect to the datum for elevations. Absolute orientation is accomplished in two distinct phases, called *scaling* and *leveling*. In order that a model may be scaled, the model must contain two horizontal control points whose positions have been plotted on the map sheet at the desired map scale. In order that a model may be leveled, the model must contain a minimum of three, but preferably four or five, vertical control points.

Before the scaling operation is discussed, it is advisable to consider the effect of an X-motion of either of two projectors on the stereoscopic model which has been obtained by relative orientation. In Fig. 12–9, in which the illumination system is not shown, projectors I and II have been relatively oriented to form a stereoscopic model indicated by the solid outline in the measuring area beneath the projectors. It is assumed that the readings of the Y-motion and the Z-motion are the same on both projectors. If projector II is moved to the right by an X-motion, the original base BX_1 has been increased by an amount ΔBX to give a new base BX_2. At the same time, the original flying height H_1 above the model terrain has been increased by an amount ΔH to give H_2. Since projector II has been moved parallel with itself, then $H_2/H_1 = BX_2/BX_1$. The ratio BX_2/BX_1 is the increase in the scale of the stereoscopic model.

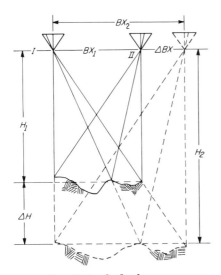

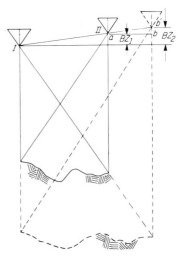

FIG. 12–9. Scale change.   FIG. 12–10. Unequal Z-settings.

The effect of a difference in the Z-settings of the two projectors is shown in Fig. 12–10. After relative orientation has been accomplished, the difference in the Z-settings is shown as BZ_1. If projector II is now moved from a to b by an X-motion, there will be y-parallax in the model because the images coming from projector II have been displaced inward relative to the new scale of the model. A Z-motion of projector II represented by bb' will eliminate the y-parallax over the entire model. The difference in the Z-settings of the two projectors is now BZ_2, which is established by the relationship $BZ_2/BZ_1 = BX_2/BX_1$.

The effect of a difference in the Y-settings of the two projectors is shown in plan view in Fig. 12–11. The solid rectangle is the outline of the neat model before scale change. The difference in Y-settings after relative orientation but before scale change is shown as BY_1. If projector II is now moved from a to c by an X-motion, there will be y-parallax in the same direction and of an equal amount over the entire model. A Y-motion of projector II represented by cc' will eliminate all of the y-parallax. The difference in the Y-settings of the two projectors is now

BY_2, the value of which is such that $BY_2/BY_1 = BX_2/BX_1$. The large dashed rectangle is the outline of the neat model after scale change.

The preceding two paragraphs reveal why it is convenient to equalize the Y- and Z-settings of the two projectors before relative orientation is performed by the first method described in Sec. 12–4. The student should satisfy himself that in the second method of relative orientation described in Sec. 12–4, the changes in BY and BZ are actually accomplished in the orientation process (see steps 1, 3, and 5 of the second method). Additional changes, however, will be necessary during the scaling process unless both BY and BZ happen to be zero.

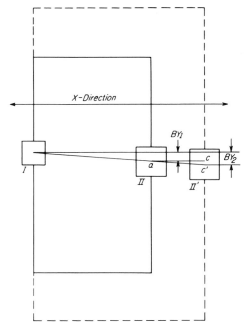

Fig. 12–11. Unequal Y-settings.

When a model is to be scaled, the map sheet containing the plotted positions of two horizontal control points is placed on the map table. The plotting pencil of the tracing table is placed on one of the map control points, and the entire map sheet is slid, carrying the tracing table with it, until the measuring mark receives the model image of the control point. This position of the tracing table is shown as point A_1 in the upper diagram of Fig. 12–12.

With the map sheet fixed in position, the tracing table is moved to the second control point in the model. The orthographic projection

B_1 of this point on the map sheet, compared with the map position of the point, will indicate the necessary amount of rotation of the map sheet and the necessary scale change. The map sheet is rotated about the point A_1 as the center until the position of the line AB as viewed in the model is in the same direction as the map position of AB. The base is now enlarged or reduced by an X-motion of one of the projectors (or both), until the distance AB as determined by a measurement in the model is the same as the map distance AB. This is a trial-and-error procedure, because the map sheet must be shifted and rotated each time the scale is changed.

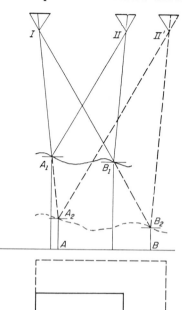

The lower portion of Fig. 12–12 is a plan view of the map sheet. The original distance A_1B_1 has been increased to the final distance A_2B_2. This latter distance must exactly agree with the map distance. Furthermore, the orientation of the map sheet must be such as to cause A_2 and B_2 to coincide exactly with the positions of these points as plotted to the desired scale on the map sheet.

During the scaling process, points *1* through *6* of Fig. 12–8 must be checked for y-parallax. If the same amount of y-parallax is introduced in the same direction at all six points when the base is changed, a Y-motion of one of the projectors will eliminate the y-parallax at all six points. If no y-parallax exists at points *1* and *2*, and if the y-parallaxes at points *3* and *5*,

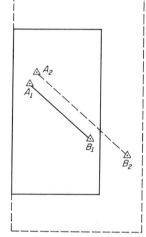

Fig. 12–12. Scaling.

or *4* and *6*, are equal and in opposing directions, a Z-motion of one of the projectors will eliminate the y-parallax at the four corners. Usually, however, both a Y-motion and a Z-motion will be required. The amount of each motion can be determined by an analysis of the amounts and directions of the y-parallaxes at the six points. The slight adjustments of the Y- and Z-motions are made simultaneously with the scaling process until all the requirements have been satisfied.

When scaling has been performed as just outlined, the model usually will not be at precisely the correct scale because it is tipped and tilted relative to the datum for elevations. After the model has been leveled to fit vertical control, the scale should be checked to determine whether or not any scaling refinements are required.

Since the reduction printer produces a diapositive which will re-create the proper angular relationship between the rays leaving the projector lens, the horizontal and vertical scales of the model formed by a pair of projectors are precisely the same. On the basis of this fact, the correct settings of the tracing-table platen can be computed for any desired elevation. Some of the more modern tracing tables contain gears which can be introduced to give a direct reading in feet of elevation to a particular scale of the model (and the map). The elevation readings may be changed without moving the platen up and down. This provision is necessary in order that the counter may be indexed to a vertical control point in the process of leveling. Many of the tracing tables still in use contain a scale or counter graduated in millimeters and tenths of a millimeter. The use of such a type will be discussed in this section.

The normal range of vertical motion of the platen is 100 mm. However, attachments with lengths of 50 mm and 100 mm can be added to increase the range to 150 mm or 200 mm. The counter registers from 0.0 mm to 99.9 mm (the use of the attachment will be ignored in this discussion). For any given vertical position of the platen, the counter may be changed to read any value from 0.0 to 99.9 mm.

Assume that a map with a 10-ft contour interval is to be compiled at a scale of 1 in. = 500 ft, and that the elevation of the terrain ranges from 350 to 550 ft. Assume that four vertical control points C, D, E, and F have elevations as follows: $h_C = 382.2$ ft; $h_D = 485.0$ ft; $h_E = 420.6$ ft; and $h_F = 372.0$ ft. When the model has been brought to the desired scale, which is the same for both horizontal and vertical distances, a 1-in. vertical movement of the platen represents a difference in elevation of 500 ft. Then typical conversion factors are as follows:

$$25.4 \text{ mm} = 500 \text{ ft}$$
$$1 \text{ mm} = 19.7 \text{ ft}$$
$$0.0508 \text{ mm} = 1 \text{ ft}$$
$$0.5080 \text{ mm} = 10 \text{ ft}$$
$$5.080 \text{ mm} = 100 \text{ ft}$$

Assume now that an arbitrary counter setting of 20.0 mm is to represent an elevation of 350 ft. For an elevation of 360 ft, the counter must then read $20.0 + 0.508 = 20.5$ mm; for an elevation of 370 ft, the counter must read $20 + (2)(0.508) = 21.0$ mm, and so on. The counter settings for all contour values are computed on the basis of the established scale relationships, and are shown in the accompanying tabulation.

SETTINGS OF TRACING-TABLE COUNTER
FOR SCALE 1 IN. = 500 FT

Contour Elevation (ft)	Setting (mm)	Contour Elevation (ft)	Setting (mm)
350	20.0	460	25.6
360	20.5	470	26.1
370	21.0	480	26.6
380	21.5	490	27.1
390	22.0	500	27.6
400	22.5	510	28.1
410	23.0	520	28.6
420	23.6	530	29.1
430	24.1	540	29.7
440	24.6	550	30.2
450	25.1		

The values of the settings for the four vertical control points are obtained by subtracting the base elevation of 350 ft from each known elevation, converting this difference in feet to a difference in millimeters, and finally adding the difference in millimeters to 20.0. This procedure is shown in tabular form.

COUNTER SETTINGS FOR VERTICAL CONTROL POINTS

Control Point	Elev. (ft)	Δh (ft)	Δh (mm)	Setting (mm)
C	382.2	32.2	1.64	21.6
D	485.0	135.0	6.86	26.9
E	420.6	70.6	3.59	23.6
F	372.0	22.0	1.12	21.1

If the scale is expressed as a representative fraction, such as $1/15,840$, typical conversion factors would be as follows:

$$1 \text{ ft} = 15,840 \text{ ft}$$
$$304.8 \text{ mm} = 15,840 \text{ ft}$$
$$1 \text{ mm} = 51.9685 \text{ ft}$$
$$0.01924 \text{ mm} = 1 \text{ ft}$$
$$0.1924 \text{ mm} = 10 \text{ ft}$$
$$1.924 \text{ mm} = 100 \text{ ft}$$

The values of the settings for all contour lines and all vertical control points may be determined at any time after the plotting scale has been selected. The control-point settings are then used to level the stereoscopic model. It should be noted that settings computed in the manner previously described are valid only after the model has, in fact, been brought to the proper scale. The slight error in the scale caused by not having the model leveled at the time of scaling has no measurable effect on the validity of the computed settings.

When the settings have been computed for the four vertical control points, the measuring mark is brought in contact with one of these control points. With the platen fixed in position, the counter reading is changed to the value of the setting for this control point. The map-sheet positions of the four control points in the preceding example are shown in Fig. 12–13. The computed settings for the points are shown in parentheses. The measuring mark is set on point C in the model, and the counter is set to read the computed value, which is 21.6 mm.

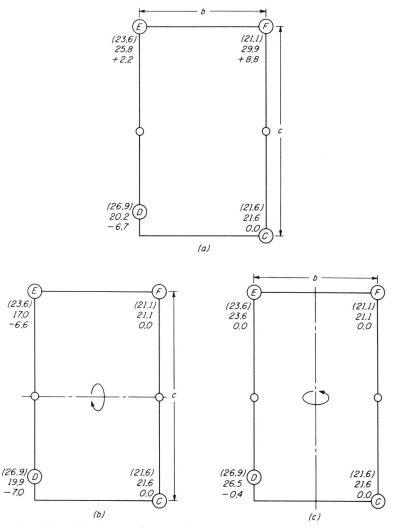

Fig. 12–13. Leveling analysis based on four vertical control points. (*a*) Readings on control prior to leveling. (*b*) Readings after rotation of model about *X*-axis. (*c*) Readings after rotation of model about *Y*-axis.

The platen is now released, and the measuring mark is set in turn on points D, E, and F. Readings are taken on these points and recorded on the map sheet, as shown in Fig. 12–13 (a). Point D is 6.7 mm too low, point E is 2.2 mm too high, and point F is 8.8 mm too high.

Consider the triangle formed by points C, F, and E. A rotation of the model about a line in the X-direction through an angle $\tan^{-1} 8.8/c$, in which c is the distance between C and F in the Y-direction, will lower the model at points E and F by 8.8 mm. The new readings at these points, after indexing the tracing table at C, will be 21.1 mm and 17.0 mm respectively as shown in Fig. 12–13 (b). The reading at D will be reduced a slight amount to 19.9 mm. The discrepancy at E is now -6.6 mm, and D, -7.0 mm.

A rotation of the model about a line in the Y-direction through an angle $\tan^{-1} 6.6/b$, in which b is the distance between E and F in the X-direction, will raise the model at points D and E by 6.6 mm. The new readings at these points, after indexing on C, will be 26.5 mm and 23.6 mm respectively, as shown in Fig. 12–13 (c). The discrepancies at C, E, and F are now reduced to zero, while at D, the discrepancy is still -0.4 mm. This discrepancy is caused by errors in the photogrammetric system, due primarily to inexact relative orientation.

Figure 12–14 shows the effect of the various relative orientation errors on the level datum. A small BY error has no effect on elevations, but simply introduces y-parallax throughout the model. A small BX error does not affect elevations by any appreciable amount unless the terrain elevation differences are sizeable. Its effect is to change the scale of the model slightly. A small BZ error has the effect of tipping the model in the X-direction which can be overcome in the leveling process. A swing error tilts the model in the Y-direction. This can be corrected in the leveling process.

A small y-tilt error causes the level datum to become slightly cylindrical. Note that the effect of this error cannot be detected by a placement of vertical control as shown in Fig. 12–13. A fifth control point in the middle of the model, will however allow for an evaluation of the y-tilt error. The effect of a small x-tilt error is to warp the model as shown in the diagram. This error can be detected by means of four corner points, as for example at point D of Fig. 12–13 (c) where the error is -0.4 mm.

In practice, a compromise is made by introducing a small but tolerable amount of x- and y-tilt into one of the projectors in order to force the vertical control points to read correctly. This introduces slight amounts of y-parallax into the model. If the amount of false x- and/or y-tilt necessary to make the vertical control fit is beyond tolerance, then the model is sometimes *broken*, that is, leveled on different groups of vertical control points during map compilation.

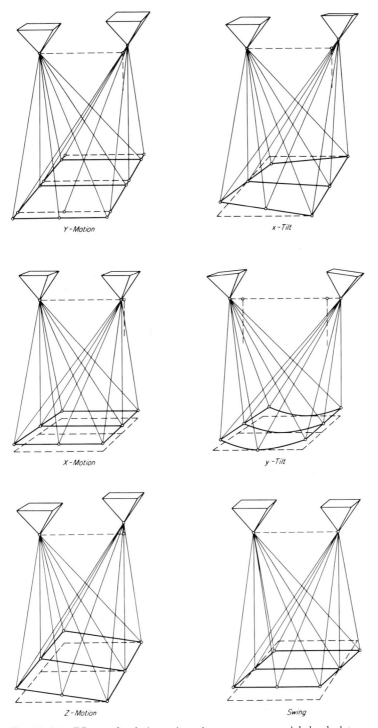

Y-Motion

x-Tilt

X-Motion

y-Tilt

Z-Motion

Swing

FIG. 12–14. Effects of relative orientation errors on model level datum.

If the distances between the control points are measured carefully, the precise amount of tip and tilt required to level the model can be computed. If, further, the Multiplex instrument were to contain graduated circles to register the tilts of the projectors, the computed tilt and tip of the model could be set off. Although some computation is involved in leveling the model, the necessary tilting and tipping is arrived at by a trial-and-error procedure.

There are three methods for leveling the model. The one to be selected depends on the type of Multiplex instrument being used. In the instrument shown in Fig. 12–15, the supporting bar remains fixed on the frame, but the map-table slab may be tipped and tilted by means of two

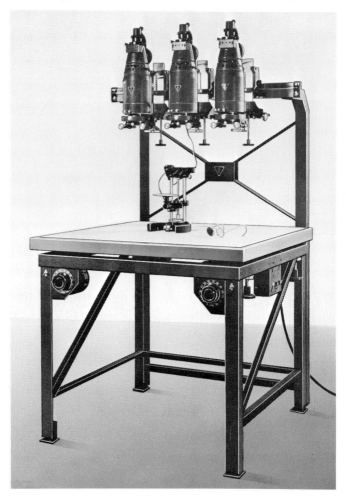

FIG. 12–15. Three-projector Multiplex plotter. (Courtesy of Bausch and Lomb Optical Co.)

large leveling screws located on both sides of the front edge of the slab. A point of support in the center of the rear edge defines the intersection of the two axes of rotation of the slab. In Fig. 12–16(*a*), a movement

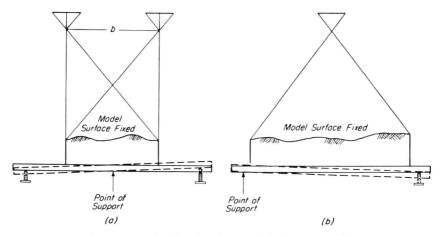

Fig. 12–16. Leveling by tilting and tipping map table.

of the left-hand leveling screw downward and an equal raising of the right-hand screw rotates the slab about a line that is perpendicular to the direction of flight and passes through the point of support. This rotation has the effect of raising the left side of the model and lowering the right side.

In Fig. 12–16(*b*) is a view looking into the side of the instrument directly along the flight line. The back edge of the map-table slab is to the left. A lowering of both leveling screws by the same amount rotates the slab about an axis that is parallel to the direction of flight and passes through the point of support. This rotation has the effect of raising the front side of the model (the side nearer the operator). By arriving at the proper combination of tilting and tipping of the table, the readings on the four vertical control points are made to agree with the computed readings. Before each successive round of readings, the counter is indexed to 21.6 at point *C*. When all four points are in agreement, the model is presumed to be leveled.

The instrument shown in Fig. 12–17 is provided with four footscrews, for tilting and tipping the supporting bar, and with a large handwheel on each column for tipping the bar in the *X*-direction. One of the columns (the left column in the picture) is jointed just above the footscrew support to prevent any stressing during a leveling operation. A stereoscopic model could be leveled simply by manipulating the footscrews and the handwheels. This procedure is not practical for a single model, however, as it requires too much rotation in the majority of cases. After leveling has

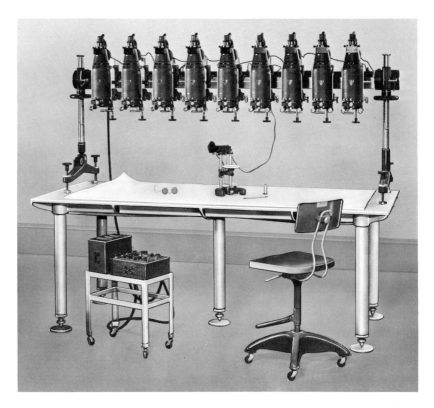

Fig. 12–17. Multiplex plotter. (Courtesy of Bausch and Lomb Optical Co.)

been accomplished by the following method, final leveling adjustments can be made by using the footscrews and the handwheels.

A model may be leveled by the rotational and translational motions of the two projectors. An equal x-tilt of both projectors will raise the near side of the model and lower the far side, or vice versa. In Fig. 12–18 is a side view of the model looking directly along the flight line. An x-tilt of one projector will introduce y-parallax throughout the model. An x-tilt of the other projector by the same amount and in the same direction will entirely eliminate the y-parallax, provided that the Y- and Z-settings of both projectors are identical. A difference in Y- and Z-settings will introduce a slight amount of y-parallax, which can be removed by the Y- and Z-motion of one projector or the other.

The entire model may be tilted from side to side in the X-direction by an equal y-tilt of both projectors followed by a Z-motion of one of the projectors, as shown in Fig. 12–19. Both projectors have been y-tilted by the same amount in a counterclockwise direction. This tilting introduces y-parallax throughout the model, except along a line through the middle

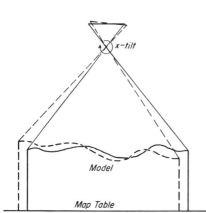

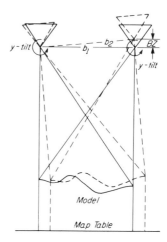

FIG. 12-18. Leveling with *x*-tilt.

FIG. 12-19. Leveling with
y-tilt and *Z*-motion.

of the model and parallel to the flight line. A Z-motion of the right-hand projector by an amount BZ will exactly eliminate the y-parallax unless the original Y- and Z-settings of both projectors differ. The residual y-parallax is eliminated by a Y-motion of either projector. In Fig. 12–19 the model has been tilted upward to the right. The introduction of the BY and BZ motions to one of the projectors during the leveling operation has the effect of rotating the base joining the two projector nodes, with respect to the supporting bar or map table.

When the model has been nearly leveled by this last-described process, the six points shown in Fig. 12–8 should be checked for y-parallax. Any residual amount can be eliminated by a slight adjustment in accordance with the procedure of relative orientation. The model is then re-scaled, because the original scaling is bound to have been slightly disturbed in the leveling process. Finally, the model may be completely leveled by means of the footscrews and the handwheels, since only slight discrepancies must be eliminated. Absolute orientation is now attained.

The entire process of relative and absolute orientation is seen to be a matter of trial and error, each phase being subject to slight adjustments after the completion of another phase. Certain errors in the entire photogrammetric system will cause difficulty in bringing a model into precise relative and absolute orientation. Likely causes of trouble in the orientation process are inexact settings in the reduction printer, inexact focal length, undetected film shrinkage, vacuum failure in the aerial camera at the instant of exposure, emulsion creep on the diapositive, residual radial distortion, tangential distortion, residual y-parallax, and errors in the photo control points. Since, after all, the stereoscopic plotting instrument is an analog computer which solves for tilt, swing, azimuth, and the space position of the exposure station of each of the photographs by orienting them to known ground control, no rigid solution would be possible in any event. Therefore, the solution of the problem of exterior orientation by means of the plotter is really a compromise which adjusts out the various sources of errors.

12–7. Map-Compilation Procedure

The first step in the compilation of a map in the plotter is the establishment of the scale to which the map is to be plotted. This topic has been discussed in Sec. 12–5. The map grid is constructed on a map sheet, which should be of well-seasoned, stable material. The horizontal control points are plotted with respect to the grid. Next the tracing-table settings for all the vertical control points and for the contour lines are computed, and a table is prepared to show these settings.

When the diapositives have been properly prepared, they are placed in the projectors and centered by means of the centering device. Before relative orientation is begun, the distance between the projectors is made approximately equal to the correct base. This separation may be established by measuring, on a contact-print photograph of one of the diapositives, the distance between the principal point and the conjugate principal point, and solving the following relationship:

$$\frac{B}{b} = \frac{\text{map scale}}{\text{average photograph scale}} \tag{12-3}$$

in which B is the distance between the two projector lenses, in millimeters; and b is the distance between the principal point and the conjugate principal point measured on the photograph, in millimeters. The Y- and Z-motions are set to read the same on both projectors. Relative orientation is then performed. If, during relative orientation, it is found that a y-tilt of one projector or the other raises or lowers the model to such an extent that the vertical motion of the tracing table is exceeded, the entire model may be raised or lowered, either by changing the base with an X-motion of one projector or by changing the Z-settings of both projectors by the same amount. If the approximately correct base has been set off as just described, then the latter method of raising or lowering the model is recommended. Note that this adjustment has no effect whatsoever on the model scale.

The stereoscopic model obtained by relative orientation is now scaled and leveled, and the relative orientation is then checked and adjusted. The final scaling and leveling ties the model to the ground control. The map sheet is checked for proper position and orientation by comparing the model positions of two horizontal control points with the plotted map positions of the two points. When they are in agreement, the map sheet is fastened to the map table.

The neat model is outlined on the map sheet. This outline extends from one principal point to the other principal point in the direction of flight, and from the center of the sidelap area of one adjacent flight strip to the center of the sidelap area of the opposite adjacent flight strip. These latter two lines may be determined with reference to the photographs of the project. The positions of the principal points are plotted on the map sheet by placing the measuring mark in contact with the model at each principal point and lowering the pencil. The principal points are plotted because it is quite often desirable to recover the map positions of the principal points in subsequent operations, even though these points may not show on the finished map.

All planimetry in the model is traced by following the features both horizontally and vertically by means of the measuring mark. Since the drainage is the primary feature that shows the influence of the topography, it must be traced out in its planimetric position with utmost care. In areas where the drainage cannot be followed easily, reversing the spectacles will give a *pseudoscopic view* of the model. The drainage will then appear as sharp ridge lines. The unnatural appearance of the drainage in a pseudoscopic model causes it to stand out more clearly in some instances, and makes it easier to follow with the measuring mark.

The tracing table is indexed on a vertical control point, and then the value for the lowest contour line, determined by inspection and measurement in the model, is set on the counter of the tracing table. The vertical motion of the platen is clamped to prevent any accidental change. The lowest contour line is traced out by following along the model at the constant elevation with the measuring mark. Succeeding contour lines are similarly traced out. The settings on the tracing table should be checked from time to time by observing the readings for the four vertical control points. This check also detects any change in orientation in the model caused by strains occurring in the instrument.

When all planimetry and topography have been compiled, a careful search is made for omissions, and all topographic tops are checked for completeness. In areas where dense ground cover, such as trees and heavy brush, obscures the ground surface of the model, it becomes difficult if not impossible to plot the contour lines in their correct positions. These areas are marked for field completion by the instrument operator. Also, planimetric features cannot always be readily interpreted and delineated in the model. These features are also noted so that they can be verified in the field.

The map sheet, or manuscript as it is sometimes called, is copied in a copying camera. Reproductions are then made available for field completion surveys and for field editing. In the field completion survey, the areas which could not be contoured in the plotter are completed in the field, usually by means of the plane table and alidade. Planimetric features which are missing are added to the field sheet. Certain planimetric features which were plotted in the plotter but which are not to show on the finished map are struck out during the field completion survey.

Field editing consists in classifying roads, highways, drainage, and other features, and in determining the accepted names for planimetric and topographic features in the map area. The field sheet is then returned to the office for final drafting, editing, and reproduction.

12–8. Horizontal-Control Extension in the Plotter

Horizontal control and, to a limited extent, vertical control may be extended in some types of plotting instruments. The control is carried through successive models until additional ground control is reached, after which an adjustment is made back through the models. The process is referred to as bridging, stereotriangulation, or aerotriangulation. Although a comprehensive discussion of the various techniques for performing aerotriangulation and for adjusting the results is well beyond the scope of an elementary textbook on photogrammetry, the principles on which the process is founded will be presented in this section.

The Multiplex instrument shown in Fig. 12–17 is capable of extending horizontal control by aerotriangulation. In fact, the reason for having more than two projectors is to enable control extension to be carried out. Assume that a strip of overlapping photographs has been prepared in diapositive form in a reduction printer, and that two horizontal control points appear in both the first overlap area and the last overlap area of the strip. Assume also that four vertical control points appear in each model. The diapositives are placed in the row of projectors in their proper sequence, and are centered by means of the centering device. The approximate base of the first pair of projectors, I and II, is determined by Eq. 12–3. The Y- and Z-motions are set with equal readings on both projectors and in their middle positions to allow for any horizontal or vertical deviation of the flight line throughout the strip.

The first pair of projectors, I and II, are brought to relative and absolute orientation. Relative orientation of projectors I and II is performed by the first method described in Sec. 12–4. After projectors I and II have been completely oriented to the ground control, a pair of pass points are chosen opposite the principal point of projector II, one point being in the middle of the sidelap area of each adjacent flight strip. These pass points are located in positions equivalent to those selected in radial-line plotting. The tracing-table elevations of these two pass points are read and recorded.

Projector III is now moved by the X-motion so that the base for projectors II and III is approximately the same as the base for I and II. The Y- and Z-motions of III are set with the same readings as are those of II. Since the first model must not be disturbed, projector III must be oriented to II by the second method described in Sec. 12–4. In this method, only projector III is moved. In Fig. 12–20, projectors I and II are oriented to ground control, forming the first model at the desired scale. Projector III has been carefully oriented to projector II by the second method described in Sec. 12–4.

The second model, formed by projectors II and III, which is shown as a solid trace, is at a larger scale than the first model. In order to bring it to the proper scale, a point P is selected in the overlap area of diapositives I and III, and near the principal point of II. With projectors I and II turned on for viewing the first model, the measuring mark is brought into

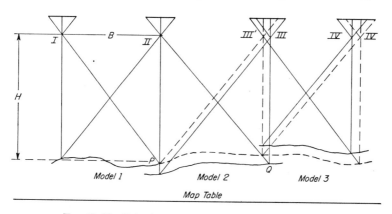

Fig. 12–20. Bringing successive models to common scale.

coincidence with the model surface at P. Now with projectors II and III turned on for viewing the second model, and without moving the tracing table, the base of II and III is altered by applying an X-motion to III to the left until the model rises up to and touches the measuring mark at P. This adjustment brings the second model to the theoretically correct scale, as shown by the dashed trace in Fig. 12–20. The BY and BZ components of the base are adjusted to eliminate any y-parallax introduced by this scale change. The tracing-table elevations of the pass points lying opposite the principal point of projector II are read and compared with the tracing-table elevations of the two points as read in the first model. If they disagree considerably, the relative orientation of projector III is checked, because a disagreement in the elevations of the pass points indicates a cross-tilting of the model resulting chiefly from improper relative orientation.

A second pair of pass points are selected opposite the principal point of projector III, and the tracing-table elevations of these forward pass points are measured and recorded. Projector IV is now oriented to projector III, to form the third model. A point Q, lying in the overlap of II and IV and lying close to the principal point of III, is measured in the second model by bringing the measuring mark in contact with the point. The original scale of the third model, shown as a solid trace in Fig. 12–20, is too small. Projector IV is now moved to the right by an X-motion until point Q of the third model is lowered to the measuring mark. This movement brings the third model to the theoretically correct scale, as shown by the dashed trace. The pass points opposite the principal point of projector III are measured, and their tracing-table elevations are compared with those previously measured, in order to detect any cross-tilting.

A forward pair of pass points are selected opposite the principal point of projector IV, and the tracing-table elevations of these pass points are measured and recorded. Projector V is next oriented to IV, the new model is brought to scale, cross-tilting is checked, and forward pass points are selected and measured. This procedure is carried out for each new model throughout the remainder of the strip. The last model formed by orienting the last projector is included. After the map sheet has been oriented in the generally correct direction, the positions, in the final model, of the two horizontal control points are plotted on the map sheet. These positions are compared with the correct map positions of the same points as previously plotted with respect to the map grid. This comparison indicates whether the scale of the entire bridge is too large or too small.

In Fig. 12–21 are shown the correct map positions of control points A, B, C, and D, together with the pass points selected in the bridging process. Points C' and D' are the positions of the corresponding two control points as plotted from the final model. The scale of the bridge is thus seen to be too small. The solid lines represent the original models. Each base must be increased slightly, in order that C' and D' will coincide with C and D. The positions of the pass points will then have to be

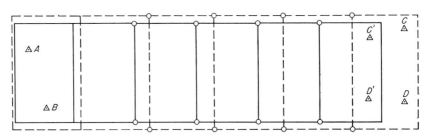

FIG. 12–21. Adjusting scale of a bridge.

adjusted, as shown at the outer edges of the adjusted models. The adjustment of the points may be carried out analytically or instrumentally.

If the work is done instrumentally, a new base must be established for the first model. The distance AC is known, or can be scaled, and the distance AC' can be scaled. The necessary factor for increasing the scale is therefore AC/AC'. The base B of the first model shown in Fig. 12–20 may be increased in the proper ratio by multiplying the flying height H by the same factor. The distance H may be scaled by placing the measuring mark on a point in the first model and measuring the vertical distance from the platen to the axis of rotation of projector I. The new value H' can be obtained by the relationship $H' = (H)(AC)/AC'$. The adjustment can be made by lowering the platen an amount corresponding to the difference $H' - H$. Finally projector II is moved slightly to the right by an X-motion until the point originally chosen is brought down to the measuring mark. This fixes the adjusted base of the first model. Extension then proceeds as before. On the completion of this second extension, points C' and D' should coincide with C and D, respectively. If they do, the second positions of all the pass points are correct. If they do not, the entire process is repeated.

The adjusted map positions of each pair of pass points in each model, together with the four vertical control points in each model, obtained by ground surveys, furnish the control needed to completely orient each model in a two-projector instrument for map compilation.

If intermediate control is available, the strip adjustment procedure is more refined. Figure 12–22 shows a strip of 13 photographs comprising

Fig. 12–22. Bridging 12 models in a strip.

12 stereoscopic models. Models *1, 5, 10* and *12* contain horizontal control points whose positions have been plotted on a gridded map sheet. The first model is oriented to points a and b, and leveled on suitable vertical control points. The extension is then carried out in which model *2* through *12* are brought to orientation and scale. The model positions of the control points and of all the selected pass points are carefully plotted on the manuscript sheet. No attempt is made to readjust the scale of the entire bridge.

Let it be assumed that the error in the plotted position of each control point is a function of the distance from the beginning control to the point. In other words, if the strip is assumed to be in the X-direction, then the positional error is a function of X. Letting the discrepancy in the X-coordinate be denoted by ΔX, and that in the Y-coordinate by ΔY, then;

$$\left.\begin{array}{l} \Delta X = a_o + a_1 X + a_2 X^2 + a_3 X^3 \\ \Delta Y = b_o + b_1 X + b_2 X^2 + b_3 X^3 \end{array}\right\} \qquad (12\text{--}4)$$

These are third-degree equations of a parabolic curve. The coefficients can be computed if there are at least four well-distributed points or groups of points in the strip. Note that there are no Y-terms in the equations. A careful scaling of the discrepancies at the seven points in strip of Fig. 12–22 together with their X-distance from some origin, will allow the coefficients to be computed by the method of least squares as applied to curve fitting. For each point, an observation equation can be formed as follows:

$$v_{X_i} = a_o + a_1 X_i + a_2 X_i^2 + a_3 X_i^3 - \Delta X_i$$

and

$$v_{Y_i} = b_o + b_1 X_i + b_2 X_i^2 + b_3 X_i^3 - \Delta Y_i$$

When these observation equations have been formed and normalized, the solution of the first set of normal equations gives $a_o \ldots a_3$, and the second set gives $b_o \ldots b_3$. With a knowledge of the coefficients of Eq. 12–4, the discrepancies in the plotted positions of the pass points can be computed. The X-distance of each pass point must of course be scaled.

This numerical adjustment can be reduced to a graphical adjustment by assuming that there exists a ficticious point on the strip X-axis for each control point or group of control ponits, and for which the discrepancy in X and Y is known. Points a and b are free of error since the first model was oriented in these two points. In Fig. 12–23, point A represents points

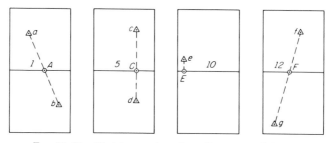

Fig. 12-23.   Ficticious points for adjustment of bridge.

a and b on the X-axis. Its X-distance is zero. This point is plotted on Fig. 12–24. The discrepancy in X at c is scaled as $+0.8$ mm and at d as

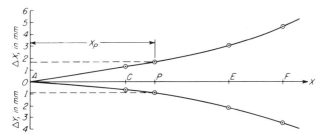

FIG. 12–24. Error curves in X and Y as functions of X.

+1.3 mm. The value of ΔX at point C which represents both points c and d is +1.1 mm by interpolation. The value of ΔY at c is −0.4 mm and at d is −0.7 mm. The value of ΔY at C is then −0.6 mm by interpolation. These values are plotted as shown in Fig. 12–24.

The discrepancies at point E must be assumed to be same as at control point e. They are $\Delta X_E = +3.0$ mm, and $\Delta Y_E = -2.2$ mm. By interpolation between the X and Y discrepancies at f and g, the values at F are $\Delta X_F = +4.6$ mm and $\Delta Y_F = -3.4$ mm. These values are plotted as shown in Fig. 12–24. A smooth curve is drawn through the ordinate points to give the error curve.

The X-distance from point A to each pass point is now scaled. This distance is used to scale off the values of the corrections $-\Delta X_P$ and $-\Delta Y_P$ as shown for one passpoint p appearing in the overlap of models 6 and 7. These corrections are then laid off on the manuscript sheet to fix the adjusted positions of the pass point.

The numerical adjustment is to be preferred over the graphical adjustment provided that the scaling can be done with great precision. It is much more direct, and the ease of solution is almost independent of the number of control points involved. One advantage to the graphical adjustment is its visual concept. A blunder in field work or in identification of control is much more easily spotted than it is in a numerical adjustment.

An examination of the curves of Fig. 12–24 shows that the discrepancy in X is not quite proportionate to X, otherwise the X-error curve would be straight. Also the Y-curve shows that the strip is bowed in azimuth. These discrepancies are caused by uncorrected systematic errors in the photogrammetric system, influenced somewhat by an accumulation of random errors.

12–9.   Horizontal-Control Extension by Stereotemplets

The extension of horizontal control by means of a radial-line plot, as described in Chapter 6, is based on the principle that angles measured at the principal point of a vertical photograph are true horizontal angles. Thus, by resection and intersection, a graphical two-dimensional triangulation network may be extended between control points to obtain the true map positions of the supplementary pass points and the principal points. With certain exceptions, the accuracy needed for horizontal control of topographic maps prepared in stereoscopic plotting instruments cannot be obtained by the radial-line method. The principal deficiencies of the radial-line method are as follows: 1) The photographs are not vertical. 2) The use of paper photographs from which to prepare the radial-line templets is undesirable because of differential paper shrinkage. 3) The scale of the photographs is too small compared with the scale of a stereoscopic model which is to be controlled by the positions of the pass points resulting from the plot.

The three-dimensional triangulation conducted by means of a sequence of projectors, as described in Sec. 12–8, can be reduced to a two-dimensional network by means of templets which are prepared, not from single photographs, but from single stereoscopic models. These templets are called *stereotemplets.* By the stereotemplet method, accurate pass-point control may be established in instruments which are not designed for aerotriangulation of a three-dimensional nature. It is presumed that the accuracy of the diapositives is preserved for the most part in the projected images of the diapositives. Since diapositives are made on glass plates, differential shrinkage is no problem. The stereotemplets may be constructed at the scale of the stereoscopic model or at a larger or smaller scale, if desired. In this discussion it is assumed that the vertical control needed to level each model is available, and that the stereotemplet will therefore be free from errors due to tilt. Since the orthographic positions of points appearing in a properly leveled model may be plotted to the scale of the model, all these points are located on a common map datum at the model scale. This being true, the angles measured at *any* of the points are true horizontal angles. Thus, in the stereotemplet, the center of rays may be taken at any point.

In preparing a theoretically correct stereotemplet, the scale of the model should be known. If the model scale is not known, it is not possible to compute the settings on the tracing table which represent the tracing-table elevations of the vertical control points, as discussed in Sec. 12–6. Therefore, the model could not be leveled. It is true that a model of unknown scale may be brought to sufficient level for stereotemplet construction by a number of methods considered to embrace the art of photogrammetry. However, since they all require experience and judgment on the part of the operator, this discussion will be confined to stereotemplet construction when the model scale has been approximately determined. Two methods in which each model may be approximately scaled are given here.

In the first method, all individual models in a strip, and which contain a control line or control points needed for scaling, are brought to absolute orientation to the desired scale at which the control line or control points have been plotted. This scale is used to compute the tracing-table elevations of the vertical control points used to level these models. After each model has been completely oriented, the base between the projectors is accurately measured. An average of all the bases is then used as the base length for *every* pair of projectors in the strip.

In the second method, a radial-line plot is prepared from the photographs of the strip to some known scale. The distance between each pair of principal points is then carefully measured on the radial-line plot. Each individual plotter base may then be computed by Eq. 3–4. Thus,

$$\frac{B}{b} = \frac{\text{desired model scale}}{\text{radial-line plot scale}}$$

in which B is the spacing of the projectors to give the desired model scale, in millimeters; and b is the distance between principal points scaled from the radial-line plot, in millimeters.

Both methods just described for bringing the individual models to scale are only approximate, but they are well within the accuracy necessary to level the individual models for the purpose of preparing the individual stereotemplets. The following analysis indicates the close approximation to a level datum which can be obtained by an approximate model scale. Assume that the base is known to within 5 per cent and that the difference in elevation between the two closest vertical control points is 500 ft. At a model scale of 1:6,000, the tracing-table difference in elevation between the two control points amounts to 25.4 mm. For a 5-per cent error in the model scale, the error in this difference in elevation is only 1.27 mm. If the model distance between the two control points is 10 in., the line between the two points will be tilted by about 17 min.

In preparing a stereotemplet, the two projectors are separated by the amount computed to give an approximate base. They are then oriented relative to one another by the first method described in Sec. 12–4, that is, by the rotational motions of both projectors. Since the scale has been established by the base separation, the absolute orientation includes the leveling procedure only. The stereotemplet method of extending horizontal control is more generally applicable to an instrument which is not capable of bridging. This is the two-projector type shown in Fig. 12–36. Consequently, the leveling is accomplished by tilting and tipping either the map table or else the bar supporting the projectors, depending on the design of the unit.

After the model has been leveled, a sheet of cardboard templet material is placed on the map table. The orthographic positions of four pass points located in the four corners of the neat model are carefully plotted on the cardboard by means of the plotting pencil. Any horizontal ground control appearing in the model is also plotted. The position of the principal point is not needed in the basic stereotemplet, but the principal point is plotted as a check on the proper identification of pass points between models. The cardboard now contains the control points, pass points, and principal points, as shown in Fig. 12–25(a). The positions

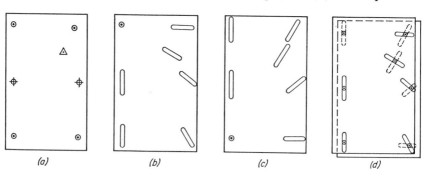

(a)   (b)   (c)   (d)

Fɪɢ. 12–25.   Stereotemplet construction.

of these points are marked on a second sheet of cardboard by pricking through the first sheet with a plotting needle.

A center of rays is now selected on one templet at one of the corner pass points, and a second center of rays is selected on the duplicate templet at some other corner point. If the templet contains a horizontal control point, the two ray centers are selected at the two corners which will give the strongest intersection angle at the control point. The first templet, shown in Fig. 12–25(b), has been completed by using the upper left pass point as the center and cutting slots through the other six points. On the duplicate templet in Fig. 12–25(c), the lower left pass point has been used as the ray center, in order to provide a strong intersection at the control point. If there is no horizontal control point on the templet, the centers of rays should be selected at two diagonally opposite pass points. The two templets that are constructed are superimposed one on another, as shown in Fig. 12–25(d). Studs placed through the intersections of the pass points complete the assembly. This is the stereotemplet.

The templet scale may be enlarged or reduced, as needed, the amount of change being limited only by the lengths of the slots. The intersections at the principal points are not used in the assembly of the stereotemplet. If the position of a pass point has been misidentified, the intersection at a principal point as defined on one stereotemplet will not coincide with the intersection as defined on the succeeding stereotemplet. Pass-point identification must then be verified, and a new stereotemplet must be constructed.

Horizontal control is plotted, and studs are secured on the base map by using the methods described for the construction of a radial-line plot. Stereotemplets are then assembled to fit the horizontal control, and the base-map positions of the pass points thus determined are pricked and identified. Finally, the positions of the pass points are carefully transferred to individual map-compilation sheets, and these points provide the horizontal control needed to scale the individual models.

A variation on the single-model templet is the use of two consecutive models for construction of the double templet. The centers of rays for the templets are taken at the two outer principal points, as shown in Fig. 12–26. Because of its increased base and stronger intersections, the con-

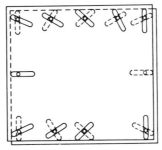

Fig. 12–26. Two-model stereotemplet.

trol obtained by an assembly of two-model templets is more accurate than one of single-model templets.

12–10. Vertical-Control Extension in the Plotter

Because of errors inherent in any photogrammetric system, and because of the high degree of accuracy required for vertical control in the stereoplotting, the extension of vertical control between fixed control points is not so satisfactory as horizontal-control extension between fixed control points. Theoretically, a series of projectors could be oriented with respect to one another through an entire strip, as described in Sec. 12–8, and then the elevations of the pass points as read in each model could be used to level individual models for subsequent map compilation.

If there were vertical control at each end of the strip, the elevations of the pass points could be adjusted to fit the end control, just as the elevations along a line of direct levels between two bench marks are adjusted. The errors in the system, however, cause the continuous strip model as a whole to bend upward or downward, to bend in a horizontal direction, or to warp or twist one way or another about some undefined axis through the strip. These distortions make a simple straight-line adjustment of elevations for vertical control approximate only, and therefore inadequate for most mapping. In this discussion, only the upward or downward bending of the vertical datum will usually be considered, and any twisting effect will be neglected unless vertical control exists midway in the flight line and on both the front side and back side of the model strip.

Let it be presumed that the first model of a bridge contains four vertical control points and two horizontal control points, and that the last model contains one vertical control point along with one horizontal control point. To start the extension, the first model is absolutely oriented to the ground control. Then, by the extension procedure described in Sec. 12–8, pass points are chosen and their tracing-table elevations are read in each of the two models in which they appear. Finally the strip is closed on the control at the far end. It is assumed that the index of the tracing table is not changed throughout the entire extension; in fact, it must not be changed for vertical-control extension.

Let it be assumed that the scale as carried through the extension and tested on the horizontal control point in the last model is in agreement with the map scale within 0.5 per cent. This is a reasonable assumption in actual operations. The results of this first extension, without the scale being changed to fit the horizontal control, are shown in Fig. 12–27. The numbers in brackets are the computed tracing-table settings in millimeters for the five vertical control points. The other values given are the tracing-table elevations read during the extension. Since

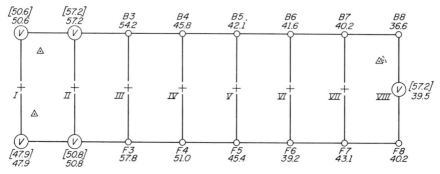

Fig. 12–27. Pass-point and control-point readings in vertical bridging.

the first model was oriented on the four control points, the values as read are identical with the computed values. The value given for each pass point *B3* through *B8* and *F3* through *F8* is the average of the values read for the point.

The discrepancy at the vertical control point in the last model is seen to be −17.7 mm. It immediately becomes apparent that the corrections to the tracing-table elevations of the pass points in Fig. 12–27 will depend on their distances in the *X*-direction from projector II. However, the amount of the correction at each pass point is not in direct proportion to this distance, because of the nature of the propagation of the errors through the strip. This propagation is shown greatly exaggerated in Fig. 12–28. When a series of projectors are oriented by successive

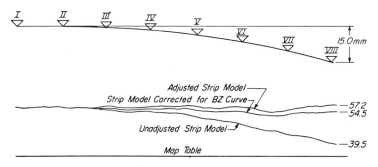

Fig. 12–28. Falling off of projectors in a vertical bridge, and adjustment.

one-projector removal of *y*-parallax, a line through the emergent nodal points of the row of projectors will nearly always form a vertical curve. The line usually curves downward, causing the elevations along the entire strip model to be too low. A smooth curve passed through the perspective centers is referred to as a *BZ curve*.

The ordinates to a BZ curve may be measured by measuring the distance from the map table up to the axis of rotation of each projector. These ordinates are then plotted with the distances from projector II to the successive projectors as the abscissas. If the line of flight is assumed to be level (this is a reasonable assumption), then the difference between the ordinate at projector II and that at any other projector represents the amount by which the measured tracing-table elevation of each pass point lying opposite the selected projector must be increased (in this example) in order to bring the level datum to a presumably level position. A curve representing these corrections for the strip in Fig. 12–27 is shown in Fig. 12–29. The tracing-table elevations of the pass points in Fig. 12–27 before and after correction for the BZ curve, are given in the

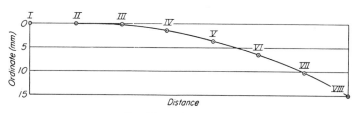

Fig. 12–29. BZ curve.

accompanying tabulation. The control point in the tabulation is the one occurring in the last model as shown in Fig. 12–27.

CORRECTIONS TO TRACING-TABLE ELEVATIONS

Point	Uncorrected Tracing-Table Reading (mm)	Correction from BZ curve (mm)	Tracing-Table Reading Corrected for BZ curve (mm)	Straight-Proportion Correction (mm)	Corrected Tracing-Table Reading (mm)
B3	54.2	+ 0.4	54.6	+0.5	55.1
B4	45.8	+ 1.7	47.5	+0.9	48.4
B5	42.1	+ 3.8	45.9	+1.4	47.3
B6	41.6	+ 6.7	48.3	+1.8	50.1
B7	40.2	+10.2	50.4	+2.3	52.7
B8	36.6	+15.0	51.6	+2.7	54.3
F3	57.8	+ 0.4	58.2	+0.5	58.7
F4	51.0	+ 1.7	52.7	+0.9	53.6
F5	45.4	+ 3.8	49.2	+1.4	50.6
F6	39.2	+ 6.7	45.9	+1.8	47.7
F7	43.1	+10.2	53.3	+2.3	55.6
F8	40.2	+15.0	55.2	+2.7	57.9
Control point	39.5	+15.0	54.5	+2.7	57.2

After the BZ-curve correction has been applied to the tracing-table elevation of the control point, this corrected reading is seen to be still low by 2.7 mm. It may be assumed that this discrepancy resulted from a straight-line accumulation of errors, independent of those producing the BZ curve. Therefore, the elevations of the intermediate pass points which have been adjusted for the BZ curve are further adjusted by straight proportion as shown in the last two columns of the preceding tabulation.

In the computations for determining the corrections in the tabulation, it was assumed that the distance between projectors was uniform and that the pass points lay directly opposite the projectors. If there were any deviation from these two assumptions, it would have been necessary to measure the X-distance from projector II to each pass point and to the control point in the last model.

A graphical portrayal of the two corrections just discussed is shown in Fig. 12–28.

If the last model, as well as the first model, contains four properly placed vertical control points, the adjustment procedure can be conducted partly by leveling the entire strip and partly by measuring the

BZ curve. Assume that the first model has been absolutely oriented, that the extension has been carried through the last model, and that the scale is found to differ by no more than 0.5 per cent. Although the pass-point elevations are noted during the extension to check cross-tilting of the models, they will not be used in the final results. The elevations of the four vertical control points in the last model are measured and their discrepancies are noted.

The far end of the bar supporting the projectors is moved up or down through such a distance that the middle of the last model has been raised or lowered by an amount equal to the algebraic average discrepancy for the four points, but in the opposite direction. This adjustment applies the straight-proportion correction to all the pass points in the strip. If all four control points do not lie exactly in the four corners of the neat model, a point at the intersection of lines joining the opposite vertical control points is used to control the vertical movement of the end of the bar. When the entire strip is leveled in this manner, the four vertical control points in the first model will be affected. The tracing table must therefore be reindexed on the two control points lying closest to and opposite projector II, and the four control points in the last model must be remeasured. A slight adjustment of the bar will again affect the control points in the first model, and the tracing table must be again reindexed on the two control points in the first model.

After a trial-and-error leveling of the entire bar, no discrepancy will exist between the measured readings and the fixed readings on the two control points in the first model. This condition is shown graphically in Fig. 12–30. Point A is the center of the last model before leveling. Point V represents the positions of the two control points in the first model lying closest to projector II. Point A'' is the center of the last model after leveling. Note that the left side of the first model has been lowered to the dashed position. This lowering is of no consequence because the first model contains four control points by which the model can be leveled for subsequent map compilation.

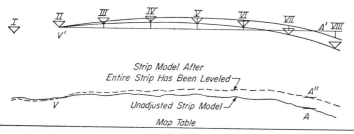

FIG. 12–30. BZ curve after leveling entire bar to fit end control.

With the entire strip model leveled, the tracing-table elevations of the pass points are now measured and recorded. Then the vertical distance from the top of the map table to the center of rotation of each projector is measured. The departure of the curve plotted from these measurements with respect to a straight line through V' and A' gives the amount by which the tracing-table elevation of each pass point must be reduced (in this example) to give the adjusted pass-point elevation. These reductions are shown as the small offsets in the upper part of Fig. 12–30.

In the method just described, one vertical control point in the last model would be sufficient to level the entire strip. The elevations of four control points, however, indicate whether or not the strip has undergone any cross-warping. This additional information will indicate the reliability of the adjusted elevations of the intermediate pass points.

When some vertical control points are located along the strip, in addition to those at the ends, a better adjustment of the elevations of the pass points may be made. Assume that, as each projector is oriented, the tracing-table elevations of the pass points and the intermediate vertical control points are measured and recorded. Also, assume that the X-distances from the beginning control point on each side of the strip to the pass points and other control points on the same side of the strip are measured and plotted as abscissas on a graph.

Assume that the twelve models of Fig. 12–31 formed by projectors I through XIII contain vertical controls points and pass points as shown.

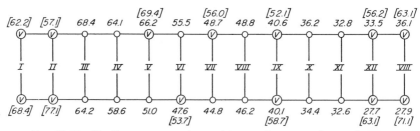

Fig. 12–31. Readings on pass points and intermediate vertical control points.

The difference between the measured tracing-table reading and the fixed or computed tracing-table setting, shown in brackets, is computed for each control point. On the graph in Fig. 12–32 these discrepancies are plotted as ordinates, with the distances from the control points in the first model as abscissas.

A smooth curve is drawn for each series of control points. The upper curve represents the line for the control points along the back edge of the strip, and the lower curve represents the line for the control points along the front edge of the strip. These curves are assumed to represent both the BZ-curve errors and the straight-proportion errors for both the

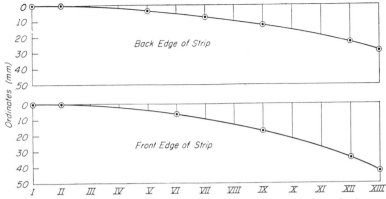

FIG. 12–32. Vertical-error curves for front and back edges of strip in a vertical bridge.

back edge and the front edge of the strip. If they are identical curves, no cross-warping or twisting of the strip has taken place. The two curves in Fig. 12–32 indicate a clockwise twisting of the strip, as evidenced by the front edge dropping faster than the back edge.

The corrections to the tracing-table elevations of the pass points which were recorded during the extension are determined by scaling the values of the ordinates at the appropriate distances along the curves.

CORRECTED TRACING-TABLE ELEVATIONS OF PASS POINTS

Point	Measured Tracing-Table Elevation (mm)	Correction from Curve (mm)	Corrected Tracing-Table Elevation (mm)
B3	68.4	+ 0.6	69.0
B4	64.1	+ 1.8	65.9
B6	55.5	+ 5.0	60.5
B8	48.8	+ 9.0	57.8
B10	36.2	+14.1	50.3
B11	32.8	+18.8	51.6
F3	64.2	+ 1.0	65.2
F4	58.6	+ 2.6	61.2
F5	51.0	+ 4.1	55.1
F7	44.8	+ 9.0	53.8
F8	46.2	+18.2	64.4
F10	34.4	+22.6	57.0
F11	32.6	+27.5	60.1

The corrected tracing-table elevations for the extension of Fig. 12–31 are shown in the accompanying tabulation. The corrections have been scaled from the curves of Fig. 12–32. The values of the adjusted tracing-table elevations are then used to level each individual model in a two-projector plotting instrument for map-compilation purposes.

The curves plotted in Fig. 12–32 represent the equation

$$\Delta Z = c_0 + c_1 X + c_2 X^2 + c_3 X^3 \qquad (12\text{–}5)$$

Note that there are no Y-terms or Z-terms in this equation. Thus, the discrepancy in elevation is assumed to be a function only of the distance along the strip. This adjustment is seen to be identical to the adjustment of the X- and Y-positions of the pass points.

12–11. Remarks on Multiplex Operations

The Multiplex instrument is considered to be a map-compilation instrument when its use is confined to two projectors. It is considered to be a bridging instrument when three or more projectors in a row are oriented together and adjusted to horizontal or vertical control or to both. The principles discussed in the foregoing sections in relation to the operations involved in the Multiplex instrument apply equally well to the stereoscopic plotting instruments to be described in the remainder of this chapter. Three of the instruments to be discussed are considered to be map-compilation instruments, although horizontal control may be extended by means of stereotemplets, prepared directly in the instrument, and by other mechanical and analytical methods. The Wild A7 Autograph and the Zeiss C8 Stereoplanigraph described in Secs. 12–16 and 12–17 are bridging instruments of great precision, even though the instruments contain only two projectors or cameras. The principles of control extension described in Secs. 12–8 and 12–10 apply equally well to the A7 Autograph and the Stereoplanigraph, although the operational procedures differ somewhat from those of the Multiplex instrument.

A review of the design and operation of the Multiplex will verify the fact that the instrument contains a projection system, a viewing system, a measuring system, and a tracing system. These components must be contained in every plotting instrument. The projection system creates a model of the terrain, in which the horizontal scale and the vertical scale are made identical by proper reduction of the diapositives. The equality of scales is a direct result of projecting the rays of light into the model space so that their angular relation to one another is the same as the relation of the corresponding rays when they entered the aerial camera at the moment of exposure. This proper orientation of rays is called interior orientation, and is accomplished by different methods in various plotting instruments.

A perfect stereoscopic model is formed by the relative orientation of two projectors. The model created, however, is at an unknown scale and is tilted with respect to the datum for elevations. By the process of absolute orientation, the model is oriented to plotted ground control. This orientation brings the model to the proper scale and level. The model thus oriented can now be measured, and its features can be plotted in the form of a topographic map. The principles of relative orientation, absolute orientation, and map compilation that apply to the Multiplex instrument are identical to those which apply to the other instruments.

12–12. Balplex Plotter

The Balplex plotter, shown in Fig. 12–33, is a map-compilation instrument with two projectors which employs the anaglyph principle of stereoscopic viewing. Each projector has six motions, which are identical to those described for the Multiplex projector. However, the design of the projector is somewhat different from that of a Multiplex projector.

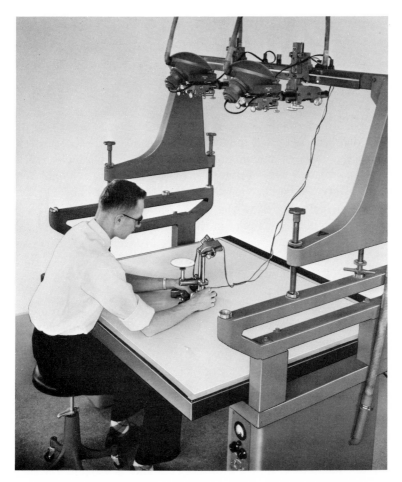

Fig. 12–33. Balplex 760 plotter. (Courtesy of Bausch and Lomb Optical Co.)

A section of the Balplex projector is shown in Fig. 12–34. The diapositive is illuminated by light from a lamp reflected from an ellipsoidal reflector surface. The lamp filament is located at one focus of the ellipsoid, and the upper nodal point of the projector lens is located at the other focus. This arrangement eliminates the need for condenser lenses because, by the

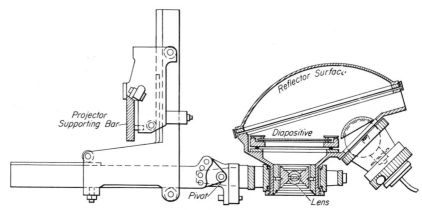

FIG. 12-34. Balplex-projector optical system.

property of an ellipsoid, a ray of light coming from one focus of the
ellipsoid and reflected from the ellipsoidal surface will pass through the
other focus. Thus, a maximum amount of available light will pass
through the projector lens. Filters provide the necessary red light or blue-
green light for anaglyphic viewing of the stereoscopic model.

The principal distance of the Balplex projector is 55 mm, compared
with a 30-mm principal distance in the Multiplex projector. The Balplex
diapositive consequently is larger than the Multiplex diapositive in the
ratio 55/30, and it contains an area greater than that of the Multiplex
diapositive in the ratio $(55/30)^2$. A special reduction printer, shown in
Fig. 12–6(b), is used to produce Balplex diapositives.

The optimum projection distance in the Balplex 525 projector is
525 mm, and that in the Balplex 760 is 760 mm. In the Multiplex projector the optimum projection distance is only 360 mm. For a given scale
of photography, therefore, the scale of the Balplex model is larger than
that of the Multiplex model, the ratio being either 525/360 or 760/360.
The vertical range of usable focus is 240 mm with the 525-mm projection
distance and 220 mm with 760-mm projection distance.

The super-wide-angle Balplex plotter, shown in Fig. 12–35, accommodates photography taken with the Wild RC9 camera, and covers an
angular field of 120°. The principal-distance setting of the projector lens
is about 32 mm. The optimum projection distance is 360 mm, the same as
the Multiplex principal distance.

Each Balplex projector is provided with a gross rotational motion
about a line parallel to the supporting bar through the point marked
"pivot" in Fig. 12–34. This motion permits the Balplex to use diapositives
made from oblique photographs. The plane of optimum focus can be
made to lie parallel to the map table by tilting the projector lens about a

FIG. 12–35. Super-wide-angle Balplex plotter. (Courtesy of Bausch and Lomb Optical Co.)

line passing through the upper nodal point so as to satisfy the Scheimpflug condition stated in Sec. 10–2.

Orientation and map-compilation procedures with the Balplex are identical to those described for the Multiplex. The greater diapositive area, the longer projection distance, and the larger model provide greater accuracy than that obtainable with the Multiplex from the same aerial photography.

12–13. Kelsh Plotter

The Kelsh plotter, shown in Fig. 12–36, is a plotting instrument of the double-projection type which is similar in principle to the Multiplex instrument. The glass diapositives are full size 9 inches square. Two different diapositive carriers can be used interchangeably on the same

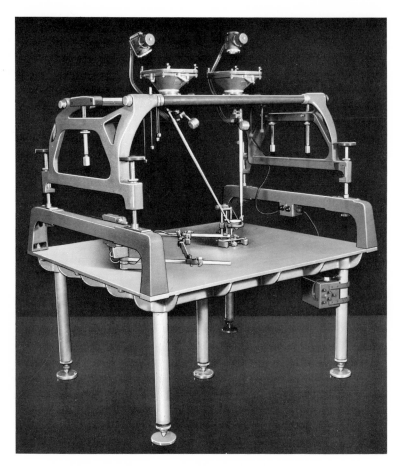

FIG. 12–36.   Kelsh plotter.   (Courtesy of Kelsh Instrument Co.)

frame.   One carrier has a nominal principal distance of 6 in., and the
other has a nominal principal distance of 8.25 in.   The Kelsh plotter can
therefore accommodate both wide-angle and normal-angle mapping
photography.

Two methods are used to achieve proper interior orientation.   In the
first method, the diapositive is prepared in a 1-to-1 printer into which
is inserted a correction plate to eliminate the lens distortion inherent in
the negative.   Provision is made to accommodate different focal lengths
of the aerial camera lenses.   The projection takes place through the
negative.   The diapositive is oriented into the carrier by means of the
fiducial marks, with the emulsion facing down toward the projector lens.

In the second method, the diapositive is prepared either in a 1-to-1
printer without a correction plate or else by contact printing of the dia-

positive through the negative. In this instance, the light source in the contact printer must be at a considerable distance from the negative; otherwise the thickness of the negative emulsion backing will cause a fuzziness or lack of sharpness in the resulting diapositive. The diapositive, which contains the distortion produced by the aerial camera lens, is placed in the carrier, and oriented by means of the fiducial marks.

To achieve proper interior orientation, the actual principal distance, which is equal to the calibrated focal length of the aerial camera used to take the photographs, is set off by means of a graduated ring that can move the projector lens vertically through a small range of focal lengths. The small diaphragm opening maintains the proper depth of focus in the model area. When the diapositives are prepared from Metrogon-lens photography, the radial distortion contained in the diapositive is offset by moving the lens vertically as different portions of the diapositive are being projected for measurement. This movement changes the principal distance from point to point.

In Fig. 12–37, it is assumed that the front and back nodal points

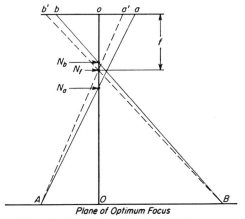

Plane of Optimum Focus

Fig. 12–37. Change in principal distance.

occupy the same position. At a principal distance equal to the focal length f, the superimposed nodal points would take the middle position N_f, as shown. Point a on the diapositive has been displaced outward from its correct position a', because of a positive radial distortion $a'a$. A ray from a' would intersect the plane of optimum focus at A. By lowering the nodal points to N_a, a ray from the displaced point a is caused to intersect at A. Thus, at least in the plane of optimum focus, the distortion effect has been eliminated. Similarly, a ray from b, which has been displaced inward, is caused to intersect the plane of optimum focus at the correct point B by raising the nodal points to N_b.

The lens is moved up and down by a cam mechanism actuated by the movement of the tracing table in the model area. The movement of the tracing table is transmitted to the cam in each of the two projectors by means of guide rods seen in Fig. 12-36. When distortion-free, wide-angle photography is used, the cams are disengaged from the guide rods, and the principal distance is kept fixed at the focal length of the aerial-camera lens. Normal-angle photography does not require the use of the cams, because the diapositives are relatively free from distortion.

Interior orientation of the diapositives is obtained by printing the diapositives, setting off the calibrated focal length, centering the diapositives in the carriers, and engaging (or disengaging) the cams.

Each carrier or projector of the Kelsh plotter contains three rotational motions and only one translational motion, which is in the X-direction. Because it is a two-projector instrument, relative orientation is accomplished by the rotational motions of both projectors. The X-motion is used to bring the model to scale. The entire frame can be tipped and tilted by means of footscrews, in order to level the model.

The illumination of the diapositives is provided by two small lamps located above the diapositives. These lamps swing in arcs about the center of the projector lenses, the motions being imparted to the lamp support arms by means of the guide rods attached to the tracing table. This arrangement can be seen in Fig. 12-36. Only a small portion of each diapositive is illuminated at any time, and that portion is projected through the lens and down onto the tracing-table platen. As the tracing table is moved about in the model area, the lamps are rotated in their arcs so as to maintain the illumination and keep the images from the two diapositives on the platen.

The optimum projection distance (which varies in different designs) is about 30 in. for the wide-angle projectors and about 33 in. for the normal-angle projectors. The usable depth of focus is about 8 or 9 in. Technical specifications relating to the Kelsh plotters must be obtained from the manufacturer.

Orientation and map-compilation procedures with the Kelsh plotter are identical to those described for the two-projector Multiplex. The 30-in. projection distance gives a Kelsh-model scale slightly more than twice as large as a Multiplex-model scale for the same aerial photography.

12–14. Wild Autograph A8

The Wild Autograph A8, shown in Fig. 12–38, is a two-projector compilation instrument, the design of which is radically different from the design of plotters of the Multiplex, Balplex, and Kelsh types. Although the four basic components exist in the A8, the design of each

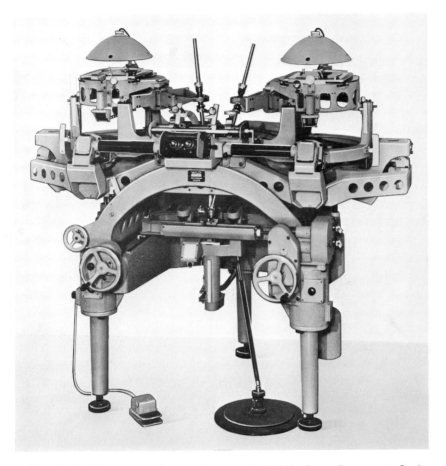

Fɪɢ. 12–38. Wild Autograph A8. (Courtesy of Wild-Heerbrugg Instruments, Inc.)

component is different from that of the corresponding component in the Multiplex-type plotter. In Fig. 12–39 is a simplified schematic diagram of the components of the projection and orientation systems of the A8. Figure 12–40 is a three-dimensional view of the workings of the instrument.

Each of the two diapositive carriers seen in Fig. 12–38 and identified in Fig. 12–39 is illuminated from above by a small bulb placed at the focus of a parabolic reflector. The diapositive carriers hold contact-print glass diapositives. Each plate carrier contains three rotational motions. Each diapositive can be rotated about its principal point, to permit the swing rotations κ' and κ'' to be set off. Also, a diapositive carrier may be raised or lowered on three columns attached to the camera body. The parallelogram link, which is attached to the underside of the diapositive carrier at a fixed pivot, is thus raised or lowered correspondingly. This

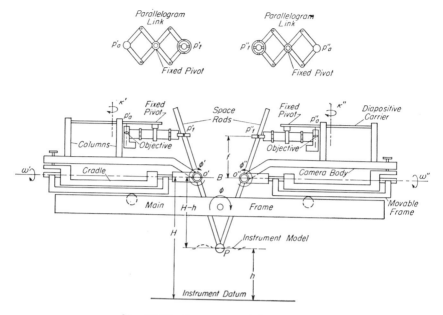

FIG. 12–39. Components of Autograph A8.

movement of the carrier sets off the desired focal length f, as shown in the figure. The camera bodies can be rotated about points o' and o'', to permit the y-tilt rotations ϕ' and ϕ'' to be set off. The cradles supporting the camera bodies can be rotated about a common axis passing through o' and o'', to permit the x-tilt rotations ω' and ω'' to be set off. The cradles are supported on frames which are movable in the X-direction, to permit the X-motion of the cameras to be set off. The movable frames are in turn supported by the main frame, which can be rotated about a y-axis through the center to permit a rotation ϕ of the entire assembly. The cameras have no Y-motion or Z-motion. The main frame is supported at the center by the yoke seen in Fig. 12–38, and the yoke is supported by the three legs of the instrument.

The projection system of the A8 is purely mechanical. Its principal components are a pair of space rods which intersect at the hinge point P. As shown in Fig. 12–39 and Fig. 12–40, the parallelogram links attached to the diapositive carriers contain sleeves at p'_t and p''_t on one end and contain objective lenses at the other end. The left-hand diapositive will be considered first. The optical axis of the objective lens is normal to the diapositive and passes through point p'_a, which is an actual point on the diapositive. The position of p'_a, and hence of the objective lens, defines a unique position of the center of the sleeve at p'_t. If p'_a is moved to the left, p'_t is moved to the right. If p'_a is moved forward out of the plane

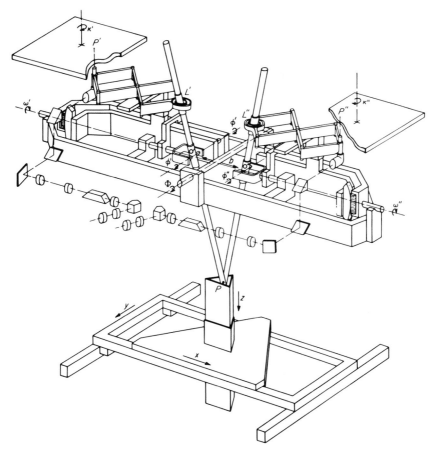

Fig. 12–40. Schematic diagram of Autograph A8 showing components and optical system.

of the figure, p'_t is moved backward. This reversal of motion is effected by the parallelogram link. All points on the diapositive are therefore transferred in reverse into a plane in which the center of the sleeve at p'_t travels. This is the effective plane of the diapositive. A similar explanation applies to the right-hand diapositive.

Point o' is the perspective center of the left-hand effective diapositive plane. The perpendicular distance from o' to this plane must be equal to the focal length of the aerial camera in which the photograph was taken, in order that the space rod, representing a projected ray of light, may occupy the correct direction in space. This distance is set off on the columns, and forms part of the interior orientation of the diapositive. The distance B, between the two perspective centers o' and o'', is varied by moving one or the other of the movable frames during the scaling process. This movement sets off the proper base. The two conjugate diapositive images p'_a and p''_a are transferred to the positions p'_t and p''_t respectively, by the two links. Since the two space rods are constrained to pass through points p'_t and o' and p''_t and o'', respectively, and since they are hinged at their junction, point P must occupy a definite position, which is located at a distance h above the instrument datum. Point P is therefore the mechanically projected position on the instrument model of the corresponding terrain point.

The viewing system consists of two optical trains, each commencing at the objective lens located beneath the diapositive and ending at the eyepiece through which the operator views the stereoscopic image. The viewing system is therefore a form of direct binocular viewing of the diapositives. The path which the rays take from the diapositives to the eyepieces can be traced in Fig. 12–40. In Fig. 12–41 is shown the plane

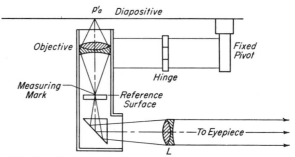

Fig. 12–41. Optical-train objectives and measuring mark of Autograph A8.

of the left-hand diapositive, with the objective lens directly beneath point p'_a. The image of p'_a is brought to focus at a reference surface, which contains a measuring mark. A second objective at L picks up the image of p'_a, together with the measuring mark, and projects them through the optical train to the left-hand eyepiece. At any time, the operator sees only a small portion of the stereoscopic image under magnification, together with the fused image of the two measuring marks. The measuring system, to be described, moves the objective lenses and the measuring marks about underneath the diapositives, so that the operator eventually can scan the entire area of overlap of the diapositives and can see the entire stereoscopic image and the fused measuring mark.

The hinge point of the space rods, shown at point P in Fig. 12–39, can be moved along a horizontal line perpendicular to the plane of the drawing by turning one of the handwheels seen in Fig. 12–38, and can be moved along a horizontal line in the plane of the drawing by turning the other handwheel. These movements give, respectively, the Y- and X-measurements of the instrument model. The base carriage, to which motion is imparted by means of the handwheels, can be seen in Fig. 12–40. The hinge point moves in the same direction as do the two objective lenses underneath the diapositives. This fact can be verified in Fig. 12–39 by assuming that the space rods rotate at the fixed perspective centers o' and o'' and that the upper ends of the space rods and the objective lenses move in opposite directions.

With point P constrained to move in a horizontal plane located at a distance h above the instrument datum, the measuring marks, which move with the objective lenses, are held at a fixed separation from each other. When viewing the stereoscopic image, the operator sees the floating mark lying above, in contact with, or below the stereoscopic image. When point P is moved upward on the base carriage, the two measuring marks are brought closer to each other, and their parallax has been increased. The floating mark thus appears to rise correspondingly. Conversely, when point P is lowered, the separation between the measuring marks is increased, and the parallax of the marks is decreased. The floating mark thus appears to fall or recede correspondingly.

A rotation of the foot disc seen in Fig. 12–38 causes the point P of the instrument model to move upward or downward. The amount of vertical movement is recorded on a Z-scale graduated to read in feet of elevation. By rotations of the two handwheels and the foot disc, the physical intersection of the axes of the space rods at P traces out the imaginary surface of the instrument model at a scale determined by the length of the base B. This scale is referred to as the instrument-model scale.

The measurement of elevations and the settings for contour lines are based on the parallax relationship given by Eq. 8–8, in which B is the instrument base; H is the vertical distance from the instrument datum to the centers of projection o' and o''; and f and p are as defined for Eq. 8–8. The parallax equation is therefore seen to be solved mechanically, once the instrument datum has been established.

The tracing system consists of a separate instrument, called a coordinatograph, which is shown in Fig. 12–42. The pencil chuck rides in the Y-direction on a girder which travels in the X-direction. The X- and Y-coordinates of any point, to the map scale, may be read directly on the coordinate scales of the coordinatograph. The rotation of the X-motion handwheel is imparted to a gear box by a coupling. The appropriate selection of gears then transmits the X-movement to the coordinatograph by a second coupling and also gives the transmitted X-movement the desired map scale. The rotation of the Y-motion handwheel is similarly transmitted through the gear box to the coordinatograph at the desired scale.

The steps in interior orientation are as follows: contact printing the diapositives; orienting the diapositives in the carriers by means of

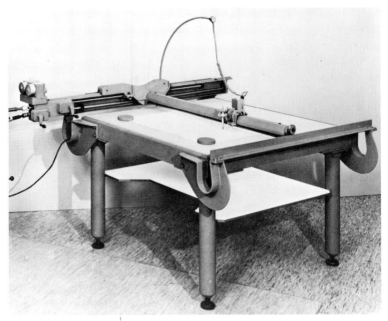

FIG. 12–42.   Coordinatograph. (Courtesy of Wild-Heerbrugg Instruments,
Inc.)

the collimation marks; inserting the appropriate correction plates a diagram of which is shown in Fig. 12–43; and finally setting off the calibrated
focal length of the aerial camera by raising or lowering the diapositive
carriers on the columns. When Metrogon-lens photography is used, glass
correction plates placed between the diapositive plane and the objective
lens eliminate all but a minor residual amount of radial distortion.

Relative orientation in the A8 is performed in the same manner
as in the Multiplex projectors. Since there is no Y-motion or Z-motion,
the relative orientation is accomplished by the rotational motions of both

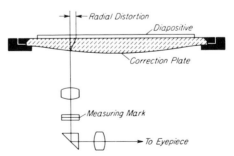

FIG. 12–43.   Correction plate for eliminating lens distortion in diapositive.

projectors. The amount of rotation about each axis can be read on scales on the instrument. When viewing the stereoscopic image through the binocular eyepiece, the operator will see the two measuring marks split in the y-direction if y-parallax exists. By going through the procedure described in Sec. 12–4, the operator systematically removes the y-parallax at the six points in the stereoscopic image.

Assume that a map sheet plotted to the desired scale and containing the map positions of two horizontal control points has been placed on the drawing surface of the coordinatograph, and that the proper gear ratio has been set in the gear box. The operator rotates the X-motion and Y-motion handwheels and the foot disc until the measuring mark appears to coincide with the image of one control point as seen in the stereoscopic image. These rotations move the pencil chuck in the X- and Y-directions. The map sheet is moved so that the plotted position of the point is directly beneath the pencil point. The operator then places the measuring mark in apparent contact with the second control point as seen in the stereoscopic image. The motions of the handwheels are transmitted to the pencil chuck and define the map position of the second control point. With the first point as the center of rotation, the map sheet is oriented so that the pencil point assumes a position on a line through the map positions of the two control points. If the pencil point falls short of the plotted position of the second point, the base must be increased by separating the cameras in the X-direction. If the pencil point falls beyond the plotted position of the second point, the base must be decreased by bringing the cameras together. The scaling is completed by this trial-and-error process, and the procedure is seen to be identical to that for scaling a Multiplex model.

The scale of the instrument model is fixed by the map scale and the gear ratio. For example, if the map scale is 1:24,000 and the gear ratio was set for $2\frac{1}{2}$ to 1 reduction, then the instrument-model scale, both horizontally and vertically, is 1:9,600. If, with the model at this scale, the intersection of the space rods is moved vertically through a distance of 1 in. by means of the foot disc, the corresponding change in elevation is 9,600 in. or 800 ft. The elevation counter is, in effect, set for a scale of 1:9,600 before leveling is performed.

Leveling is accomplished by tilting both cradles about the x-tilt axis (the ω' and ω'' axes) by the same amount and in the same direction, and also by tipping the entire assembly about the ϕ axis. Equal ω' and ω'' rotations are set off by means of the graduated scales for measuring these rotations. One vertical control point is used for indexing the elevation counter during the trial-and-error leveling process. Tilting and tipping of the cameras cause the imaginary instrument model to tilt and tip with respect to the instrument datum. Indexing the elevation counter on a vertical control point, in effect, establishes the value of H in Fig. 12–39.

Focal lengths of from 4 to 8.25 in. may be accommodated over the continuous range by vertical movement of the diapositive carriers on the columns. The vertical distance between the perspective centers and the intersection of the space rods ranges from 175 mm to 350 mm. This range physically limits the vertical range that may be accommodated in the instrument.

The student will observe that there are four distinct scales in the instrument: the diapositive scale, the instrument-model scale, the stereoscopic-image scale, and the plotting scale. The diapositive scale is determined by the focal length and the flying height of the photography. The instrument-model scale is fixed by the base separation. The stereoscopic-image scale is determined by the magnification of the optical train. The A8 magnifies the diapositive scale 6 times for stereoscopic viewing. The plotting scale is, of course, fixed by the instrument-model scale and the gear ratio. The ratio of the diapositive scale to the plotting scale varies from $\frac{1}{4}$ to 4.

When the diapositives have been oriented to the ground control by relative and absolute orientation, the map sheet is fastened in position on the drawing surface of the coordinatograph. The operator then views the stereoscopic image, and by means of the foot disc he sets the measuring mark in apparent contact with the image at a feature which is to be traced. He next lowers the pencil point to the map sheet. By rotation of the two handwheels, the measuring mark is apparently moved along the feature being traced. At the same time the two handwheel movements are transmitted to the pencil. As the terrain rises or falls, the measuring mark is raised or lowered by rotation of the foot disc. The pencil thus traces out the feature in an orthographic projection on the map sheet.

When a contour line is to be plotted, the pencil chuck is raised, the elevation scale is set at the desired contour elevation by rotating the foot disc, the measuring mark is moved by the handwheels until it comes in apparent contact with the stereoscopic image, and the pencil is lowered to the map sheet. As the operator then guides the measuring mark along the surface of the stereoscopic image by simultaneous rotations of the handwheels, a contour line is traced in orthographic projection on the map sheet at the scale of the map.

12–15. Control Extension by Independent Models

The Balplex, Kelsh, and Autograph A8 plotters are essentially two-projector instruments, designed for compilation of planimetry and topography from near-vertical photographs. Balplex projectors can be oriented on a long bar to form a strip model for the extension of control by the methods discussed in Sec. 12–8. They also accept convergent photographs, as discussed in Sec. 13–34. Various versions of the Kelsh plotter have been constructed to accommodate as many as four projectors, allowing control extension through three models. The Autograph A8, however, is capable of setting up only one model at a time. These three instruments are used to perform what is referred to as semianalytical control extension, inasmuch as the instruments perform the relative orientation and initial-model resection, while the control is carried by joining the models analytically.

At present, highly satisfactory results are being realized in the extension of horizontal control by semianalytic methods. The success of this technique is due for the most part to the increase in precision with which coordinates of the pass points are measured in the Balplex and Kelsh plotters and the precision inherent in the Autograph A8. This increased precision in the first two instruments is obtained by substituting an X-Y coordinatograph for hand movement of the tracing table. Then, by encoding the X-, Y-, and Z-spindles of the instruments, all control point and pass-point coordinates are directly digitized for data processing.

Only a general outline of the technique will be given here. The student should consult the bibliography for an exhaustive treatment of this most productive subject. Assume that a series of diapositives have been prepared for control extension and map compilation, the first four of which are shown in Fig. 12–44. Ground control points are identified on each diapositive on which they appear, either by pre-marking, post-marking or selection of natural features as discussed in Chapter 5. Following this identification, pass points are selected exactly as done for radial line extension discussed in Chapter 6, or for stereotriangulation as discussed in Sec. 12–8. A carry-over point is selected at or near each principal point. These selected points are all marked with a marking instrument and transferred by means of a point-transfer instrument as discussed in Chapter 1. They are designated a through l in Fig. 12–44.

Diapositives 1 and 2 are oriented in the two projectors to form model I. This first model is then oriented to control, as points A and B of Fig.

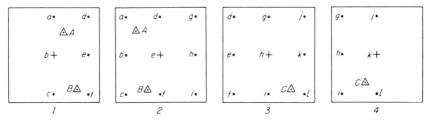

Fig. 12–44. Diapositives prepared for control extension.

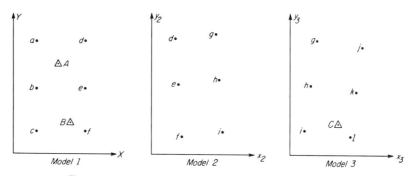

FIG. 12–45. Independent coordinate axes of three models.

12–44, and leveled on vertical control in the model. If there is not a sufficient amount of horizontal control necessary to scale the model, it is brought to approximate scale by methods discussed in Sec. 12–9. The instrument or machine coordinates of the control points and pass points are read or automatically recorded by means of the model-to-digital encoders. These coordinates are referred to the coordinate axes of this first model as established by the position of the model with respect to the coordinatograph, and is shown in Fig. 12–45.

The second model is now set up using diapositives *2* and *3*, and brought to approximate scale using pass points *d* and *f*. All the pass point coordinates of *d* through *i* are read or automatically recorded. Note that in Fig. 12–45, these coordinates are now referred to a local instrument coordinate system, unrelated to that of the initial model.

The third model is next set up using diapositives *3* and *4*. This model is scaled approximately to pass points *g* and *i*. All pass-point instrument coordinates as well as the instrument coordinates of control point *C* are read or recorded. This process is repeated for each subsequent model. The instrument coordinates of each set of pass points (except at the two ends of the strip) is thus referred to two different pairs of coordinate axes, all independent and unrelated.

Reference is made to Fig. 12–45 in which the first three independent coordinate systems are shown. The axes of the first or initial model are designated by X and Y. This set of axes will be taken as the strip coordinate axes. Thus, the strip coordinates of pass points *a* through *f* are designated X_a, Y_a, . . ., X_f, Y_f, and those of the control points as X_A, Y_A, X_B and Y_B. It is possible to rotate, translate and enlarge or reduce the coordinate system x_2, y_2 so that the coordinates of *d* and *f* of the second model are transformed into their equivalent strip coordinates. The enlargement or reduction factor is

$$m = \frac{[(X_f - X_d)^2 + (Y_f - Y_d)^2]^{\frac{1}{2}}}{[(x_{2_f} - x_{2_d})^2 + (y_{2_f} - y_{2_d})^2]^{\frac{1}{2}}}$$

The rotation angle is given by

$$\theta = \tan^{-1}\frac{Y_f - Y_d}{X_f - X_d} - \tan^{-1}\frac{y_{2_f} - y_{2_d}}{x_{2_f} - x_{2_d}}$$

The translation is then given by

$$\Delta X = X - X \text{ (scaled and rotated)}$$
$$\Delta Y = Y - Y \text{ (scaled and rotated)}$$

This transformation of the coordinates of d and f from the second to the strip coordinate system can be accomplished quite simply by the transformation equations

$$X = a_1 + a_3 x - a_4 y$$
$$Y = a_2 + a_3 y + a_4 x$$

in which X and Y are the strip coordinates and x and y are the coordinates of d and f in the second model, all in the same units. Since X, Y, x, and y are known, the transformation coefficients $a_1 \ldots a_4$ can be computed. However, since there are three points common to models 1 and 2, the transformation equations can be stated as observation equations, thus

$$vX_d = a_1 + a_3 x_d - a_4 y_d - X_d$$
$$vX_e = a_1 + a_3 x_e - a_4 y_e - X_e$$
$$vX_f = a_1 + a_3 x_f - a_4 y_f - X_f$$
$$vY_d = a_2 + a_3 y_d + a_4 x_d - Y_d$$
$$vY_e = a_2 + a_3 y_e + a_4 x_e - Y_e$$
$$vY_f = a_2 + a_3 y_f + a_4 x_f - Y_f$$

These observation equations, weighted or unweighted, are then reduced by the method of least squares to give the values of $a_1 \ldots a_4$. The transformation equations are then solved for X_g, Y_g, X_h, Y_h, X_i, Y_i by substitution of the instrument coordinates of these points from the second model, together with the transformation coefficients.

The instrument coordinates of the pass points and control point of model 3 can be transformed into strip coordinates by a least squares fit on the strip coordinates of points g, h, and i. This process is carried through the entire strip, producing strip coordinates of all the pass points and the control points as diagrammed in Fig. 12–46. This completes the control extension through a series of independent models. The student should note the similarity of this method to that of stereotriangulation discussed in Sec. 12–8. The one-projector orientation of each new model performs the same transformation instrumentally as the transformation equations do analytically.

The strip coordinates of all the control points, together with their

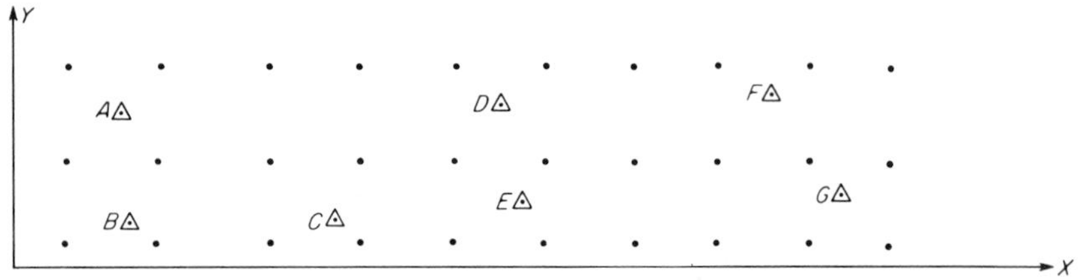

FIG. 12–46.   Strip coordinate axes.

known ground coordinates are now used to transform the strip coordinates of all the pass points into their adjusted ground control points. Different methods are employed for this transformation, one of which is given by Eq. 12–4 or by its observation equation counterpart. The pass points then furnish control for scaling each individual model for subsequent map compilation, and for relating all the map compilation sheets in one system.

In the practical application of the method of control extension by semianalytical methods, selected pass points are used also as tie points in order to relate adjacent strips. These tie points, together with the ground control points are used to perform an over-all fit of several flight strips by what is referred to as a block adjustment. This performs the same general function of a radial line plot or a stereotemplet assembly.

12–16.   Wild Autograph A7

The Autograph A7, shown in Fig. 12–47, is a two-projector instrument designed to measure and plot from terrestrial as well as from aerial photo-

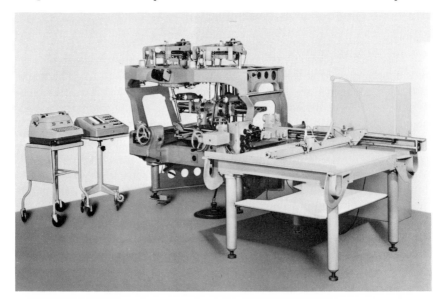

FIG. 12–47.   Wild Autograph A7. (Courtesy of Wild-Heerbrugg Instruments, Inc.)

graphs. It is extremely precise and stable, and this together with its capability of extending control by stereotriangulation, makes it a most versatile instrument. The viewing system, measuring system and tracing system is identical in all respects to that of the Autograph A8.

The plate carriers are capable of receiving and orienting all sizes of terrestrial plates and aerial diapositives up to 9- by 9-in. in size. Each carrier is capable of being set for a principal distance ranging from 98 to 215 mm, which is essentially the same range accommodated in the Autograph A8. As shown in Fig. 12–48, the cameras rotate inde-

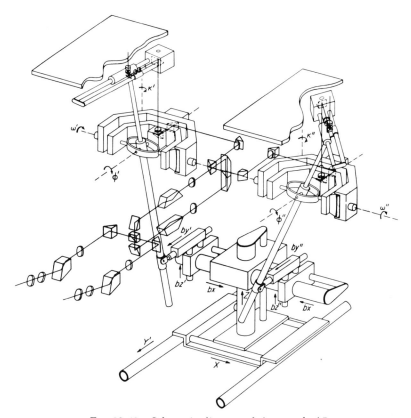

Fig. 12–48. Schematic diagram of Autograph A7.

pendently about the primary ω-' and ω-" -axes, the secondary ϕ-' and ϕ" -axes and the tertiary κ-' and κ-" -axes. These axes are seen to intersect in the centers of the gimbals through which pass the space rods. Notice that these points lie beneath the diapositives, whereas they are displaced toward the middle of the Autograph A8 by means of the parallelogram links. These points constitute the mechanical perspective centers of the diapositives.

The distance between the perspective centers can be varied in the Autograph A8 in order to set off the proper base B as shown in Fig. 12–39. However, in the Autograph A7, the distance between the perspective centers is fixed. In fact, the perspective centers are fixed in space relative to the frame of the instrument. Because of the necessary physical separation of the diapositive carriers, the space rods do not physically intersect within the limits of the instrument. Instead, they are separated, for normal viewing of vertical aerial photographs, as shown in Fig. 12–49.

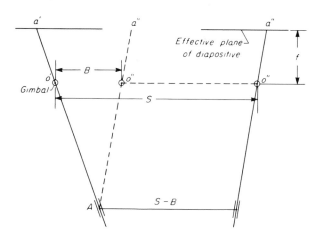

FIG. 12–49. Separation of space rods in A7, and formation of Zeiss parallelogram.

Here, the perspective centers are separated by the constant distance S. An imaginary shifting of the right hand space rod from its actual position to the dashed position produces an imaginary point at A. This shift indicates the actual base B as the distance between the left perspective center o' and the displaced perspective center o''. The parallelogram formed by the two positions of o'', the two positions of the right-hand space rod, and the line joining the lower pivot points of the space rods is called the *Zeiss parallelogram*. The model point A can be considered to lie anywhere along the latter line, since the two lower pivot points of the space rods are moved in unison as can be concluded by a study of Fig. 12–48.

In order to set off the necessary BY and BZ motions for relative orientation, and the BX motion for scaling the model, the lower pivot points of the space rods are translated relative to the cameras or diapositive carriers. In Fig. 12–50(a) is shown a pair of Multiplex projectors in schematic form, the right projector of which has been given a BY and a BZ motion as shown. This is necessary in order to orient the right projector to the left projector in the one-projector relative orientation process.

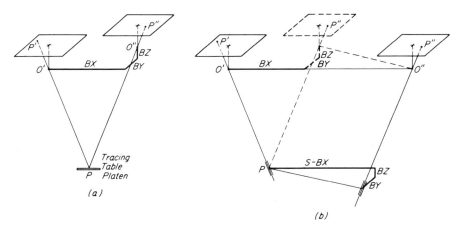

Fig. 12–50. Comparison between base components of Multiplex projectors and those of Autograph A7 space rod pivot points.

The proper base is set off by a *BX* motion of the right-hand projector during the orientation and scaling process.

In Fig. 12–50(*b*) is shown a schematic diagram of the Autograph A7. In order to achieve the proper base settings, the lower pivot of the right-hand space rod has been moved through *BY* and *BZ*, but in a direction *opposite* to the same motions of the right-hand Multiplex projector of Fig. 12–50(*a*). An imaginary shift of the right-hand space rod to its dashed position forms the Zeiss parallelogram and places the imaginary right carrier in the same relative position with respect to the left carrier as is the case in Fig. 12–50(*a*). The proper base *BX* is set off in the orientation process by displacing the lower pivot points of the space rods toward or away from one another, thus establishing the distance $S-BX$. This *BX* movement is split equally between the two space-rod pivot-points. The student will note that both space rods can be brought to a vertical position, in which $S-BX=S$, $BY=0$, and $BZ=0$; or in other words, a zero base can be established. This would be physically impossible in an instrument such as those previously discussed.

The relative orientation process in the Autograph A7 is identical to that in the Multiplex-type instruments, using either the one- or the two-projector scheme. Numerical methods, based on measured *y*-parallax at the orientation points shown in Fig. 12–8, are employed, as well as trial-and-error methods. The justification for numerical methods lies in the fact that *y*-parallax on the order of accuracy of 0.01 mm can be measured by means of the graduated *BY* motions, and that all rotational elements can be read and set to 0.01^g or about ½ min of angle. In order to facilitate the measurement of *y*-parallax, the field of view of each eyepiece can be rotated through 90°, thus converting *y*-parallax to *x*-parallax. The operator then displaces one of the space rods by a BY motion until the measuring mark comes in contact with the now flat-looking model. The necessary amount of BY motion is recorded as the y-parallax at the point.

Scaling of the model is performed by the BX motion of the space-rod pivot-points, followed by the necessary amount of BY and BZ to remove any y-parallax motion introduced by the BX motion. This is the same method used to scale the Multiplex model.

Since the two perspective centers of the Autograph A7 are fixed in space relative to the instrument frame, the leveling operation is accomplished by a combination of the rotations about the common ω' and ω'' axes, the rotations about the independent ϕ' and ϕ'' axes, and a rotation of the imaginary line joining the lower pivots of the space rods.

Assume that BY', and BZ', BY'', and BZ'' are all zero, that is $B = BX$ only. Then an equal amount of ω' and ω'' rotations will have the effect of raising or lowering the front of the model. Suppose, however that the base components are BX, $BY = BY' - BY''$, $BZ = BZ' - BZ''$. Then referring to Fig. 12–51, and looking in the direction of the X-axis of the instru-

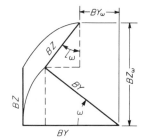

Fig. 12–51. Base rotation about X-axis.

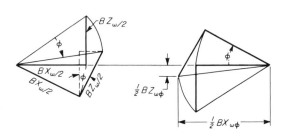

Fig. 12–52. Base rotation about Y-axis.

ment, the new base components after a rotation through ω about the X-axis become

$$
\left.
\begin{aligned}
BX_\omega &= BX \\
BY_\omega &= BY \cos \omega - BZ \sin \omega \\
BZ_\omega &= BY \sin \omega + BZ \cos \omega
\end{aligned}
\right\}
\qquad (12\text{–}6)
$$

or

$$
\begin{bmatrix} BX_\omega \\ BY_\omega \\ BZ_\omega \end{bmatrix}
=
\begin{bmatrix}
1 & 0 & 0 \\
0 & \cos \omega & -\sin \omega \\
0 & \sin \omega & \cos \omega
\end{bmatrix}
\begin{bmatrix} BX \\ BY \\ BZ \end{bmatrix}
= \mathbf{A}_\omega
\begin{bmatrix} BX \\ BY \\ BZ \end{bmatrix}
\qquad (12\text{–}6a)
$$

Next, imagine looking at the base along the Y-axis of the instrument, as shown in Fig. 12–52. Each projector has been given an equal ϕ-rotation. The BX and BZ components are assumed to be split equally between the two space-rod pivot-points. Then

$$\left.\begin{array}{l} BX_{\omega\phi}=BX_{\omega}\,\cos\,\phi+BZ_{\omega}\,\sin\,\phi \\ BY_{\omega\phi}=BY_{\omega} \\ BZ_{\omega\phi}\,=-BX_{\omega}\,\sin\,\phi+BZ_{\omega}\,\cos\,\phi \end{array}\right\} \qquad (12\text{--}7)$$

or

$$\begin{bmatrix} BX_{\omega\phi} \\ BY_{\omega\phi} \\ BZ_{\omega\phi} \end{bmatrix} = \begin{bmatrix} \cos\,\phi & 0 & \sin\,\phi \\ 0 & 1 & 0 \\ -\sin\,\phi & 0 & \cos\,\phi \end{bmatrix} \begin{bmatrix} BX_{\omega} \\ BY_{\omega} \\ BZ_{\omega} \end{bmatrix} = \mathbf{A}_{\phi} \begin{bmatrix} BX_{\omega} \\ BY_{\omega} \\ BZ_{\omega} \end{bmatrix} \; (12\text{--}7a)$$

Combining Eq. 12–6a and 12–7a gives

$$\begin{bmatrix} BX_{\omega\phi} \\ BY_{\omega\phi} \\ BZ_{\omega\phi} \end{bmatrix} = \mathbf{A}_{\phi}\mathbf{A}_{\omega} \begin{bmatrix} BX \\ BY \\ BZ \end{bmatrix}$$

$$= \begin{bmatrix} \cos\,\phi & \sin\,\omega\,\sin\,\phi & \cos\,\omega\,\sin\,\phi \\ 0 & \cos\,\omega & -\sin\,\omega \\ -\sin\,\phi & \sin\,\omega\,\cos\,\phi & \cos\,\omega\,\cos\,\phi \end{bmatrix} \begin{bmatrix} BX \\ BY \\ BZ \end{bmatrix} \quad (12\text{--}8)$$

or

$$\left.\begin{array}{l} BX_{\omega\phi}=BX\,\cos\,\phi+BY\,\sin\,\omega\,\sin\,\phi+BZ\,\cos\,\omega\,\sin\,\phi \\ BY_{\omega\phi}=BY\,\cos\,\omega-BZ\,\sin\,\omega \\ BZ_{\omega\phi}\,=-BX\,\sin\,\phi+BY\,\sin\,\omega\,\cos\,\phi+BZ\,\cos\,\omega\,\cos\,\phi \end{array}\right\} (12\text{--}8a)$$

The values of ω and ϕ are determined by an analysis of the readings of the vertical control points before leveling, as discussed in Sec. 12–6. The values of BX, BY and BZ are obtained by reading the base settings of the two space rod pivot points, following relative orientation and scaling, but before leveling. The readings of ω' and ω'' must then be increased by the necessary model rotation ω. The readings of ϕ' and ϕ'' must be increased by the required ϕ-rotation of the model. The new value of BX, which is now $BX_{\omega\phi}$ is set off. Finally, the new values of BY and BZ, which are now $BY_{\omega\phi}$ and $BZ_{\omega\phi}$, are used to establish new settings of BY', BY'', BZ' and BZ''. The differences between BY and $BY_{\omega\phi}$ and between BZ and $BZ_{\omega\phi}$ are split equally by the two space rods, added to one rod and subtracted from the other.

Compilation of a map is accomplished in exactly the same fashion as in the Autograph A8. The two handwheels move the base carriage in X and Y directions, as shown in Fig. 12–48. These motions are transmitted through the gear box to the coordinatograph. An upward movement of the base carriage by means of the foot disk causes the upper ends of the space rods, and thus the measuring marks, to spread apart, increasing their parallax. This causes the mark to appear to rise in the viewing model space.

The A7 can extend control through any desired number of models by means of an optical switch at the binocular eyepiece, and by alternately switching the base from a normal position to an outside position. Suppose that the strip of four overlapping photographs shown in Fig. 12–53(a) is to be extended in the A7 for the purpose of bridging control. The overlap area between photographs *1* and *2* is designated *a*, that between photographs *2* and *3* is *b*, and that between *3* and *4* is *c*. It is assumed that there is sufficient control in the first overlap area to permit absolute orientation of the first model.

Diapositives *1* and *2* are oriented in the two carriers by means of the fiducial marks. All the rotational motions of the carriers are set to zero, BY' is set equal to BY'', BZ' is set equal to BZ'', and an approximate BX-setting is introduced. This latter value depends on the scale of the photography and on the desired average Z-position of the base carriage. The two carriers are then oriented to one another by the rotational motions of both carriers. They are then scaled and leveled to ground control. The result is shown diagrammatically in Fig. 12–53(b), in which diapositive *1* is on the left and is viewed with the left eye, while diapositive *2* is on the right and is viewed with the right eye. The common overlap area is situated at *a* on both diapositives. Scaling has fixed base B_a. The elevation of a carry-over point near the principal point of diapositive *2* is now measured and recorded.

Diapositive *1* is removed from the left carrier and is replaced by diapositive *3*, as shown in Fig. 12–53(c). Diapositive *3* is then oriented by use of the fiducial marks. When the optical switch at the eyepiece is thrown, the left eye views the right diapositive while the right eye views the left diapositive. The common overlap area is situated at *b* on both diapositives. The base is now run out to its outside position in order to allow the observer to view the common overlap area. Since orientation of diapositive *2* must not be disturbed, diapositive *3* is oriented to diapositive *2* by rotations of the carrier and the BY and BZ motions of the left space rod pivots.

The model is scaled by first setting the elevation counter to the recorded elevation of the carry-over point, since it will have been changed during the process of relative orientation. Then the base is changed with a BX motion, followed by an X-movement of the base carriage by means of the handwheel, until the measuring mark touches the stereoscopic image at the carry-over point. This is identical to scaling the new models in a Multiplex bridge. The X-, Y-, and Z-coordinates of the two pass points are recorded. A new carry-over point and pass points are selected, and their instrument space positions are recorded. In Fig. 12–53(c), the base formed by the Zeiss parallelogram is seen to lay outside the camera lens. This is called the *base-out* position, whereas the situation in Fig. 12–53(b) is referred to as the *base-in* position.

Diapositive *2* is now replaced by diapositive *4*, the space rods are run into the base-in position, and the optical switch is now thrown for

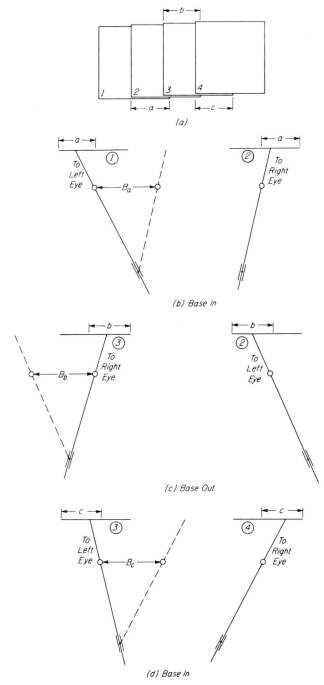

FIG. 12–53. Optical switch and base reversal in control
extension with Autograph A7.

direct viewing. The common overlap area is then area c, as shown in Fig. 12–53(d). Diapositive 4 is oriented to diapositive 3, the new model is brought to scale by means of the carry-over point, and the pass-points are read and recorded. A new carry-over point and pass points are selected and measured.

Alternating the position of the base and the position of the optical switch will permit an indefinite number of models to be oriented to form a stereotriangulation bridge. The bridge is then adjusted analytically in order to establish the adjusted instrument coordinates and elevations of the pass points. These points are then used for absolute orientation in a map-compilation instrument.

The use of the Autograph A7 for measuring and plotting from terrestrial photographs is discussed in Sec. 14–18.

12–17. Zeiss Stereoplanigraph C8

The Zeiss Stereoplanigraph C8, shown in Fig. 12–54, is a two-projector instrument for compilation and bridging. The projection of images from contact-print diapositives takes place through a pair of lenses similar to the lens of aerial camera with which the photographs were taken. The projectors are, in fact, referred to as the cameras of the instrument. By a reversal of the rays through a lens identical to the one through which the photographs were exposed, any radial distortion is exactly compensated for.

In Fig. 12–55, the diapositive has been oriented in the camera by means of the fiducial marks. Point a is the diapositive position of a point which, at the time of photography, was displaced outward from a' by a positive radial distortion. On reprojection through a lens with the same focal length and the same distortion characteristics, the bundle of parallel rays is leaving the lens at the correct angle with the optical axis. This principle of projection that is applied to cancel the effects of lens distortions is known as the *Porro-Koppe principle*. Since the Stereoplanigraph C8 is designed to accommodate photography taken with lenses of varying distortion characteristics, the Porro-Koppe principle is not strictly adhered to. Compensation for distortion is provided either by means of a corrective plate in the diapositive printer, or else by a compensation plate under the diapositives in the projector-cameras similar to that shown in Fig. 12–43.

Because the emergent rays are parallel, they will never come to focus at a finite distance unless an auxiliary lens system intercepts the collimated rays. This auxiliary system is shown diagrammatically in Fig. 12–55. The function of this system is to bring the rays to focus at A in the reference plane.

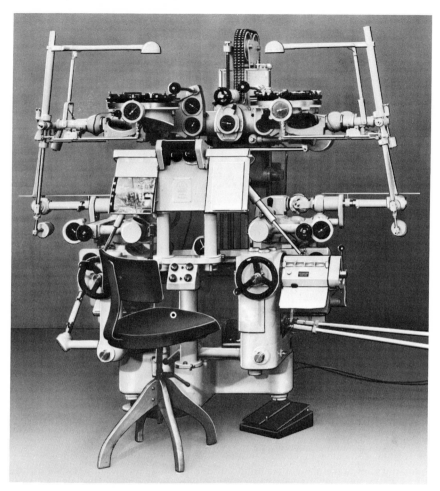

Fig. 12–54. Zeiss Stereoplanigraph C8. (Courtesy of Carl Zeiss, Oberkochen.)

The auxiliary system is made to swing under the lens about point N by motions imparted by the handwheels. The entire diapositive can thus be scanned directly through the lens. Since the distance NA is greater than the distance NO, the focal length of the auxiliary system must be varied to maintain sharp focus in the reference plane. The change of focus is effected by changing the separation s of the elements of the lens system. The distance s is varied by a cam rod which is actuated by the rotation of the handwheels. If the cameras are to be raised or lowered with respect to the reference surface, in order to obtain a corresponding increase or decrease in the projection distance, the separation of the elements is also regulated by the cam rods in order to maintain focus in the reference plane.

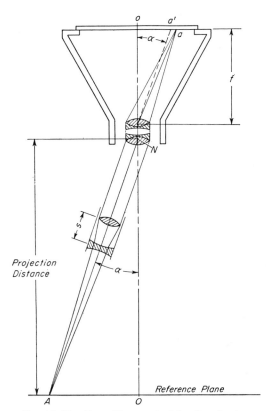

Fig. 12-55. Porro-Koppe principle of projection.

Each camera can be rotated about the three mutually-perpendicular axes passing through the nodal point N. These rotations, denoted by ϕ, ω, and κ, correspond to the y-tilt, x-tilt, and swing of the Multiplex projectors. Although the cameras themselves have no X-, Y-, and Z-motions corresponding to the three translational motions of the Multiplex projectors, the two measuring marks may be translated in the three directions independent of each other. The displacement of each measuring mark, identified in Fig. 12-56, is similar to the displacement of the space rod pivot points of the Autograph A7.

In Fig. 12-56 is a schematic diagram of the C8, showing the projection system, the rotations of the two cameras, the three motions of each measuring mark, designated bx, by, and bz, the viewing system, and the measuring system. It is to be noted that this diagram shows the instrument in its base zero position. A pair of conjugate points are projected through the camera lenses and the auxiliary lens systems, and come to focus on reference mirrors m and m'. The reference mirrors contain

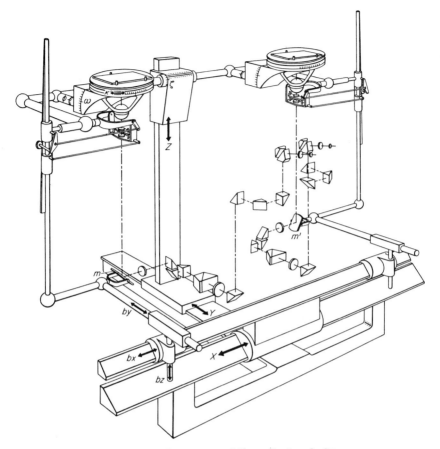

FIG. 12–56. Components of Stereoplanigraph C8.

the measuring marks, which lie in the reference planes of the cameras shown in Fig. 12–55. From the reference mirrors, the images of the points, together with the measuring marks, are brought to the eyepieces by means of the optical trains.

The relative orientation may be accomplished by the rotational motions of both cameras, or by the rotational motion of one camera together with the by- and bz-motions of its measuring mark. The methods are described in Sec. 12–4.

The instrument model is formed at the apparent intersection of the rays coming from the two cameras. In Fig. 12–57, the two images a and a' are projected into the instrument-model space onto the reference mirrors m and m'. An imaginary shift of the ray $m'a'$ so as to cause an intersection with the ray am at A forms the Zeiss parallelogram whose

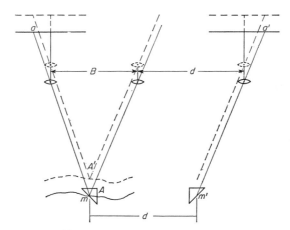

Fɪɢ. 12–57. Zeiss parallelogram.

base is equal to the separation d of the two measuring marks. The distance B is the camera base, and it defines the scale of the instrument model. The model is measured in the vertical direction by moving the two cameras up or down as a unit. The instrument model is thus raised or lowered. This movement, in effect, raises or lowers the measuring marks, which are seen as a single floating mark through the binocular eyepiece.

The instrument model is brought to scale by a bx-motion of one measuring mark or the other. The separation d of the measuring marks, and hence the camera base B, is thus changed. The process of scaling is identical to that described for the Wild Autograph A7.

The rotation of the X-motion handwheel imparts an X-movement to the two measuring marks as a unit. This movement is transmitted through a gear box to the coordinatograph. The rotation of the Y-motion handwheel imparts a Y-movement to the entire column which supports the projectors, as shown in Fig. 12–56. This movement is transmitted to the coordinatograph through the gear box. The entire model is therefore moved in the Y-direction. A rotation of the foot disc moves the camera assembly up or down on the supporting column. The instrument model is thus raised or lowered.

Leveling is performed by equal ω- and ϕ-rotations of the cameras together with the base rotations, as discussed in Sec. 12–16 for the Autograph A7.

The procedure for map compilation in the C8 is similar to that described for the Wild Autograph A7 and A8. Rotations of the handwheels cause the coordinatograph pencil to move correspondingly, but to the scale of the map. Rotation of the foot disc causes the stereoscopic image to rise or fall, the corresponding movement of the instrument model registering on an elevation counter.

Like the Autograph A7, the Stereoplanigraph is an extremely precise and stable instrument. It is capable of extending control through a strip of photographs by means of an optical switch, and by alternating from a base-in to a base-out position. Stereotriangulation in the C8 is identical to that in the A7.

The foregoing sections discussing the principles of design and operating procedures of the different stereoscopic plotting instruments are not intended to be an operational manual for the instruments. Technical specifications and operational procedures should be obtained from the manufacturers of the instruments. In order to get more insight into the operation of these ingenious photogrammetric instruments, the student is advised to read selections from the bibliography.

12—18. Automation in Stereoscopic Plotting Instruments

A new generation of instruments which is expected to eliminate much of the tedious work of compiling contour lines and planimetric features is presently in the development stage. This development is made possible by the improvement and perfection of electronic scanning devices and related circuitry together with the increase in the speed of electronic computers.

The function of a stereoscopic plotting instrument, aside from stereotriangulation, is the creation of a stereoscopic model by the orientation processes discussed earlier in this chapter. The operator can then compile planimetric features and trace contour lines by traversing the model in all three dimensions using the measuring mark. Recognition of planimetric features by the human brain is by pattern and form. This is created in the stereoscopic model by varying image densities and density gradients inherent in the diapositives.

Density variations and density gradients in the diapositive are capable of being digitized through measurement of light intensity by means of a photoelectric cell, having assigned numerical values to various levels of intensity at discrete points on the diapositives. The digitized data can then be analyzed and processed to locate planimetry and contour lines. A contour line is established at points where comparison of the data from the two diapositives indicate equal amounts of a given x-parallax. Planimetry is compiled by a process opposite to that which produced the data from the diapositives; thus, a traveling light source of an intensity which is made to vary from point to point can paint an image onto a sensitized sheet of film. The film is then used for making reproductions. This system makes possible an automatic analog-to-digital conversion of data without human intervention. In the data reduction process, the elements of orientation are computed, and their effects on each point are continuously determined in the computer.

A technique which is less oriented toward digital computer solution is that in which the pattern formed on each diapositive by a scanning spot generated by a cathode ray tube (CRT) and projected through the projector lenses are compared with one another electronically to detect x- and y-parallax. The y-discrepancy at the six orientation points shown in Fig. 12–8 are used to control servo motors which impart the rotational and translational motions to the projectors. Automatic iteration of this process minimizes the y-parallaxes and performs automatic relative orientation.

The x-parallaxes detected throughout the model can be used in a variety of ways to perform functions automatically. One function is automatic profiling. Imagine a CRT to be traveling back and forth in the model, generating a scanning pattern onto each diapositive. The electronic pickup via a pair of photoelectric cells analyzes the x-discrepancy at all points and then generates a signal which drives a servo motor, causing a tracing device to be raised or lowered in order to keep the x-parallax to a minimum. This vertical motion produces a profile along the travel of the CRT.

Taking automatic profiling a step further, imagine that as the tracing device is moved upward past a contour elevation value, the pencil makes contact with the drawing medium and remains in contact until the next higher contour is reached. The pencil is then automatically raised and held in the raised position until the next contour is reached. A repetition of this process at every contour value creates a series of dashed lines and spaces equal in length to the spacings of the contour lines. As the CRT travels back and forth over the model, these lines produce a system of lines and spaces as shown in Fig. 12–58(a). The resulting contour lines are shown in Fig. 12–58(b). This is the *drop-line* technique for locating contour lines.

(a)   (b)

Fig. 12–58. Contour lines produced by drop-line technique.

Now suppose that the up-and-down motion is used to pick up the image projected through one of the projector lenses just as an image could be visualized as being received on a very small portion of the Multiplex tracing table as the table is raised or lowered in the stereoscopic model. If this small image is detected by a photoelectric cell, the variation in intensity due to variation in the density of the diapositive from point to point allows a reproduction to be made on film by the process in reverse. Thus, a series of small image bands are painted on the film each time the CRT traverses the stereoscopic model. The resulting picture is called an *orthophoto* because it is an orthographic projection of the image appearing in perspective projection on the diapositive.

An instrument called the Orthophotoscope works on the general geometric principle as stated above except that it is not at present a fully-automated instrument. The tracing table of the Balplex plotter is replaced by a film holder larger than the stereoscopic model. The film surface is covered except for a small rectangular window surrounded by a small platen on which the stereoscopic model can be viewed.

The entire film holder can be raised and lowered in order to keep the small rectangular window and thus a small portion of the film in contact with the the surface of the model. This small window, which serves as the floating mark, is moved back and forth in the Y-direction by means of a curtain arrangement, being stepped in the X-direction, an amount equal to the width of the window, after each traverse. The traverse motion is effected by a driving mechanism. The up-and-down motion of the entire assembly is controlled by means of a hand crank turned by the operator while viewing the model stereoscopically. The film is sensitive to blue light but not to red light. Thus, because of the red filter used in one projector, only the image of the other diapositive is exposed onto the film. This therefore is an orthographic projection of one of the diapositives which is itself a perspective projection. The resulting orthophoto is a true map with a uniform scale throughout its entire area. It has the advantage of showing the planimetric features by their pictorial impression rather than by map symbolism.

Perhaps the most advanced method for locating contours is that in which the scanning pattern received by the photoelectric cells after having passed through the diapositives is analyzed in the electronic circuitry to give the direction of steepest slope. Servo motors then guide a tracing device in the X- and Y-direction, always staying normal to the direction of slope. This traces out the contour line. The operator must intervene in order to step up or down to the next contour to be traced.

Figure 12–59 is a schematic diagram of the automation of the Wild Aviograph B8, which is called Stereomat. The cathode ray tubes which generate the scanning pattern on the diapositives are held stationary. Underneath the diapositives, the photo multipliers which are also stationary, pick up the pattern and create a current i. For each point P in

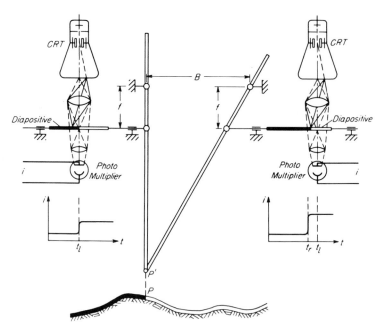

Fɪɢ. 12–59. Principle of automation of Wild B8 Stereomat.

the instrument model space, the current from the left photo cell will be either in phase or out of phase with that from the right cell. In the diagram, the intersection of the space rods at P' is seen to be too high, and the two currents are shown to be out of phase. A signal is received by the servo which controls the Z-motion of the space rod intersection causing it to move down to the correct point P. Since the base B is held fixed according to the orientation process, the diapositives are forced to move apart, decreasing the parallax and consequently decreasing the phase difference. Note the reversal of the positions of the space rod pivots and the base when compared with their positions on the Autograph A8.

Figure 12–60 shows the method of viewing the diapositive. Light from a small lamp is reflected from a dicroic mirror S to the diapositive. The image of the diapositive is brought to focus via the half-silvered mirror H at the measuring mark M by means of the objective lens O. From the mark, the image is carried to the eye by an optical train similar to that of the Autograph A8. The blue light from the CRT is separated from the yellow viewing light from the lamp by means of filters.

The Stereomat performs automatic relative orientation, profiling, contour tracing and orthophotography. The instrument can be made to step automatically in running profiles and orthophotos by outlining the area limits with reflective tape placed on the plotting table. A light-

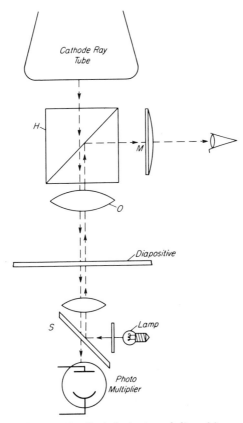

Fig. 12–60. Optical viewing of diapositive
in Wild B8 Stereomat.

sensitive sensor signals for the next line as soon as the boundary has been reached.

All of the automated stereoscopic plotting instruments contain complicated circuitry which must operate at near-peak performance at all times. They are subject to errors of interpretation if not monitored by a human operator. For example, automatic contour-tracing devices will contour the tops of trees; they will become "confused" at buildings or bridges or bodies of water; and they may get lost and come to a halt. The operator must then intervene to straighten things out. Nevertheless, the progress made in developing these ingenious instruments to their present state is truly remarkable.

12–19. Analytical Plotter

The principles of analytical photogrammetry developed in Chapter 3 have been successfully applied to a stereoscopic plotting instrument called the analytical plotter and designated AP. The commercial version of the analytical plotter, designated AP/C is shown in Fig. 12–61. The most distinct and noteworthy feature of this instrument is its adaptability to virtually any type of photography. This includes narrow-angle, normal-angle, wide-angle, super-wide-angle photography; focal lengths from zero to 1220 mm, and vertical, tilted, convergent, oblique or panoramic photography. The plotter will take into account any type of lens distortion, film shrinkage, atmospheric refraction, and earth curvature. It is of simple design from a mechanical standpoint and has very few moving parts.

Fɪɢ. 12–61. Analytical plotter AP/C. (Courtesy of OMI Corp.)

The analytical plotter consists of three main parts; a stereo-viewing unit, a high-speed digital computer, and a plotting coordinatograph. These separate parts can be identified in Fig. 12–61. The viewing unit is identical to a stereocomparator. It contains two stages for holding diapositives up to 9- by 9-in. in size. These diapositive holders are coplanar and are constrained to move in a horizontal plane and in the Y-direction only, each holder moving independently. The viewing optics move in the X-direction, each side moving independently. Thus, by a combination of these four motions any pair of conjugate images from the two diapositives can be brought exactly under each viewing objective to form a stereoscopic impression at the eyepieces. The measuring mark is comprised of two half-marks, each located on the axes of the two optical viewing trains. It is positioned in X, Y, and Z by means of the two hand wheels and the foot disc. The diapositive holders do not contain any rotational motions, and thus the stereo-viewing unit is extremely simple in design and very stable mechanically.

The computer consists of two parts. The first is a general purpose computer which is used to compute interior, relative and absolute orientation of the diapositive pair, as well as to receive the data necessary to allow for the systematic errors such as lens distortion, film shrinkage, atmospheric refraction, and earth curvature. The second part is a digital differential analyzer which is a real-time computer used to compute the appropriate positions of the diapositives and viewing system for any position of the measuring mark. A computation is made for each 5-micron displacement of the measuring mark in both X-, Y-, and Z-direction.

The coordinatograph is driven in X and Y by rotations of the hand-wheels of the viewing unit through synchro links. Its operation is identical to those of the instruments previously discussed.

After the various quantities such as focal length, lens distortion, and so on, have been introduced into and stored by the computer, the operator sets the mark on the fiducial marks of each diapositive in turn, signaling the computer to receive these values as plate coordinates. The computer then computes the position of the principal point, based on pre-stored camera calibration data, together with the directions of the coordinate axes of each plate. This completes interior orientation. Note that the diapositives need not be centered as they must in the conventional stereoscopic plotting instrument.

In order to perform relative orientation, the operator measures the y-parallax at from 6 to 14 points in the overlap area by independent motions previously cited. The computer automatically stores these displacements as quantative values of y-parallax. When all points have been read, the operator signals the computer to determine the rotational and base elements of relative orientation based on analytical formulae for numerical relative orientation. Since only five points are needed for a unique relative orientation, the redundant measurements are reduced by the method of least squares to give the most likely values for the relative orientation elements. These elements are then stored in the computer.

The operator now moves to all horizontal and vertical control points, placing the measuring mark on each point in turn. This is introduced into the computer as the x and y plate coordinates. These values, together with the relative orientation elements are used to automatically compute the absolute orientation of the model. The results are two orientation matrices given by Eq. 3–51, one for each photograph, together with the instrument X_L, Y_L, Z_L coordinates of each exposure station. These are all stored in the computer for subsequent use.

The overlap area is now ready to be measured in order to compile a map. Each position of the hand wheel and the foot disc represents a unique instrument position for a ground point P. This position is sensed by the digital differential analyzer as the values of X_P, Y_P, Z_P of Eq. 3–77. The computer solves for the x- and y-photographic coordinates of the point for each diapositive by means of Eq. 3–77. A signal is then relayed to the viewing unit, imparting the proper motions to the plate carriers and the viewing objectives to place the conjugate images of the corresponding point in fusion at the measuring mark.

In plotting from convergent photography, for example, the two conjugate images will be at different viewing scales. Or if the flying heights of the two diapositives are different, or if the focal lengths are different (a rare occasion), the viewing scales must be equalized for proper stereoscopic viewing. This is provided for by the computer which actuates the Zoom section of the optics to effect this equality. Also, if the diapositives are not placed on the carriers so that the flight line is aligned with the X-direction of the instrument (see Secs. 7–6 and 8–5), one or another of the images seen through the eyepiece must be rotated. This is accomplished by a signal from the computer which actuates a dove prism. It is thus seen that ideal stereoscopic viewing is maintained.

As the operator moves the hand wheels while following a contour line, the value of Z_P is held constant while the digital differential analyzer receives a signal for each 5-micron motion in the X- and Y-direction, draws data from the computer, and solves the collinearity equation for each photograph. This computation is performed in real time at the rate of 10 milliseconds per cycle. The output is then used to drive the diapositive carriers independently in the Y-direction, the optics independently in the X-direction, control the Zoom optics, rotate the dove prisms, and impart motion to the coordinatograph pencil, all in real time. The direction of the measuring mark is controlled by the motions of the hand wheels as is the case in the Autograph A8 for example.

When planimetric features are being traced, the operator must impart a Z-motion by means of the foot disc, as well as the X and Y motions, in order to keep the measuring mark in apparent contact with the surface of the model. The digital differential analyzer receives this movement also in 5-micron increments. Thus all three values X_P, Y_P, and Z_P of Eq. 3–77 are used to compute the proper x and y plate coordinates of the corresponding point.

At the present time, many of the operations of the analytical plotter are in the process of being automated. The automation will be accomplished generally by the methods discussed in Sec. 12–18.

Bibliography

AHREND, M., BRUCKLACHER, W., MEIER, H. K., and UTZ, H. "The Gigas-Zeiss Orthoprojector," *Photogrammetric Engineering*, Vol. XXXI (1965), p. 1039.

ALTENHOFEN, R. E. "Analytical Adjustment of Horizontal Aerotriangulation," *Photogrammetric Engineering*, Vol. XXXII (1966), p. 1047.

AMERICAN SOCIETY OF PHOTOGRAMMETRY. *Manual of Photogrammetry* (Menasha, Wisc.: George Banta Co., 1952), Chapters 14 and 15.

————. *Manual of Photogrammetry* (Menasha, Wisc.: George Banta Co., 1966), Chapters 9, 13, 14, and 15.

BEAN, R. K. "Development of the ER–55 Projector," *Photogrammetric Engineering,* Vol. XIX (1953), p. 71.

BERTRAM, S. "The Universal Automatic Map Compilation Equipment," *Photogrammetric Engineering,* Vol. XXXI (1965), p. 244.

BIRNBAUM, M. M., and SALOMON, P. M. "A High-Speed, Inertia-Free Autotmatic Stereoplotting Instrument," *Photogrammetric Engineering,* Vol. XXX (1964), p. 842.

BLUM, JOSEPH. "An Orientation Analysis of the Multiplex Model," *Photogrammetric Engineering,* Vol. XVI (1950), p. 166.

BRANDENBERGER, A. J. "An Analysis of Super-Long Aerial Triangulation and Its Applicability in Practice," *Photogrammetric Engineering,* Vol. XXX (1964), p. 977.

BRANDT, R. S. "Aerial Triangulation with the Stereoplanigraph," *Photogrammetric Engineering,* Vol. XVI (1950), p. 577.

————. "Discussion of Spatial Triangulation with the Zeiss Stereoplanigraph," *Photogrammetric Engineering,* Vol. XIV (1948), p. 425.

————. "Resume of Aerial Triangulation Adjustment of the Army Map Service," *Photogrammetric Engineering,* Vol. XVII (1951), p. 806.

COLCORD, J. E. "Aerial Triangulation Strip Adjustment with Independent Geodetic Control," *Photogrammetric Engineering,* Vol. XXVII (1961), p. 117.

COTTRELL, C. M. "Operation and Comparison of the Stereoplanigraph," *Photogrammetric Engineering,* Vol. XV (1949), p. 103.

COULTHART, D. E. "The Army Map Service M-2 Stereoplotter," *Photogrammetric Engineering,* Vol. XXVI, No. 4 (Sept. 1960), p. 657.

DEGRAAF, R. M. "Automation Characteristics of the Stereomat B-8," *Photogrammetric Engineering,* Vol. XXX (1964), p. 818.

DEMETER, E. R. "Latest Advances in Automatic Mapping," *Photogrammetric Engineering,* Vol. XXIX (1963), p. 1027.

DICKERSON, L. E. "Control Extension by Photogrammetric Methods," *Photogrammetric Engineering,* Vol. XIX (1953), p. 533.

DWYER, R. F., JR. "Visual Factors in Stereoscopic Plotting," *Photogrammetric Engineering,* Vol. XXVI (1960), p. 557.

EDEN, J. A. "The Conditions Necessary for Plotting Stereo Models in which the Set Principal Distance is not the Same as that of the Taking Camera," *Photogrammetric Engineering,* Vol. XXVIII (1962), p. 73.

————. "The Relation of Scale and Height Errors in a Multiplex Extension and a Possible Application to Mapping," *Photogrammetric Engineering,* Vol. XIV (1948), p. 556.

EDSON, D. T. "Time-Shared Readout," *Photogrammetric Engineering,* Vol. XXXII (1966), p. 383.

ESTEN, R. D. "Automatic Photogrammetric Instruments," *Photogrammetric Engineering,* Vol. XXX (1964), p. 544.

FOREST, R. B. "AP-C Plotter Orientation," *Photogrammetric Engineering,* Vol. XXXI (1966), p. 1024.

FRIEDMAN, S. J. "Aerotriangulation with the Kelsh Plotter," *Photogrammetric Engineering,* Vol. XIX (1953), p. 51.

GHOSH, S. K. "Determination of Weights of Parallax Observations for Numerical Relative Orientation," *Photogrammetric Engineering,* Vol. XXIX (1963), p. 887.

———. "Experience of Model Orientation in Wild A8 Stereo-Plotters," *Photogrammetric Engineering*, Vol. XXX (1964), p. 89.

———. "Relative Orientation Improvement," *Photogrammetric Engineering*, Vol. XXXII (1966), p. 410.

———. "Strip Triangulation with Independent Geodetic Control," *Photogrammetric Engineering*, Vol. XXVIII (1962), p. 810.

HALBROOK, J. W. "Modification of the Zeiss Stereoplanigraph Model C5 to Accommodate 9- by 9-Inch Photography Taken with a 6-Inch Metrogon Lens," *Photogrammetric Engineering*, Vol. XV (1949), p. 418.

HALLERT, B. *Photogrammetry* (New York: McGraw-Hill Book Co., 1960), Chapter 3.

———. "Practical Tests of the Theoretical Accuracy of Aerial Triangulation," *Photogrammetric Engineering*, Vol. XXVIII (1962), p. 707.

———. "Weight Distribution in Stereoscopic Models after Adjustment of Coordinates in Plan and Height," *Photogrammetric Engineering*, Vol. XV (1949), p. 177.

HARDY, G. D. "The Galileo Santoni Stereosimplex Model III," *Photogrammetric Engineering*, Vol. XXII (1956), p. 397.

HELAVA, U. V. "A Fast Automatic Plotter," *Photogrammetric Engineering*, Vol. XXXII (1966), p. 58.

———. "Some Thoughts on Automation in Photogrammetry," *Canadian Surveyor*, Vol. XVIII (1964), p. 399.

HOBROUGH, G. L. "Automation in Photogrammetric Instruments," *Photogrammetric Engineering*, Vol. XXXI (1965), p. 595.

HOTHMER, J. "Possibilities and Limitations for Elimination of Distortion in Aerial Photographs," *Photogrammetric Record*, Vol. II (1958), p. 426. Concluded in Vol. III (1959), p. 60.

JANICOT, R. "General View of French Photogrammetric Equipment," *Photogrammetric Engineering*, Vol. XV (1949), p. 360.

JERIE, H. G. "A Contribution to the Problems of Analytical Aerial Triangulation," *Photogrammetric Engineering*, Vol. XXII (1956), p. 41.

JOCKMANN, H. "Number of Orientation Points," *Photogrammetric Engineering*, Vol. XXXI (1965), p. 670.

JOHNSON, E. C. "Systems Design of a Digital Control Computer for an Analytical Stereoplotter," *Photogrammetric Engineering*, Vol. XXVII (1961), p. 583.

KARARA, H. M. "Maximum Bridging Distance in Spatial Aerotriangulation," *Photogrammetric Engineering*, Vol. XXVII (1961), p. 542.

KASPER, HUGO. "Graphical Determination of the Over-Correction Factor for Use in the Relative Orientation of Vertical Photographs in any Terrain," *Photogrammetric Engineering*, Vol. XXII (1956), p. 239.

———. "The Wild B8 Aviograph—A Simple Photogrammetric Plotter," *Photogrammetric Engineering*, Vol. XXVII (1961), p. 590.

KATIBAH, G. P. "Model Flatness—A Guide for Stereo-Operators," *Photogrammetric Engineering*, Vol. XXX (1964), p. 299.

KELSH, H. T. "Kelsh Plotter," *Photogrammetric Engineering*, Vol. XIV (1948), p. 11.

———. "The Kelsh Plotter and Its Place in Photogrammetry," *Photogrammetric Engineering*, Vol. XV (1949), p. 397.

KORKONEN, U. K. "A Preliminary Investigation into the Use of Superwide-Angle Photographs on the Wild A9 Autograph," *Canadian Surveyor*, Vol. XI (1960), p. 317.

KRAMES, M. J. "About a New Graphical Method of Orienting a Pair of Aerial Photographs," *Photogrammetric Engineering*, Vol. XVI (1950), p. 556.

LANDEN, D. "Photomaps for Urban Planning," *Photogrammetric Engineering*, Vol. XXXII (1966), p. 136.

LÖSCHER, W. "The B8 Stereomat," *Photogrammetric Record,* Vol. IV (1964), p. 476.

MALCHOW, S. "A New Super-Wide-Angle Lens for Projection Plotters," *Photogrammetric Engineering,* Vol. XXX (1964), p. 942.

MASSERANO, GUIDO. "Stereocartograph Model IV," *Photogrammetric Engineering,* Vol. XV (1949), p. 346.

McKENZIE, M. L. "Adjustment of Elevations Derived from Instrumentally Bridged Aerial Photographs," *Photogrammetric Engineering,* Vol. XXX (1964), p. 272.

McMILLEN, H. J. "An Operational Report on Stereo-Templates," *Photogrammetric Engineering,* Vol. XXIII (1957), p. 708.

MEADOWS, P. L. "B8 Contouring Accuracy," *Photogrammetric Engineering,* Vol. XXXI (1965), p. 695.

MISULIA, M. G. "Investigation of the Camera Rotation System of Aerial Triangulation," *Photogrammetric Engineering,* Vol. XXX (1964), p. 230.

MROZ, A. "Relative Orientation," *Photogrammetric Record,* Vol. V (1966), p. 198.

"New Developments in Photogrammetric Equipment" (A Symposium), *Photogrammetric Engineering,* Vol. XX (1954), p. 621.

NISTRI, U. "A Practical Procedure to Carry Out Spatial Stereotriangulation," *Photogrammetric Enginering,* Vol. XXI (1955), p. 132.

NORWICKI, A. L., and BORN, C. J. "Improved Stereotriangulation Adjustments with Electronic Computers, *Photogrammetric Engineering,* Vol. XXVI (1960), p. 599.

PERKS, M. "A Numerical Adjustment Procedure for Aerotriangulation Programmed for IBM 650 Computer," *Canadian Surveyor,* Vol. XVI (1962), p. 116.

"Proceedings of Second International Photogrammetric Conference on the Analytical Plotter," *Canadian Surveyor,* Vol. XVII (1963), p. 130.

PROCTOR, D. W. "The Adjustment of Aerial Triangulation by Electronic Digital Computers," *Photogrammetric Record,* Vol. IV (1962), p. 24.

ROOK, TOMASO. "Stereosimplex Model II," *Photogrammetric Engineering,* Vol. XV (1949), p. 343.

SARALEGUI, A. M. "Accuracy and Efficiency of Stereo-Plotting Instruments," *Photogrammetric Engineering,* Vol. XVIII (1952), p. 901. Errata, Vol. XIX (1953), p. 151.

SCHER, M. B. "Stereotemplate Triangulation," *Photogrammetric Engineering,* Vol. XXI (1955), p. 655.

SCHMUTTER, B. "On Certain Instrumental Errors in the A7," *Photogrammetric Engineering,* Vol. XXVII (1961), p. 471.

SCHUT, G. H. "A Method of Block Adjustment for Horizontal Coordinates," *Canadian Surveyor,* Vol. XV (1961), p. 376.

———. "The Use of Polynomials in the Three-Dimensional Adjustment of Triangulated Strips," *Canadian Surveyor,* Vol. XVI (1962), p. 132.

SCHWIDEFSKY, K. *An Outline of Photogrammetry* (New York: Pitman Publishing Corp., 1959), Chapter 7.

SHARP, J. V. "Basic Factors in Photogrammetric Instrument Performance," *Photogrammetric Engineering,* Vol. XVI (1950), p. 118.

———. "Increased Accuracy of the Multiplex System," *Photogrammetric Engineering,* Vol. XV (1949), p. 430.

———. "Quantitative Basis for Comparison of Systems of Mapping," *Photogrammetric Engineering,* Vol. XVI (1948), p. 547.

———, CHRISTENSEN, R. L., GILMAN, W. L., and SCHULMAN, F. D. "Automatic Map Compilation Using Digital Techniques," *Photogrammetric Engineering,* Vol. XXXI (1965), p. 223.

———, and HAYES, H. H. "Effects on Map Production of Distortions in Photogrammetric Systems," *Photogrammetric Engineering,* Vol. XV (1949), p. 159.

———, and SPARLING, R. J. "A Functional Comparison of Stereoscopic Plotting Instruments," *Photogrammetric Engineering,* Vol. XIV (1948), p. 358.

STRUCK, LUIS. "The Multiplex, Kelsh Plotter, and Wild Autographs," *Photogrammetric Engineering,* Vol. XVIII (1952), p. 84.

TEWINKEL, G. C. "Numerical Relative Orientation," *Photogrammetric Enginneering,* Vol. XIX (1953), p. 841.

———. "Slope Corrections in Aerotriangulation Adjustments," *Photogrammetric Engineering,* Vol. XXXI (1965), p. 180.

———. "Stereoscopic Plotting Instruments," *Photogrammetric Engineering,* Vol. XVII (1951), p. 635.

———. "The Reading Plotter," *Photogrammetric Engineering,* Vol. XV (1949), p. 394.

THERRIEN, J. J. "A Simultaneous Section Adjustment for small Computers," *Canadian Surveyor,* Vol. XVII (1963), p. 405.

THOMPSON, E. H. "A Rational Algebraic Formulation of the Problem of Relative Orientation," *Photogrammetric Record,* Vol. III (1959), p. 152.

———. "The Thompson-Watts Plotter Model 2," *Photogrammetric Record,* Vol. IV (1964), p. 337.

THOMPSON, M. M., and LEWIS, J. G. "Practical Improvements in Stereoplotting Instruments," *Photogrammetric Engineering,* Vol. XXX (1964), p. 802.

TROW, S. W., and KELLER, M. "Transfer of Absolute Orientation From One Type of Stereoscopic Plotting Instrument to Another," *Photogrammetric Engineering,* Vol. XIX (1953), p. 831.

U. S. COAST AND GEODETIC SURVEY. "Topographic Manual," Part II, *Special Publication* No. 249 (Washington, D. C.: Government Printing Office, 1949), Chapter 5.

U. S. WAR DEPARTMENT. "Multiplex Mapping Equipment," *Technical Manual 5–244.* Washington, D.C.: Government Printing Office, 1943.

VAN WIJK, M. C. "The Effect of "Unflatness" and Bending of Diapositive Plates," *Canadian Surveyor,* Vol. XV (1961), p. 439.

———. "The Use of the A9-B9 System in Aerial Surveying," *Photogrammetric Engineering,* Vol. XXX (1964), p. 83.

VLCEK, J. "Adjustment of a Strip Using Orthogonal Polynomials," *Photogrammetric Engineering,* Vol. XXXI (1965), p. 363.

VON GRUBER, O. *Photogrammetry* (Boston: American Photographic Publishing Co., 1942), Chapters 9 and 11.

YZERMAN, H. "The Kern PG2 Photogrammetric Plotter," *Photogrammetric Record,* Vol. IV (1963), p. 218.

ZARZYCKI, J. M. "Graphical Interpolation-Adjustment of a Double Strip," *Photogrammetric Engineering,* Vol. XV (1949), p. 666.

———. "Some Theoretical and Practical Problems in Photogrammetric Bridging," *Photogrammetric Engineering,* Vol. XXI (1955), p. 725.

Problems

12–1. The focal-plane opening of an aerial camera measures 230.00 by 230.10 mm when the camera is calibrated. The calibrated focal length is 152.68 mm. What are the theoretical dimensions of the photographic image on a Multiplex diapositive?

12–2. Let Fig. 12–8 represent a pair of 9- by 9-in. photographs taken with a 6-in. focal length lens and containing 60 per cent overlap. Points *1, 2, 4,* and *3* form a square, as do points *1, 2, 6,* and *5.* If a Multiplex projector is used, what is the effect, in millimeters, of 3° swing of projector I on the *y*-displacement of point *4* in the plane of optimum definition? Of point *2*?

12–3. If projector I in Fig. 12–8 is *y*-tilted 3°, what is the *y*-displacement, in millimeters, of point *4* in the plane of optimum definition?

12–4. If projector II in Fig. 12–8 is *x*-tilted 3°, what is the *y*-displacement, in millimeters, of point *3* in the plane of optimum definition? Of point *1*?

12–5. A pair of Multiplex projectors are spaced so that the distance between their nodal points is 205 mm. A pair of conjugate points intersect on the tracing-table platen at a projection distance of 380 mm. What will be the *x*-displacement of the image of one point with respect to the other if the platen is moved upward 20 mm? Downward 20 mm?

12–6. In Prob. 12–5, the conjugate images coincide at a projection distance of 300 mm. Compute the *x*-displacements for an upward movement of 20 mm and a downward movement of 20 mm.

12–7. Plot a 6- by 12-in. rectangle on a sheet of drafting paper, and locate positions *1* through *6* of Fig. 12–8. Let these be the projected images coming from projector I. The initial *y*-displacements, when the direction from *1* to *3* is considered positive, are $\Delta y_1 = -0.10$ in.; $\Delta y_2 = -0.25$ in.; $\Delta y_3 = +0.10$ in.; $\Delta y_4 = -0.20$ in.; and $\Delta y_5 = 0$. By means of several sheets of tracing paper, determine the motions necessary to eliminate the *y*-displacements, and show the relative positions of the points on a separate sheet of tracing paper after each motion. Solve the orientation by the two-projector method and by the one-projector method.

12–8. Photography at an average scale of 1 in.=600 ft is taken with a lens having a 6.00-in. focal length. Compute the optimum Multiplex compilation scale in representative-fraction form.

12–9. For the photography of Prob. 12–8 and a Multiplex plotting scale of 1:3,800 what is the average projection distance, in millimeters?

12–10. In Prob 12–9, how much difference in elevation, in feet, above and below the average elevation, can be accommodated at the given plotting scale? Draw a diagram to scale, illustrating this situation.

12–11. Before a stereoscopic model is brought to scale, the control line as measured in the model is 10.200 in. long. As plotted on the map sheet, the length of the control line is 11.000 in. If, before scaling, the vertical distance from the projectors to a point lying at the average elevation is 325 mm, how many millimeters has the model been raised or lowered at this point after scaling?

12–12. Plotting at a scale of 1 in.=250 ft is to be performed in a Multiplex plotter. A tracing-table reading of 40.0 is to represent an elevation of 300 ft. Compute the tracing-table settings for 5-ft contour lines from 400 ft to 500 ft.

12–13. In Prob. 12–12, the elevations of five vertical control points are as follows: V–1=387.2 ft; V–2=477.7 ft; V–3=461.1 ft; V–4=572.5 ft; V–5=505.7 ft. Compute the tracing-table settings for these control points.

12–14. In Prob. 12–12, the tracing-table readings of five points taken in a scaled and leveled model are 47.7, 51.6, 67.7, 91.2, and 38.6 mm. Compute the elevations of the points.

12–15. In Fig. 12–13, $EF=7.00$ in., $FC=13.6$ in., and $ED=11.6$ in. How many degrees must the model be tilted in the x-direction and in the y-direction in order to bring it to level?

12–16. For the conditions in Prob. 12–15, the distance between the leveling screws in Fig. 12–16(a) is 32.0 in. If the pitch of the screws is 14 per inch, how many rotations of the leveling screws are required to level the model in the x-direction?

12–17. If, for the conditions in Prob. 12–15, the distance between the point of support and the leveling screws in Fig. 12–16(b) is 26.0 in., how many turns of the leveling screws are required to level the model of Fig. 12–13 in the y-direction?

12–18. Solve Prob. 12–1 for a Balplex diapositive.

12–19. Solve Probs. 12–2, 12–3, and 12–4 for a Balplex 760 plotter.

12–20. Solve Prob. 12–8 when a Balplex 525 plotter is used.

12–21. When a Balplex 760 plotter is used at the optimum scale, what range of relief can be accommodated if the plotting scale is 1 in.$=50$ ft?

12–22. Solve Probs. 12–2, 12–3, and 12–4 for a wide-angle Kelsh plotter.

12–23. Solve Prob. 12–8 when using a wide-angle Kelsh plotter.

12–24. The distortion curve of Fig. 2–25 applies to the lens used to take photographs for use in a Kelsh projector. In order to eliminate the effect of radial distortion in the stereoscopic model, what should be the theoretical principal distances in the projector for a) the principal point; b) a point at 30° from the optical axis; and c) a point at 45° from the optical axis?

12–25. The air base of an overlapping pair of photographs is 4,500 ft. If the coordinatograph of an Autograph A8 plotter is set for a 4-time reduction to give a plotting scale of 1:24,000 what will be the resultant distance $o'\,o''$ of Fig. 12–39?

12–26. In Prob. 12–25, how many millimeters must point P of Fig. 12–39 be moved vertically to represent a difference in elevation of 625 ft?

12–27. If, for the conditions in Prob. 12–25, the viewing magnification is 6 times, what is the apparent viewing scale of the stereoscopic image?

12–28. Photography at an average scale of 1:10,000 is taken with a lens having a 6-in. focal length. The coordinatograph of a Stereoplanigraph C8 is set for a 2-time enlargement. If the plotting scale is 1:1,500, what is the average projection distance NO of Fig. 12–55?

12–29. In Prob. 12–28, what difference in elevation, in feet, is represented by a vertical movement of the instrument model of 75 mm?

12–30. The average scale of photography flown for mapping in the Autograph A7 is 1:45,000. Focal length is 113.00 mm. A reduction of ⅓ between the instrument and the coordinatograph is set off and a model is oriented to ground control which is plotted to a scale of 1:60,000. What is the average projection distance from the perspective centers of the space rods to their pivot points in the base carriage?

12–31. In Prob. 12–30, $BX=151.25$ mm, $BY=8.64$ mm, and $BZ=6.20$ mm. Compute the actual distance, in feet, between the exposure stations.

12–32. Relative orientation and scaling have been performed in the Autograph A7. The dial readings are as follows: $\phi'=102.^g60$, $\phi''=100.^g84$, $\omega'=97.^g62$, $\omega''=99.^g80$, $BY'=0$, $BY''=+7.63$ mm, $BZ'=+1.06$ mm, $BZ''=+10.88$ mm, $BX=174.50$ mm. An analysis of the vertical control indicates the need to rotate the model $+1°$ 14.5' about the Y-axis and $+1°$ 38.0' about the X-axis. $100^g=90°$. Compute the new settings on the dials in order to bring the model to level.

12–33. Control extension is to be performed in the Autograph A8 by the method of independent models. The first model is set up and oriented to horizontal and vertical control. The coordinates of two forward pass points m and n are read as $X_m=280.10$ mm, $Y_m=62.58$ mm, $X_n=286.14$ mm, $Y_n=420.65$ mm. On the second model set-up, the coordinates of the two pass-points m and n, together with the next two pass points p and q are read as follows:

Point	x_2 (mm)	y_2 (mm)
m	46.80	12.65
n	109.00	364.89
p	291.45	8.64
q	351.20	363.20

Compute the coordinates of p and q with respect to the instrument coordinate axes (strip axes) of the first model.

Oblique Photography 13

13-1. Uses of Obliques

An oblique photograph, as defined in Chapter 1, is an aerial photograph exposed with the optical axis of the camera lens intentionally tilted from the vertical. High obliques, which are tilted sufficiently to expose the horizon, are used for mapping and charting at relatively small scale. The singular advantage of the high oblique in small-scale charting is its great coverage. When taken in sequence along a flight line, as discussed in Secs. 13–19 and 13–27, the photographs cover a strip of terrain from the left horizon to the right horizon. Although the entire area covered by an oblique cannot be mapped from the photograph because of small scale and loss of detail in the background area, nevertheless the usable coverage is sufficient to allow a wide spacing between adjacent flight lines.

Two widely-used methods of mapping from high obliques will be described in this chapter. These are the *trimetrogon* method and the *Canadian-grid* method. Three cameras are used in each system. Both methods produce small-scale planimetric maps, and contour lines of relatively low accuracy can also be delineated on the maps produced by the trimetrogon procedure.

Low obliques, on which the horizon does not appear, are used to compile topographic maps with a relatively high degree of accuracy. The nine-lens camera of the Coast and Geodetic Survey, described in Chapter 2, exposes eight low obliques at each exposure station. These photographs are transformed into the plane of the central near-vertical photograph by a transformer printer, and the nine-photograph composite is then rectified to an equivalent single vertical photograph. A pair of these equivalent verticals are oriented in a specially designed stereoscopic plotting instrument, called the Reading plotter, in which a topographic map is compiled.

Single-lens low obliques are exposed in sequence along a flight line to produce pairs of convergent photographs, as shown in Fig. 1–3. Continuous stereoscopic coverage of the terrain permits the compilation of topographic maps in some of the stereoscopic plotting instruments discussed in Chapter 12. The advantage of convergent low-oblique photography is the increased base-height ratio, which enables contour lines to be delineated more accurately in the plotter.

13–2. Apparent and True Horizon

The apparent horizon of a high oblique is the visible line of demarkation between the terrain and the sky. If the terrain is perfectly level, the apparent horizon will appear as a slightly-curved line near the upper edge of the photograph. This line is a trace of the curved surface of the earth. If the terrain is mountainous, and the topography is therefore irregular, the apparent horizon will appear as a broken line in which the slight curvature may or may not be discernible.

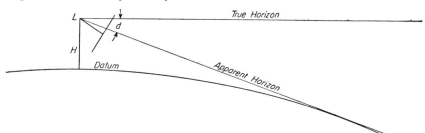

Fig. 13–1. Principal-plane section of high oblique photograph.

The true horizon of a high oblique is the photographic trace of a horizontal plane containing the exposure station. It is the intersection of that horizontal plane with the plane of the photograph. The true horizon is an imaginary line. Therefore, it does not appear on the photograph through exposure.

In Fig. 13–1, a high oblique is taken at exposure station L from a

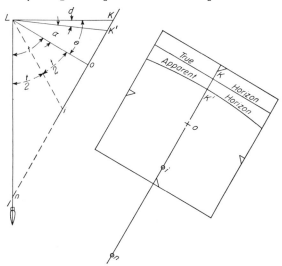

Fig. 13–2. True and apparent horizon of oblique photograph, and true and apparent depression angle.

flying height H above the datum at the earth's surface. The apparent horizon is shown as the plane that passes through the exposure station and is tangent to the earth's surface. This apparent-horizon plane, which intersects the plane of the photograph as shown in Fig. 13–2, is actually a doubly-curved surface. Its curvature normal to the drawing in Fig. 13–1 is the earth's curvature. Also it is convex upward in the plane of the drawing in Fig. 13–1, because of atmospheric refraction.

Since the true horizon is a plane surface, it is straight in the plane of the drawing in Fig. 13–1, and its trace on an oblique photograph also is straight, as shown in Fig. 13–2. The plane of the left-hand drawing of Fig. 13–2 is the principal plane of the photograph. A line constructed on the photograph so that it is perpendicular to the trace of the true horizon (called simply the true horizon) and passes through the principal point, is the principal line as defined in Sec. 3–2. Thus, Kon is the principal line.

13–3. Dip Angle

The dip angle, designated as d in Fig. 13–1 and Fig. 13–2, is the angle measured in the principal plane between the true horizon and the apparent horizon. The dip angle increases as the flying height becomes greater. In Fig. 13–3, L is an exposure station at a flying height H above the surface of the earth, O is the center of the earth, the line LK is the trace of the true horizon, and the line LK' is the trace of the apparent horizon in the plane of the drawing. For simplicity, atmospheric refraction has been neglected. The sides of the angle formed at O between the radii to exposure station L and the point of tangency K' of the apparent horizon are perpendicular to the sides

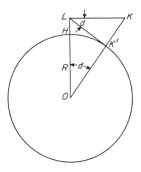

Fig. 13–3. Dip angle.

of the angle d at L between the true and apparent horizons. Hence, the angle at O is also equal to d. If R denotes the radius of the earth,

$$\tan d = \frac{LK'}{OK'} = \frac{LK'}{R}$$

By the Pythagorean theorem,

$$LK' = \sqrt{\overline{LO^2} - \overline{OK'^2}} = \sqrt{(R+H)^2 - R^2} = \sqrt{2RH + H^2}$$

Therefore,

$$\tan d = \frac{\sqrt{2RH + H^2}}{R}$$

Because H is small compared to R, this equation reduces to

$$\tan d = \frac{\sqrt{2R\,H}}{R} = \sqrt{\frac{2}{R}}\,\sqrt{H} \qquad (13\text{-}1)$$

Since the dip angle is always small, $\tan d = d'' \tan 1''$, and Eq. 13–1 becomes

$$d'' = \frac{1}{\tan 1''}\sqrt{\frac{2}{R}}\,\sqrt{H} \qquad (13\text{-}2)$$

In this expression it is assumed that the apparent-horizon trace LK' is a straight line. Atmospheric refraction will decrease the value of d in Eq. 13–2. When the approximate average value of the radius of the earth, or 20.9×10^6 ft, is used and the value of d is decreased to allow for refraction, Eq. 13–2 is reduced to

$$d'' = 58.8\sqrt{H} \qquad (13\text{-}3)$$

in which d'' is the dip angle, in seconds, and H is the flying height above the datum, in feet.

The dip angle is given approximately by the relationship

$$d' = \sqrt{H} \qquad (13\text{-}4)$$

in which d' is the dip angle, in minutes. The result obtained by Eq. 13–4 is within about 2 per cent of the correct value given by Eq. 13–3.

13–4. Apparent Depression Angle

The apparent depression angle of a high oblique is the angle measured in the principal plane between the apparent horizon and the optical axis of the camera lens. This is the angle α in Fig. 13–2. Since oK' is perpendicular to Lo,

$$\tan \alpha = \frac{oK'}{f} \qquad (13\text{-}5)$$

in which oK' is the distance measured on the photograph along the principal line between the principal point and the apparent horizon, in inches; and f is the focal length of the lens, in inches.

Before the distance oK' can be measured, the principal line must be defined on the photograph. If points on the apparent horizon at the left and right edges of the photograph can be identified, a chord can be drawn to join these two points and the principal line can then be drawn through the principal point and perpendicular to the chord. If the ends of the apparent horizon cannot be defined easily, a line is drawn generally through as many points on the apparent horizon as can be identified. The principal line is then drawn perpendicular to this line.

13–5. Depression Angle

The depression angle of an oblique photograph is the angle measured in the principal plane between the true horizon and the camera axis. In Fig. 13–2, it is the angle θ. Obviously,

$$\theta = \alpha + d \tag{13–6}$$

in which θ, α, and d are expressed in angular units.

13–6. Position of True Horizon

The true horizon may be drawn in its correct position on the photograph after the depression angle has been determined. In Fig. 13–2,

$$\tan \theta = \frac{oK}{f}$$

and
$$oK = f \tan \theta \tag{13–7}$$

in which oK is the distance measured along the principal line between the principal point and the true horizon, in inches; and f and θ are as previously defined.

When the distance oK has been computed, it is laid off on the principal line to locate point K. The true horizon is then drawn through K and perpendicular to the principal line.

13–7. Nadir Point

The nadir point, as n in Fig. 13–2, of an oblique is the point at which a plumb line passing through the exposure station pierces the plane of the photograph (extended). The nadir point can be located on the downward side of the photograph by measuring a distance $f \tan t$ from the principal point along the principal line. As seen in Fig. 13–2,

$$t = 90° - \theta \quad \text{and} \quad \theta = 90° - t \tag{13–8}$$

Therefore, the distance on is also equal to $f \cot \theta$.

13–8. Isocenter

The isocenter, as i in Fig. 13–2, of an oblique is the point at which the bisector of the angle of tilt pierces the photograph. It can be located by measuring a distance $f \tan (t/2)$ downward from the principal point along the principal line. A line on the photograph passing through the isocenter and parallel to the true horizon would have the same scale as a vertical photograph taken with the same camera and from the same exposure station.

13–9. Scale of an Oblique Photograph

The scale of an oblique is constant along any line that is parallel to the true horizon, but the scale varies along any other line. Furthermore, if a series of constant-scale lines were drawn on the photograph beginning at the true horizon and ending at the lower edge of the photograph, each succeeding line would have a greater scale than the previous line. The scale of an oblique along one of these constant-scale lines is called the *x*-scale, designated as S_x, along the line.

The scale of a line drawn perpendicular to the constant-scale lines, that is, parallel to the principal line, varies throughout its length. The scale at a point on an oblique in a direction parallel to the principal line is called the *y*-scale, designated as S_y, at the point.

In Fig. 13–4 a high oblique, for which the depression angle is θ, is exposed at L from a flying height H above the datum. Point w on the principal line is the image of the datum point W, and a ray to it makes an angle ϕ with the optical axis Lo. Point a is the image of the datum point A. The line wa is parallel to the true horizon, and the line WA is a horizontal line.

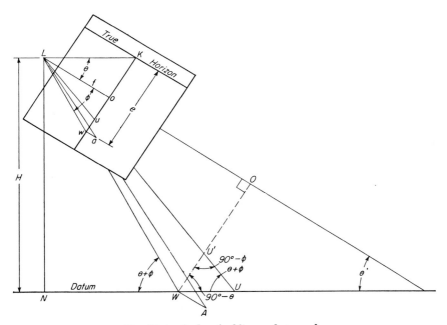

Fig. 13–4. Scale of oblique photograph.

The x-scale along the line wa is

$$S_x = \frac{wa}{WA}$$

By similar triangles,

$$\frac{wa}{WA} = \frac{Lw}{LW} = \frac{Lo/\cos\phi}{LN/\cos\left[90° - (\phi+\theta)\right]}$$

Substituting f for Lo and H for LN, and simplifying, gives

$$S_x = \frac{f \sin (\theta+\phi)}{H \cos \phi} \qquad (13\text{–}9)$$

in which S_x is the scale of an oblique photograph along a line parallel to the true horizon; f is the focal length of the lens, in inches or feet; H is the flying height, in feet; θ is the depression angle; and ϕ is the angle measured at the exposure station between the principal point and the point at which the scale line crosses the principal line. If f is in inches, the scale is an engineer's scale; if f is expressed in feet, the scale is a representative fraction.

The x-scale may be expressed in terms of the distance e, which is measured from the true horizon to the line, and the depression angle θ. As seen in Fig. 13–4,

$$e = f \tan \theta + f \tan \phi = f (\tan \theta + \tan \phi) \qquad (13\text{–}10)$$

By identity,

$$f (\tan \theta + \tan \phi) \cos \theta = \frac{f \sin (\theta+\phi)}{\cos \phi} \qquad (13\text{–}11)$$

So, from Eqs. 13–10 and 13–11,

$$\frac{f \sin (\theta+\phi)}{\cos \phi} = e \cos \theta \qquad (13\text{–}12)$$

Substituting Eq. 13–12 in Eq. 13–9 gives

$$S_x = \frac{e \cos \theta}{H} \qquad (13\text{–}13)$$

EXAMPLE 13–1. An oblique photograph is taken from a height of 10,000 ft with a camera whose focal length is 6.000 in. The distance measured on the photograph between the apparent horizon and the principal point is 3.850 in. Determine the scale along the apparent horizon and along a constant-scale line through the principal point.

Solution: By Eq. 13–3, the dip angle, in seconds, is

$$d'' = 58.8 \sqrt{10,000} = 5,880''$$

So $d = 1° 38'$

By Eq. 13–5,

$$\tan \alpha = \frac{3.850}{6.000} = 0.641667$$

from which $\alpha = 32° 41'$.

By Eq. 13-6, the depression angle is

$$\theta = 32°\ 41' + 1°\ 38' = 34°\ 19'$$

Then

$$\tan \theta = 0.682580 \text{ and } \cos \theta = 0.825934$$

The apparent horizon lies at a distance f ($\tan \theta - \tan \alpha$) down from the true horizon. Thus, the distance $c_{K'}$ is 0.245 in. The principal point lies at a distance $f \tan \theta$ down from the true horizon. So the distance e_o is 4.095 in. Finally, by Eq. 13-13, the scales at the apparent horizon and at the principal point are

$$S_{x_{K'}} = \frac{0.245 \text{ in.} \times \cos 34°\ 19' / 12 \text{ in./ft}}{10{,}000 \text{ ft}} = \frac{1}{594{,}000}$$

$$S_{x_o} = \frac{4.095 \text{ in.} \times \cos 34°\ 19' / 12 \text{ in./ft}}{10{,}000 \text{ ft}} = \frac{1}{35{,}480}$$

An expression for the y-scale at a point on an oblique may be determined by referring to Fig. 13-4. Since the scale in the y-direction (parallel with the principal line) varies from point to point, the y-scale can be considered constant for only an infinitesimal distance. In Fig. 13-4, let the distance wu be an infinitesimal y-distance, corresponding to the infinitesimal datum distance WU. The scale of this short segment is

$$S_y = \frac{wu}{WU} \tag{13-14}$$

The line WU' in triangle LWU' is parallel to the principal line. In the similar triangles LWU' and Lwu,

$$\frac{wu}{WU'} = \frac{Lw}{LW} = \frac{wa}{WA} \tag{13-15}$$

However, by Eq. 13-9,

$$\frac{wa}{WA} = S_x = \frac{f \sin (\theta + \phi)}{H \cos \phi}$$

Therefore,

$$\frac{wu}{WU'} = \frac{f \sin (\theta + \phi)}{H \cos \phi} \tag{13-16}$$

In triangle $WU'U$, $\angle W = (90° - \theta)$, $\angle U' = (90° - \phi)$ since LW may be assumed to be parallel to $LU'U$ when WU is infinitesimal, and $\angle U = (\theta + \phi)$. By the law of sines,

$$\frac{WU}{\sin (90 - \phi)} = \frac{WU'}{\sin (\theta + \phi)}$$

So

$$WU = \frac{WU' \cos \phi}{\sin (\theta + \phi)} \tag{13-17}$$

Substituting Eq. 13-17 in Eq. 13-14 gives

$$S_y = \frac{wu \sin (\theta + \phi)}{WU' \cos \phi} \tag{13-18}$$

Substituting the value of wu/WU' from Eq. 13–16 in Eq. 13–18 gives

$$S_y = \frac{f}{H}\left[\frac{\sin(\theta+\phi)}{\cos\phi}\right]^2 \qquad (13\text{–}19)$$

in which S_y is the instantaneous scale of an oblique photograph at a point in the direction of the principal line, expressed either as an engineer's scale or as a representative fraction; and the remaining quantities are as previously defined.

The y-scale at a point may also be expressed in terms of the depression angle and the distance e from the true horizon to the point by the equation

$$S_y = \frac{e^2 \cos^2\theta}{Hf} \qquad (13\text{–}20)$$

When Eqs. 13–9 and 13–19 are used, the angle ϕ is considered positive if measured downward from the optical axis and is negative if measured upward from the optical axis.

As shown in Fig. 13–2, the isocenter lies at a distance $Ki = f\,[\tan(t/2)+\tan\theta]$ from the true horizon. It can be shown that this distance is equal to $f \sec\theta$ in the following manner. A trigonometric identity is

$$\tan\frac{t}{2}+\cot t = \csc t$$

Since $t = 90-\theta$,

$$\tan\frac{t}{2}+\tan\theta = \sec\theta$$

Therefore,

$$Ki = e_i = f\sec\theta \qquad (13\text{–}21)$$

in which e_i is the distance from the true horizon to the isocenter.

The x-scale at the isocenter may be determined by substituting the value of e_i from Eq. 13–21 in Eq. 13–13. The result is

$$S_{x_i} = \frac{f\sec\theta\cos\theta}{H} = \frac{f}{H}$$

This relationship was implied in Sec. 13–8.

EXAMPLE 13–2. Determine the y-scale at the principal point of the photograph in Example 13–1.

Solution: By Eq. 13–20,

$$S_{y_o} = \frac{(4.095 \text{ in.})^2 \cos^2 34° 19'/12 \text{ in./ft}}{10,000 \text{ ft}\times 6 \text{ in.}} = \frac{1}{62,940}$$

13–10. Horizontal Angle from Coordinate Measurements on Oblique Photograph

Let the x-axis of a high oblique coincide with the true horizon, and let the y-axis coincide with the principal line. Also, let the positive y-direction be taken upward, as from o to K in Fig. 13–5. The line pL

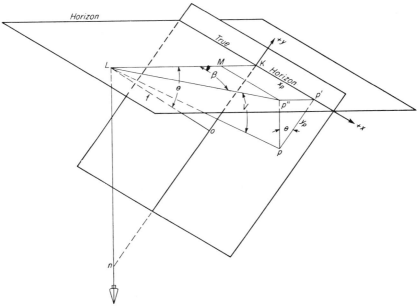

Fig. 13–5. Horizontal and vertical angles from oblique photograph.

is the ray directed from ground point P to the exposure station L. A vertical plane containing this line intersects the horizon through L along the line Lp''. The angle between the vertical plane $p''Lp$ and the principal plane, or the horizontal angle to ground point P with respect to the principal plane, is the angle $MLp'' = \beta$. In the diagram,

$$\tan \beta = \frac{Mp''}{LM} = \frac{x_p}{LK - MK} \qquad (13\text{–}22)$$

In triangle $pp'p''$,

$$p''p' = -y_p \sin \theta = MK \qquad (13\text{–}23)$$

The minus sign is used with y_p to make MK positive when the point p lies below the true horizon.

In triangle oLK,

$$LK = f \sec \theta \qquad (13\text{–}24)$$

Substituting the values from Eqs. 13–23 and 13–24 in Eq. 13–22 gives

$$\tan \beta = \frac{x_p}{f \sec \theta + y_p \sin \theta} \qquad (13\text{–}25)$$

in which β is the horizontal angle measured at the exposure station between the principal plane and a ground point P whose image p appears on the photograph; x_p and y_p are the coordinates, in inches, with respect to an x-axis coinciding with the true horizon and a y-axis coinciding with the principal line; f is the focal length, in inches; and θ is the depression angle of the oblique photograph. Due regard must be given to the algebraic signs of x_p and y_p. The positive directions are indicated in Fig. 13–5.

The horizontal angle measured at the exposure station between two ground points A and B whose images appear on the photograph is given by the relationship

$$\angle ALB = \beta_B - \beta_A \tag{13-26}$$

in which β_A and β_B are each determined by Eq. 13–25.

EXAMPLE 13-3. The images a and b of ground points A and B appear on an oblique taken with a lens having a 6-in. focal length and containing a depression angle of 28° 10′. The x-coordinates of the two images, with respect to the principal line, are $x_a = -3.26$ in. and $x_b = -0.74$ in. Point a lies 1.98 in. below the true horizon, and point b lies 5.05 in. below the true horizon; that is, $y_a = -1.98$ in. and $y_b = -5.05$ in. Determine the horizontal angle at L from A to B.

Solution: In Eq. 13–25,

$$\sin \theta = 0.47204 \quad \text{and} \quad \sec \theta = 1.13433$$

Hence,

$$\tan \beta_A = \frac{-3.26}{6.00 \times 1.13433 - 1.98 \times 0.47204} = -0.55536$$

and

$$\tan \beta_B = \frac{-0.74}{6.00 \times 1.13433 - 5.05 \times 0.47204} = -0.16735$$

Then

$$\beta_A = -29° 03′ \quad \text{and} \quad \beta_B = -9° 30′$$

By Eq. 13–26,

$$\angle ALB = -9°.30′ - (-29° 03′) = 19° 33′$$

13–11. Vertical Angle from Coordinate Measurements on Oblique Photograph

In Fig. 13–5, the vertical angle at L to ground point P (considered negative if measured downward as in surveying) is the angle $p''Lp = V$. Hence,

$$\tan V = \frac{pp''}{Lp''} \tag{13-27}$$

In triangle $pp'p''$,

$$pp'' = y_p \cos \theta \tag{13-28}$$

In triangle LMp'',

$$Lp'' = \frac{Mp''}{\sin \beta} = \frac{x_p}{\sin \beta} \tag{13-29}$$

Also, in triangle LMp'',

$$Lp'' = \frac{LM}{\cos \beta} = \frac{f \sec \theta + y_p \sin \theta}{\cos \beta} \qquad (13\text{-}30)$$

Substituting the values of Eqs. 13-28 and 13-29 in Eq. 13-27 gives

$$\tan V = \frac{y_p \cos \theta \sin \beta}{x_p} \qquad (13\text{-}31)$$

Substituting the values of Eqs. 13-28 and 13-30 in Eq. 13-27 gives

$$\tan V = \frac{y_p \cos \theta \cos \beta}{f \sec \theta + y_p \sin \theta} \qquad (13\text{-}32)$$

Due regard must be given to the signs of x_p, y_p, and β in Eqs. 13-31 and 13-32. If y_p is positive, the point lies above the true horizon, and the vertical angle is an elevation $(+)$ angle; if y_p is negative, the points lies below the true horizon, and the vertical angle is a depression $(-)$ angle, according to the usual surveying designation.

When x_p is greater than $(f \sec \theta + y_p \sin \theta)$, Eq. 13-31 is used to compute a vertical angle. When x_p is less than $(f \sec \theta + y_p \sin \theta)$, Eq. 13-32 is used.

EXAMPLE 13-4. Determine the vertical angles to points A and B by the measurements given in Example 13-3.

Solution: Since the value of $(f \sec \theta + y \sin \theta)$ is greater than both x_a and x_b, this problem is solved by applying Eq. 13-32. Thus,

$$\cos \beta_A = +0.87420 \qquad \cos \beta_B = +0.98629 \qquad \cos \theta = 0.88158$$

$$\tan V_A = \frac{-1.98 \times 0.88158 \times 0.87420}{6.00 \times 1.13433 - 1.98 \times 0.47204} = -0.25996$$

$$\tan V_B = \frac{-5.05 \times 0.88158 \times 0.98629}{6.00 \times 1.13433 - 5.05 \times 0.47204} = -0.99299$$

$$V_A = -14° 35' \qquad \text{and} \qquad V_B = -44° 48'$$

By Eq. 13-31,

$$\tan V_A = \frac{-1.98 \cos 28° 10' \sin (-29° 03')}{-3.26} = -0.26006$$

$$V_A = -14° 35'$$

13-12. Horizontal Angle by Construction

In Fig. 13-6, photo point r is the image on an oblique photograph of ground point R. A vertical plane containing the plumb line Ln and passing through r cuts the trace Lr' in the horizon, and intersects the plane of the photograph along the line nrr'. The angle λ is formed in the plane of the photograph between the principal line (or the principal plane) and point r. This angle is measured about the nadir point n.

The angle β, measured at the exposure station L, is the horizontal

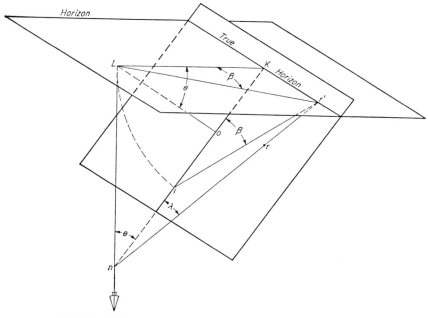

Fɪɢ. 13–6. Rotation of horizon into plane of oblique photograph.

angle between the principal plane and the point, according to Sec. 13–10. If the triangle LKr' is imagined to be rotated about line Kr' into the plane of the photograph, the vertex of angle β will be located at the iso-center, since both LK and iK are equal to $f \sec \theta$.

The nadir point lies at a distance $f (\cot \theta + \tan \theta)$ down from the true horizon. It usually falls off the photograph itself. Consequently,

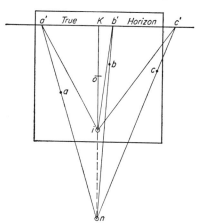

Fɪɢ. 13–7. Horizontal angle by
construction.

when the nadir point is to be located, the photograph must be secured to a sheet of drafting paper, and the principal line must be extended down a sufficient distance.

In Fig. 13–7, the true horizon, the nadir point, and the isocenter have been located in their correct positions. The horizontal angles at the exposure station between A and B and between B and C are to be determined by construction. Lines originating at n and passing through the images a, b, and c are drawn to intersect the true horizon at a', b', and c', respectively. Next, lines are drawn from the three points a', b', and c' back through the isocenter. The angles $a'ib'$ and $b'ic'$ are the desired horizontal angles.

13–13. Horizontal Angles by Using the Rectoblique Plotter

The principle of construction of horizontal angles presented in Sec. 13–12 is applied to a mechanical solution of the same problem by means of a device called the *rectoblique plotter*. In Fig. 13–8, an auxiliary horizon lies above the horizon containing the exposure station L. The position of the exposure station is projected vertically upward to L'. The principal line is extended to K'' on the auxiliary horizon. A line from n, passing through p, intersects the true horizon at p' and intersects

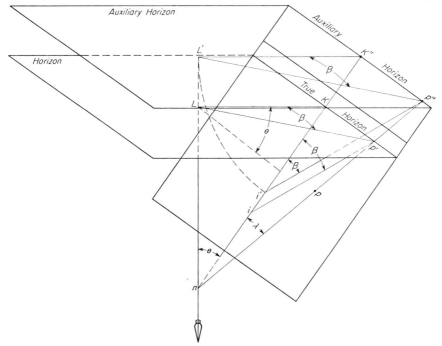

Fig. 13–8. Auxiliary horizon.

the auxiliary horizon at p''. The vertical plane nLp' is extended upward to intersect the auxiliary horizon along the line $L'p''$, which makes the angle β with the principal plane.

By the principle discussed in Sec. 13–12, the isocenter i is the vertex of horizontal angles measured in the plane of the photograph. The auxiliary point i' is the vertex of horizontal angles measured in the plane of the photograph when the triangle $K''L'p''$ is rotated about the line $K''p''$ into the plane of the photograph.

The distance KK'' is a physical distance fixed in the rectoblique plotter. The distance $K''i'$ is a distance to be set off in the plotter. It depends on the distance KK'', the focal length f, and the depression angle θ. In triangle LKn,

$$Kn = f\ (\cot\theta + \tan\theta) \qquad\qquad (13\text{--}33)$$

Therefore,

$$K''n = KK'' + f\ (\cot\theta + \tan\theta)$$

Also, in triangle $L'K''n$,

$$K''L' = K''n\ \sin\theta$$

Since $K''i' = K''L'$,

$$K''i' = K''n\ \sin\theta \qquad\qquad (13\text{--}34)$$

The rectoblique plotter is shown diagrammatically in Fig. 13–9. It consists of a horizon bar that is attached to a desk top and contains

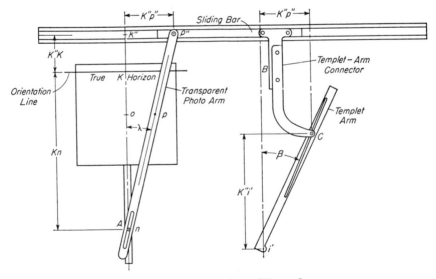

Fig. 13–9.   Diagram of rectoblique plotter.

a groove in which a moving bar slides. As the moving bar slides through a given distance (representing the distance $K''p''$ of Fig. 13–8), it imparts an equal horizontal motion to both the pivot point p'' of the transparent photo arm and the templet-arm connector. The templet arm rotates about a fixed point at i'. The photo arm rotates about and slides along the pivot point n, which represents the photo nadir point.

The oblique is oriented to the desk top by setting the photo arm (and consequently the templet arm) to a zero position, and orienting the principal line of the photograph to the center line of the photo arm. The photograph is then moved up or down until the true horizon coincides with the orientation line, as shown. Finally the photograph is taped to the desk top. The distance from the center line of the horizon bar to the true horizon represents the distance $K''K$ of Fig. 13–8.

The pivot point n is set off at a distance from the orientation line equal to Kn of Fig. 13–8. This setting is made by means of a scale at A in Fig. 13–9, and the operation solves Eq. 13–33.

The templet-arm connector may be moved up or down. By reference to a scale at B, the connector is locked in such a position that the distance $K''i'$ in Fig. 13–8 is set off between the fixed pivot at i' and the line along which the pivot point C moves. This procedure solves Eq. 13–34 mechanically. The positions of the photo arm and the templet arm shown in Fig. 13–9 are analogous, respectively, to the two lines np'' and $i'p''$ of Fig. 13–8.

The rectoblique plotter is used to prepare templets for the construction of a radial-line plot involving oblique photographs. A sheet of tracing paper, containing a point marking the tracing-paper position of the nadir point, is oriented under the templet arm, with the fixed pivot i' passing through the tracing-paper nadir point. The tracing paper is then secured to the desk top.

As the movable bar is slid in the horizon bar, the etched center line of the photo arm passes through successive points on the photograph, thus setting off various values of λ. At the same time, the templet arm assumes various values of the horizontal angle β. A ray is drawn on the tracing paper along the edge of the templet arm as the photo arm is brought over each photo point in succession. The resulting angles between the rays thus drawn are horizontal angles, measured about the exposure station.

13–14. Horizontal and Vertical Angles by Using Photoalidade

The photoalidade, shown in Fig. 1–7, is used to measure horizontal and vertical angles on oblique photographs by a graphical-instrumental method. The photograph is placed in the frame in front of the telescope of the alidade, and the frame is set at a distance f from the center of rotation of the alidade. The vertical circle is set to correspond to the depression angle. The entire frame, held by a yoke, may be rotated about a horizontal axis passing through the center of the alidade. The yoke is rotated until the cross hairs of the telescope intersect the principal point. This sets the photograph at the proper depression angle.

If the line of sight is now raised to a horizontal position (vertical-circle reading corresponding to 90°), the intersection of the cross hairs should lie on the true horizon of the photograph. The photograph is rotated in its own plane about the principal point in such a way as to meet the following requirement: When the alidade is rotated in azimuth, the intersection of the cross hairs tracks along the true horizon. This procedure sets off the proper swing of the photograph.

A sheet of paper with a center of rays marked on it is placed beneath the photoalidade, and the center of rays is brought directly beneath the alidade. This positioning is accomplished by means of an optical plummet. The sheet is normally a portion of a map manuscript, and the photograph nadir point is located on the sheet in its map position by means of a radial-line plot. This being the case, the nadir point is oriented beneath the alidade. The map sheet is then secured to the table or desk top.

With the photograph properly oriented in the photoalidade, as just described, the setup is analogous to a surveying instrument located in space at the camera exposure station. The telescope can be rotated in altitude and azimuth to give lines of sight to various image points appearing on the photograph. The altitude, or vertical angle, to a point is read on the vertical circle of the alidade. As the telescope is rotated through a horizontal angle, a blade lying on the map sheet is also rotated about the nadir point through the same horizontal angle. The blade can be identified in Fig. 1–7. Thus, the direction to a point is obtained, not by a horizontal-circle reading, but by drawing a ray along the blade. The angle between two rays is the horizontal angle measured at the exposure station between the corresponding two points.

13–15. Map Position of Nadir Point by Resection

The true map position of the nadir point of a high oblique photograph can be determined quite readily, provided that the photograph contains at least three well-placed points whose horizontal positions are known.

The true horizontal angles between the left and middle image points and between the middle and right image points can be determined by any of the methods discussed in Secs. 13–10, 13–12, 13–13, and 13–14. If the angles have been determined by coordinate measurement, they may be laid off on a sheet of tracing paper by means of a protractor. If the method of Sec. 13–12 has been used, the construction lines are traced directly on the tracing paper. When either the rectoblique plotter or the photoalidade is used, the tracing paper is used as the drawing medium directly.

The positions of the three control points are plotted with respect to a grid at the desired map scale. The tracing paper containing the two horizontal angles between the three points is then oriented over the map sheet, and the three rays are caused to pass through the three plotted control points. The position of the ray center (the vertex of the angles) thus defines the nadir point of the photograph.

Although the purposes for which obliques are used do not warrant extreme precision, the position of the nadir point may be determined by an analytic solution of the three-point problem described in any good surveying textbook. Such a procedure would be justified only if the photographic coordinates, as discussed in Sec. 13–10, have been precisely measured. The angles computed by applying Eq. 13–26 are used in the analytic solution.

13–16. Map Positions of Image Points by Intersection

If the map positions of the nadir points of two successively exposed oblique photographs have been located by the principles discussed in Sec. 13–15, the map position of any point whose image appears on both photographs may be determined by the method of intersection.

In Fig. 13–10, the map positions of the two nadir points n_1 and n_2 have been determined by resecting on the map positions of control points

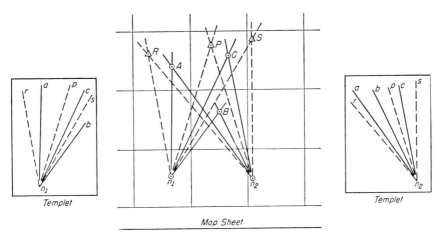

Fig. 13–10. Intersection.

P, R, and S. The resection lines are shown as dashed lines. On the same tracing-paper templet containing the resection lines, rays to image points a, b, and c are also drawn. These rays represent the horizontal directions to the three points from each nadir point. When the templets are superimposed over one another on the map sheet, the intersections of the rays determine the true map positions of the points.

13–17. Determination of Flying Height of High Oblique

The value of the flying height of an oblique determined by the reading of an aircraft altimeter is accurate enough for computing the dip angle. When the dip angle is known, the depression angle may be determined as discussed in Sec. 13–5.

When the flying height given by the altimeter is not sufficiently accurate (except for computing the dip angle), the photograph must contain the image of at least one vertical control point (but it is preferable to use three such points). The vertical angle to the point either is computed as described in Sec. 13–11 or is measured directly in the photoalidade. The horizontal distance from the exposure station to the point is scaled from an intersection plot similar to that shown in Fig. 13–10.

In Fig. 13–11, point P is at a known elevation h above the datum.

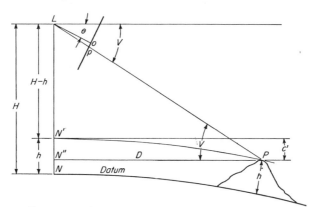

Fig. 13–11. Flying height of oblique, and elevation of ground point.

An oblique containing the image of P is taken from a flying height H above the datum at a depression angle θ. The distance D has been determined by scaling the distance from the nadir point to the intersected point on an intersection plot. If refraction is disregarded, the observed difference in elevation LN'' between the exposure station and point P is

$$LN'' = -D \tan V \qquad (13\text{--}35)$$

The minus sign is used to give the quantity LN'' a positive value, since

V is a negative angle. The difference in elevation computed by Eq. 13–35 is seen to be too great by an amount $N''N' = c'$ because of curvature of the earth. The distance c' is reduced to a distance c when atmospheric refraction is allowed for. If distance $N''N'$ is denoted by c to allow for both curvature of the earth and refraction of the atmosphere, the true difference in elevation between the exposure station and a ground point is

$$H - h = -D \tan V - c \qquad (13\text{–}36)$$

The value of c is obtained by the relationship

$$c = 0.0206 \left(\frac{D}{1,000} \right)^2$$

in which c is the combined effect of curvature and refraction, in feet; and D is the horizontal distance from the exposure station (or from the ground nadir point) to the selected ground point, in feet.

The value of the flying height is obtained by rearranging the terms in Eq. 13–36. Thus,

$$H = h - D \tan V - c \qquad (13\text{–}37)$$

in which H is the flying height, in feet; h is the known elevation of a ground point, in feet; V is the vertical angle to the point obtained from the photograph; and c is the correction for curvature and refraction, in feet. Due regard must be given to the algebraic sign of V.

When the images of three vertical control points appear on the photograph, it is possible to determine three independent values of the flying height. An analysis of the discrepancies in the three values makes it possible to determine corrections that can be applied to the swing angle and the depression angle as set off in the photoalidade. The student is referred to the *Manual of Photogrammetry*, 1966, Chapter 18, for a discussion of this analysis.

13–18. Elevations by Measurements on Oblique Photographs

The elevation of a ground point whose image appears on two oblique photographs may be determined by measuring the vertical angle and scaling the horizontal distance from the exposure station to the point. The vertical angle may be computed as described in Sec. 13–11, or it may be measured directly in the photoalidade. The horizontal distance between the nadir point of one photograph and the point is scaled from an intersection plot. By rearranging Eq. 13–36, the relationship found for the elevation of the ground point is

$$h = H + D \tan V + c \qquad (13\text{–}38)$$

in which the quantities are as previously defined. The vertical angle is positive $(+)$ if the point lies above the true horizon, and is negative $(-)$ if the point lies below the true horizon.

EXAMPLE 13–5. Assume that the flying height of the photograph in Examples 13–3 and 13–4 is 18,000 ft, and the distances LA and LB as scaled from a map are 52,500 ft and 16,300 ft, respectively. Determine the elevations of the two points.

Solution: The corrections for curvature and refraction for the two points are

$$c_A = 0.0206\left(\frac{52,500}{1000}\right)^2 = 57 \text{ ft} \qquad \text{and} \qquad c_B = 0.0206\left(\frac{16,300}{1000}\right)^2 = 5 \text{ ft}$$

By Eq. 13–38,

$$h_A = 18,000 + 52,500 \tan\,(-29° 03') + 57$$
$$= 18,000 - 13,648 + 57 = 4,409 \text{ ft}$$

Also,

$$h_B = 18,000 + 16,300 \tan\,(-44° 48') + 5$$
$$= 18,000 - 16,186 + 5 = 1,819 \text{ ft}$$

13–19. Camera Installation for Trimetrogon Charting

The trimetrogon system of small-scale charting uses successively exposed sets of three photographs from which to compile planimetry and, in some instances, topography in the form of contour lines. Three cameras are so installed in a mounting frame that they are rigidly oriented together to form one unit. As shown in Fig. 13–12, the central camera points vertically downward, while the left camera points to the left of the flight line at a depression angle of approximately 30° and the right camera points to the right of the flight line also with a depression angle of about 30°. The name trimetrogon is derived from the fact that each of the three cameras contains a metrogon lens having a nominal 6-in. focal length.

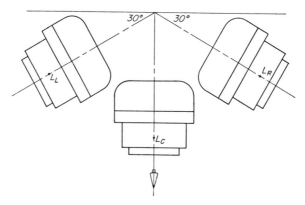

FIG. 13–12. Camera arrangement for trimetrogon
photography.

13–20. Relative Orientation Between Photographs

In Fig. 13-12, the exposure stations L_L, L_C, and L_R of the three cameras do not coincide with one another. However, since the distances between these three points are extremely small in relation to the flying height and other distances involved, all three camera stations are assumed to be coincident. An array of three photographs may then be represented as shown in Fig. 13–13. The central photograph is assumed to be vertical in this drawing. The lines of intersection of the two wing photographs with the plane of the central photograph are called the *isolines*.

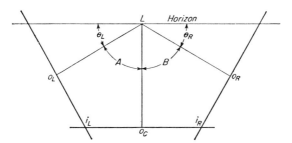

Fig. 13–13. Relation between central and wing photographs.

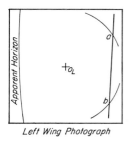 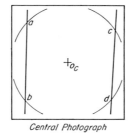 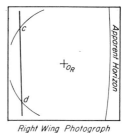

Left Wing Photograph   Central Photograph   Right Wing Photograph

Fig. 13–14. Location of isolines.

If a single exposure station is considered to be effective for all three photographs of a set, and if all three optical axes lie in one plane, the traces of the two isolines on the central photograph will be parallel with each other. When the three axes are not coplanar, the traces of the isolines on the central photograph will converge either fore or aft of the flight. The angle between the two isolines is referred to as the *relative setting*. The acute dihedral angle between the plane containing the axes Lo_L and Lo_C and the plane containing the axes Lo_C and Lo_R (which angle causes the relative setting) is called the *break angle*.

The method of locating the isolines is indicated in Fig. 13–14. If it is assumed that the focal lengths of all three cameras are identical, a circle having a radius of about 4.5 in. is drawn on the central photograph, with the principal point as the center. Two arcs having exactly the same radius as that used on the central photograph are drawn on each of the wing photographs, as shown in Fig. 13–14. Any point on either isoline must lie at the same distance from the principal point of the central photograph as it lies from the principal point of the corresponding wing photograph. Therefore, if two well-defined image points, as a and b, are found to lie on the arcs on two photographs, as shown in the drawing, the two points define one isoline. Points c and d are similarly located on the central photograph and the right wing photograph to define the second isoline.

If the focal lengths of the three cameras differ appreciably, the radii of the arcs drawn on the photographs must be proportional to the focal lengths.

The angles A and B of Fig. 13–13 between the central axis and the wing axes are called the *interlocking angles*. The angle between the isoline on a wing photograph and a line joining the x-fiducial marks is referred to as the *relative swing* of the wing photograph.

All the quantities just defined are elements of relative orientation and should remain constant during a flight. These elements may be determined from the positions of the isolines on the three photographs by methods discussed in the reference cited in Sec. 13–17.

13–21. Determination of Tilt of Three-Camera Array

The tilt of the entire three-camera assembly in a direction normal to the line of flight, or the x-tilt, is obtained by comparing the depression angle of one of the wing photographs with its corresponding interlocking angle. If there is no x-tilt, $\theta_L = 90° - A$, and $\theta_R = 90° - B$. If an x-tilt is present, these relations are not true. The x-tilt in Fig. 13–15 is seen to be equal to $\theta_L + A - 90°$. It is also equal to $90° - \theta_R - B$. Thus, when

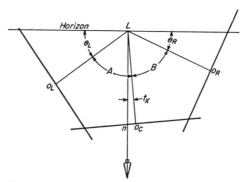

Fig. 13–15. The x-tilt of trimetrogon photography.

both depression angles may be determined, a check is provided on the computed x-tilt.

Quite often one apparent horizon or the other cannot be identified because of cloud layers, haze, or mountain ranges. The x-tilt can then be computed from only one depression angle. If both horizons are equally clear, the average of the two computed values of the x-tilt is adopted.

The tilt in the direction of flight, or the y-tilt, is determined by measuring the angle between the true horizon and the isoline of a wing photograph. This angle is the y-tilt in the plane of the photograph. It is projected into a vertical plane by multiplying the measured value by the cosine of the depression angle. When both horizons can be identified with equal clarity, the two values of y-tilt obtained from each wing photograph are averaged.

The direction of the x-tilt should be obvious to the student; the direction of the y-tilt is not so readily apparent. If the value $s - \kappa$ is positive, where s is the swing of the oblique as defined in Sec. 3–2 and κ is the relative swing, the camera array is tilted in the forward direction of the flight line.

The position of the nadir point of the central photograph can be located after the x- and y-tilts have been determined. The photographic coordinates of the nadir point with respect to lines joining opposite fiducial marks are given by the following relationships:

$$x_n = -f \tan (y\text{-tilt}) \tag{13–39}$$

$$y_n = -f \tan (x\text{-tilt}) \tag{13–40}$$

in which f is the focal length of the central camera. These values are laid off with reference to the coordinate axes to define the position of the nadir point.

13–22. Coverage of Trimetrogon Photography

Each set of exposures of a trimetrogon array covers a strip of terrain from horizon to horizon and normal to the direction of the flight line. The usable coverage on the photographs, in addition to the entire central photograph, extends from the lower edge of each oblique to a horizontal line from $\frac{1}{2}$ to 1 in. above the principal point. This coverage, for three flight lines, is shown in Fig. 13–16. With the tremendous lateral coverage afforded by the wing photographs, the flight lines are spaced at distances varying from 15 miles to 30 miles. The actual spacing depends on the flying height and the scale at which the charting is to be compiled or published.

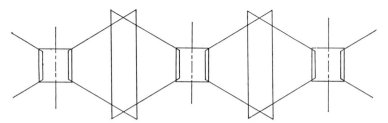

Fig. 13–16.   Trimetrogon coverage.

The overlap in the line of flight is normally about 60 per cent measured on the central photograph. This overlap affords continuous stereoscopic coverage and allows horizontal control to be extended by radial-line plotting.

13–23.   Radial Plotting for Control of Trimetrogon Compilation

Trimetrogon charting is usually conducted in large, and sometimes remote and sparsely inhabited, areas in which very little horizontal control exists. However, the process lends itself very well to horizontal-control extension by the principles of radial-line plotting discussed in Chapter 6.

In radial triangulation for trimetrogon mapping, every second set of photographs is used. In Fig. 13–17 are shown two alternate sets of photographs. The intermediate vertical photograph, shown without the

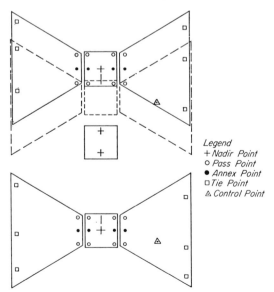

Legend
+ *Nadir Point*
o *Pass Point*
● *Annex Point*
□ *Tie Point*
△ *Control Point*

Fig. 13–17.   Points used for radial-line control of
trimetrogon photography.

wing photographs, is used to locate azimuth lines on the two alternate central photographs, which will be described in this section. The nadir point is located on each photograph from a tilt analysis, discussed in Sec. 13–21 and described in the reference cited in Sec. 13–17. The legend on Fig. 13–17 identifies the types of points used.

Pass points are selected in the small overlap area of the alternate vertical photographs, and are transferred to the adjacent vertical photographs and to the wing photographs as shown. An annex point is carefully chosen on each side of the nadir point of each central photograph. The annex points are then transferred to the wing photographs.

Tie points, which are points common to adjacent flights, are chosen along a line midway between adjacent flight lines. These tie points will normally be located on the wing photographs along transverse lines slightly above the principal points. The selection of tie points is more difficult than the selection of pass points because the appearance of a point as seen from one flight line is quite different from the appearance of the same point as seen from the adjacent flight line. When no positive identification between adjacent flight lines is possible, the tie point is omitted. However, an outer pass point is selected in the general vicinity of the normal position of the tie point. The pass point is then transferred to the next alternate wing photograph in the same flight line.

Conjugate nadir points cannot be transferred between alternate vertical photographs because of insufficient overlap. So the intermediate photograph is used to establish azimuth lines on the alternate photographs. This process is shown in Fig. 13–18. Nadir points n_1 and n_3

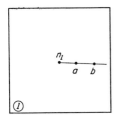 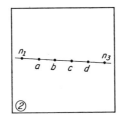 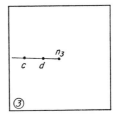

Fig. 13–18. Azimuth line.

are transferred stereoscopically (see Sec. 8–4) to the intermediate photograph. A line through n_1 and n_3 is then drawn across the photograph. Several points such as a and b, which are common to photographs *1* and *2* and which lie on line n_1n_3, are visually transferred to photograph *1*. The line n_1ab is the azimuth line for photograph *1*. Similarly, points such as c and d are transferred to photograph *3* to define the azimuth line for photograph *3*.

A tracing-paper templet, with one long dimension oriented normal to the direction of flight, is placed over each vertical photograph. Rays are drawn from the nadir point through the four pass points and the two annex points, and along the azimuth line, as shown in Fig. 13–19.

The tracing-paper templet is now placed under the templet arm of the rectoblique plotter, and one wing photograph is oriented under the photo arm. The photo arm is set to pass through the annex point on the photograph. The tracing-paper templet is then rotated about the

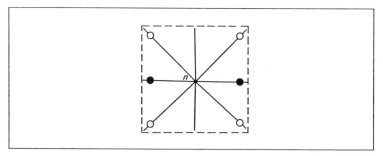

Fig. 13–19. Radial-line templet for central photograph.

nadir point at position i' of Fig. 13–9 until the edge of the templet arm coincides with the ray drawn through the annex point. This procedure orients the templet in the rectoblique plotter.

The photo arm is caused to pass through all pass points, tie points, and control points appearing on the wing photograph, and the corresponding rays are drawn along the templet arm. This procedure ties the templet for the wing photograph directly to the central templet. The rays directed to the points on the opposite wing photograph are drawn by repeating the process just described. The resulting composite templet is shown in Fig. 13–20.

Control for the radial-line plot is plotted at a scale approximately one-half the scale of the central photographs. A preliminary lay down

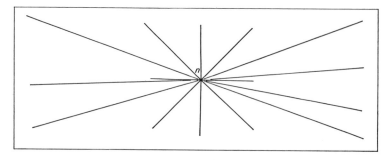

Fig. 13–20. Composite templet.

of the paper templets to fit the plotted control will indicate the approximate point along each tracing-paper ray at which an intersection will occur. These intersection points are marked to aid in the preparation of metal-arm templets.

The tracing-paper templets are now used in the construction of metal-arm templets. The slotted metal arms are selected with such lengths that the mid-points of the slots will fall at the points indicating intersections. These metal arms are fastened together as discussed in Sec. 6–8, the tracing-paper rays being used as guides for the orientation of the arms.

The final lay down of the metal-arm templets to fit the plotted control completes the radial-line plot. The procedure is identical to that described in Chapter 6. As the templets are removed, the positions of the nadir points, the tie points, the pass points, and the annex points are identified for use in planimetric compilation.

13–24. Compilation of Planimetry

Because of the large area covered by trimetrogon photography, it is not feasible to compile the planimetry on a single map sheet. Individual compilation sheets are prepared, and the positions of the control points are transferred from the radial-line plot to the sheets. The base map on which the radial-line plot is assembled is sometimes prepared by piecing several sheets together before the assembly is made. In this instance, the individual sheets can later be separated and used directly as compilation sheets.

The planimetry is transferred from the central, or vertical, photographs to the compilation sheet by using the vertical sketchmaster shown in Fig. 6–19 and following the procedure outlined in Sec. 6–13. The compilation scale is reduced to about one-half the scale of the photograph directly in the sketchmaster.

The planimetry is transferred from the wing photographs to the compilation sheet by using an instrument called an *oblique sketchmaster*, which is pictured in Fig. 13–21. A diagram of this instrument is shown in Fig. 13–22. The wing photograph is placed in the photo holder. A mirror at M and a half-silvered mirror at H reflect the image of the photograph to the eyepiece at e.

The half-silvered mirror allows the compiler also to view the map sheet on which is superimposed the image of the photograph. Each planimetric feature is traced by keeping the pencil point at p_m in apparent contact with the photographic image p_p of the feature.

The photograph may be raised or lowered to fit the compilation scale. It may be swung in its own plane and may be tilted by three

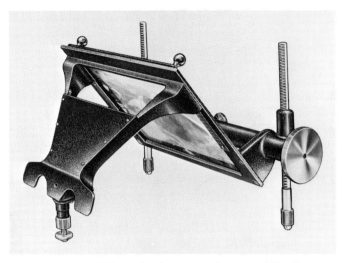

Fig. 13–21. Oblique sketchmaster. (Courtesy of Harrison
Ryker, Inc.)

supporting legs, so that the photographic images of the control points
are made to apparently coincide with the map positions of the same points.

The oblique sketchmaster is seen to be a variation of the basic camera
lucida discussed in Sec. 6–13. Compilation by using the instrument follows the general procedures discussed in Chapter 6 for transferring planimetry from near-vertical photographs.

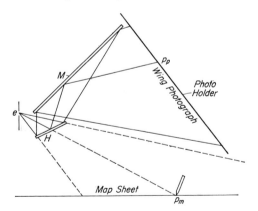

Fig. 13–22. Diagram of oblique sketchmaster.

13–25. Delineation of Contour Lines

If a chart prepared from trimetrogon photographs is to contain
topography in the form of contour lines, each photograph must contain

some vertical control. Although the contour lines can be compiled by orienting the wing photographs in specially designed stereoscopic plotting instruments, the majority of this compilation is done by means of the photoalidade and a simple stereoscope.

The wing photograph is oriented in the photoalidade, and a flying height is determined as discussed in Sec. 13–17. The elevations of several carefully selected points are determined by reading vertical angles to these points in the photoalidade and applying the principles developed in Sec. 13–18. These points are selected to aid in sketching the contour lines.

The obliques are oriented in pairs under a mirror stereoscope to give a stereoscopic image of the terrain. Because of the great scale change from the near side to the far side of an oblique, the photographs must be continually shifted under the stereoscope in order to perceive the stereoscopic image in the entire overlap area. Using the three-dimensional image of the terrain as a guide, the compiler sketches in the contour lines to conform with the elevations of the points measured in the photoalidade.

Values of contour intervals ranging from 200 ft to 1,000 ft are used in trimetrogon charting. The student can see that, because of the great flying heights involved in this process and because of the relatively small photographic scale in the background area of the obliques, the method does not lend itself to accurate contour-line delineation.

Compilation of topography from the central photographs can be conducted in the Multiplex instrument. The requirements for vertical control necessary for topographic mapping discussed in Chapters 5 and 12 need not be met in this type of compilation because of the large contour intervals involved. Vertical-control bridging between several photographs would be quite satisfactory for leveling the individual models.

13–26. Canadian-Grid Mapping

The Canadian-grid method of mapping derives its name from the fact that it was developed in Canada to map large expanses of flat country, and from the fact that a perspective grid is used to transfer detail from the photographs to the map manuscript. Map compilation by this method truly combines the art and the science of photogrammetry, and its success is attributed chiefly to the judicious application of the art.

No attempt will be made here to discuss the minute details involved in map compilation. The basic principles alone will be presented. The use of the perspective grid for the graphical rectification of oblique photographs taken for Canadian-grid mapping can be applied generally to any oblique photograph.

13–27. Photography for Canadian-Grid Mapping

Three cameras with equal or nearly equal focal lengths are employed for photographing three obliques at each exposure station. The central camera axis is directed forward along the line of flight at a depression angle of from 20° to 25°. Each wing camera is pointed in a general forward direction, with the axes making an angle of about 45° with the flight line. The axes of the wing cameras also are depressed at an angle of between 20° and 25°. The arrangement of the camera axes and the resultant ground coverage are shown in Fig. 13–23.

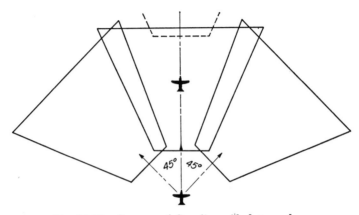

Fig. 13–23. Coverage of Canadian-grid photography.

The flying height is maintained at approximately 5,000 ft by means of a barometer. Exposures are made at an interval of 2 miles in order to take advantage of the foreground portions of the oblique photographs. A greater interval would require that compilation be made too far into the background of the oblique photographs, where the scale becomes smaller than desired and where it is difficult to distinguish planimetric features. The flight lines are oriented in an east-west direction and are spaced at 6-mile intervals. In sectionized country, the flight lines can be laid out along township lines where ground control is more conveniently located.

13–28. Azimuth Line

In order to control the compilation of the details from the central photographs, and to control any tendency of the compilation to swing to one side or another, a common azimuth line is projected onto each central oblique photograph. This line serves the same purpose as does the azimuth line discussed in Sec. 11–7 for controlling a mosaic strip.

In Fig. 13–24, point *B* is a well-defined point lying in the center and near the apparent horizon of the first central photograph of a strip. This background point is identified and marked on each succeeding central photograph. A second point, as *a*, is selected in the foreground of photograph *1*. The line *aB* constitutes an azimuth line which is to be projected across each photograph.

A well-defined point *b*, which appears in the foreground of photograph *2*, is chosen along the line *aB* of photograph *1*. This point is transferred visually to photograph *2*, and the line *bB* thus defines the azimuth line on the second photograph. Points *c*, *d*, and *e* are likewise selected on the line *aB* to appear in the foreground of photographs *3*, *4*, and *5*, respectively. The lines *cB*, *dB*, and *eB* are the segments of the common azimuth line projected onto these three photographs.

Each azimuth line is begun on a photograph containing the image of a ground control point lying near the foreground, and is extended through successive photographs until another ground control point is reached. If ground control occurs quite frequently, a single azimuth line may be extended through several photographs containing the images of the control points lying in the foreground. A new azimuth line is then initiated and extended to a new control point, as just described.

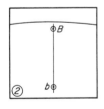

13–29. Perspective Grid

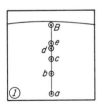

If the focal length, flying height, and depression angle of an oblique photograph are known, it is possible to draw on the photograph a grid which will represent a rectangular grid lying in a horizontal plane. The grid drawn on the oblique is a perspective projection of an imaginary rectangular grid laid out on the (level) ground and photographed on the oblique. The rectangles representing the terrain grid may have any desired dimensions, but are usually taken to represent squares 1 mile on a side. These main squares are in turn subdivided to represent squares ⅛ mile on a side.

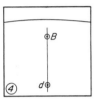

Fig. 13–24. Azimuth line.

In the Canadian-grid system, the perspective grid is computed to give a compilation scale of 1 in. = 1 mile. However, a perspective grid representing a ground grid other than ⅛ mile on a side may be selected when the perspective grid is to be applied to obliques in general.

In Fig. 13–25 is shown a high oblique taken from an altitude *H* with a camera having a focal length f, and containing a depression angle θ. The principal line Ko is extended downward to intersect the ground at P. The line PO is the trace of the principal plane in the ground plane. A line on the ground is constructed so as to pass through P and be perpendicular to the principal plane. Distances of 10 ch. are laid out on this line to locate points A through F. Lines are constructed through these points in the ground plane, each parallel to the principal-plane trace PO. These lines, AA' through FF', constitute one set of rectangular grid lines in the ground plane.

By the principles of projective geometry, the set of lines in the horizontal plane that are parallel to the principal plane (or normal to the horizon trace) will be projected onto the oblique plane (the plane of the photograph) in such positions that they will converge at the intersection of the true horizon and the principal line. This intersection is at point K in Fig. 13–25. These projections are the lines such as AK, BK, and CK.

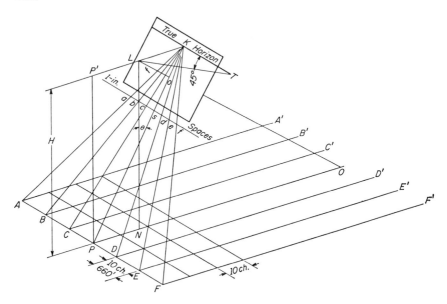

Fig. 13–25. Perspective grid.

A line af is now constructed in the plane of the photograph in such a position that the line is parallel to the true horizon and the length of each intercept, as ab or bc, between two successive converging lines is 1 in. The position of this line af fixes the x-scale of the perspective grid as 1 in. = 10 ch. Before the position of the intercept line can be determined, the distance Ks must be computed. By Eq. 13–13,

$$Ks = e = \frac{S_x H}{\cos \theta} = \frac{1 \text{ in.} \times H}{660 \text{ ft} \times \cos \theta}$$

in which Ks is expressed in inches and H is expressed in feet. Thus,

$$Ks = \frac{H \sec \theta}{660} \tag{13-41}$$

This equation may also be derived from the relationship between Ks and KP in the similar triangles Ksd and KPD. For Ks in inches and KP in feet,

$$\frac{Ks}{KP} = \frac{1 \text{ in.}}{660 \text{ ft}}$$

Since $KP = H \sec \theta$,

$$Ks = \frac{H \sec \theta}{660}$$

If Ks is in inches and H is expressed in chains, Eq. 13–41 becomes

$$Ks = \frac{H \sec \theta}{10} \tag{13-42}$$

For any value other than that selected specifically for Canadian-grid mapping, the desired scale is substituted in Eq. 13–13 as the x-scale (S_x), and the computed value of e is the distance from the true horizon at which the line for the 1-in. intercepts should be constructed.

The set of parallel lines in the ground rectangular grid that are parallel to the horizon trace (normal to the principal line) are next projected into the plane of the oblique. By projective geometry, however, the ground lines that are parallel to the horizon trace do not converge at a point when projected onto the oblique plane. Their projections must therefore be determined indirectly.

In Fig. 13–25, the horizontal line LT makes a true horizontal angle of 45° with the principal plane. The two distances LK and KT are therefore equal. Since the distance LK is equal to $f \sec \theta$,

$$KT = f \sec \theta \tag{13-43}$$

By projective geometry, any set of parallel lines lying in the horizontal ground plane, other than those lying parallel with the horizon trace, must converge at one point on the true horizon when projected onto the plane of the oblique. Point T is the point at which one set of parallel ground lines—the lines making an angle of 45° with the principal plane—will converge on the oblique photograph.

In Fig. 13–26(a), the ground lines parallel with the principal plane are shown. These correspond to the lines in Fig. 13–25 that are lettered in the same way. In Fig. 13–26(b), the projections of these lines on the oblique photograph are shown. These projections also correspond to the lines similarly lettered in Fig. 13–25. Any ground line such as line *RS* or *UV* of Fig. 13–26(*a*), which makes an angle of 45° with the principal plane, will pass through point *T* of Fig. 13–26(*b*) when projected onto the plane of the oblique. The lines *rT* and *uT* are the projections of the lines *RS* and *UV*. All lines of a set of parallel ground lines making an angle of 45° with the principal plane but running perpendicular to *RS* and *UV* would converge at *T′* of Fig. 13–26(*b*) when projected onto the oblique plane.

If lines were constructed so as to pass through the intersection of the line *UV* with the lines such as *AA′* and *BB′* of Fig. 13–26(*a*) and so as to be parallel to the line *AF*, the result would be a grid composed of squares 10 ch. on a side. If lines were drawn so as to pass through the intersections of the line *uT* with the lines such as *aK* and *bK* of Fig. 13–26(*b*) and so as to be parallel to the line *af* (or parallel to the true horizon), the result would be a perspective grid composed of trapezoids. These trapezoids, diminishing in size from the foreground to the background, represent ground squares 10 ch. on a side.

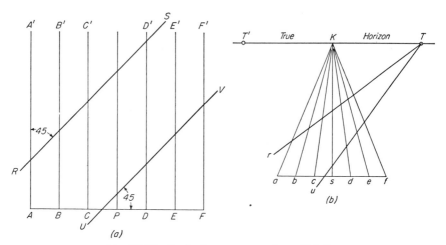

Fig. 13–26. Projective geometry of parallel lines.

In Fig. 13–27, an oblique photograph has been taped to a large sheet of drafting paper. The measurements necessary to determine the depression angle have been made, and the true horizon has been constructed. Next, the distance *Ks* has been computed by Eq. 13–41, and a line parallel to the true horizon has been drawn through *s*. The distances *KT* and *KT′* have been computed and laid off.

Tick marks spaced 1-in. apart are now laid off on the line through *s*. Lines representing the set of ground lines that are parallel to the

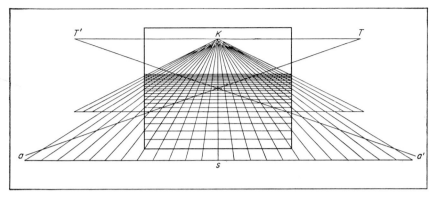

Fɪɢ. 13–27. Location of 45° lines on perspective grid.

principal plane are next drawn through the tick marks to converge at K. The lines Ta and $T'a'$ are drawn so as to pass through the principal point. This location is selected because it is convenient to have a grid intersection occur at the principal point. Any line through T would be suitable for constructing the perspective grid.

If the lines Ta and $T'a'$ have been carefully constructed, and if the drafting paper is oriented so that the true horizon coincides with the edge of a T-square, then, as the T-square is moved down, it should successively pass precisely through two intersections. After the drafting paper has been so oriented, the set of lines parallel to the true horizon are drawn through the successive pairs of intersections. This operation completes the perspective grid.

The grid is extended from the foreground upward to a distance of about 1 in. above the principal point. Beyond this limit, the scale of the oblique is too small to be usable for compilation purposes. The 2-mile exposure spacing in Canadian-grid photography provides sufficient detail overlap from one set of photographs to the next. Occasionally, however, when the 6-mile flight spacing is exceeded, the grids for the wing photographs must be extended beyond the 1-in. limit just mentioned.

The principles involved in the construction of a perspective grid for an oblique photograph can be applied to an oblique taken at any flying height and with any depression angle. Furthermore, a scale other than 1 in. = 10 ch. may be selected.

When an extensive area is mapped by using the perspective grid, it is desirable for practical reasons to hold the flying height and the depression angle constant within limits. The same ranges of flying heights and depression angles may be carried over from one mapping project to another. Consequently, it is convenient to construct a cross file of grids to represent a limited range of flying heights in increments of 25 or 50 ft and a limited range of depression angles in increments of 10 or 20 min. These grids are constructed at four times the size at which they are to be used, and are then reduced photographically onto sensitized material which is transparent after being processed. When a flying height and a depression angle have been computed, the proper grid may then be selected from the cross file. The prepared grid is oriented to the photograph by the principal point and the apparent horizon (which appears on the prepared grid).

13–30. Compilation of Planimetry

The individual compilation sheets consist of $\frac{1}{8}$-in. ruled grid paper with each inch-line emphasized. Thus at a compilation scale of 1 in.= 80 ch. (1 mile to the inch), each trapezoid on the perspective grid represents a $\frac{1}{8}$-in. square on the compilation sheet. Planimetric detail is transferred visually from a trapezoid to its corresponding square. The accented inch-lines are used to aid in selecting the proper squares on the compilation sheet. This transfer process is, in effect, a graphical transformation or rectification of the oblique photograph into a vertical photograph which is at a scale of 1 in.= 80 ch.

Because the method is restricted to flat terrain, no serious errors are introduced into planimetric positions because of relief displacement. Occasionally, however, a hill will obscure some detail lying beyond it. The compiler must then use his judgment in delineating the hidden features in their correct positions on the compilation sheet. Also, if a planimetric feature appears to lie considerably above the datum, the compiler must imagine the position at which the feature would lie if projected vertically onto the datum, and then transfer the detail accordingly.

13–31. Preparation of the Central Strip

In this section, it is assumed that a cross file of grids is available. Otherwise, an individual grid must be constructed for each central photograph, whenever the need arises.

Of the quantities needed to construct a perspective grid to the proper scale, only the flying height is subject to error. The focal length is determined by calibration (see Chapter 2), and the depression angle is computed indirectly from a photographic measurement. It is true that the depression angle depends on the dip angle, which in turn is computed from the flying height. A serious error in the flying height (within reason), however, will produce only a slight error in the dip angle.

Assume that the following preliminary work has been done: The flying height at each exposure station has been obtained from altimeter readings. Each depression angle has been determined, and a grid has been selected from the cross file (or constructed) for each central photograph. The azimuth line, described in Sec. 13–28, has been located and the ground control has been identified on each photograph.

The position of the azimuth line of the first photograph is located on a sheet of ⅛-in. grid paper by using the perspective grid for the first photograph and transferring the positions of points a and b of Fig. 13–24 from the photograph to the grid paper. Control point M, shown in Fig. 13–28, is also transferred from the photograph to the grid sheet. On a long sheet of tracing paper, a straight line is drawn along its center to represent the azimuth line. The tracing paper is shown to the right in Fig. 13–28. The individual plot of points a, b, and M obtained from photograph 1 is oriented under the tracing paper by means of the azimuth line. The positions of points a, b, and M are then plotted on the tracing paper.

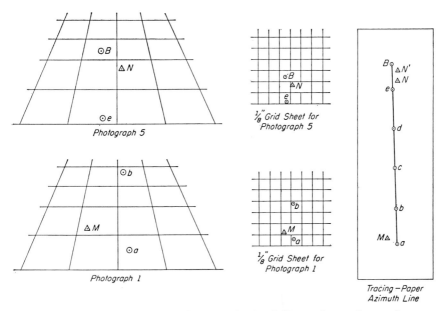

Photograph 5

⅛" Grid Sheet for Photograph 5

Photograph 1

⅛" Grid Sheet for Photograph 1

Tracing – Paper Azimuth Line

Fɪɢ. 13–28. Tracing-paper location of azimuth line and ground control.

The position of the azimuth line of photograph 2 is located on an individual grid sheet by using the perspective grid selected (or constructed) for photograph 2 and transferring the positions of points b and c of Fig. 13–24 from the photograph to the grid sheet. This grid sheet is then oriented under the tracing paper by making the azimuth line coincide and by bringing the tracing-paper position of *b* directly over its position on the grid sheet. Point *c* is then plotted on the tracing paper.

The tracing-paper position of point *d* is obtained by using photograph *3;* that of point *e* by using photograph *4;* and that of the background point *B* by using photograph *5.* When the individual plot for photograph *5* is prepared, the position of control point *N* is also transferred to the tracing paper as point *N'*, as shown in Fig. 13–28.

The distance *MN'* scaled from the tracing paper is compared with the known distance *MN.* If *MN'* is too large, the flying heights used to select the perspective grids were too large. New flying heights are determined by the following ratio:

$$\frac{\text{New } H}{\text{Preliminary } H} = \frac{\text{correct } MN}{\text{scaled } MN'} \qquad (13\text{--}44)$$

The process just described is repeated with a new set of perspective grids which correspond to the new value of the flying height. (Note that the depression angles need not be recomputed.) Finally, the distance *MN'* will agree with the known length. Although there are refinements and variations in the method for scaling the central strip, the principles discussed in this section are considered sufficient to explain this phase of the mapping.

The tracing paper is now laid over the map manuscript on which have been plotted the positions of the control points, and it is oriented to the control. Points *a* through *e* are pricked through and marked on the manuscript, and the azimuth line is drawn through the points. The entire process is repeated for each succeeding strip of central photographs. An examination of the manuscript positions of the azimuth lines indicates the areas in which the 6-mile flight spacing has been exceeded. The wing photographs covering these areas must be used beyond the limit discussed in Sec. 13–29.

13–32. Planimetric Mapping of Central Photographs

An individual compilation of planimetry is made for each central photograph by using the correct perspective grids. The procedure is outlined in Sec. 13–30. The positions of the azimuth line, the points on the azimuth line, and any control point appearing on the photograph are plotted on the compilation sheet. On each side of the central photograph a pair of points are selected which are common to the two wing photographs. These points are carefully transferred to the compilation sheet. They are called tie points because they serve to subsequently orient the individual wing-photograph compilations to the manuscript. Tie points, along with the other essential points, are shown in Fig. 13–29.

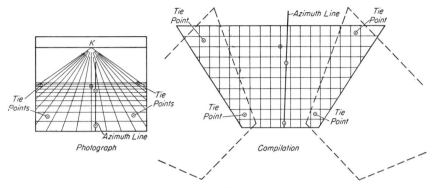

FIG. 13–29. Tie points.

The individual compilations of the central photographs are next transferred to the manuscript. If the material of the manuscript is translucent, each compilation in turn is oriented underneath the manuscript by means of the azimuth line and the points on the azimuth line. The positions of the tie points are plotted and these points are identified. The planimetry is then traced onto the manuscript.

13–33. Planimetric Mapping of Wing Photographs

The flying height for the wing photographs of a set is the same as the adjusted flying height of the corresponding central photograph. Therefore, only the depression angle need be computed. The proper grid is selected (or constructed) for each wing photograph in succession, and individual compilations are made on sheets of ⅛-in. grid paper. The tie points, which have been previously marked and identified, are transferred to the compilation sheets along with the map features.

The compilation sheets are then oriented under the map manuscript one at a time by means of the tie points, and the map details are traced. The compiler must continually make adjustments for mismatching between individual compilations, as the features are traced onto the map manuscript. The successful compilation of an entire manuscript requires considerable experience and judgment on the part of the draftsman.

13–34. Convergent Photography

The term convergent photography refers to a pair of low oblique aerial photographs which cover the same terrain and are taken with a precision camera (or a pair of cameras) for topographic-map compilation. Three systems may be used for taking the photographs. In each system, a low oblique is exposed forward and another is exposed backward along the flight line.

In Fig. 13–30 is shown one method for exposing convergent low obliques. The aircraft contains two cartographic cameras mounted together in a single frame. The frame can be swung, tipped, and tilted

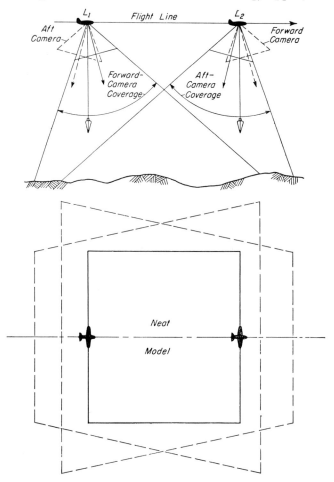

Fɪɢ. 13–30. Convergent-photography coverage.

in the camera mount. This arrangement is seen in Fig. 13–31. It is assumed that the two front nodal points occupy one position in space. Consequently, there is but one exposure station for each set of photographs. When the forward camera is at L_1 in Fig. 13–30 and is tilted at approximately 20°, part of the area covered is the same as when the aft camera is at L_2 and is tilted the same amount. These two photographs include an overlap area shown in Fig. 13–30. The neat area, which extends from one nadir point to the next in the line of flight, is seen to be square.

A second system for exposing convergent low obliques uses only one

Fig. 13–31. Zeiss 2 × RMK 21/18 convergent cameras and mount. (Courtesy of Carl Zeiss, Oberkochen.)

camera. As shown in Fig. 13–32, the camera is first swung aft and an exposure is made, and the camera is then swung forward and another exposure is made. This sequence is performed as rapidly as possible. Stops are provided on the camera mount to set off the approximate tilt angle both fore and aft. In this system, there are two separate exposure stations for each set of photographs. The objection to this system is that

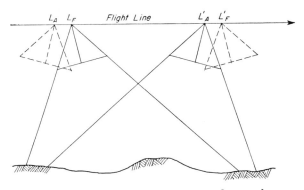

Fig. 13–32. Single-camera convergent photography.

frequent gapping occurs along the flight line, and costly reflights are thus made necessary.

In the third system, one camera containing two lenses and two focal planes is used. This is the most desirable of the three systems because the shutters, being actuated by the same mechanism, are opened and closed at virtually the same instant.

13–35. Topographic Mapping from Convergent Photographs

The general procedure for compiling topographic maps in a stereo-scopic plotting instrument by use of convergent photographs is the same

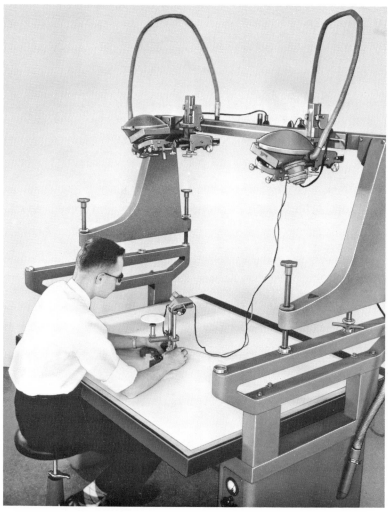

Fig. 13–33. Balplex 760 oriented for plotting from convergent photographs. (Courtesy of Bausch and Lomb Optical Co.)

as that outlined in Chapter 12 for vertical photographs. Diapositives are prepared from the negatives, the proper focal lengths being set off when the reduction printers are used. The diapositives are oriented in the plotting cameras or projectors, and are tied to one another by the process of relative orientation. The model thus formed is scaled and leveled as outlined in Chapter 12, and finally the topography is compiled by means of the measuring and tracing system.

In Fig. 13–33 are shown a pair of Balplex 760 plotters containing convergent diapositives and oriented for compilation. Because the projector lenses may be rotated about their upper nodal points, it is possible to make the diapositive plane, the lens plane, and the plane of optimum definition intersect along one line, and thus to fulfill the Scheimpflug condition stated in Sec. 10–2. This adjustment maintains optimum definition over the entire model area.

If the instrument used is a double-projection plotter the lenses of which cannot be rotated, the planes of optimum definition intersect along a line in the middle of the model, as shown in Fig. 13–34. At any other

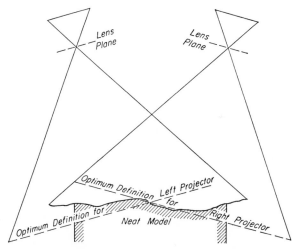

Fig. 13–34. Planes of optimum definition using convergent photography in projectors with nontilting lenses.

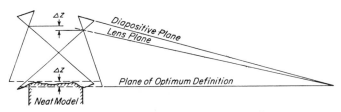

Fig. 13–35. Scheimpflug condition in projection of convergent photography.

point, the model departs from these planes and it becomes difficult to plot features near the edges of the neat-model area. On the other hand, if the lenses can be rotated, the two planes very nearly coincide, except for a vertical distance ΔZ between the projectors. This condition is diagrammed in Fig. 13–35.

In Fig. 13–36 are shown a pair of convergent diapositives oriented in a Zeiss Stereoplanigraph C8. Notice that the cameras are set in the

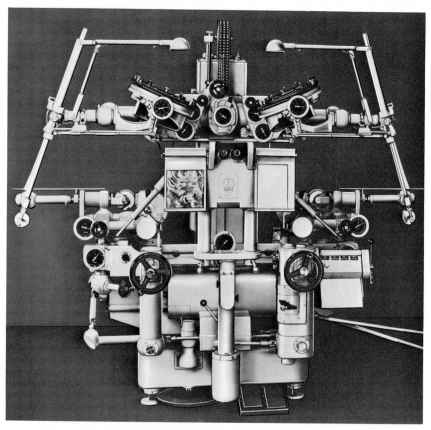

Fig. 13–36. Stereoplanigraph C8 oriented for plotting from convergent photographs. (Courtesy of Carl Zeiss, Oberkochen.)

base-out position. Because the diapositives are viewed directly through the optical viewing system, all areas of the stereoscopic model are seen with equally sharp definition.

13–36. Advantage of Convergent Photography

One advantage of convergent photography, when it is used for topographic mapping, is the increase in the base-height ratio. Whereas the ratio B/H for standard vertical photography is about 0.60, convergent photography can increase this ratio to as high as 1.20, although 1.00 is considered to be the most desirable ratio. This large ratio increases the precision with which elevations can be measured in the plotter, and it allows the operator to trace contour lines with more positive assurance.

A second advantage of the use of convergent photography is the increase in model size. This increase results in a reduction of the amount of horizontal and vertical control needed for orienting the models.

Bibliography

AMERICAN SOCIETY OF PHOTOGRAMMETRY. *Manual of Photogrammetry* (Menasha, Wisc.: George Banta Publishing Co., 1952), Chapter 16.

――――. *Manual of Photogrammetry* (Menasha, Wisc.: George Banta Co., 1966), Chapter 18.

――――. *Manual of Photographic Interpretation* (Menasha, Wisc.: George Banta Co., 1960), Chapters 2 and 3.

DONNELLY, C. B. C. "Trimetrogon Photogrammetry, Some Usages in the Preparation of the Canadian Aeronautical Chart," *Photogrammetric Engineering*, Vol. XV (1949), p. 22.

GAY, S. P., JR. "Measurement of Vertical Heights from Single Oblique Aerial Photographs," *Photogrammetric Engineering*, Vol. XXIII (1957), p. 900.

――――. "Nomographic Solution to Oblique Photo Mensuration," *Photogrammetric Engineering*, Vol. XXII (1956), p. 76.

GRIFFIN, E. P. "20-Degree Convergent versus Vertical Photography for Aerotriangulation," *Photogrammetric Engineering*, Vol. XXVI (1960), p. 59.

HERZOG, MERIAM. "Two Sketching Devices for Oblique Aerial Photographs," *Photogrammetric Engineering*, Vol. XXIV (1958), p. 138.

KATZ, A. H. "Contributions to the Theory and Mechanics of Photo-Interpretation from Vertical and Oblique Photographs," *Photogrammetric Engineering*, Vol. XVI (1950), p. 339.

KONECNY, G. "Interior Orientation and Convergent Photography," *Photogrammetric Engineering*, Vol. XXXI (1965), p. 625.

LANDON, DAVID. "Reconnaissance Mapping with Photoalidade," *Photogrammetric Engineering*, Vol. XIV (1948), p. 46.

LANE, B. B., JR. "Scales of Oblique Photographs," *Photogrammetric Engineering*, Vol. XVI (1950), p. 409.

LOVING, H. B. "Twin Photography for Mapping Alaska's Brooks Range," *Surveying and Mapping*, Vol. XVII (1957), p. 263.

McNEIL, G. T. "Oblique Plotting Scale," *Photogrammetric Engineering*, Vol. XV (1949), p. 455.

PENNINGTON, J. T. "Aerotriangulation with Convergent Photography," *Photogrammetric Engineering*, Vol. XX (1954), p. 76.

RADLINSKI, W. A. "Convergent Low Oblique Photography and Its Application to the Twinplex," *Photogrammetric Engineering*, Vol. XVIII (1952), p. 591.

RAISZ, E. "Direct Use of Oblique Air Photos for Small-Scale Maps," *Surveying and Mapping*, Vol. XIII (1953), p. 496.

SEELY, H. E. "The Forestry Tri-Camera Method of Air Photography," *Photogrammetric Engineering*, Vol. XV (1949), p. 461.

SWASEY, EDMUND. "Half-Base Convergent Photography," *Photogrammetric Engineering,* Vol. XXIX (1963), p. 58.

STEWART, R. A. "The Application of the Balplex Plotter to Trimetrogon Obliques," *Photogrammetric Engineering,* Vol. XXIII (1957), p. 697.

TEWINKEL, G. C. "The Reading Plotter," *Photogrammetric Engineering,* Vol. XIII (1947), p. 257.

TISCHLER, S. A. "Procedural Developments in Trimetrogon Compilation," *Photogrammetric Engineering,* Vol. XIV (1948), p. 53.

WOO, H. W. "The Oblique Wide-Angle Multiplex Projector," *Photogrammetric Engineering,* Vol. XV (1949), p. 423.

WRIGHT, J. W. "An Account of the Simplified Methods of Mapping from Trimetrogon Photographs Used in the Anglo-Egyptian Sudan," *Photogrammetric Engineering,* Vol. XVII (1951), p. 522.

ZELLER, M. *Textbook of Photogrammetry* (London: H. K. Lewis and Co., Ltd., 1952), Chapter 3.

Problems

13–1. The distance measured along the principal line from the principal point to the apparent horizon of an oblique photograph is 3.55 in. The flying height is 10,400 ft, and the focal length of the camera lens is 8.50 in. Compute the angle of dip and the depression angle.

13–2. For the photograph of Prob. 13–1, compute the distances from the principal point to the true horizon, to the nadir point, and to the isocenter.

13–3. A high oblique, taken from an altitude of 14,000 ft with a lens having a 6-in. focal length, contains a depression angle of 26° 30′. What is the x-scale at the principal point? at the isocenter? Along the apparent horizon?

13–4. If the true horizon of Prob. 13–3 is assumed to be parallel to the edge of a 9- by 9-in. photograph, what is the approximate length along the apparent horizon, in miles, from one edge of the photograph to the opposite edge?

13–5. A high oblique, taken from an altitude of 6,000 ft with a lens having an 8.25 in. focal length, contains a 25° depression angle. What is the y-scale at the principal point? At the isocenter? At a point 2 in. down from the true horizon?

13–6. An oblique photograph taken with a lens having a 6-in. focal length contains a depression angle of 28° 20′. On the oblique there are three points whose coordinates, with respect to the horizon line as the x-axis, are $x_a = +3.955$ in. and $y_a = -2.120$ in.; $x_b = -4.062$ in. and $y_b = -1.545$ in.; $x_c = +0.422$ in. and $y_c = +0.035$ in. Compute the horizontal angle at the exposure station between B and A and the angle between B and C.

13–7. For the data of Prob. 13–6, compute the vertical angles to points A, B, and C.

13–8. On a sheet of drafting paper, carefully construct a set of rectangular coordinate axes, and plot the positions of points a, b, and c of Prob 13–6. Determine the horizontal angle between B and A and the angle between B and C by construction.

13–9. Computed values of the vertical angles to points P, Q, and R, whose images appear on an oblique photograph are $V_P = -16°\ 09′$, $V_Q = -17°\ 52′$, and $V_R = -7°\ 28′$. The distances from the ground nadir point N to the three points, determined by intersection, are $NP=42,000$ ft, $NQ=49,200$ ft, and $NR=75,600$ ft. The elevation of point P is 8,700 ft above sea level. Compute the flying height of the aircraft, and the elevations of points Q and R.

13–10. The interlocking angles of a trimetrogon installation are $A=58°$ 52′ and $B=61°$ 03′. The depression angles, determined by measurement on the photograph, are $\phi_L=29°$ 42′ and $\phi_R=30°$ 13′. Compute the amount and direction of the x-tilt of the assembly.

13–11. In Prob. 13–10, the isoline on the left wing photograph makes an angle of 3° 12′ with the true horizon, and the isoline on the right wing photograph makes an angle of 3° 07′ with the true horizon. In both instances, the intersection of the isoline with the true horizon is in the aft direction. What are the amount and direction of the y-tilt of the assembly?

13–12. The focal length of the central photograph in Prob. 13–10 is 153.06 mm. What is the position of the nadir point on the central photograph with respect to the lines joining the fiducial marks?

13–13. Trimetrogon flight lines are spaced 30 miles apart. The flying height is planned to be 42,000 ft above the datum. Assuming depression angles of 30° and focal lengths of 6 in., determine the x-scale of the wing photographs along a line midway between flight lines.

13–14. Flying for Canadian-grid mapping is to be at 5,000 ft above the terrain. The nominal focal length of the camera is 8.25 in. The depression angle is assumed to be 19°. If the ground nadir point of each central photograph is to coincide with the ground principal point of each preceding central photograph, and if the ground speed of the aircraft is 180 mph, what will be the exposure interval, in seconds?

13–15. Compute and plot a perspective grid to be superimposed over a 7- by 9-in. photograph. Each perspective square is to represent 10 ch. on a side. The true horizon falls along the 9-in. side of the photograph. The flying height is 5,200 ft; the depression angle is 16° 00′; the focal length is 8.25 in. Carry the construction ½ in. above the principal point.

13–16. The depression angle of an oblique photograph is 27° 10′ and the focal length is 6 in. For a set of parallel lines making an angle of 60° with the principal plane of the photograph, where will the vanishing point be located on the true horizon?

13–17. Compute and plot a perspective grid to represent ground squares 1 mile on a side for an oblique photograph taken at a 29° depression angle, with a lens having a 6-in. focal length, on a 9- by 9-in. format, and from a flying height of 30,000 ft above the terrain. Carry the construction ½ in. above the principal point.

13–18. Convergent photography is taken with a tilt angle of 16°, giving a total convergence of 32°. The ratio B/H is 0.90, based on the spacing between exposures. The flying height is 8,000 ft above the average terrain elevation. If the map is to be plotted with a wide-angle Kelsh plotter for which the optimum projection distance is 30 in. and the usable plotting depth is 8 in., what is the optimum plotting scale?

13–19. In Prob. 13–18, how far vertically does the average model elevation depart from the plane of optimum definition? Express the distance in inches.

13–20. In Prob. 13–18, what amount of relief, above and below the average elevation, can be accommodated within the usable plotting depth?

Terrestrial Photogrammetry 14

14–1. Classification

Terrestrial photogrammetry is the science of photographic measurement wherein the photographs have been exposed from a camera station on the ground. The camera station is usually fixed in position. It may be a field point, or it may be located inside a laboratory. Photographs taken from the tops of towers and buildings, or from moving vehicles, such as ships, boats, automobiles, trucks, and trains, are all considered to be terrestrial photographs. If they are taken from a moving vehicle, however, the exposure station is not fixed.

The photography is classified as *still* photography when the object being photographed is stationary or nearly so. For example, still photography is employed if the face of a building is to be measured by means of a pair of photographs taken from the ends of a fixed base. Since there is no necessity for making the two exposures simultaneously, only one camera is required. The two photographs may even be taken on different days.

A series of photographs taken in fairly rapid sequence in order to picture the positions of a slow-moving object or set of objects at various instants, constitutes *quasi-static* photography. Thus, if the study of traffic flow or traffic weaving patterns is to be determined by photographing the street network from a tall building or a bridge tower every 10 seconds or so, the photography is considered to be quasi-static.

Dynamic photography involves motion-picture cameras, in which several frames a second are exposed. Usually, but not always, the camera station is fixed, in order to eliminate many otherwise unknown elements of orientation of the camera. Dynamic photography must be employed when measurements are to be made on an object which changes its size, shape, position, or orientation from one instant to another. Examples of measurements of this nature include those of waves, moving machinery parts, the human form in motion, vehicles, missiles, and aircraft.

Photographs taken from a moving vehicle may be classified as still, quasi-static, or dynamic, the decision depending on the time sequence. However, they usually fall under the latter two classifications.

Terrestrial photogrammetry may be concerned with measurements made on single photographs or with measurements in a stereoscopic image or model. Where still photography is employed to obtain a stereo pair, a single camera can be used. Where quasi-static or dynamic photography is used to obtain the stereo pairs, two cameras are necessary. Furthermore, the successive pairs of photographs must be exposed simultaneously in order to obtain reliable measurements.

14–2. Terrestrial Cameras and Their Orientation

A terrestrial camera employed for still photography contains many elements of an aerial camera. These include a lens, a cone, a focal plane, a set of fiducial marks in the focal plane, and a film holder. Most terrestrial cameras are equipped with shutters. However some are not so equipped. These use slow film emulsions, and the consequent relatively long exposure time is controlled by a lens cap. Glass plates are used exclusively in lieu of the rolls of acetate-base film used in aerial cameras. So there is no need for the elaborate film-flattening and film-advancing mechanism found in the magazine of an aerial camera. Instead, the camera contains a simple housing to receive a plate holder, and is provided with a hand-operated lever device for bringing the glass plate into the focal plane.

The terrestrial camera sits on a tripod. A set of level bubbles normal to one another are used to level both the optical axis and the photograph horizon line. The camera's use in the field is comparable to the use of a transit or theodolite; in fact, it accomplishes the same results. The camera can be centered over an exposure station by means of a plumb bob or an optical plummet. The optical axis is oriented in azimuth with reference to either a horizontal circle or a series of optically flat faces built into the camera.

A *phototheodolite,* shown in Fig. 14–1, is a combination of a 1-second theodolite and a terrestrial camera. The theodolite portion is a repeating instrument in the sense that it contains a lower motion and an upper motion. The vertical circle, as well as the horizontal circle, can be read directly to 1 second. The theodolite is thus capable of observations for second-order triangulation under favorable conditions.

The camera is supported in two V-shaped bearings by means of a pair of trunnions attached to the cone. The axis of the trunnions intersects the optical axis of the camera lens. With the theodolite leveled, the optical axis can be set in a level position, or at an elevation angle of 7^g ($6° 18'$), or at a depression angle of 7^g, 14^g, or 21^g. The desired position is obtained by means of a tilt-setting bar, which is located on the front of the camera and contains five precisely machined stops.

The lower motion of the theodolite allows the alidade and the camera to rotate in azimuth as a unit. The upper motion allows the alidade to rotate in azimuth with respect to the camera. When the alidade is

Fig. 14–1. Wild phototheodolite. (Courtesy of Wild-Heerbrugg Instruments, Inc.)

oriented to give a reading of 0° 00′ 00″ on the horizontal circle, the telescope axis of the alidade and the optical axis of the camera lie in the same vertical plane. A horizontal-circle reading of 90° 00′ 00″ indicates that the telescope optical axis is oriented in azimuth at right angles to the camera axis and the angle is measured in a clockwise direction. The motion of the alidade relative to the camera allows the camera axis to be oriented in any direction with respect to a given line.

Let it be supposed that the phototheodolite occupies the left end of the base line, or station L in Fig. 14–2, and that the camera axis is to be oriented at right angles to the base in the direction LP. The horizontal circle is set to read 90° by means of the upper-motion clamp and tangent screw. A backsight is taken by sighting on station R through the telescope and using the lower motion. This operation gives the camera axis the desired orientation. If the azimuth of the line LR is 62° 22′ 14″, as shown in Fig. 14–2, the azimuth of the camera axis is 62° 22′ 14″ − 90° = 332° 22′ 14″. For any setting, the azimuth α_C of the camera axis is given by the relationship

$$\alpha_C = \alpha_{LR} - \text{horizontal-circle reading} \qquad (14\text{-}1)$$

in which α_{LR} is the azimuth of the base line in the direction of the line of sight.

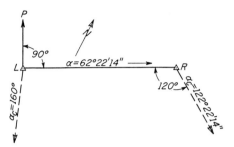

Fig. 14–2. Camera orientation.

EXAMPLE 14–1. The phototheodolite occupies station R of Fig. 14-2, and the camera is oriented by backsighting on station L with a circle reading of 120°. Determine the camera azimuth.

Solution: The azimuth of the base line in the direction of the line of sight is 242° 22′ 14″. The camera azimuth is, by Eq. 14-1,

$$\alpha_c = 242° \ 22′ \ 14″ - 120° = 122° \ 22′ \ 14″$$

EXAMPLE 14–2. With the phototheodolite set up over station L of Fig. 14-2, the camera axis is to be oriented so that its azimuth is 160°. Determine the horizontal-circle reading required for a backsight on station R to give the proper azimuth.

Solution: By Eq. 14-1,

$$160° = 62° \ 22′ \ 14″ - \text{horizontal-circle reading}$$

The required horizontal-circle reading is 62° 22′ 14″ − 160° = 262° 22′ 14″.

It is to be noted that the camera azimuth is the same as the azimuth of the principal plane, as defined in Sec. 3–2. By means of a phototheodolite, the camera azimuth can be readily determined or conveniently set to any value, as illustrated by Examples 14–1 and 14–2.

The tilt of the camera axis is determined by the tilt-bar setting, and ranges from 79^g to 107^g in four steps of 7^g. The five settings correspond to tilts of 71° 06′, 77° 24′, 83° 42′, 90° 00′, and 96° 18′. Expressed as angles with the horizontal, these are, respectively, depression angles of 18° 54′, 12° 36′, 6° 18′, and 0° 00′, and an elevation angle of 6° 18′.

The swing of the photograph, as defined in Sec. 3–2, is controlled by the inclination of the level bubble that is transverse to the direction of the camera axis. In Fig. 14–3, the line joining opposite fiducial marks in the x-direction is horizontal only when the transverse-level bubble is centered. (It is assumed, of course, that the level bubble is in adjustment.) If the principal line, which is defined by the fiducial marks

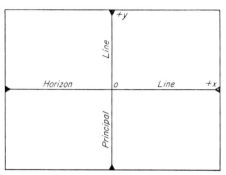

Fɪɢ. 14–3. Terrestrial photograph axes.

at the top and bottom of the photograph, is perpendicular to the horizon line, the swing of the photograph is either 0° or 180°. The swing is 0° when the camera axis is elevated above the horizon, and is 180° when the camera axis is level or is depressed below the horizon.

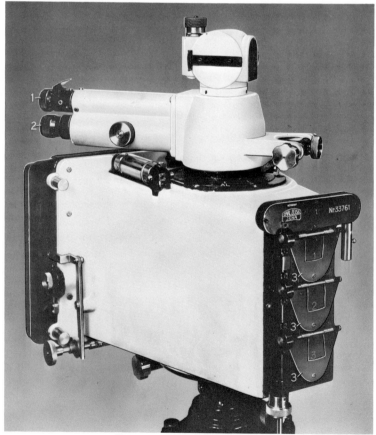

Fɪɢ. 14–4. Terrestrial camera.

The camera shown in Fig. 14–4 contains a sighting telescope, a collimating telescope, and an orienting prism containing eight reflecting surfaces. All these are mounted directly atop the camera cone. Although the sighting telescope is fixed in a horizontal position, the line of sight may be raised or lowered by means of a prism which is tilted by a knurled knob. The elevation or depression angle of the line of sight is read on a graduated drum on the knob.

The axis of the collimating telescope and that of the sighting telescope lie in the same vertical plane when the transverse-level bubble is centered. The camera axis is oriented with respect to the collimating-telescope axis (and thus to the line of sight) by auto-reflection on the eight-faced prism. The conditions are illustrated in Fig. 14–5. The prism is fixed in position on the camera cone. The collimating and sighting telescopes may be rotated about the prism and positioned by means of a clamp and a tangent screw. Eight graduations on the top of the camera cone indicate the approximate positions of the collimating tele-

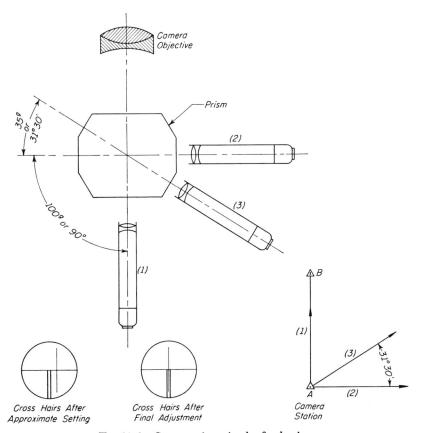

Fig. 14–5. Camera orientation by fixed prism.

scope which will cause the collimation axis to become normal to one of the eight prism faces. By turning the tangent screw, the collimation cross hairs are made to coincide with their reflections off the face of the prism. This adjustment sets the camera axis at a known angle with the line of sight to within about 10 seconds.

When the collimating telescope is oriented at position (1) of Fig. 14–5, the azimuth of the camera axis is coincident with the line of sight. Thus, with the camera at station A and the line of sight directed to station B, the camera axis also points at station B as shown by the arrow. When the collimating telescope is oriented at position (2), the azimuth of the camera axis is 90° greater than that of the line of sight. At position (3) the camera axis makes a horizontal angle of 65^g or 58° 30′ with the line of sight, or an angle of 35^g or 31° 30′ with a normal to the line of sight.

When the camera is to be oriented by reflection, the azimuth of the camera can be set off with respect to the base line only at one of the eight angles which correspond to the directions of the prism faces. Any other azimuth must be set off by using a transit or a theodolite. Suppose that the camera is to be oriented at 45° with the base line. The transit is set up, leveled, and backsighted on the far end of the base line. A 45° angle is set off with reference to the horizontal circle, and a well-defined point falling on the line of sight is selected. The transit is removed, and the camera is set up. The collimating telescope is oriented to position (1) of Fig. 14–5, and the line of sight is directed at the selected point by rotating the camera and the line of sight as a unit. This pointing orients the camera axis in the desired direction.

The camera azimuth may be determined indirectly by measurements on the photograph, as explained in Sec. 14–7.

The axis of the camera shown in Fig. 14–4 cannot be raised or lowered through a vertical angle after it has been fixed in a horizontal position by centering the longitudinal-level bubble. However, the camera contains three lenses whose axes are parallel and coplanar. The three lenses allow the necessary coverage which might extend upward or downward in rugged terrain. The horizon line for each lens is defined by separate fiducial marks, as shown in Fig. 14–6. The tilt of any photograph taken with this camera is always 90°. So the depression angle is zero. The swing is therefore 180°.

The camera shown in Fig. 14–7 is a form of a phototheodolite, in that it contains a full horizontal circle beneath the camera. The camera is oriented by sighting directly through the camera objective by means of either of two oculars located in the camera back. If the camera axis is to be oriented at a given angle off the base line, the other end of the base

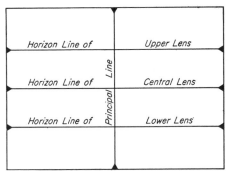

Horizon Line of	Upper Lens
Horizon Line of	Central Lens
Horizon Line of	Lower Lens

FIG. 14–6. Horizon lines of three-lens terrestrial camera.

FIG. 14–7. TAF phototheodolite.

line is sighted through the objective by means of one of the oculars, and the circle is read. The desired angle is added to or subtracted from the circle reading. The camera is then turned through the approximate angle and clamped in position, and the computed circle reading which will give the correct camera azimuth is set off precisely by using the tangent screw.

The camera contains only one lens, the axis of which cannot be inclined up or down. The tilt is consequently fixed at 90°. Vertical coverage is obtained by raising or lowering the lens by means of a rack and pinion. The vertical movement of the lens from the horizon line is determined by the reading on a scale which gives indirectly the tangent of the vertical angle formed by the line of sight.

The conditions for a certain camera are represented in Fig. 14–8. When the lens is in the central position, the horizon line is defined by the line joining the fiducial marks. For this position of the lens, the calibrated reading S of the scale is 150, and either ocular may be used. If the scale reading for an exposure is greater than 150, the upper ocular is used. If the reading is less than 150, the lower ocular is used.

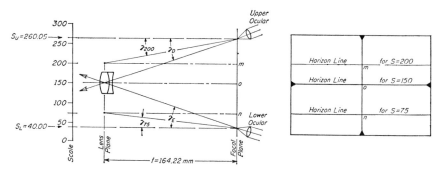

FIG. 14–8. Vertical angles in TAF camera.

When the upper ocular is used, the tangent of the angle of inclination of the line of sight is obtained by subtracting a calibrated constant reading S_U from the central reading and then dividing the difference by a calibrated coefficient D. For the camera in Fig. 14–8, $S_U = 260.05$ and $D = 327.0$. So

$$\tan \gamma_D = \frac{S_{150} - S_U}{D} = \frac{150 - 260.05}{327.0} = -0.336544$$

and

$$\gamma_D = -18° 36'$$

When the lower ocular is used, the tangent of the angle of inclination of the line of sight is obtained by subtracting a calibrated constant S_L from the central reading and then dividing the difference by a calibrated coefficient H. For the camera in Fig. 14–8, $S_L = 40.00$ and $H = 327.6$. So

$$\tan \gamma_E = \frac{150 - 40.00}{327.6} = +0.335775$$

and

$$\gamma_E = +18° 34'$$

Suppose that a photograph is exposed when the scale reading is 200.00, and it is required to establish the horizon line on the photograph. The upper ocular would be used, and the tangent of the depression angle of the line of sight corresponding to the scale reading is

$$\tan \gamma_{200} = \frac{200.00 - 260.05}{327.0} = -0.183639$$

So $\qquad \gamma_{200} = -10° 24'$

The distance *om* of Fig. 14–8 is then obtained as follows:

$$om = f \ (\tan \gamma_D - \tan \gamma_{200})$$

$$= 164.22 \ (0.336544 - 0.183639) = 25.11 \ \text{mm}$$

Therefore the horizon line lies 25.11 mm above and parallel to the line joining the fiducial marks.

Similarly, when the lens is set so that the scale reading is 75.00, the lower ocular would be used, and the tangent of the elevation angle of the line of sight corresponding to the scale reading is

$$\tan \gamma_{75} = \frac{75.00 - 40.00}{327.6} = 0.281441$$

So $\qquad \gamma_{75} = +15° 43'$

Also,

$$on = f \ (\tan \gamma_E - \tan \gamma_{75})$$

$$= 164.22 \ (0.335775 - 0.106838) = 37.60 \ \text{mm}$$

The horizon line thus lies 37.60 mm below and parallel with the line joining the fiducial marks.

The three types of cameras described in this section are used on any project in which the object being photographed will not move either during the exposure or between exposures. The exposure time is quite long, ranging from 2 seconds to 20 seconds. The best time depends on the type of film emulsion, the size of diaphragm, the type of filter, and the focal length.

When the camera is to be used to determine horizontal positions and elevations of points lying in the object space, two photographs are taken, one from each of two ground stations which have been established by ground surveys. Distances can be determined from the photographs graphically, analytically, or instrumentally. Occasionally, the two camera stations are at the ends of a base line, and at each station the camera axis is oriented so as to be normal to the base line. The pair of terrestrial photographs thus obtained may be observed and measured stereoscopically.

Terrestrial cameras were developed originally to produce photographs from which topographic maps of rugged terrain could be compiled. The walls of the canyon of the Colorado River at the site of Hoover Dam were mapped by taking photographs from various survey base lines and compiling the maps in a stereoscopic plotting instrument. Although certain types of geological maps and sections are still compiled by terrestrial photogrammetry, the science is more frequently applied at present to the procurement of supplementary control points in mountainous country. The control points in turn are used to control topographic maps produced by aerial-photogrammetric methods. One exposure made at a ground station with a terrestrial camera whose exterior orientation is known is equivalent to an infinite number of horizontal and vertical angles measured at the same station by using a transit or theodolite. Since the field time is thus reduced, the observations are less dependent on weather conditions than otherwise. The horizontal and vertical angles are determined by measurements made directly on the photographs.

The use of terrestrial cameras is not confined to activities which involve surveying and mapping. They can be used wherever the space

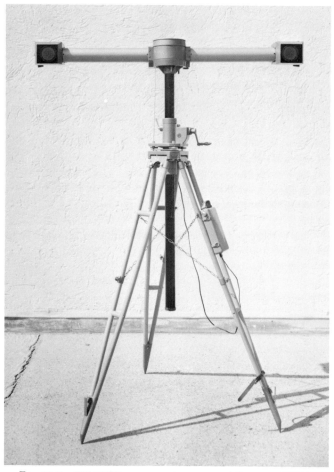

FIG. 14–9. Wild C120 stereometric camera. (Courtesy of Wild-Heerbrugg Instruments, Inc.)

positions of points must be determined but the direct measurement of distances or angles is impossible or inconvenient. Terrestrial photogrammetry solves many problems in which inaccessibility of the object being measured would otherwise preclude the measurements.

When an object is in a state of change from one instant to the next, photographs taken from two viewpoints to obtain a stereoscopic model must be both exposed at exactly the same instant in order to stereoscopically "freeze" the motion. This implies either the use of two cameras or else a single camera with a split field. A stereo camera containing a base of 120 cm is shown in Fig. 14–9. Each camera contains a low-distortion normal angle lens with a focal length of 90 mm and a plate size of 6.5 by 9 cm. The focal plane of each camera contains fiducial marks to define the position of the principal point. The depth of field ranges from 6 meters to 80 meters or from about 20 ft to 260 ft. The base can be rotated about its own axis to provide for elevated or depressed views of the cameras. The shutters are tripped simultaneously by means of a single cable release. The camera base can be raised and lowered as seen from the figure. It is leveled by means of the leveling head of the tripod.

The stereo camera shown in Fig. 14–10 contains wide-angle, low-distortion lenses of 60-mm focal length. The plate size is 9 cm by 12 cm. The depth of field ranges from 5 meters, or 16 ft, to infinity. The camera base is fixed in a horizontal position as shown in Fig. 14–10. However, by means of an adapter, the base can be rotated to give elevation angles up to 90°, that is, the cameras point vertically upward, and depression angles down to 90°. The base can also be oriented in a vertical position for special purposes.

The advantages of the stereometric cameras exemplified by the Wild C120 and the Zeiss SMK120 instruments are fixed relative orientation between the two cameras, and the ability to freeze a changing object at some point in time by means of the simultaneous exposure of each plate. The resulting photographs can be measured quite precisely by means of a parallax bar as discussed in Sec. 14–14, or else in a stereoscopic plotting instrument as discussed in Sec. 14–20.

If an object is in a state of change and is to be measured sequentially at closely spaced time intervals, the photographs must be taken in fairly rapid sequence. It is then necessary to use a pair of motion-picture cameras which are situated at two known and fixed camera stations and the shutters of which operate synchronously. The camera frames must contain fiducial marks in order to define the principal point on each exposure. In most instances, the principal distance (the distance from the rear nodal point of the lens to the film) must be known.

Various methods of obtaining synchronization are used in motion-picture photogrammetry. In one method, a clock with a sweep hand is

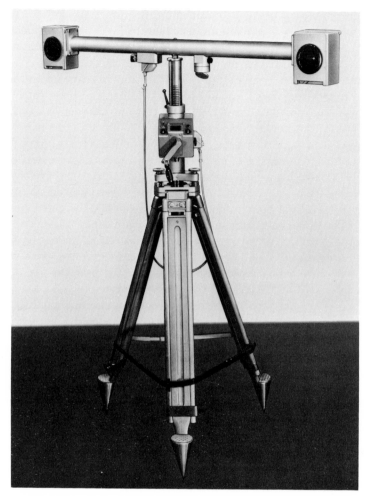

FIG. 14–10. Zeiss SMK stereometric camera. (Courtesy of Carl Zeiss, Oberkochen.)

placed in the field of view of both cameras. Then, after the film has been processed, the frames can be matched by reference to the time. This method is applicable only when the camera-to-object distance is relatively small. In other methods, the shutters are caused to operate together by various mechanical and electrical devices.

The *cinetheodolite* is a motion-picture camera in which the azimuth and altitude of the optical axis are determined from photographs taken of the horizontal and vertical circles of the instrument each time a frame is exposed. The cinetheodolite is used to track and photograph fast-moving objects, such as aircraft and missiles. Two widely separated camera stations are established, and their positions are determined from ground surveys. Each camera can then be initially oriented by means of the horizontal circle. As the object is being tracked, the auxiliary photographs of the circles afford an automatic record of the camera azimuth and the elevation (or depression) angle of the optical axis for each individual exposure. Fiducial marks in the focal plane, which appear on the exposed frames, allow points to be measured on the photographs. From the results of the motion-picture records at each camera station, the space position of the object can be determined at any instant of time by application of the principles to be discussed in the following sections.

14–3. Horizontal Angles from Terrestrial Photographs

The horizontal angle, at the ground exposure station, between two points whose images appear on a terrestrial photograph can be determined graphically, analytically, or instrumentally. In the first situation to be discussed, it is assumed that the camera axis is truly horizontal (the plane of the photograph is vertical). Such a photograph is shown in Fig. 14–11.

Fig. 14–11. Terrestrial photograph with camera axis horizontal.

The horizon line, discussed in Sec. 14–2, is the intersection of the horizontal plane, containing the front nodal point of the lens, with the plane of the photograph. The horizon line is thus seen to be identical with the true horizon defined in Sec. 13–3.

In Fig. 14–12, a photograph is taken at L (the position of the front nodal point, which is directly over the ground station) with a camera whose focal length is f. The images of ground points A and B appear at a and b as shown. The projection of a onto the horizon line defines point

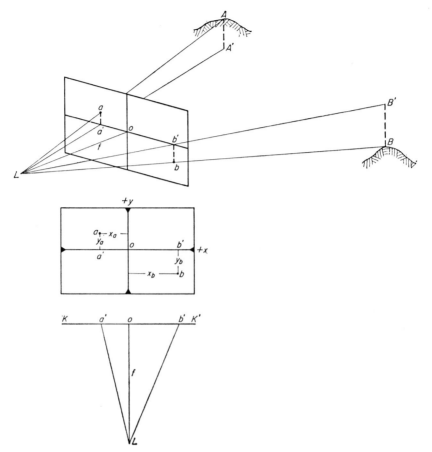

Fɪɢ. 14–12. Horizontal and vertical angles from terrestrial photograph,
with camera axis horizontal.

a', and the projection of b onto the horizon line defines point b'. The
horizontal angle at L from A to B is $\angle\, a'Lb'$. This is equal to $\angle\, a'Lo +$
$\angle\, oLb'$. The angles may be found analytically from the relationships

$$\tan \angle a'Lo = \frac{|x_a|}{f} \qquad \text{and} \qquad \tan \angle oLb' = \frac{|x_b|}{f} \qquad (14\text{--}2)$$

in which $|x_a|$ and $|x_b|$ are the absolute values of the photographic x-co-
ordinates of a and b with respect to the principal line as the y-axis; and
f is the focal length. All quantities are expressed in the same units. The
coordinate values may be measured with a simple scale described in
Sec. 1–4 or by means of a comparator.

The angle β measured from the principal plane to a point is computed by the relationship

$$\tan \beta = \frac{x}{f} \qquad (14\text{-}3)$$

in which the quantities are as previously defined. The algebraic sign of the x-coordinate indicates whether the angle is clockwise (for $+x$) or counterclockwise (for $-x$) with respect to the principal plane.

The angles $a'Lo$ and oLb' can be determined graphically as follows. Construct a line KK' to represent the true horizon of the photograph, as shown in Fig. 14–12, and construct a second line oL, which is perpendicular to KK', to represent the optical axis. Lay off the distance oL, which is equal to f. With a pair of dividers, lay off the values of the x-coordinates of the points along the line KK' from point o. These are the distances oa' and ob'. Draw lines from L through a' and b'. The angle between these lines is the horizontal angle between the corresponding two points. To improve the precision, make the distance oL equal to $2\,f$ and transfer the x-coordinate values from the photograph to the line KK' by means of proportionate dividers set for a 2-to-1 ratio. Lines from L through the two points thus marked form the desired horizontal angle.

The horizontal angle between two points or between the principal plane and any point may be obtained by measurements made in a goniometer or a photoalidade. This procedure has been described in previous chapters, and will not be repeated here.

In the second situation to be discussed, the optical axis is inclined up or down; that is, there is an elevation angle or a depression angle. A photograph taken with the optical axis elevated 7^g is shown in Fig. 14–13. Note that this situation can arise when the phototheodolite shown in Fig. 14–1 is used. However, when the camera shown in Fig. 14–4 or that

Fig. 14–13.   Terrestrial photograph with camera axis elevated 7^g.

shown in Fig. 14–7 is used, the optical axis is always horizontal, and the horizon line can be defined as explained in Sec. 14–2.

In Fig. 14–14, the distance from the principal point to the horizon line is

$$oK = f \tan \theta_D \qquad (14\text{--}4)$$

in which θ_D is the depression angle, which is determined from the setting of the tilt bar and is considered positive. Also, the distance y' measured from the horizon line to point p is

$$y' = y - oK$$

or

$$y' = y - f \tan \theta_D \qquad (14\text{--}5)$$

in which y' is the y-coordinate of the point with respect to an x'-axis coinciding with the horizon line; and y is the y-coordinate of the point

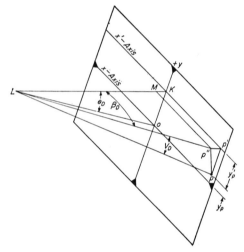

Fig. 14–14. Horizontal and vertical angles from terrestrial photograph, with camera axis depressed.

with respect to the photographic x-axis defined by the fiducial marks. The problem is thus reduced to that of determining the horizontal angle from measurements on an oblique photograph, discussed in Sec. 13–10.

The notations in Fig. 14–14 are the same as those shown in Fig. 13–5. The angle β_D can be found from the relationship

$$\tan \beta_D = \frac{x}{f \sec \theta_D + y' \sin \theta_D} \qquad (14\text{--}6)$$

in which β_D is the horizontal angle measured from the principal plane to the point; x is the photographic x-coordinate measured from the principal line; y' is the distance from the horizon line to the point, obtained by Eq. 14–5; f is the focal length; and θ_D is the depression angle of the optical axis, being considered positive. Due regard must be given to the algebraic signs of x and y'. If x is plus, the angle from the principal plane to the point is clockwise; if x is minus, the angle is counterclockwise. It is seen that Eq. 14–6 is identical with Eq. 13–25 in Sec. 13–10.

EXAMPLE 14–3. The camera axis of a phototheodolite was set at a depression angle of 12° 36′, and an exposure was made. The focal length of the camera is 178.20 mm. Two points a and b appear on the resulting photograph, and their coordinates, reduced from comparator measurements, are as follows: $x_a = -74.20$ mm and $y_a = -26.31$ mm; $x_b = +10.03$ mm and $y_b = +11.25$ mm. Compute the horizontal angle at the exposure station L between the corresponding points A and B.

Solution: Since θ_D is 12° 36′, $\sin \theta_D = +0.218143$; $\tan \theta_D = +0.223526$; $\sec \theta_D = +1.02468$. By Eq. 14–5,

$$y'_a = -26.31 - 178.20 \tan 12° 36' = -66.14 \text{ mm}$$
$$y'_b = +11.25 - 178.20 \tan 12° 36' = -28.58 \text{ mm}$$

By Eq. 14–6,

$$\tan \beta_{D_a} = \frac{-74.20}{178.20 \sec 12° 36' - 66.14 \sin 12° 36'} = -0.441220$$

$$\tan \beta_{D_b} = \frac{+10.03}{178.20 \sec 12° 36' - 28.58 \sin 12° 36'} = +0.056869$$

So, $\beta_{D_a} = -23° 48'$ and $\beta_{D_b} = +3° 15'$.

The angle at L between A and B is the sum of the absolute values of β_{D_a} and β_{D_b}, because these angles have opposite signs. Thus,

$$\angle ALB = 23° 48' + 3° 15' = 27° 03'$$

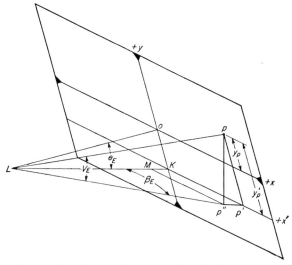

FIG. 14–15. Horizontal and vertical angles from terrestrial photograph, with camera axis elevated.

When the camera axis is directed upward through an elevation angle θ_E, as shown in Fig. 14–15, the y'-coordinate of a point with respect to the horizon line is given by the relationship

$$y' = y + f \tan \theta_E \qquad (14\text{–}7)$$

in which y is the y-coordinate of the point with respect to the x-axis defined by the fiducial marks.

The horizontal angle β_E between the principal plane and the point is obtained from the following relationship:

$$\tan \beta_E = \frac{x}{f \sec \theta_E - y' \sin \theta_E} \qquad (14\text{–}8)$$

in which the quantities are as previously defined. Due regard must be given to the algebraic signs of x and y'.

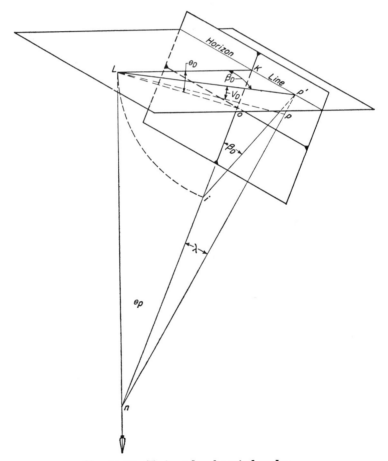

Fig. 14–16. Horizontal and vertical angles.

Horizontal angles may be determined graphically on a terrestrial photograph containing a depression angle by the principles discussed in Sec. 13–12. In Fig. 14–16, the distance from the principal point to the nadir point is

$$on = f \cot \theta_D \qquad (14\text{–}9)$$

The distance from the principal point to the horizon line is

$$oK = f \tan \theta_D \qquad (14\text{–}10)$$

The distance between the horizon line and the isocenter is

$$Ki = f \sec \theta_D \qquad (14\text{–}11)$$

By applying Eqs. 14–9, 14–10, and 14–11, the horizon line, the nadir point, and the isocenter may be located. The photograph must be taped to a sheet of drafting paper because the nadir point, and sometimes the isocenter, will fall off the photograph. In Fig. 14–17, a line extended

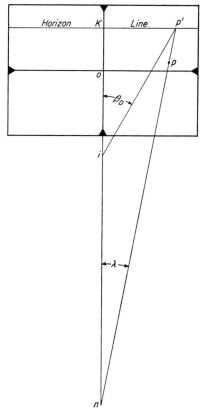

Fɪɢ. 14–17. Horizontal angle by construction, with camera axis depressed.

from the nadir point at n through the image p will intersect the horizon line at p'. A line is then drawn from the isocenter at i through p'. This line makes the desired horizontal angle β_D with the principal plane.

If the optical axis is raised at an elevation angle, the nadir point and the isocenter will lie above the principal point, and the horizon line will lie below the principal point. The graphical determination of a horizontal angle under these circumstances is shown in Fig. 14–18.

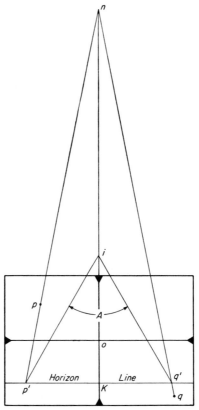

Fɪɢ. 14–18. Horizontal angle by construction, with camera axis elevated.

The lines np and nq intersect the horizon line at p' and q'. The lines ip' and iq' define the horizontal angle A.

Horizontal angles can be determined from a terrestrial photograph which contains an elevation angle up to 15° or a depression angle down to 37° by measurements made in the photoalidade illustrated in Fig. 1–7.

14–4. Vertical Angles from Terrestrial Photographs

The vertical angle above or below the camera horizon can be determined from terrestrial photographs graphically, analytically, or instrumentally.

In Fig. 14–12, the camera axis is in a horizontal position, and $\theta = 0°$. The vertical angle to point A is the angle aLa', since the line La' lies in the camera horizon. The angle aLa' can be found from the relationship

$$\tan \angle aLa' = \frac{aa'}{La'} \tag{14-12}$$

But

$$aa' = y_a \tag{14-13}$$

and

$$La' = f \sec \angle a'Lo \tag{14-14}$$

in which $\angle a'Lo$ is the horizontal angle at L from the principal plane to A, as found from Eq. 14-2.

Substituting Eqs. 14-13 and 14-14 in Eq. 14-12 gives

$$\tan \angle aLa' = \frac{y_a}{f \sec \angle a'Lo} \tag{14-15}$$

In Eq. 14-15, the algebraic sign of the vertical angle depends on the sign of the y-coordinate. If the point lies above the horizon line, the vertical angle is plus; if the point is below the horizon line, the vertical angle is minus.

The vertical angle to B is obtained from the relationship

$$\tan \angle b'Lb = \frac{y_b}{f \sec \angle oLb'}$$

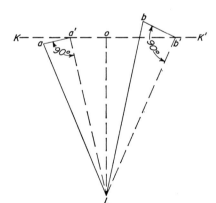

FIG. 14–19. Vertical angle by construction, with camera axis horizontal.

This angle is seen to be a depression angle, since b lies below the horizon line.

The vertical angles aLa' and $b'Lb$ may be determined graphically as follows. In Fig. 14–19, the dashed lines are the construction lines for determining the horizontal angles graphically, this construction being shown in the lower portion of Fig. 14–12. In Fig. 14–19, perpendiculars to lines La' and Lb' are drawn at a' and b', respectively. The values of the y-coordinates of the two points are transferred to these two perpendiculars by a pair of dividers, and these distances locate points a and b, respectively. The angles aLa' and $b'Lb$ are the desired vertical angles.

The vertical angle to a point also may be obtained by orienting the photograph in the photoalidade, sighting the point, and reading the vertical circle. This is possible for photographs containing elevation angles up to 15° or depression angles down to 37°.

The vertical angle to a point can be determined on a terrestrial photograph containing a depression angle θ_D by the principles given in Sec. 13–11. Thus, the angle V_D in Fig. 14–14 can be obtained from the relationship

$$\tan V_D = \frac{y' \cos \theta_D \cos \beta_D}{f \sec \theta_D + y' \sin \theta_D} \qquad (14–16)$$

in which V_D is the vertical angle to the point; y' is the distance from the horizon line to the point, as found by Eq. 14–5; θ_D is the depression angle of the photograph; and β_D is the horizontal angle between the principal plane and the point, as found from Eq. 14–6. The vertical angle is plus or minus, the sign depending on whether the point lies above or below the horizon line (or whether y' as obtained from Eq. 14–5 is positive or negative).

EXAMPLE 14–4. Determine the vertical angles to points A and B of Example 14–3.

Solution: From Example 14–3, $\beta_{D_a} = -23° 48'$, $\beta_{D_b} = +3° 15'$, and $\theta_D = 12° 36'$. So $\cos \beta_{D_a} = +0.914960$; $\cos \beta_{D_b} = +0.998392$; $\cos \theta_D = +0.975917$. By Eq. 14–16,

$$\tan V_{D_a} = \frac{-66.14 \cos 12° 36' \cos (-23° 48')}{178.20 \sec 12° 36' - 66.14 \sin 12° 36'} = -0.35117$$

$$\tan V_{D_b} = \frac{-28.58 \cos 12° 36' \cos 3° 15'}{178.20 \sec 12° 36' - 28.58 \sin 12° 36'} = -0.15789$$

Therefore, $V_{D_a} = -19° 21'$ and $V_{D_b} = -8° 58'$.

If the terrestrial photograph contains an elevation angle θ_E, as shown in Fig. 14–15, the vertical angle to a point may be found from the relationship

$$\tan V_E = \frac{y' \cos \theta_E \cos \beta_E}{f \sec \theta_E - y' \sin \theta_E} \qquad (14–17)$$

in which V_E is the vertical angle to the point; y' is the distance from the horizon line to the point, as found by Eq. 14–7; θ_E is the elevation angle of the photograph; and β_E is the horizontal angle between the principal plane and the point, as found from Eq. 14–8. The vertical angle is plus or minus, the sign depending on whether the point lies above or below the horizon line (or whether y' as obtained by Eq. 14–7 is positive or negative).

The vertical angle to a point appearing on a depressed photograph may be determined graphically, as indicated in Fig. 14–20. Mount the photograph on a sheet of drafting paper. Then, after having computed

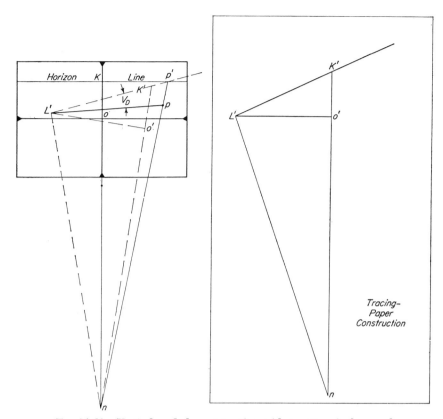

Fɪɢ. 14–20. Vertical angle by construction, with camera axis depressed.

the distance oK by Eq. 14–4, locate point K on the principal line. Mark the position of the horizon line by ruling through K a line that is perpendicular to the principal line. Extend the principal line downward and locate the position of the nadir point n. Pass a line from n through the point p to intersect the horizon line at p'. On a sheet of tracing paper, construct a line $K'o'n$, and lay off points K' and n from o', as shown to the right in Fig. 14–20. Erect a perpendicular to this line at o', and on it make the distance $o'L'$ equal to f. Draw a line from L' through K' to extend beyond K'.

Lay the tracing paper over the photograph so that the tracing-paper position of n coincides with the nadir point. Rotate the tracing paper about n until the line $L'K'$ passes through p'. The angle at L' from p' to p, shown on the left part of Fig. 14–20, is the vertical angle to image point p. The vertical plane LKn in Fig. 14–16 corresponds to the tracing-paper figure $L'K'n$ in Fig. 14–20. If plane LKn of Fig. 14–16 is imagined to be rotated about line Ln through the angle β_D, the resulting vertical plane $Lp'n$ is seen to contain the image point p. If the plane $Lp'n$ of Fig. 14–16 is now rotated about the line $p'n$ into the plane of the photograph, it will assume a position shown on the left in Fig. 14–20. Thus, $\angle p'Lp = \angle p'L'p = V_D$.

In Fig. 14–21 is shown the graphical solution for measuring vertical angles on a photograph whose camera axis is elevated. The horizon line lies below the line joining fiducial marks. In Fig. 14–21(a), a point r lies above the horizon line. A line from n through r intersects the

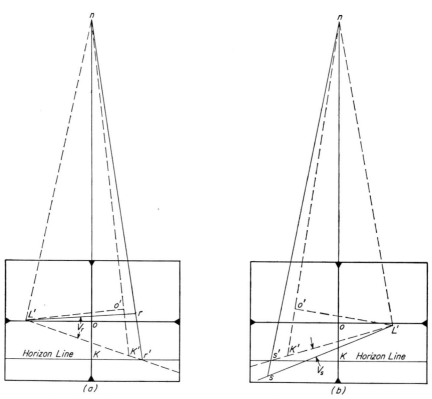

Fig. 14–21. Vertical angles by construction, with camera axis elevated.

horizon line at r'. When the tracing-paper construction of plane $L'K'n$ is oriented over the photograph at n so that the line $L'K'$ passes through r', the vertical angle V_r to r can be measured. The line $L'r$ makes the positive vertical angle $rL'r'$ with the line $L'r'$.

In Fig. 14–21(b), point s lies below the horizon line, and the vertical angle to this point is negative. By use of the tracing-paper construction of the plane $L'K'n$, the vertical angle V_s or $s'L's$ may be determined.

14–5. Control Surveys for Terrestrial Photogrammetry

The purpose of control surveys for terrestrial photogrammetry is to determine the horizontal positions and elevations of carefully selected camera stations from which the photographs will be taken. The camera stations are chosen so as to give as much coverage of the terrain as possible. For this reason, they are usually located on points of higher elevation than the surrounding terrain. Thus, a camera station is likely to be a good triangulation station.

The methods discussed in Chapter 5 for establishing basic horizontal control are generally applicable to terrestrial photogrammetry. When triangulation is employed, supplementary unoccupied points are observed and established by intersection. These points, such as towers, poles, peaks, and lone trees, can be used to locate auxiliary camera stations as outlined in Sec. 14–6. The positions of these intersected points are not, however, so precisely located as the stations in the main triangulation net.

Quite often, desirable camera stations cannot be included directly in the triangulation system. Trig and subtense traversing can be used to good advantage in such a situation. The traverse is then run between, and adjusted to, two triangulation stations.

When terrestrial photogrammetry is used for obtaining picture-point control for aerial mapping, the camera stations usually stand alone and are interconnected by a triangulation system. When terrestrial photographs are taken to measure a three-dimensional model in a stereoscopic plotting instrument, camera stations are located in pairs. These pairs of stations are considered the ends of base lines, and are analogous to two consecutive aerial-camera stations from which are taken a set of overlapping photographs.

In a limited project, the horizontal control often consists of but one base line. When a camera base line is to be established in a triangulation net (not to be confused with the triangulation base line), a triangulation station forms one end of the base. The other end is established by a direct measurement from the triangulation station, as by turning an angle and measuring a distance. The direction to the far end of the camera base should be included directly in the triangulation observation. The distance can be determined by taping, subtense angle, or trig-traverse angle.

The area in Fig. 14–22 enclosed by the dashed outline is to be mapped by aerial photogrammetry. This area may comprise several quadrangle sheets of very rugged, inaccessible terrain. An arc is carried from two existing triangulation stations and is closed on a third fixed station, these three stations being shown by solid triangles. Prominent

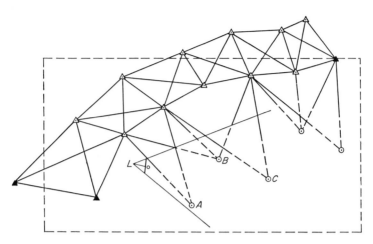

Fɪɢ. 14–22. Triangulation for terrestrial photogrammetry.

points are selected as intersection stations and are observed from the arc. These stations are shown by circles. At the time the triangulation angles are observed at each station, a series of terrestrial photographs are exposed. The camera orientation can be made by sighting on any adjacent triangulation station. Then, after the azimuth of the orientation line has been determined by the triangulation computations, the azimuth

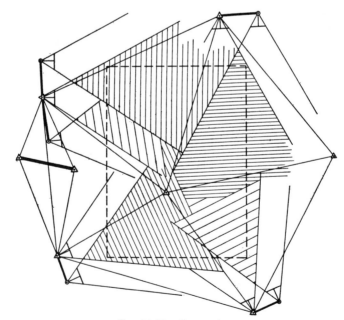

Fɪɢ. 14–23. Camera bases.

of each photograph can be computed in accordance with principles of Sec. 14–2. The photographs are then used to determine positions and elevations of picture points by methods to be discussed in Secs. 14–9, 14–10, 14–12, and 14–13.

A limited area, as outlined by the dashed lines in Fig. 14–23, is to be mapped from terrestrial photographs. A rather simple triangulation system is laid out and the necessary measurements are made. A camera base is established at each triangulation station, and the directions to the ends of these bases are observed along with the directions to the triangulation stations. The field work at each triangulation station also includes the photography from both ends of the camera base.

As shown in Fig. 14–24, an elevation view of the side of a building

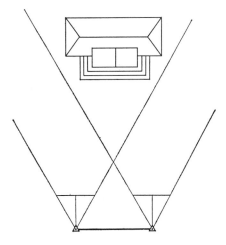

FIG. 14–24. Base for photographing building.

is to be detailed from a pair of terrestrial photographs taken from two ends of a base. In this case, the horizontal control consists of one base line between the two camera stations.

Vertical control is necessary to establish the ground elevations of the camera stations. When the camera is set up, a simple measurement from the ground up to the camera lens then gives the actual height of the camera lens above the datum for elevations. The principles governing vertical-control surveys discussed in Chapter 5 apply to terrestrial photogrammetry. The choice of methods to be used is governed by the desired accuracy, the type of terrain, and the purpose for which the photography is taken. For obtaining supplementary vertical photo control from terrestrial photographs, trig leveling is conducted by using a theodolite giving second-order or better accuracy. Because the distances involved are usually quite long, reciprocal observations must be made in order to eliminate uncertainties in refraction along the lines of sight.

14–6. Camera Position by Resection

Ordinarily, each camera position is located by a horizontal-control survey. Occasionally, however, it is more convenient to establish a camera station by the principle of resection. Assume that a camera station is selected at point L of Fig. 14–22, and that a photograph is taken in the direction shown. The camera station is not a triangulation station; however, the positions of the three intersection stations A, B, and C are included in the photograph, as shown in Fig. 14–25.

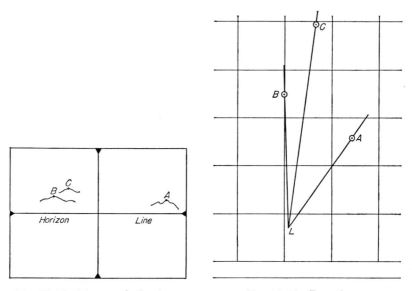

Fig. 14–25. Photograph showing intersection stations.

Fig. 14–26. Resection.

By the methods described in Sec. 14–3, the angles BLC and CLA in Fig. 14–22 may be determined. If they have been determined graphically, a tracing-paper resection on the map positions of the three intersection points will fix the map position of the camera station. This method is shown in Fig. 14–26. If the angles have been computed analytically, or measured in a photoalidade or a goniometer, the values may be set off on a three-armed protractor. The camera station L can then be located graphically, as in Fig. 14–26. Angles derived analytically or instrumentally can also be used to solve the three-point problem for determining the position of the camera station.

14-7. Camera Azimuth

The camera azimuth, or the azimuth of the principal plane, is the ground-survey direction of the camera axis. The camera azimuth can be computed directly by orienting the camera with respect to a line of known azimuth, as described in Sec. 14–2.

Quite often it becomes necessary to determine the camera azimuth by measurements after the photograph has been processed. Assume that the position of L in Fig. 14–26 has been established by resection. The angle between the principal plane of the photograph and any other line may be computed by use of Eq. 14–3 (when the camera axis is level), or by the use of Eq. 14–6 or Eq. 14–8 (when the camera axis is inclined). If the positions of A, B, and L in Fig. 14–27 are known, the azimuths

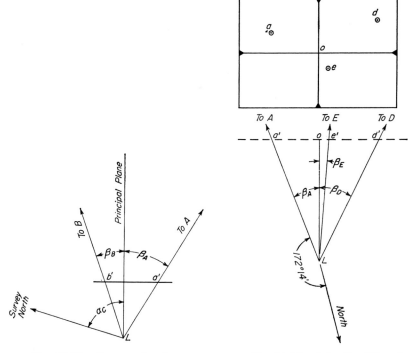

FIG. 14–27. Camera azimuth.   FIG. 14–28. Azimuths of lines from terrestrial photograph.

of the lines LB and LA are also known. The angle β_B is negative, and the angle β_A is positive. So the azimuth α_C of the principal plane may be found by either of the following equations:

$$\alpha_C = \alpha_{LB} + (-\beta_B) = \alpha_{LB} - \beta_B$$

or

$$\alpha_C = \alpha_{LA} - \beta_A$$

Therefore, the camera azimuth can be determined by:

$$\alpha_C = \alpha_{LP} - \beta \qquad (14\text{--}18)$$

in which α_C is the camera azimuth; α_{LP} is the azimuth of the known line directed to a point P; and β is the angle between the principal plane and the point. Due regard must be given to the algebraic sign of β as computed from Eq. 14–3, Eq. 14–6, or Eq. 14–8.

14–8. Azimuth of a Line from Photographic Measurement

If the azimuth of the principal plane of a terrestrial photograph is known, the azimuth of a line directed from the camera station to a point whose image appears on the photograph may be determined by rearranging the terms of Eq. 14–18. Thus,

$$\alpha_{LP} = \alpha_C + \beta \qquad (14\text{--}19)$$

in which the quantities are as previously defined. Again, due regard must be given to the algebraic sign of β.

EXAMPLE 14–5. In Fig. 14–28 the coordinates of points a, d, and e, with respect to the lines joining the fiducial marks on the photograph, are $x_a = -55.20$ mm and $y_a = +27.51$ mm; $x_d = +62.03$ mm and $y_d = +48.62$ mm; $x_e = +10.09$ mm and $y_e = -19.80$ mm. The axis of the camera was level at the time of exposure at station L. The focal length is 178.90 mm. If the azimuth of the line LA is $172°\ 14'$, what are the azimuths of the lines LD and LE?

Solution: Since the camera axis is level, Eq. 14–3 is applied. Then

So
$$\tan \beta_A = \frac{-55.20}{178.90} \qquad \tan \beta_D = \frac{+62.03}{178.90} \qquad \tan \beta_E = \frac{+10.09}{178.90}$$

$$\beta_A = -17°\ 09' \qquad \beta_D = +19°\ 07' \qquad \beta_E = +3°\ 14'$$

The camera azimuth, determined by Eq. 14–18, is

$$\alpha_C = 172°\ 14' - (-17°\ 09') = 189°\ 23'$$

The azimuths of the lines LD and LE are then computed by Eq. 14–19. Thus,

$$\alpha_{LD} = 189°\ 23' + 19°\ 07' = 208°\ 30'$$
$$\alpha_{LE} = 189°\ 23' + \ 3°\ 14' = 192°\ 37'$$

14–9. Analytical Determination of Horizontal Position of a Point from Photographic Measurement

In order to determine the positions of points from measurements on terrestrial photographs, each point must appear on at least two photographs, each taken from a different camera station. The positions of the camera stations must be known, either as a result of ground surveys or by the principle of resection discussed in Sec. 14–6. The camera azimuth α_C must also be known. This azimuth is computed either from the camera orientation described in Sec. 14–2 or from coordinate measurements as outlined in Sec. 14–7.

In Fig. 14–29, an exposure is made at camera station L_1 whose ground coordinates are X_1 and Y_1. An elevation angle θ_E gives a horizon line as shown. The camera azimuth measured clockwise from north is determined to be α_C. The image of a ground point P appears at p on

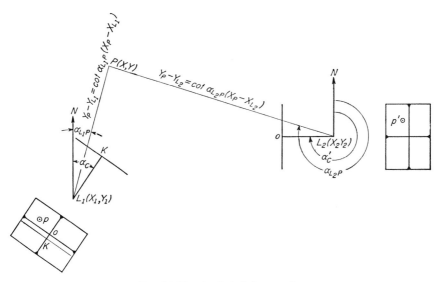

Fig. 14–29. Analytical intersection.

this photograph. At camera station L_2, whose ground coordinates are X_2 and Y_2, an exposure is made with the camera axis level. The camera azimuth measured clockwise from north is α'_C, as shown on the right side of the diagram. The image of the ground point P appears at p' on this photograph.

By the principles of Sec. 14–3 and Sec. 14–8, the azimuths of the lines L_1P and L_2P can be computed.

In analytic geometry, the point-slope form of the equation of a straight line is as follows:

$$y - y_0 = m \ (x - x_0) \tag{14–20}$$

in which x and y are the coordinates of any unknown point lying on the line; x_0 and y_0 are the coordinates of the known point on the line; and

m is the tangent of the angle θ formed between the line and the $+x$-axis. These quantities are shown in Fig. 14–30(a).

In Fig. 14–30(b), it is seen that tan $\theta =$ cot α, in which α is the azimuth, measured clockwise from north, of the same line as that of Fig. 14–30(a). Therefore, the equation of a line which passes through a point with known ground coordinates, and the azimuth of which is known, is

$$Y - Y_0 = \cot \alpha \ (X - X_0) \tag{14-21}$$

In this equation, X and Y are the ground-survey coordinates of any unknown point lying on the line; X_0 and Y_0 are the ground-survey coordinates of the known point on the line; and α is the azimuth of the line.

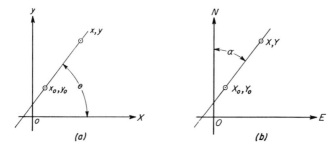

Fig. 14–30. Slope and azimuth of a line.

In Fig. 14–29, the equations of lines L_1P and L_2P are shown. In order to determine the coordinates of the point of intersection P of these two lines, the two equations are solved simultaneously for X_P and Y_P.

EXAMPLE 14–6. The ground-survey coordinates of L_1 and L_2 shown in Fig. 14–29 are as follows: $X_{L_1}=25,225.4$ ft and $Y_{L_1}=9,642.0$ ft; and $X_{L_2}=29,770.3$ ft and $Y_{L_2}=10,721.5$ ft. The azimuths of the two lines L_1P and L_2P, determined from photographic measurements, are $\alpha_{L_1P}=15° \ 12'$ and $\alpha_{L_2P}=293° \ 45'$. Compute the ground-survey coordinates of point P.

Solution: By Eq. 14–21, the equation of the line L_1P is

$$Y_P - 9,642.0 = \cot \ 15° \ 12' \ (X_P - 25,225.4) \tag{1a}$$

and the equation of the line L_2P is

$$Y_P - 10,721.5 = \cot \ 293° \ 45' \ (X_P - 29,770.3) \tag{2a}$$

Substituting the values of cot $15° \ 12'$ and cot $293° \ 45'$ in Eqs. 1a and 2a gives

$$Y_P - \ 9,642.0 = +3.680611 \ (X_P - 25,225.4) \tag{1b}$$

$$Y_P - 10,721.5 = -0.440010 \ (X_P - 29,770.3) \tag{2b}$$

Removing the parentheses, rearranging, and solving for X_P gives the following result:

$$-3.680611\ X_P + Y_P = -\ 83{,}202.9 \qquad \text{(1c)}$$
$$+0.440010\ X_P + Y_P = +\ 23{,}820.7 \qquad \text{(2c)}$$

$$-4.120621\ X_P \qquad = -107{,}023.6$$
$$X_P \quad = \quad 25{,}972.7\ \text{ft}$$

Substituting the value of X_P in Eq. 1c or 2c gives

$$Y_P = 12{,}392.4\ \text{ft}$$

The analytic solution for determining the horizontal position of a point from photographic measurements presented in this section is applicable to any situation in which a pair of photographs have been taken from two exposure stations. The positions of the exposure stations and the camera azimuths must be known. It is further required that precise coordinate measurements be made on the photographic plates in order to determine the value of β from Eq. 14–3, Eq. 14–6, or Eq. 14–8. These measurements are made most conveniently by means of a comparator, the coordinates being referred to the axes defined by the fiducial marks on the plate.

The method of intersection by the simultaneous solution of a pair of linear equations is easily programmed for computation in a high-speed digital computer. Thus, the coordinates of any number of points may be computed in a relatively short time. The input data for each point consist of the camera focal length, the elevation angles or depression angles, the ground coordinates of the exposure stations, the camera azimuths, and the photographic-coordinate measurements of the image points.

14–10. Graphical Location of a Point

The map position of a point appearing on two photographs, each taken from a different camera station, can be determined graphically in any one of several ways. The extent of the graphics involved depends on the number of unknown factors of camera orientation. The position of the exposure station and the camera azimuth may be known, as a result of ground surveys and deliberate camera orientation. Often, however, a photograph may be taken from a known position, but the camera azimuth may not be known. Finally, the situation exists wherein neither the camera position nor its azimuth is known.

In Fig. 14–31, R and S are two known camera stations which have been plotted in their correct map positions. Both camera azimuths are known, and the lines Ro and So' can be drawn in their proper directions. The distances Ro and So' are laid off equal to twice the focal length of the camera, as shown. Lines are constructed through o and o' perpendicular to Ro and So', respectively. These are the map traces of

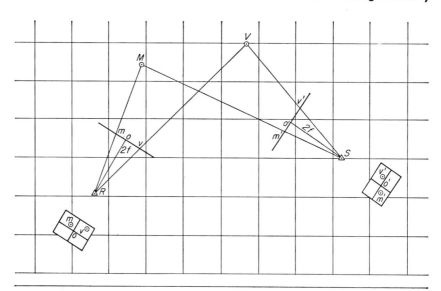

F𝗂𝗀. 14–31. Graphical intersection.

the planes of the photographs. On each photograph, the x-coordinates
of points m and v have been scaled by a pair of proportionate dividers
set for a 2-to-1 ratio, and transferred to the photograph traces as shown
(both camera axes assumed to be horizontal at the time of exposure.) The
lines Rm and Sm' extended will intersect on the map sheet at the correct
position of M. Similarly, lines Rv and Sv' extended determine the map
position of V.

If one exposure or the other was made with the axis inclined, the
method just described must be modified as follows. In Fig. 14–32, a

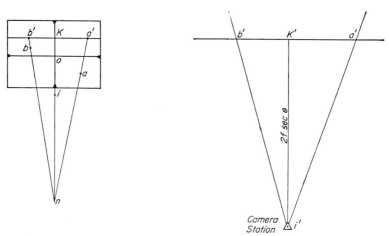

F𝗂𝗀. 14–32. Horizontal directions by construction from depressed photograph.

photograph containing a depression angle θ is fastened to a sheet of drafting paper, and the horizon line is identified. The principal line Kn is drawn through o and perpendicular to the horizon line (by reference to the upper and lower fiducial marks). The distance Kn is computed from the known focal length and depression angle, and the nadir point n is plotted. Lines are drawn from n through image points a and b, whose map positions are to be determined, to intersect at a' and b' on the horizon line.

The map position of the exposure station is plotted, and the camera azimuth is laid off. The distance $i'K'$, which equals $2\,f \sec\,\theta$, is laid off along the line representing the camera azimuth from point i' coinciding with the position of the exposure station. A line is constructed through K' perpendicular to $i'K'$. This represents the horizon line of the photograph. Now, with the proportionate dividers set for a 2-to-1 ratio, the distances Ka' and Kb' are measured on the actual horizon line of the photograph and are transferred to the map position of the horizon line as the distances $K'a'$ and $K'b'$. Lines from i' through points a'

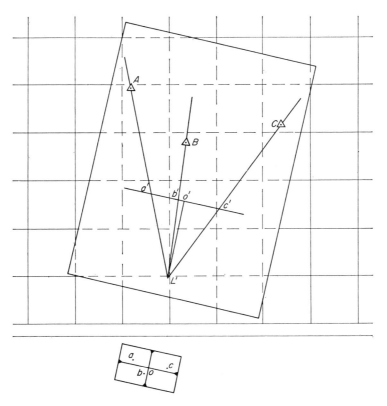

Fɪɢ. 14–33. Tracing-paper resection.

and b' on the map horizon line are the true horizontal directions from the camera station to the two points. Then the method of locating points by intersection is identical with that described in the first part of this section.

If the positions of the camera stations are not known, they can be located by graphical resection as described in Sec. 14–6. The camera axis is fixed in its proper direction, or azimuth, as a result of the resection. In Fig. 14–33, a tracing-paper templet has been prepared by constructing the line $L'o'$ equal to twice the focal length and then laying off the distances $o'a'$, $o'b'$, and $o'c'$ along the templet horizon line $a'c'$. These distances are transferred from the photograph by means of proportionate dividers in the manner previously described. Finally the lines $L'a'$, $L'b'$, and $L'c'$ are drawn to complete the templet. When the tracing paper has been oriented to the plotted positions of A, B, and C, the camera axis $L'o'$ is automatically oriented in its correct azimuth. The method of intersection can then be applied as for other conditions.

14–11. Determination of Camera Height

The height of the camera is the elevation of the lens above the datum. This height is usually established directly by vertical-control surveys. When the camera is set up over the station, the vertical distance is measured from the ground up to the camera lens. This distance is then added to the known elevation of the ground station to give the camera height.

When a camera is set up over a point whose elevation is not known, the camera height must be determined by measurements made on the photograph. Let it be supposed that the elevations of both points A and B of Fig. 14–12 are known, and that their horizontal positions are known or have been computed by intersection. The horizontal position of the exposure station has been determined either by ground control surveys or by resection. Thus, the horizontal distances LA' and LB' can be computed.

The difference in elevation between point A and point L of Fig. 14–12 is the negative vertical distance AA'. The difference in elevation between points B and L is the positive vertical distance BB'. If the angle ALA' is designated as V_A and $B'LB$ is called V_B, the differences in elevation between the two points of known elevation, A and B, and the exposure station L are given by the relationships

$$AA' = -LA' \tan V_A$$

and

$$BB' = -LB' \tan V_B$$

The elevation H_L of L is then computed by either of the following equations:

$$H_L = h_A - LA' \tan V_A$$

or

$$H_L = h_B - LB' \tan V_B$$

When subscripts are dropped to denote a general point, the camera height is given by the equation

$$H_L = h - D \tan V \qquad (14\text{--}22)$$

in which H_L is the camera height (elevation of the camera lens above the datum for elevations), in feet; h is the known elevation of a point whose image appears on the photograph, in feet; D is the horizontal distance from the camera station to the point, in feet; and V is the vertical angle measured from the exposure station to the point. Due regard must be given to the algebraic sign of V.

When the distance to the point is beyond 2,000 ft, the effect of curvature of the earth and atmospheric refraction must be allowed for, and Eq. 14–22 becomes

$$H_L = h - D \tan V - c \qquad (14\text{--}23)$$

in which H_L, h, D, and V are as previously defined; and c is the correction for curvature and refraction, in feet. The value of c is given by the relationship

$$c = 0.0206 \left(\frac{D}{1,000} \right)^2$$

Equation 14–23 is identical with Eq. 13–37, which expresses the flying height of an oblique photograph from measurement of a point of known elevation.

EXAMPLE 14-7. The distances from the camera to points A and B of Example 14-4 are $D_A = 1,714.2$ ft and $D_B = 3,050.6$ ft. The vertical angles have been computed as shown in that example. If the elevation of A is 1,649.7 ft and that of B is 1,768.8 ft, what are the two values of the camera height?

Solution: By Eq. 14–23, in which point A is considered and curvature and refraction are neglected,

$$H_L = 1,649.7 - 1,714.2 \tan(-19° \, 21') = 2,251.7 \text{ ft}$$

When point B is considered,

$$H_L = 1,768.8 - 3,050.6 \tan(-8° \, 58') - 0.0206 \left(\frac{3,050.6}{1,000} \right)^2 = 2,250.0 \text{ ft}$$

14–12. Elevation of a Point by Photographic Measurement

The elevation of a point, whose images appear on two photographs taken from different camera stations, may be determined from measured coordinates of the images. The position and the azimuth of the camera at each station must be known. The camera height at one station must also be known. The horizontal angle formed by the principal plane and the line directed to the point is computed for each camera station by Eq. 14–3, Eq. 14–6, or Eq. 14–8. The azimuth of the line directed from each camera station to the point is then determined as described in Sec. 14–8. The horizontal position of the point is located by intersection as described in Sec. 14–9.

After the horizontal position of the point has been established, the distance from the camera station of known elevation to the point is computed. The vertical angle at this station to the point can be determined by Eq. 14–15, Eq. 14–16, or Eq. 14–17. By rearranging the terms in Eq. 14–23, the elevation of the point is then given by the relationship

$$h = H_L + D \tan V + c \qquad (14\text{–}24)$$

in which h is the elevation of the point, in feet; H_L is the camera height, in feet; D is the horizontal distance to the point, in feet; V is the vertical angle to the point; and c is the correction for curvature and refraction, in feet. Due regard must be given to the algebraic sign of V. It is to be noted that Eq. 14–24 is identical with Eq. 13–38, which gives the elevation of a point from measurements made on an oblique photograph.

14–13. Elevation of a Point by Graphical Construction

When a terrestrial-photogrammetry problem is solved by graphical methods, the map positions of points whose images appear on the photographs are located by intersection of lines directed toward the points. Vertical angles can then be determined graphically by procedures outlined in Sec. 14–4. The distance, at the map scale, from the camera station to the point, together with the graphical vertical angle, are then used to scale the difference in elevation between the camera station and the point.

In Fig. 14–34, the vertical angles V_A and V_B to A and B have been determined graphically by the method given in Sec. 14–4. The map positions of A and B have been fixed by graphical intersection from two camera stations. A perpendicular is erected to the line LA at point A, and the vertical angle V_A is laid off at L to locate line La. Line La is then extended to intersect the perpendicular at A''. The distance AA'', to the scale of the map, is the difference in elevation between the camera and the ground point A; it is positive in this instance. Similarly, a perpendicular is erected to the line LB at B, and line Lb is located at an angle V_B with LB. Line Lb is then extended to intersect the perpendicular at B''. The scaled distance BB'' is the difference in elevation between the camera and ground point B; it is negative in this instance.

If the camera axis is inclined, the simple construction just described is not possible. However, the difference in elevation can be determined

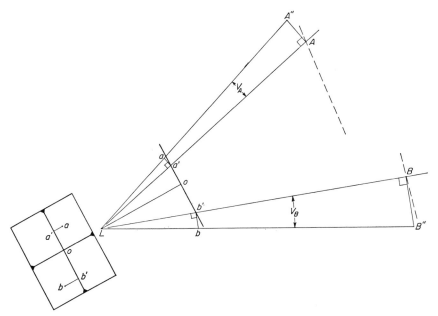

F<small>IG.</small> 14–34. Elevation by graphical construction, with camera axis horizontal.

graphically in the following manner. First, a line is drawn to represent the line joining the camera station with the ground point, as in Fig. 14–35.

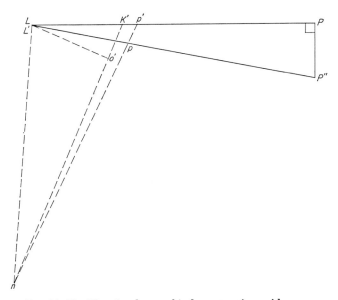

F<small>IG.</small> 14–35. Elevation by graphical construction, with camera axis inclined.

On this line is laid off the scaled distance between the camera station and the ground point. The tracing-paper solution for determining the vertical angle, shown for example in Fig. 14–20, is now superimposed on the line LP of Fig. 14–35 so that L' coincides with L and $L'p'$ coincides with LP. A perpendicular is erected to the line LP at P, as shown. Finally, the line Lp is extended to intersect the perpendicular at P''. The scaled distance PP'' is the difference in elevation between the camera and the ground point.

The value of the scaled difference in elevation is added to or subtracted from the camera height, whichever the case may be, to obtain the elevation of the ground point. Because the solution is graphical, the correction for curvature and refraction may be ignored.

14–14. Position and Elevation of a Point by Parallax Equations

As mentioned in Sec. 14–5, the photography involved in terrestrial photogrammetry quite often consists of a pair of photographs exposed from the two ends of a base line. The camera axes are normal to the base and assume a horizontal position. Thus, both camera plates lie in the same vertical plane. The overlap area of the resulting stereoscopic pair depends on the angular coverage of the plate, and also on the length of the base.

In Fig. 14–36, exposures at L and L' overlap the area beyond the distance D in front of the base. The angular coverage of one half of the plate is the angle α. It is seen that the distance D is equal to $(B/2) \cot \alpha$.

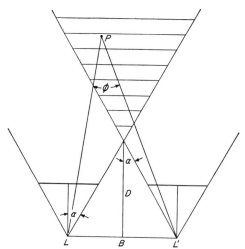

Fig. 14–36.   Coverage of a pair of terrestrial photographs.

The far limits of photographic overlap are fixed by the distance at which the parallactic angle ϕ subtended by the base becomes too small to realize an accurate intersection at a point in the overlap area. When one of the terrestrial cameras described in Sec. 14–2 is used, this distance ranges from 15 to 20 times the length of the camera base.

In Fig. 14–37, two cameras are set up at equal heights at two ends

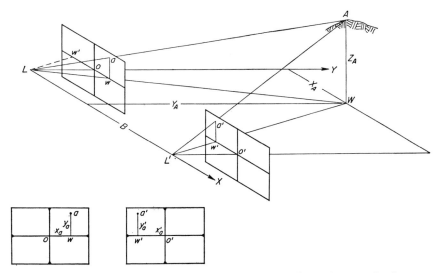

FIG. 14–37. Coordinates from parallax measurement, with equal camera heights.

of a base, and their axes are oriented normal to the base. (Actually the same camera is used at both ends.) The horizon lines of the resulting two photographs are colinear. Thus, the x-axes formed by the x-fiducial marks are colinear. The image of a ground point A appears at a on the left-hand photograph with coordinates x_a and y_a, and appears at a' on the right-hand photograph with coordinates x'_a and y'_a. The air base LL' is designated as B.

With an origin of ground coordinates at L, and a ground Y-axis coinciding with the direction of the left-hand camera axis, the ground coordinates of A are X_A and Y_A, as shown. The difference in elevation between L and A is the distance WA, and it is designated as Z_A.

The line $L'w'$ is transferred to the left-hand photograph, as shown in Fig. 14–37. In the triangles $Lw'w$ and $WL'L$, LW is coincident and parallel with Lw, LL' is parallel with $w'w$, and $L'W$ is parallel with Lw'. Therefore, triangles $Lw'w$ and $WL'L$ are similar. Accordingly,

$$\frac{f}{Y_A} = \frac{w'w}{LL'} = \frac{ow}{X_A} = \frac{wa}{Z_A} \qquad (14\text{--}25)$$

The quantity $w'w$ is the parallax of the point, and is

$$p = x_a - x'_a \qquad (14\text{--}26)$$

Since $ow = x_a$ and $wa = y_a$, the results obtained by combining Eq. 14–26 with Eq. 14–25 and dropping subscripts are the following parallax equations:

$$X = \frac{B}{p} x \qquad (14\text{--}27)$$

$$Y = \frac{B}{p} f \qquad (14\text{--}28)$$

$$Z = \frac{B}{p} y \qquad (14\text{--}29)$$

in which X, Y, and Z are the space coordinates, in feet, of a point with respect to a set of axes whose origin is at the left-hand exposure station, and whose Y-axis coincides with the left-hand camera axis; B is the distance between the camera stations, in feet; p is the parallax of the point; f is the camera focal length; and x and y are the photographic coordinates of the point measured on the left-hand photograph with respect to the axes defined by the fiducial marks. The quantities p, f, x, and y are all in the same units, either inches or millimeters. Equations 14–27, 14–28, and 14–29 apply to measurements made on photographs taken at the same camera height.

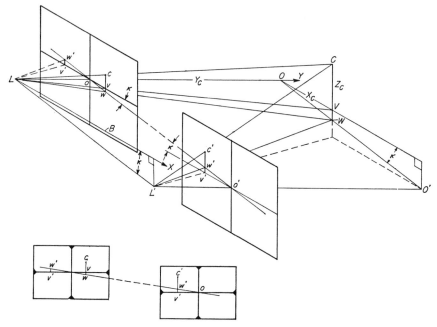

Fig. 14–38. Coordinates from parallax measurement, with unequal camera heights.

The elevation of a point is determined by adding the quantity Z computed by Eq. 14–29 to the camera height. That is,

$$h = H + Z + c \qquad (14\text{--}30)$$

in which h is the elevation of the point, H is the camera height at the left exposure station, and c is the correction for curvature and refraction. The distance necessary to obtain the value of c is computed by the distance formula

$$D = \sqrt{X^2 + Y^2}$$

The correction for curvature and refraction can be ignored if the distance is less than 2,000 ft.

In Fig. 14–38, photographs are taken at two ends of a base, but the camera height at L is greater than that at L'. The survey length of the base is B. The angle κ, formed between a line joining the principal points of the photographs and the horizon lines, is found from the relationship

$$\tan \kappa = \frac{H_L - H_{L'}}{B} \qquad (14\text{--}31)$$

in which H_L and $H_{L'}$ are the camera heights at the left-hand and right-hand camera stations, in feet; and B is the survey length of the base.

In the sloping plane $LL'O'O$ in Fig. 14–38,

$$\triangle\, LL'W \sim \triangle\, Lww'$$

in which the line $L'w'$ has been transferred to the left-hand photograph as the line Lw'. By similar triangles, therefore,

$$\frac{Lo}{LO} = \frac{w'w}{LL'} \qquad (14\text{--}32)$$

But

$$w'w = v'v \sec \kappa = (x_c - x'_c) \sec \kappa = p'_c \sec \kappa \qquad (14\text{--}33)$$

and

$$LL' = B \sec \kappa \qquad (14\text{--}34)$$

Substituting Eqs. 14–33 and 14–34 in Eq. 14–32 and letting $Lo = f$ and $LO = Y_C$ gives the following result:

$$\frac{f}{Y_C} = \frac{p'_c \sec \kappa}{B \sec \kappa} = \frac{p'_c}{B} \qquad (14\text{--}35)$$

In the triangles Lov and LOV,

$$\frac{Lo}{LO} = \frac{Lv}{LV} = \frac{ov}{OV} = \frac{f}{Y_C} \qquad (14\text{--}36)$$

From Eqs. 14–35 and 14–36,

$$\frac{ov}{OV} = \frac{x_c}{X_C} = \frac{p'_c}{B} \qquad (14\text{--}37)$$

Also, in the triangles Lvc and LVC,

$$\frac{Lv}{LV} = \frac{cv}{CV} = \frac{y_c}{Z_C} \tag{14-38}$$

Combining Eqs. 14-35, 14-36, and 14-38 gives

$$\frac{y_c}{Z_C} = \frac{p'_c}{B} \tag{14-39}$$

By solving for X_C, Y_C, and Z_C in Eqs. 14-35, 14-37, and 14-39, and dropping subscripts, the following parallax equations are obtained:

$$X = \frac{B}{p'} x \tag{14-40}$$

$$Y = \frac{B}{p'} f \tag{14-41}$$

$$Z = \frac{B}{p'} y \tag{14-42}$$

in which X, Y, and Z are the space coordinates, in feet, of a point with respect to a set of axes whose origin is at the left-hand exposure station, and whose Y-axis coincides with the left-hand camera axis; B is the horizontal distance between the two camera stations (survey length of the base), in feet; p' is the difference in the photographic x-coordinates of the point; f is the focal length; x and y are the photographic coordinates of the point measured on the left-hand photograph with respect to the axes defined by the fiducial marks. The quantities p', f, x, and y are all in the same units, either inches or millimeters.

The elevation of the point is determined by Eq. 14-30, in which Z is the vertical distance computed by Eq. 14-42.

The value of p given in Eqs. 14-27, 14-28, and 14-29 is the true parallax of the point as defined in Sec. 8-2, because the x-axes of the two photographs defined by the fiducial marks are parallel with the line LL' of Fig. 14-37.

The value of p' given in Eqs. 14-40, 14-41, and 14-42 is not the true parallax of the point, but is the projection of the true parallax, $w'w$ of Fig. 14-38, onto the x-axis defined by fiducial marks.

Suppose that the two photographs of Fig. 14-37 are to be oriented under a stereoscope for parallax-bar measurements. A straight line, defining the eye-base of the stereoscope, would coincide with the x-axes defined by fiducial marks, as shown in Fig. 14-39. The line passing through any pair of conjugate images is parallel to the eye-base. The parallaxes obtained by the parallax-bar measurements represent the true parallaxes.

If the two photographs of Fig. 14-38 are to be oriented under the

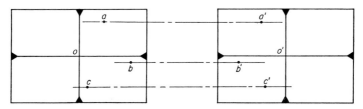

FIG. 14–39. Photographs oriented for stereoscopic measurement, with equal camera heights.

stereoscope, the right-hand photograph must be displaced downward, as shown in Fig. 14–40. The line joining the two principal points defines the stereoscope eye-base. Parallax-bar measurements then give the true parallaxes of the conjugate points. The projection of the parallax of a point onto the x-axis of the left-hand photograph is then obtained by the relationship

$$p' = p \cos \kappa \qquad (14\text{--}43)$$

in which p is the true parallax of the point obtained by parallax-bar measurement.

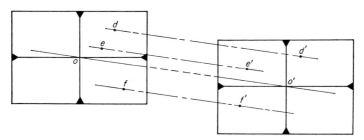

FIG. 14–40. Photographs oriented for stereoscopic measurement, with unequal camera heights.

EXAMPLE 14–8. The air base of Fig. 14–37 is 956.22 ft long. The camera focal length is 172.20 mm. The height of both cameras is 583.4 ft above sea level. The coordinates of two points a and b measured on the left-hand photograph are $x_a = -27.21$ mm and $y_a = +8.95$ mm; $x_b = +50.20$ mm and $y_b = -21.80$ mm. The x-coordinates measured on the right-hand photograph are $x'_a = -81.70$ mm and $x'_b = -71.22$ mm. Determine the ground coordinates and elevations of A and B.

Solution: By Eq. 14–26,

$$p_a = -27.21 - (-81.70) = 54.49 \text{ mm}$$
$$p_b = +50.20 - (-71.22) = 121.42 \text{ mm}$$

By Eq. 14–27,

$$X_A = \frac{956.22}{54.49} \times (-27.21) = -477.5 \text{ ft} \qquad \text{and} \qquad X_B = \frac{956.22}{121.42} \times 50.20 = +395.4 \text{ ft}$$

By Eq. 14–28,

$$Y_A = \frac{956.22}{54.49} \times 172.20 = +3,021.9 \text{ ft} \qquad \text{and} \qquad Y_B = \frac{956.22}{121.42} \times 172.20 = +1,356.1 \text{ ft}$$

By Eq. 14–29,

$$Z_A = \frac{956.22}{54.49} \times 8.95 = +157.1 \text{ ft} \qquad \text{and} \qquad Z_B = \frac{956.22}{121.42} \times (-21.80) = -171.7 \text{ ft}$$

By the distance formula,

$$D_A = \sqrt{477.5^2 + 3,021.9^2} = 3,076.3 \text{ ft}$$

$$D_B = \sqrt{395.4^2 + 1,356.1^2} = 1,412.6 \text{ ft}$$

The correction for curvature and refraction to the elevation of A is

$$c_A = 0.0206 \left(\frac{3,076.3}{1,000}\right)^2 = 0.2 \text{ ft}$$

That for B can be neglected.

By Eq. 14–30,

$$h_A = 583.4 + 157.1 + 0.2 = 740.7 \text{ ft}$$

$$h_B = 583.4 - 171.7 = 411.7 \text{ ft}$$

EXAMPLE 14–9. The air base of Fig. 14–38 is 453.70 ft long. The camera focal length is 168.45 mm. The elevation of the left camera is 1,754.2 ft. and the elevation of the right camera is 1821.6 ft. The coordinates of two points m and n measured on the left-hand photograph are $x_m = +20.25$ mm and $y_m = -16.41$ mm; $x_n = +72.75$ mm and $y_n = -3.02$ mm. The photographs were oriented under a stereoscope, and parallax-bar measurements gave the following values: $p_m = 67.80$ mm and $p_n = 55.23$ mm. Determine the ground coordinates and elevation of M and N.

Solution: By Eq. 14–31,

$$\tan \kappa = \frac{1,754.2 - 1,821.6}{453.70} = -0.14856$$

Then $\kappa = -8°\,27'$ and $\cos \kappa = 0.98914$.

By Eq. 14–43,

$$p'_m = 67.80 \times 0.98914 = 67.06 \text{ mm}$$

$$p'_n = 55.23 \times 0.98914 = 54.63 \text{ mm}$$

By Eq. 14–40,

$$X_M = \frac{453.70}{67.06} \times 20.25 = +137.0 \text{ ft} \qquad \text{and} \qquad X_N = \frac{453.70}{54.63} \times 72.75 = +604.2 \text{ ft}$$

By Eq. 14–41,

$$Y_M = \frac{453.70}{67.06} \times 168.45 = +1,139.7 \text{ ft} \qquad \text{and} \qquad Y_N = \frac{453.70}{54.63} \times 168.45 = +1,399.0 \text{ ft}$$

By Eq. 14–42,

$$Z_M = \frac{453.70}{67.06} \times (-16.41) = -111.0 \text{ ft} \qquad \text{and} \qquad Z_N = \frac{453.70}{54.63} \times (-3.02) = -25.1 \text{ ft}$$

Since the distance to each point is less than 2,000 ft, the allowance for curvature and refraction may be ignored. Then by Eq. 14–30,

$$h_M = 1,754.2 - 111.0 = 1,643.2 \text{ ft}$$

$$h_N = 1,754.2 - 25.1 = 1,729.1 \text{ ft}$$

14–15. Survey Coordinates of a Point

The X- and Y-coordinates of a point given by Eqs. 14–27, 14–28, 14–40, and 14–41 are with respect to an assumed set of X- and Y-axes coinciding, respectively, with the camera base and the axis of the left-hand camera lens. If the left-hand camera azimuth and the survey coordinates of the left-hand camera station are known, the survey coordinates of a point can then be determined by rotation and translation formulas.

In Fig. 14–41, the survey axes are designated X_S and Y_S, and their

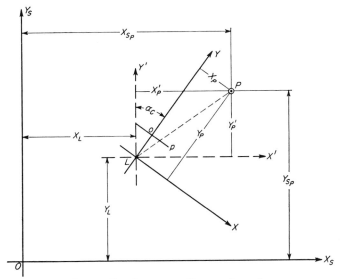

Fɪɢ. 14–41.   Survey coordinates of a point.

origin is at O. The axes with respect to the photograph base and the left-hand camera axis are noted as X and Y. The coordinates of P with respect to this set of axes are X_P and Y_P. If the X- and Y-axes are rotated in a counterclockwise direction (considered positive in analytic geometry) through the angle α_C, the resulting X'- and Y'-axes are parallel with the ground-survey X_S- and Y_S-axes. The coordinates of P with respect to these axes are given by the rotational equations, as follows:

$$X'_P = X_P \cos \alpha_C + Y_P \sin \alpha_C \qquad (14\text{–}44)$$

$$Y'_P = -X_P \sin \alpha_C + Y_P \cos \alpha_C \qquad (14\text{–}45)$$

in which α_C is the camera azimuth of the left-hand photograph.

The survey coordinates of P are obtained by adding the survey coordinates of the exposure station to the coordinates computed in Eqs. 14–44 and 14–45. Thus,

$$X_{S_P} = X'_P + X_L \qquad (14\text{–}46)$$

$$Y_{S_P} = Y'_P + Y_L \qquad (14\text{–}47)$$

in which X_{S_P} and Y_{S_P} are the survey coordinates of point P; and X_L and Y_L are the survey coordinates of the exposure station, as shown in Fig. 14–41.

The rotational equations, Eqs. 14–44 and 14–45, may be combined with the translational equations, Eqs. 14–46 and 14–47. The results are

$$X_{S_P} = X_P \cos \alpha_C + Y_P \sin \alpha_C + X_L \qquad (14\text{–}48)$$

$$Y_{S_P} = -X_P \sin \alpha_C + Y_P \cos \alpha_C + Y_L \qquad (14\text{–}49)$$

EXAMPLE 14–10. The camera azimuth of Example 14–9 is 146° 22′ 10″, and the survey coordinates of the camera station are $X_L = 1,642,220.0$ ft and $Y_L = 544,184.9$ ft. Compute the survey coordinates of points M and N.

Solution: It is found that sin 146° 22′ 10″ = +0.553836 and cos 146° 22′ 10″ = −0.832626.

By Eq. 14–48,

$X_{S_M} = (137.0)(-0.832626) + (1,139.7)(0.553836) + 1,642,220.0 = 1,642,737.1$ ft

$X_{S_N} = (604.2)(-0.832626) + (1,399.0)(0.553836) + 1,642,220.0 = 1,642,491.7$ ft

By Eq. 14–49,

$Y_{S_M} = -(137.0)(0.553836) + (1,139.7)(-0.832626) + 544,184.9 = 543,160.1$ ft

$Y_{S_N} = -(604.2)(0.553836) + (1,399.0)(-0.832626) + 544,184.9 = 542,685.4$ ft

14–16. Space Coordinates of a Point by Direction Cosines

Many problems in terrestrial photogrammetry, in which the space positions of several discrete points must be determined from simple plate-coordinate measurements, can be readily solved by the method of direction cosines introduced in Sec. 3–13 through Sec. 3–16. This approach is made practical by the use of high-speed electronic computers.

The complete orientation of a terrestrial camera is usually known, or can be determined quite readily by the principles discussed in this chapter. The space coordinates X_L, Y_L, and Z_L of the camera station are obtained by field surveys or by laboratory measurements. These coordinates may be established with respect to either a fixed coordinate system or an assumed coordinate system. The tilt, swing, and azimuth of the photograph are usually known, or can be easily determined.

The tilt of a photograph, whose camera axis is horizontal, is 90°. The tilt of a depressed photograph is given by the relationship

$$t_D = 90° - \theta_D \qquad (14\text{–}50)$$

in which θ_D is the depression angle, deliberately set off on the camera. The tilt of an elevated photograph is given by the equation

$$t_E = 90° + \theta_E \qquad (14\text{-}51)$$

in which θ_E is the elevation angle, deliberately set off on the camera.

The swing of a terrestrial photograph that contains a tilt of 90° or less is always 180°, provided that the camera has been leveled transverse to the direction of the optical axis. The swing of a terrestrial photograph that contains a tilt greater than 90° is always 0° under the same provision. If the camera is not level in the transverse direction, the angle of swing is still considered to be the clockwise angle measured in the plane of the photograph from the positive y-axis to the nadir point. This is the same definition given for the swing of an aerial photograph.

The azimuth α_C of a terrestrial photograph is the ground survey direction of the camera axis, as is the case for an aerial photograph. It is determined by the methods described in Sec. 14–2 and Sec. 14–7.

The x_T, y_T, z_T coordinates of a point with respect to a set of axes parallel with the ground survey axes in terms of the photographic coordinates of the point together with the orientation angles t, s, and α_C are then given by Eq. 3–34, as

$$\begin{bmatrix} x_T \\ y_T \\ z_T \end{bmatrix} = \mathbf{M}^T \begin{bmatrix} x \\ y \\ z \end{bmatrix} \qquad (14\text{-}52)$$

in which the orientation matrix $\mathbf{M}^T$ is given by Eq. 3–44, as

$$\mathbf{M}^T = \begin{bmatrix} -\cos s \cos \alpha_C - \sin s \cos t \sin \alpha_C & \sin s \cos \alpha_C - \cos s \cos t \sin \alpha_C & -\sin t \sin \alpha_C \\ \cos s \sin \alpha_C - \sin s \cos t \cos \alpha_C & -\sin s \cos \alpha_C - \cos s \cos t \cos \alpha_C & -\sin t \cos \alpha_C \\ -\sin s \sin t & -\cos s \sin t & \cos t \end{bmatrix} \qquad (14\text{-}53)$$

In Fig. 14–42, the photographic x- and y-axes are defined by lines joining fiducial marks, and the photographic z-axis coincides with the optical axis and is positive in the direction oL. By the principles discussed in Sec. 3–14, the direction cosines of the line pL with respect to the photographic coordinates axes are given by the following expressions:

$$\cos mpL = \frac{-x_p}{\sqrt{x_p^2 + y_p^2 + f^2}}$$

$$\cos npL = \frac{-y_p}{\sqrt{x_p^2 + y_p^2 + f^2}}$$

$$\cos kpL = \frac{+f}{\sqrt{x_p^2 + y_p^2 + f^2}}$$

in which x_p and y_p are the measured photographic coordinates, and f is the camera focal length. These values of the cosines are based on the condition that the optical axis intersects the photograph at the point where lines joining the fiducial marks cross one another.

If the lens of the camera shown in Fig. 14–7 has been moved up or down from its central position, then the value of the y-coordinate of the point as measured with respect to the fiducial marks must be modified accordingly before the direction cosines mpL, npL, and kpL can be computed.

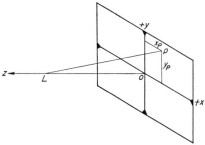

If the upper or lower lens of the camera shown in Fig. 14–4 is used in making an exposure, the y-coordinate

FIG. 14–42. Photographic space-coordinate axes.

of the point must be measured with respect to the appropriate set of fiducial marks.

After the orientation matrix $\mathbf{M}^T$ has been computed for the photograph based on known exterior orientation elements, the directions of the various lines with respect to the ground X-, Y-, and Z-axes can then be determined by Eq. 3–68, thus

$$\begin{bmatrix} \cos MPL \\ \cos NPL \\ \cos KPL \end{bmatrix} = \mathbf{M}^T \begin{bmatrix} \cos mpL \\ \cos npL \\ \cos kpL \end{bmatrix} \qquad (14\text{–}54)$$

In Fig. 14–43, exposures at the two camera stations L and L' result in two photographs, the position and orientation of each of which are known. The coordinates are X_L, Y_L, and Z_L and $X_{L'}$, $Y_{L'}$, and $Z_{L'}$,

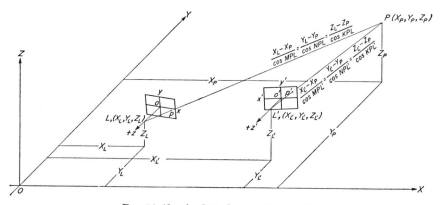

FIG. 14–43. Analytical space intersection.

respectively. The orientations are t, s, and α_C and t', s', and α'_C, respectively. An orientation matrix is prepared for each photograph. The plate coordinates of the image of the space point P are measured on both photographs, giving x_p, y_p, x'_p, and y'_p. By Eq. 14–54, the values of cos MPL, cos NPL, cos KPL, cos MPL', cos NPL', and cos KPL' are computed to establish the directions of lines PL and PL' with respect to the ground axes.

According to Eq. 3–70, the equations of the lines PL and PL' in space are, respectively,

$$\frac{X_L - X_P}{\cos MPL} = \frac{Y_L - Y_P}{\cos NPL} = \frac{Z_L - Z_P}{\cos KPL}$$

and

$$\frac{X_{L'} - X_P}{\cos MPL'} = \frac{Y_{L'} - Y_P}{\cos NPL'} = \frac{Z_{L'} - Z_P}{\cos KPL'}$$

The equations of these two lines are shown in Fig. 14–43. If these two equations are solved simultaneously, the results yield the ground coordinates X_P, Y_P, and Z_P. If X_P and Y_P are computed first, two values of Z_P (the elevation of P) will result. A discrepancy between these two values is caused by errors in the photogrammetric system. Similarly, if X_P and Z_P or Y_P and Z_P are computed first, a discrepancy in the two values of Y_P or the two values of X_P will reflect errors in the system.

Let it be supposed that a camera is set up and leveled in both directions, and is oriented normal to the camera base. Let it be further assumed that the camera axis is oriented in a horizontal position. Under these conditions, $t = 90°$ and $s = 180°$. The orientation matrix $\mathbf{M}^T$ then becomes

$$\mathbf{M}^T_{\substack{t=90° \\ s=180°}} = \begin{bmatrix} \cos \alpha_C & 0 & -\sin \alpha_C \\ -\sin \alpha_C & 0 & -\cos \alpha_C \\ 0 & 1 & 0 \end{bmatrix} \tag{14–55}$$

Suppose now that the survey X-axis is assumed to coincide with the camera base and that the camera axis is oriented normal to the base, making $\alpha_C = 0$. Then the orientation matrix $\mathbf{M}^T$ becomes

$$\mathbf{M}^T_{\substack{t=90° \\ s=180° \\ \alpha_C=0°}} = \begin{bmatrix} 1 & 0 & 0 \\ 0 & 0 & -1 \\ 0 & 1 & 0 \end{bmatrix} \tag{14–56}$$

The photographic coordinates of a point can be expressed in terms of the elements of exterior orientation together with the x_T, y_T, z_T coordinates of the point in which the latter set of coordinates are with respect to a set of coordinate axes parallel with the ground survey axes, but translated in space so that the origin is coincident with the nodal point of the photograph. In this instance, the z-coordinate of a photographic image is $-f$. The transformation is, by Eq. 3–30,

$$\begin{bmatrix} x \\ y \\ z \end{bmatrix} = \mathbf{M} \begin{bmatrix} x_T \\ y_T \\ z_T \end{bmatrix} \qquad (14\text{–}57)$$

in which the orientation matrix $\mathbf{M}$ is given by Eq. 3–29 as

$$\mathbf{M} = \begin{bmatrix} -\cos s \cos \alpha_c - \sin s \cos t \sin \alpha_c & \cos s \sin \alpha_c - \sin s \cos t \cos \alpha_c & -\sin s \sin t \\ \sin s \cos \alpha_c - \cos s \cos t \sin \alpha_c & -\sin s \cos \alpha_c - \cos s \cos t \cos \alpha_c & -\cos s \sin t \\ -\sin t \sin \alpha_c & -\sin t \cos \alpha_c & \cos t \end{bmatrix} \qquad (14\text{–}58)$$

Letting matrix $\mathbf{M}$ be represented as in Sec. 3–13,

$$\mathbf{M} = \begin{bmatrix} m_{11} & m_{12} & m_{13} \\ m_{21} & m_{22} & m_{23} \\ m_{31} & m_{32} & m_{33} \end{bmatrix}$$

and performing the multiplication in Eq. 14–57, the photographic coordinates are given as

$$\left. \begin{aligned} x &= m_{11}x_T + m_{12}y_T + m_{13}z_T \\ y &= m_{21}x_T + m_{22}y_T + m_{23}z_T \\ z &= m_{31}x_T + m_{32}y_T + m_{33}z_T \end{aligned} \right\} \qquad (14\text{–}59)$$

By Fig. 14–44, the following relationships are evident

$$x_T = \frac{-z_T(X_P - X_L)}{Y_P - Y_L} \qquad (14\text{–}60)$$

$$y_T = \frac{-z_T(Z_P - Z_L)}{Y_P - Y_L} \qquad (14\text{–}61)$$

and by identity

$$-z_T = \frac{-z_T(Y_P - Y_L)}{Y_P - Y_L} \qquad (14\text{–}62)$$

Substituting Eqs. 14–60, 14–61, and 14–62 into Eq. 14–59, and dividing x and y by z gives the collinearity equations

$$\left. \begin{aligned} \frac{x}{z} &= \frac{m_{11}(X_P - X_L) + m_{12}(Z_P - Z_L) + m_{13}(Y_P - Y_L)}{m_{31}(X_P - X_L) + m_{32}(Z_P - Z_L) + m_{33}(Y_P - Y_L)} \\[2ex] \frac{y}{z} &= \frac{m_{21}(X_P - X_L) + m_{22}(Z_P - Z_L) + m_{23}(Y_P - Y_L)}{m_{31}(X_P - X_L) + m_{32}(Z_P - Z_L) + m_{33}(Y_P - Y_L)} \end{aligned} \right\} \qquad (14\text{–}63)$$

The values of the photographic x- and y-coordinates are thus,

$$\left. \begin{array}{l} x = z\left[\dfrac{m_{11}(X_P-X_L)+m_{12}(Z_P-Z_L)+m_{13}(Y_P-Y_L)}{m_{31}(X_P-X_L)+m_{32}(Z_P-Z_L)+m_{33}(Y_P-Y_L)} \right] \\[4mm] y = z\left[\dfrac{m_{21}(X_P-X_L)+m_{22}(Z_P-Z_L)+m_{23}(Y_P-Y_L)}{m_{31}(X_P-X_L)+m_{32}(Z_P-Z_L)+m_{33}(Y_P-Y_L)} \right] \end{array} \right\} \quad (14\text{--}64)$$

The quantity z in Eq. 14–64 is equal to $-f$ of the camera lens. Comparing Eq. 14–63 with Eq. 3–77 shows the effect of having the y-axis of a terrestrial photograph essentially in the direction of the Z-axis of the ground system and the camera axis oriented generally in the horizontal position.

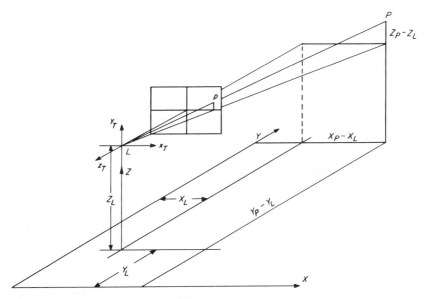

FIG. 14–44. Projective transformation.

If at least three points in the object space of a terrestrial photograph are known in X, Y, and Z, then by the use of the partial differential coefficients of Eq. 14–64, as discussed in Sec. 9–6, the values of X_L, Y_L, Z_L, t, s, and α_C can be approximated, and the corrections dX_L, dY_L, dZ_L, dt, ds, and $d\alpha_C$ to these approximate values can be computed by iteration. Furthermore, if more than three points are known, the most probable values can be determined by the method of least squares.

Direction cosines which make up the orientation matrices $\mathbf{M}$ and $\mathbf{M}^T$ can also be expressed in terms of sequential rotations α_C about a vertical line, ω about a horizontal line, and κ about the camera axis, in that order. In Fig. 14–45, the x_T-, y_T-, and z_T-axes are parallel with the ground survey axes, but translated to the principal point of the terrestrial photograph. A

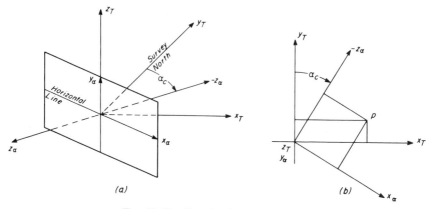

Fig. 14–45. Rotation in azimuth (α_C).

rotation about the z_T-axis through an angle α_C results in the primarily rotated x_a-, y_a- and z_a-axes are shown in Fig. 14–45(a). According to Fig. 14–45(b), the coordinates of a point p following this rotation, considering that α_C is a negative rotation according to a right-hand system, are

$$x_a = x_T \cos(-\alpha_C) + y_T \sin(-\alpha_C)$$
$$y_a = z_T$$
$$-z_a = -x_T \sin(-\alpha_C) + y_T \cos(-\alpha_C)$$

or

$$\left. \begin{array}{l} x_a = x_T \cos \alpha_C - y_T \sin \alpha_C \\ y_a = z_T \\ z_a = -x_T \sin \alpha_C - y_T \cos \alpha_C \end{array} \right\} \qquad (14\text{--}65)$$

In matrix form, the coefficient matrix $\mathbf{M}_a$ is

$$\mathbf{M}_a = \begin{bmatrix} \cos \alpha_C & -\sin \alpha_C & 0 \\ 0 & 0 & 1 \\ -\sin \alpha_C & -\cos \alpha_C & 0 \end{bmatrix} \qquad (14\text{--}66)$$

and

$$\begin{bmatrix} x_a \\ y_a \\ z_a \end{bmatrix} = \mathbf{M}_a \begin{bmatrix} x_T \\ y_T \\ z_T \end{bmatrix} \qquad (14\text{--}67)$$

In Fig. 14–46(a), the once-rotated x_a-, y_a-, z_a-axes are now rotated about the x_a-axis through the positive angle ω. According to Fig. 14–46(b), the rotated coordinates of p become

$$\left. \begin{array}{l} x_{a\omega} = x_a \\ y_{a\omega} = y_a \cos \omega + z_a \sin \omega \\ z_{a\omega} = -y_a \sin \omega + z_a \cos \omega \end{array} \right\} \qquad (14\text{--}68)$$

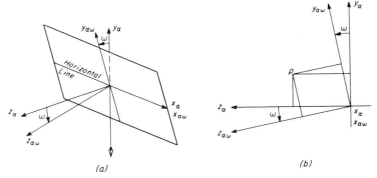

FIG. 14-46. Rotation about horizontal line (ω).

The matrix of coefficients of Eq. 14-68 are given by

$$\mathbf{M}_\omega = \begin{bmatrix} 1 & 0 & 0 \\ 0 & \cos \omega & \sin \omega \\ 0 & -\sin \omega & \cos \omega \end{bmatrix} \qquad (14\text{-}69)$$

and

$$\begin{bmatrix} x_{a\omega} \\ y_{a\omega} \\ z_{a\omega} \end{bmatrix} = \mathbf{M}_\omega \begin{bmatrix} x_a \\ y_a \\ z_a \end{bmatrix} \qquad (14\text{-}70)$$

Finally, a positive rotation κ is made to bring the axes into their position on the photograph, as shown in Fig. 14-47. The final rotated coordinates, which are the photographic coordinates of the point, are given by

$$\left. \begin{aligned} x &= x_{a\omega\kappa} = x_{a\omega} \cos \kappa + y_{a\omega} \sin \kappa \\ y &= y_{a\omega\kappa} = -x_{a\omega} \sin \kappa + y_{a\omega} \cos \kappa \\ z &= z_{a\omega\kappa} = z_{a\omega} \end{aligned} \right\} \qquad (14\text{-}71)$$

The matrix of coefficients of Eq. 14-71 are given by

$$\mathbf{M}_\kappa = \begin{bmatrix} \cos \kappa & \sin \kappa & 0 \\ -\sin \kappa & \cos \kappa & 0 \\ 0 & 0 & 1 \end{bmatrix} \qquad (14\text{-}72)$$

and

$$\begin{bmatrix} x \\ y \\ z \end{bmatrix} = \mathbf{M}_\kappa \begin{bmatrix} x_{a\omega} \\ y_{a\omega} \\ z_{a\omega} \end{bmatrix} \qquad (14\text{-}73)$$

Combining the results of Eqs. 14-67, 14-70, and 14-73 gives

$$\begin{bmatrix} x \\ y \\ z \end{bmatrix} = \mathbf{M}_\kappa \mathbf{M}_\omega \mathbf{M}_a \begin{bmatrix} x_T \\ y_T \\ z_T \end{bmatrix} \qquad (14\text{-}74)$$

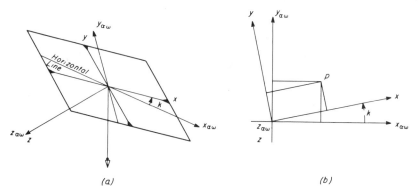

FIG. 14–47.   Rotation about camera axis (κ).

The product of the individual matrices gives the orientation matrix **M**, Thus,

$$\mathbf{M} = \mathbf{M}_\kappa \mathbf{M}_\omega \mathbf{M}_\alpha \tag{14–75}$$

and by Eqs. 14–66, 14–69, and 14–72;

$$\mathbf{M} = \begin{bmatrix} \cos \kappa & \sin \kappa & 0 \\ -\sin \kappa & \cos \kappa & 0 \\ 0 & 0 & 1 \end{bmatrix} \begin{bmatrix} 1 & 0 & 0 \\ 0 & \cos \omega & \sin \omega \\ 0 & -\sin \omega & \cos \omega \end{bmatrix} \begin{bmatrix} \cos \alpha_C & -\sin \alpha_C & 0 \\ 0 & 0 & 1 \\ -\sin \alpha_C & -\cos \alpha_C & 0 \end{bmatrix} \tag{14–76}$$

Multiplication of the coefficient matrices of Eq. 14–76 gives the orientation matrix **M** in final form as

$$\mathbf{M} = \begin{bmatrix} \cos \alpha_C \cos \kappa - \sin \alpha_C \sin \omega \sin \kappa & -\sin \alpha_C \cos \kappa - \cos \alpha_C \sin \omega \sin \kappa & \cos \omega \sin \kappa \\ -\cos \alpha_C \sin \kappa - \sin \alpha_C \sin \omega \cos \kappa & \sin \alpha_C \sin \kappa - \cos \alpha_C \sin \omega \cos \kappa & \cos \omega \cos \kappa \\ -\sin \alpha_C \cos \omega & -\cos \alpha_C \cos \omega & -\sin \omega \end{bmatrix} \tag{14–77}$$

The photographic coordinates of the point are then expressed as

$$\begin{bmatrix} x \\ y \\ z \end{bmatrix} = \mathbf{M} \begin{bmatrix} x_T \\ y_T \\ z_T \end{bmatrix} \tag{14–78}$$

The inverse of Eq. 14–78 gives the translated coordinates of a point as

$$\begin{bmatrix} x_T \\ y_T \\ z_T \end{bmatrix} = \mathbf{M}^T \begin{bmatrix} x \\ z \\ y \end{bmatrix} \tag{14–79}$$

A comparison between the angles t, s, α_C, and ω, κ, α_C shows that the azimuth angle is identical in each case. Angle t is the tilt of the optical axis from a vertical position, while ω is the rotation of the photograph about the x-axis, or more strictly speaking, about the horizon line of the photograph. Angle s is the clockwise angle measured in the plane of the photograph from the positive y-axis of the photograph to the nadir point, while κ is the angle measured in the plane of the photograph from a horizontal line on the photograph to the photographic x-axis.

Suppose for example that a terrestrial photograph has been taken with the camera pointed 60° in azimuth, with the optical axis elevated through an angle of $\theta_E = 30°$, and the camera has not been leveled transversely such that the positive end of the photographic x-axis is tilted upward 10°. In this case

$$t = 90° + 30° = 120° \qquad \omega = +30°$$
$$s = 10° \qquad \kappa = +10°$$
$$\alpha_C = 60° \qquad \alpha_C = 60°$$

The values of the elements of the matrices given by Eqs. 14–58 and 14–77 are numerically equal, element for element. Thus, analytical solutions to any problem in terrestrial photogrammetry can be performed in either system of exterior orientation.

The principles discussed in this section are applicable to any system in which a calibrated camera containing fiducial marks is used. Calibration implies a knowledge of the focal length and the lens distortion characteristics. The camera need not have been designed particularly for photogrammetric work. In fact, a hand-held still camera with a quality lens, and equipped with some form of fiducial marks can be used for analytical solutions to the problems discussed in this chapter, provided that the necessary controls have been established in the object space.

For the most satisfactory results, the photographs should be exposed on glass plates or else printed on glass plates from film negatives and measured in a comparator or stereocomparator. The effect of film shrinkage in the latter case must be accounted for. If plate measurements are made directly on the emulsion side of the negative, then the negative plate x-coordinates must all be reversed in sign. This results in the values of the coordinates as though they were measured on a positive photograph, which is the basis for the discussion in this section.

14–17. Establishing Controls in a Limited Object Space

In this section, it is assumed that the camera contains a set of fiducial marks to define the coordinate axes and the principal point, but that the camera cannot be oriented at a definite tilt, swing, and camera azimuth. This condition exists if an aerial camera is to be used for ground photography, or if two calibrated motion-picture or still cameras are employed. Because the cinetheodolite contains plate bubbles and graduated circles, its orientation is known at all times, and no auxiliary controls need be established.

Assume that a camera is to occupy a station whose position and elevation have been established by field surveys. In the object space to be photographed, a set of two or three leveling rods are fastened to supports and are brought vertical by means of a plumb line or the vertical cross hair of a surveying instrument. The rods should be set along a straight line normal to the direction of the camera axis. By using a level or a transit, the elevation of the camera lens is determined. This elevation is then set on the rods by means of rod targets. The line passing through the targets is presumably horizontal over the limited distance, and provides a horizon line on the photograph.

In Fig. 14–48, targets at *A*, *B*, and *C* have been set at the same eleva-

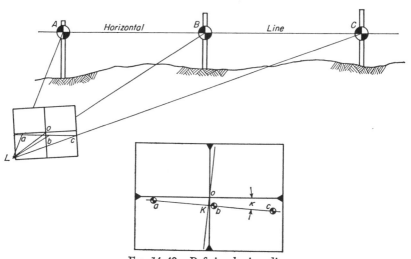

Fig. 14–48.   Defining horizon line.

tion as *L* and establish a horizontal plane *LABC*. The intersection of this plane with the plane of the photograph is the horizon line *abc*. In this example, the principal point *o* falls above the horizon line. So the camera axis is elevated. Also, since the line *abc* is not parallel with the photographic *x*-axis defined by fiducial marks, the swing is not 0°. The angle κ may be determined analytically by the relationship

$$\tan \kappa = \frac{y_c - y_a}{x_c - x_a} \tag{14–80}$$

If the horizon line makes a clockwise angle with the positive *x*-axis, and the camera axis is elevated (as in Fig. 14–48), the swing of the photograph is

$$s = \kappa \tag{14–81}$$

If the horizon line makes a clockwise angle with the positive x-axis, and the camera axis is depressed, the swing of the photograph is

$$s = 180° + \kappa \tag{14–82}$$

The distance oK can be determined analytically by expressing the equation of the line ac in the normal form and solving for the distance from the line to the origin at o. The result is

$$oK = \frac{[(y_c - y_a)/(x_c - x_a)]\, x_a - y_a}{\sqrt{[(y_c - y_a)/(x_c - x_a)]^2 + 1}} \tag{14–83}$$

The elevation angle, or depression angle, is then obtained by the relationship

$$\tan \theta = \frac{oK}{f} \tag{14–84}$$

The tilt can then be computed by either Eq. 14–50 or Eq. 14–51.

Before the camera azimuth can be determined, the azimuth of line LA, LB, or LC of Fig. 14–48 must be known. Let it be supposed that the azimuth of the line LA has been determined by a field survey. The angle formed at L between a and K on the photograph is the horizontal angle between the line LA and the principal plane of the photograph, and is determined by the relationship

$$\tan \beta_A = \frac{aK}{f} \tag{14–85}$$

In order to determine the length of aK analytically, the photographic coordinates of K must be determined. These are

$$x_K = oK \sin \kappa \tag{14–86}$$

$$y_K = oK \cos \kappa \tag{14–87}$$

The algebraic signs of x_K and y_K are determined by inspection. The length of aK is then determined by the distance formula. Thus,

$$aK = \sqrt{(x_K - x_a)^2 + (y_K - y_a)^2}$$

The camera azimuth is computed by Eq. 14–18. If x_a is algebraically less than x_K, then β_A is negative; if x_a is greater than x_K, then β_A is positive. Due regard must be given to the algebraic sign of β_A when Eq. 14–18 is applied.

When the auxiliary controls discussed in this section have been established for a terrestrial photograph, the photographic measurements can take any one of three forms. If horizontal and vertical angles are to be computed by using Eq. 14–6, Eq. 14–8, Eq. 14–16, or Eq. 14–17, the x- and y-coordinates may be measured with respect to the horizon line defined by the line of targets as the x-axis, and with respect to the principal line (normal to the horizon line and passing through the principal point) as the y-axis. For these measurements the horizon line and the principal line must be scribed on the photograph.

If Eq. 14–6, Eq. 14–8, Eq. 14–16, or Eq. 14–17 is to be applied, but the x- and y-coordinates are to be measured with respect to the fiducial marks, the axes must be rotated and translated by the following formulas:

$$x' = x \cos \kappa - y \sin \kappa \qquad (14\text{–}88)$$

$$y' = x \sin \kappa + y \cos \kappa + f \tan \theta_E \qquad (14\text{–}89)$$

$$y' = x \sin \kappa + y \cos \kappa - f \tan \theta_D \qquad (14\text{–}89a)$$

in which x' and y' are the photographic coordinates of the point with respect to the horizon line and the principal point; x and y are the photographic coordinates with respect to the fiducial marks; κ is the angle which the horizon line makes with the positive x-axis, considered positive if measured in a clockwise direction; f is the focal length; and θ_E or θ_D is the elevation angle or depression angle of the camera axis, as the case may be.

In Fig. 14–49(a), κ is seen to be positive and the camera axis is

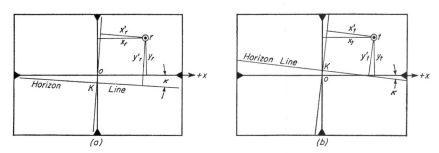

FIG. 14–49. Photographic coordinates with respect to fiducial marks, and with respect to horizon line and principal line.

elevated. The coordinates x_r, y_r, x'_r, and y'_r of point r are shown. In Fig. 14–49(b), κ is positive and the camera axis is depressed. The coordinates x_t, y_t, x'_t, and y'_t of point t are shown.

A graphical solution of horizontal and vertical angles must make use of the horizon line and the principal line, both of which are defined on the photograph by construction.

When the principles of Sec. 14–16 are applied, the x- and y-coordinates of all points are measured with respect to the axes defined by the fiducial marks. The orientation matrix for each photograph is computed from the values of the tilt, swing, and camera azimuth determined as outlined in this section.

14-18. Resection to Establish Camera Position and Orientation

If three or more control points, whose object space X-, Y-, and Z-coordinates are known, have been established, the orientation of the photograph and the position of the camera station can be computed by resection as outlined in Sec. 9-6. If two photographs of the object space have been taken, each may be resected to establish two orientation matrices and two-exposure positions. With these data known, a complete three-dimensional survey of the object area covered by the two photographs can be conducted from measured plate coordinates, and by application of the principle of intersection discussed in Sec. 14-16.

If the length of the line joining the two camera stations is accurately known, an additional condition can be introduced into the solution of the resections. Letting the length of the line be B, then

$$B = [(X_{L'} - X_L)^2 + (Y_{L'} - Y_L)^2 + (Z_{L'} - Z_L)^2]^{\frac{1}{2}}$$

and

$$dB = \frac{\partial B}{\partial X_L} \, dX_L + \frac{\partial B}{\partial X_{L'}} \, dX_{L'} + \frac{\partial B}{\partial Y_L} \, dY_L + \frac{\partial B}{\partial Y_{L'}} \, dY_{L'} + \frac{\partial B}{\partial Z_L} \, dZ_L + \frac{\partial B}{\partial Z_{L'}} \, dZ_{L'}$$

If B is to be held fixed, then dB must be set equal to zero. Thus, as the iterations are performed, dB is always held equal to zero.

14-19. Finite Focusing Using Fixed-Focus Camera

Much close-up photogrammetry requires that the fixed principal distance of the camera or cameras be modified in order to obtain a sharp image. Consider for example the use of a camera, in which the lens is set for infinity focus, for photographing an object, say 6 ft away. Clearly, the camera lens will not provide sharp focus at this near object distance. There are three ways in which the object can be brought to focus. First, the negative plane can be moved back and held at the principal distance required for correct focus by means of spacer-shims. Or the lens mount can be moved forward to obtain the required principal distance. The proper principal distance is given by

$$\frac{1}{p} + \frac{1}{q} = \frac{1}{f} \tag{14-90}$$

in which p is the principal distance, q is the object distance, and f is the camera focal length, all expressed in the same units. The thickness of the shims is then $p - f$. These two methods require physical modification of the camera and disturb its interior orientation. Although they have been successfully employed, they are not recommended without the aid of a competent machinist.

The third method employs an auxiliary lens fitted to the front of the camera lens just as a filter is attached to the lens. In Fig. 14–50(a), the object is at distance q_L which is infinity, and the image is formed at a distance p_L from the rear nodal point of the lens. This is equal to the focal length of the lens, f_L, and is focussed sharply in the fixed focal plane.

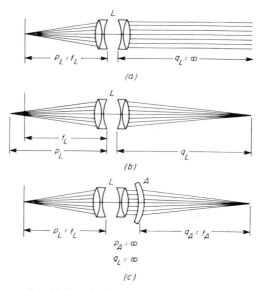

Fig. 14–50. Auxiliary lens used for bringing object at finite distance to focus in focal plane of camera.

In Fig. 14–50(b), an object lies at a finite distance q_L in front of the lens, and is brought to focus behind the focal plane at a distance p_L. The image is thus out of focus.

In Fig. 14–50(c), an auxiliary lens A of focal length f_A equal to the object distance q_A has been placed in front of lens L. Since the object lies in the focal plane of the auxiliary lens, its image will be formed at infinity; thus $p_A = \infty$. Now as far as the camera lens is concerned, its object distance q_L is at infinity, and the lens will bring the parallel rays to focus in the camera focal plane. Thus $p_L = f_L$.

The power of the auxiliary lens is expressed in diopters, which is the reciprocal of the focal length in meters. With a given object distance expressed in meters, an auxiliary lens with a power equal to the reciprocal of the object distance will bring the object to focus in the focal plane. With an object distance of 6 ft, or 1.83 meters, a lens of 0.55 diopter will bring the object to focus in the camera focal plane, provided that the camera lens is fixed at infinity focus.

Figure 14–51 shows a stereo pair of photographs taken with the photo-

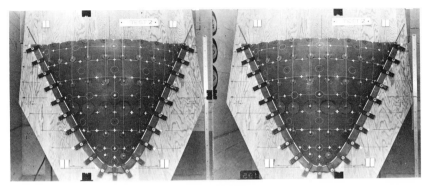

Fig. 14–51. Stereopair of rubber membrane model of concrete arch dam.

theodolite shown in Fig. 14–1. A 0.50 diopter lens was used. The camera base was 10 in., with both photographs taken normal to the base. The object is a rubber membrane model of a concrete arch dam photographed to determine the surface configuration for design purposes. The camera arrangement is shown in Fig. 14–52.

In close-up photogrammetry such as this example, alignment of the base is extremely critical. In Fig. 14–52, two tripods are set up and each tribrach centered over the reference line by means of an optical plummet. A reference mark is located approximately 40 ft away. The photo-theodolite is placed in each tribrach in turn to make the exposures. The optical axis in each instance is made normal to the base line by the principles discussed in Sec. 14–2, with a backsight made on the reference mark in each case.

The two photographs shown in Fig. 14–51 were printed on stable base paper and measured by means of a parallax bar under a mirror stereoscope. The position and elevation of each cross mark was computed by Eqs. 14–27, 14–28, and 14–29. The results are shown in the form of contour lines in Fig. 14–53.

The advantage of the auxiliary lens is its simplicity of use and the fact that it does not destroy the original interior orientation of the camera. Objects at varying distances can be brought to focus simply by changing auxiliary lenses. The chief disadvantage in their use is the introduction of serious lens distortions. These distortions can be evaluated by camera calibration, however, and can be allowed for in the photogrammetric reduction process.

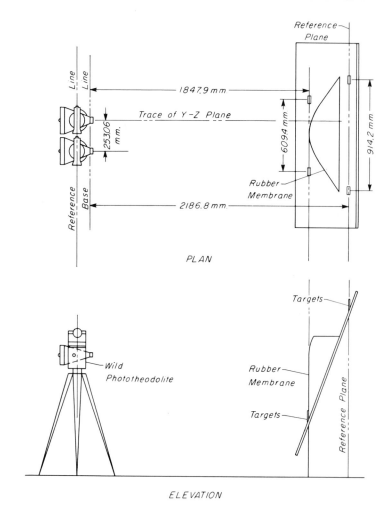

Fɪɢ. 14–52. Camera arrangement for photographing rubber membrane model.

A reasonably satisfactory method for calibrating a camera with an auxiliary lens is by photographing a large precisely-ruled grid from two different distances, with the difference in the distance being accurately measured. In Fig. 14–54, the camera is set up and leveled, and brought normal to a grid located in the easel plane of a large reproduction copy camera. By careful attention to orientation, the focal plane can be made parallel to the plane of the grid. An exposure is now made, with the appropriate auxiliary lens fitted to the camera lens. The easel is then moved away from the camera through a distance at least twice the length of the approximate principal distance. The displacement ΔY of the easel

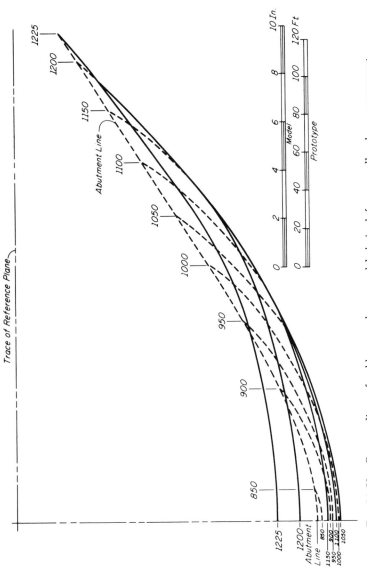

Fig. 14-53. Contour lines of rubber membrane model derived from parallax bar measurements.

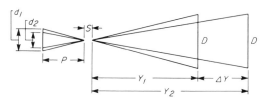

Fig. 14–54. Determination of principal distance of camera lens-auxiliary lens combination.

is measured with respect to the scales on the reproduction camera. A second exposure is now made.

The distances d_1 and d_2 of Fig. 14–54 are the measurements made in a comparator between two grid intersections lying symmetrically, or nearly so, about the principal point. Distance d_1 is measured on the first exposure, and d_2 on the second exposure. These two distances actually represent the average of several distances measured around the principal point of the photograph. The distance D is the known grid spacing; p is the principal distance of the camera lens-auxiliary lens combination; s is the spacing of the nodal points of this combination; and Y_1 and Y_2 are the distances from the front nodal point to the two positions of the grid. The two latter distances cannot be measured precisely since the position of the front nodal point is not known.

By similar triangles:

$$\frac{d_1}{p} = \frac{D}{Y_1} \quad \text{and} \quad \frac{d_2}{p} = \frac{D}{Y_2}$$

from whence

$$Y_1 = \frac{pD}{d_1} \quad \text{and} \quad Y_2 = \frac{pD}{d_2}$$

then

$$\Delta Y = Y_2 - Y_1 = \frac{pD}{d_2} - \frac{pD}{d_1} = \frac{pD(d_1 - d_2)}{d_1 d_2}$$

Finally

$$p = \frac{\Delta Y d_1 d_2}{D(d_1 - d_2)}$$

Using the computed value of p, the theoretically correct position of all the grid intersection images can be determined. These are compared with their actual positions as measured on the plate, from whence the lens distortion at each point can be determined. If the distances Y_1 and Y_2

are selected as the outer limits of critical focus, determined by experimentation, then multiple exposures can be made through the range of the depth of field. This will permit the computation of different values of p and different values of lens distortion for a range of Y-values.

14–20. Use of Plotting Instruments

The plotting instruments discussed in Chapter 12 can be used under certain conditions to measure the space positions of points appearing in the overlap area of a pair of terrestrial photographs. In general, the plotters are not used to compile topographic maps. They are used rather to make measurements of an object which would otherwise be impossible or impractical.

Because instruments of the double-projection type are specifically designed for plotting from aerial photographs, the measurement in the Z-direction of the instrument is limited to a fractional part of the optimum projection distance. In other words, the amount of elevation difference which can be measured in the instrument is limited to a fractional part of the flying height.

The Z-direction in aerial photogrammetry corresponds to the Y-direction in terrestrial photogrammetry. Let it be assumed that a pair of Multiplex diapositives have been properly prepared from the pair of terrestrial photographs shown in Fig. 14–55. When the projectors have

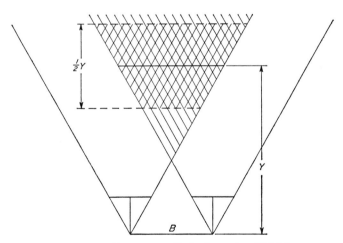

Fig. 14–55. Object space limitation using Multiplex.

been oriented, the distance between the projector lenses corresponds to the camera base B, and the optimum projection distance (360 mm) corresponds to the distance Y of Fig. 14–55. The limiting depth which can be measured in the Y-direction is $Y/2$. The corresponding distance in the

Multiplex model is 180 mm. Therefore, at a given model scale, the Multiplex can be used to plot or measure from terrestrial photographs only in the double crosshatched area shown in Fig. 14–55.

If the object depth must be exceeded, the model scale must be decreased or increased. In Fig. 14–56 (a), the projector base b_1 forms a model with an optimum projection distance of 360 mm. This represents the distance Y_1, from the camera base into the object area. Let it be supposed that the camera base is 1,000 ft and Y_1 is to be 1,800 ft. The model scale is thus approximately 1:1,520 (see Sec. 12–5), and the physical distance b_1 is 1,000/1,520 = 0.66 ft or about 200 mm. The range of depth, normal to the camera base, in which measurements can be made at this scale is from 1,350 ft to 2,250 ft. The corresponding range in the model is from 270 mm to 450 mm.

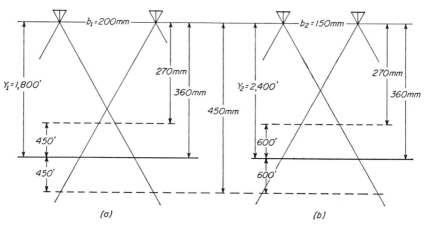

Fig. 14–56. Increasing object depth by decreasing Multiplex base.

In Fig. 14–56 (b), the same two photographs are used, but the distance Y_2 is to be 2,400 ft and the model scale is about 1:2,040. The distance b_2 is 1,000/2,040 = 0.49 ft, or about 150 mm. The depth ranges from 1,800 ft to 3,000 ft at this scale, and the corresponding range in the model is from 270 mm to 450 mm. Because of the physical size of the Multiplex projectors, they cannot be brought very close. The minimum distance between projector lenses is about 150 mm. So no measurements are possible beyond a certain outer depth in the object area.

The Balplex and Kelsh plotters impose a greater restriction on the measurable depth in the Y-direction. For a particular plotter, the limiting range in depth can be determined by comparing the optimum projection distance and the usable depth of focus of the plotter. The physical and optical limitations of the plotters must be thoroughly investigated before the photography is planned. These limitations fix the length of the camera base to be laid out.

If the object to be measured is relatively shallow in the Y-direction, the precision with which the depth can be measured can be increased by taking the photographs convergent inward from normals to the base. The Balplex plotter is capable of accepting convergent photography because of the canting arrangement of the projector lens. Thus, it is suitable for this type of photography. Most terrestrial cameras have a fairly narrow angular coverage compared with aerial cameras. Convergent photography has the effect of increasing the angular coverage, giving a stronger parallactic angle. Architectural detail, for example, can be measured very successfully in a Balplex plotter from convergent terrestrial photography.

The projection distance in the Autograph A8 ranges from 175 mm to 350 mm. The projection base is limited by the permissible amount of X-movement of the photo carriers away from and toward one another. The range of the projection distance and that of the base are the controlling factors in planning the photography and selecting the instrument scale. By means of the gear box, various instrument scales can be reduced to a common plotting or coordinatograph scale.

The Multiplex, Kelsh, Balplex, and Autograph A8 plotters, and other instruments designed specifically for aerial photographs, cannot be used to plot continuous contour lines from terrestrial photographs. If the measuring mark is fixed in one vertical position, and a line is traced by keeping the mark in apparent contact with the terrain, the line plotted by the tracing pencil is a vertical profile of the terrain. A change in the height of the measuring mark corresponds to a change in the Y-direction in the terrestrial model. Thus, the contour lines plotted from aerial photographs correspond to vertical sections plotted from terrestrial photographs.

The Autograph A7 and the Stereoplanigraph C8 are universal plotting instruments designed for both aerial and terrestrial photographs. The C8 and a modified version of the A7 will accept convergent photography. (See Fig. 13–36.) The projection distance in the A7 ranges from 140 mm to 490 mm. By means of the Zeiss parallelogram the base can be set from 0 mm to 280 mm. The projection distance in the C8 ranges from 170 mm to 605 mm. The base can be set from 0 mm to 310 mm. In both of these instruments, the Y- and Z-spindles may be interchanged to permit continuous tracing of contour lines on the coordinatograph.

One of the major difficulties encountered in plotting or measuring from terrestrial photographs is the absence of an image above the horizon line. When the plotter does not contain rotational scales, relative orientation must be performed by clearing y-parallax from the stereoscopic model. Images must then be located in the four corners of the model.

The upper corners of a terrestrial photograph do not contain images, unless the photography has been taken in mountainous terrain or across a canyon.

Artificial relative orientation may be performed by preparing identical grid diapositives, and then clearing the parallax from the grid intersections. Since this process makes the diapositives coplanar, then a pair of diapositives prepared from a pair of coplanar terrestrial photographs will contain the proper angular relationship when placed in the projectors. All that remains is to eliminate the y-parallax, which is caused by improper swing relationship. The desired result is obtained by referring to images in the vicinity of the principal points.

Another difficulty in using terrestrial photographs in a plotter is the unsatisfactory placement of control used to level the model. This difficulty is not encountered, however, in an instrument which contains rotational settings, because the known terrestrial camera orientations can be set off deliberately on the projectors. In fact, when an instrument of this type is used, relative and absolute orientation can be accomplished entirely by means of the settings on the instrument.

When the object space to be measured from terrestrial photographs is of limited extent, as in a laboratory, artificial control can be arranged

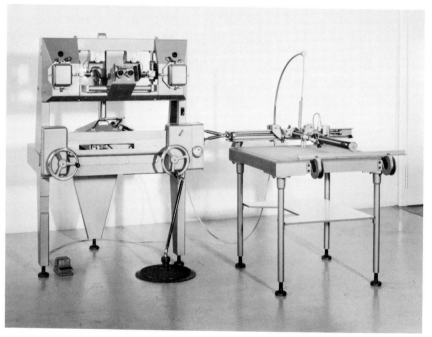

Fig. 14–57. Wild Autograph A40. (Courtesy of Wild-Heerbrugg Instruments, Inc.)

in the object space. Ideally, this control consists of six points which will fall at the four corners of the model and at the two principal points. These points must, of course, be plainly visible on the photography. They serve not only to aid in clearing y-parallax, but also to perform absolute orientation. The six points should lie in, or nearly in, a vertical plane at the middle point of the object space to be measured. The space positions of the six points are determined with respect to the camera base.

Stereoscopic plotting instruments designed specifically for plotting from normal stereopairs eliminate all but a slight amount of relative and absolute orientation. The Wild C120 stereometric camera and the Zeiss SMK stereometric camera produce photographs which are coplanar. This

Fig. 14–58. Zeiss Terragraph. (Courtesy of Carl Zeiss, Oberkochen.)

constitutes the normal case of stereophotography. The normal case is achieved by orienting a terrestrial camera normal to each end of the base, and leveling the optical axis at each end so that the plate lies in a vertical plane. Under these circumstances, the only motions necessary for relative and absolute orientation are a BY-motion (actually BZ in the survey system) to account for difference in camera heights, and a BX-motion for setting off the appropriate base.

The Wild Autograph A40 shown in Fig. 14–57, and the Zeiss Terragraph shown in Fig. 14–58 are both designed to plot from photographs taken in the normal case. The plate holders have no rotational motions, although equal elevation or depression angles at the two ends of the base can be accommodated. The measuring mark is moved in the instrument model space by means of hand wheels and the foot disc. The Y- and Z-spindles can be interchanged to plot either contour lines or vertical sections. These two instruments are used most efficiently for plotting from photographs taken with the stereometric cameras.

14–21. Preparation of Diapositives from Terrestrial Photographs

The preparation of Multiplex diapositives from aerial photographs taken with a camera having a nominal 6-in. focal length was discussed in Sec. 12–3. By means of the reduction printer, the 6-in. photography is made compatible with the 30-mm principal distance of the Multiplex. If Multiplex diapositives are to be prepared from photography taken with a camera having any other focal length, the enlargement ratio must be $30/f$, where f is expressed in millimeters. For example, suppose that Multiplex diapositives are to be prepared from motion-picture photography taken with a lens having a 25-mm focal length. The negatives must be enlarged in the ratio $30/25$. Since no photogrammetric reduction printer presently available will produce this enlargement, a high-quality photographic enlarger must be used. The resulting diapositive will not be so satisfactory as one prepared in a reduction printer from an aerial negative. However, if the diapositive is made carefully, it can be used to obtain measurements that are fairly accurate.

The negative plane, the lens plane, and the easel plane of the enlarger must lie parallel to one another. This parallelism can be tested by photographing a grid and making a contact-print slide from the resulting negative. The negative is placed in the negative carrier, and the contact-print slide is placed on the easel. The enlarger is set for a 1-to-1 enlargement, and the image projected from the negative is superimposed on the slide. If the lines coincide throughout the area, then the negative plane, lens plane, and easel plane are parallel. If the lines do not coincide, tilting and tipping the easel will remedy all but a slight amount of the mismatch. Although this method of making the lines coincide is not theoretically correct, diapositives produced with the easel shimmed in position will be fairly satisfactory.

The grid is used also to obtain the proper enlargement factor. The distance between two widely-spaced grid lines is carefully measured. This distance is multiplied by the enlargement factor to give a scale length. The enlarger is then set so that the distance between the grid lines as projected onto a plate resting on the easel is equal to the scale length. The plate must have the same thickness as the diapositive glass. Finally, the terrestrial negative is placed in the negative carrier, diapositive glass is placed on the easel, and an exposure is made.

Figure 14–59 shows a reduction printer constructed for preparing

FIG. 14–59. Universal reduction printer for preparation of diapositives.

Multiplex, Balplex, and Autograph diapositives from a wide range of camera focal lengths. The maximum distance between object plane (the negative) and image plane (the diapositive) is about 2,500 mm. It contains a high-resolution process lens of approximately 415 mm focal length. Because of this relatively long focal length, the angular coverage required for small-format negatives is extremely narrow. The conjugate distances required for proper enlargement or reduction are set off by gage rods, and refined by the longitudinal micrometer movement of the lens mount and the negative carrier. No provisions are made for removing lens distortions by means of correction plates. Thus, the distortion contained in the negative is reproduced in the diapositive.

The enlargement factor for the Balplex plotter is $55/f$, where f is in millimeters. If diapositives are to be prepared for the Kelsh plotter, the ratio should be f_c/f, where f_c is the middle focal-length setting on the projector lens.

The Autograph A8 accommodates a continuous range of focal lengths from 4 in. to 8.25 in. Thus, if the focal length of the terrestrial camera lies in this range, the diapositives can be made by contact-printing the negative. If the camera focal length is outside this range, the negative must be enlarged or reduced so that the principal distance of the enlarged or reduced diapositive is between 4 and 8.25 in. The appropriate principal distance is then set off in the instrument. The Autograph A7 accommodates focal lengths ranging from 4 to 8.50 in.

The Stereoplanigraph C8 accommodates focal lengths of from 3.75 in. to 12 in. either by interchangeability of the lenses of the plotting cameras or by a combination of such interchangeability and the use of a reduction printer. The diapositive may therefore be prepared either by contact printing alone or with the aid of the reduction printer.

The three requirements for a properly prepared diapositive are: 1) The fiducial marks must show on the diapositive. 2) The size of the diapositive must be such that it will fit in the carrier of the instrument. 3) The proper enlargement or reduction must be made. If these three requirements have been fulfilled, interior orientation of the diapositives may be accomplished.

14–22. Measurement in the Plotter

After a pair of diapositives have been oriented in the carriers with respect to the fiducial marks or the principal point (determined by the fiducial marks), they must be oriented first relative to one another and then relative to ground control. When an instrument of the double-projection type is used, the relative orientation is effected by removing y-parallax in accordance with the principles discussed in Sec. 12–4. If the camera orientations are precisely known, and if the projectors such as the Autographs and the Stereoplanigraph contain rotational and base settings, the complete camera orientation can be re-created by setting off the elevation or depression angles as the ω-rotations; the horizontal angles between the camera axes and the photo base normals as the ϕ-rotations; and the swing angles as the κ-rotations. For the so-called normal case, all rotation settings would be zero.

The difference in camera heights, reduced to plotter or machine scale, is set off as a BY motion of one or the other projector or base element so that $BY = H_L - H_{L'}$, where these heights are expressed to the plotter scale. The camera base, to the plotter scale, is set off as a BX motion. The plotter scale must be selected so as not to exceed the physical measuring depth of the instrument as discussed in Sec. 14–20. If the instrument does not contain BX scales, the plotter base may be established by carefully measuring the distance between the projector centers. When distances between control points in the model are scaled, this distance may have to be slightly modified.

Setting off the known elements directly in the plotter should theoretically produce a perfect stereoscopic model at the desired scale. Because of random errors, however, these settings must be slightly modified by the absolute-orientation process. This modification establishes a compromise between known camera-orientation elements and fixed ground control.

The Autograph A40, the Zeiss Terragraph, and other plotters specifically designed to plot from normal photography are not susceptible to errors of rotation because of their design. Errors in orientation produced by photographs exposed in a well-aligned stereometric camera and measured in these specialized plotters are very minimal.

When measurements to a point are made in a universal plotter, the Y- and Z-coordinates are switched. The measurements are then made by placing the measuring mark in apparent contact with the point in the stereoscopic model. The instrument X-, Y-, and Z-coordinates then give the space position of the point, to the plotter scale.

When use is made of a plotter designed specifically for aerial photography, the measuring mark is brought in apparent contact with the desired point. The plotted tracing-table (or coordinatograph) position of the point gives its location in the X-Z plane. The tracing-table reading (or the elevation-counter reading) gives the location of the point in the Y-direction. Therefore, the X- and Z-coordinates must be scaled from the map sheet. These can, of course, be read directly from scales on the coordinatograph.

Bibliography

AMERICAN SOCIETY OF PHOTOGRAMMETRY. *Manual of Photogrammetry* (Menasha, Wisc.: George Banta Co., 1966), Chapter 19.

AVERA, H. Q. "The Miniature Camera Calibrator—Its Design, Development and Use," *Photogrammetric Engineering,* Vol. XXIII (1957), p. 601.

BAZHAW, W. O. "Geophotometric Mapping," *Photogrammetric Engineering,* Vol. XV (1949), p. 114.

BLESH, T. E. "Postural Analysis of Yale University Freshmen," *Photogrammetric Engineering,* Vol. XXII (1956), p. 357.

BORCHERS, P. E. "Architectural Photogrammetry at Ohio State University—First Phase," *Photogrammetric Engineering,* Vol. XXIII (1957), p. 937.

———. "Choice of Station and Control for Efficient Orientation and Plotting in Architectural Photogrammetry," *Photogrammetric Engineering,* Vol. XXVI (1960), p. 713.

———. "The Photogrammetric Study of Structural Movements in Architecture," *Photogrammetric Engineering,* Vol. XXX (1964), p. 809.

BORRELL, S. M. "Terrestrial Photography for Establishing Supplemental Control," *Photogrammetric Engineering,* Vol. XXIII (1957), p. 58.

BURKHARDT, R. "Short Range Photogrammetry with Miniature Camera and Multiplex," *Photogrammetric Engineering,* Vol. XIX (1953), p. 723.

COLCORD, J. E. "The TAF Phototheodolite and Its Use in Glacier Surveys," *Photogrammetric Engineering,* Vol. XXIII (1957), p. 552.

ELMER, C. H. "Photography in the Rocket-Test Program," *Photogrammetric Engineering,* Vol. XVIII (1952), p. 686.

ENGLEMANN, W. F. "Photogrammetry Applied to Making Sculptured Portraits," *Photogrammetric Engineering,* Vol. XXII (1956), p. 366.

GARFIELD, J. F. "The Photogrammetry of the Tracks of Elementary Particles in Bubble Chambers," *Photogrammetric Engineering,* Vol. XXX (1964), p. 824.

GRUNER, HEINZ. "New Aspects of Mono-Photogrammetry," *Photogrammetric Engineering,* Vol. XXI (1955), p. 39.

HALLERT, BERTIL. "Deformation Measurements by Photogrammetric Methods," *Photogrammetric Engineering,* Vol. XX (1954), p. 836.

——. "Determination of the Accuracy of Terrestrial Stereophotogrammetric Procedures," *Photogrammetric Engineering,* Vol. XXI (1955), p. 84.

——. "Determination of the Interior Orientation of Cameras for Non-Topographic Photogrammetry, Microscopes, X-Ray Instruments and Television Images," *Photogrammetric Engineering,* Vol. XXVI (1960), p. 748.

——. *Photogrammetry* (New York: McGraw-Hill Co., 1960), Chapter 2.

HALSMAN, J. "Stereoscopic Medical Photography," *Photogrammetric Engineering,* Vol. XXII (1956), p. 374.

HELMCKE, J. G., KLEINN, W., and BURKHARDT, R. "Quantitative Electron Microscopy," *Photogrammetric Engineering,* Vol. XXXI (1965), p. 796.

HERTZBERG, H. T. E. "Stereophotogrammetry as an Anthropometric Tool," *Photogrammetric Engineering,* Vol. XXIII (1957), p. 942.

HEYDEN, F. J. "Photogrammetry in Astronomy," *Photogrammetric Engineering,* Vol. XVI (1950), p. 66.

JURY, H. L. "An Application of Terrestrial Photogrammetry to Glaciology in Greenland," *Photogrammetric Engineering,* Vol. XXIII (1957), p. 543.

KONECNY, G. "Glacial Surveys in Western Canada," *Photogrammetric Engineering,* Vol. XXX (1964), p. 64.

KONECNY, G. "Structural Engineering Application of the Stereometric Camera," *Photogrammetric Engineering,* Vol. XXXI (1965), p. 96.

KOWALCZYK, Z. "Certain Applications of Photogrammetry in Underground Mining," *Canadian Surveyor,* Vol. XIX (1965), p. 428.

LEYDOLPH, W. K. "Stereophotogrammetry in Animal Husbandry," *Photogrammetric Engineering,* Vol. XX (1954), p. 804.

MANN, R. W. "Stereophotogrammetry Applied to Hydraulic Analogue Studies of Unsteady Gas Flow," *Photogrammetric Engineering,* Vol. XXVIII (1962), p. 615.

McNEIL, G. T. "Macrophotogrammetry with the Donaldson Stereo-Camera," *Photogrammetric Engineering,* Vol. XXII (1956), p. 379.

——. "Metrical Photography, *ibid.,* Vol. XXIII (1957), p. 667.

——. "Nav Scan: A Dual Purpose Panoramic Camera," *Photogrammetric Engineering,* Vol. XXVII (1961), p. 407.

——. "X-Ray Stereo Photogrammetry," *Photogrammetric Engineering,* Vol. XXXII (1966), p. 993.

MERRITT, E. L. "Principles of Design and the Applications of the MM 101 Surveying Camera," *Photogrammetric Engineering,* Vol. XIX (1953), p. 779.

————. "Selections of Camera Stations in Terrestrial Photogrammetry," *ibid.*, Vol. XIV (1948), p. 421.

————. "System-Testing Cinetheodolites by Stars," *ibid.*, Vol. XXII (1956), p. 286.

————, and LUNDAHL, A. C. "A Reconsideration of Terrestrial Photogrammetry," *Photogrammetric Engineering*, Vol. XIII (1947), p. 295.

"Non-Topographic Photogrammetry" (A Symposium), *Photogrammetric Engineering*, Vol. XIX (1953), p. 651.

ORVILLE, H. D. "Cumulus Cloud Photogrammetry," *Photogrammetric Engineering*, Vol. XXVII (1961), p. 787.

PIERSON, W. R. "Photogrammetric Determination of Surface Area," *Photogrammetric Engineering*, Vol. XXVII (1961), p. 99.

ROCK, DORIS L. "Field Determination of the Center Cross," *Photogrammetric Engineering*, Vol. XVII (1951), p. 596.

ROSENFIELD, G. H. "Present and Future Capability of Optical Systems with Emphasis on the Ballistic Camera Operation," *Photogrammetric Engineering*, Vol. XXVII (1961), p. 51.

SARALEGUI, A. M. "What is Photosculpture?," *Photogrammetric Engineering*, Vol. XX (1954), p. 29.

SCHWIDEFSKY, K. *An Outline of Photogrammetry* (New York: Pitman Publishing Corp.), 1959, Chapter 3.

SCOTT, D. B. "Microscopic Topography by Means of Surface Replicas," *Photogrammetric Engineering*, Vol. XXII (1956), p. 326.

SOLARI, F., and WILD, D. P. "Plane Table Photogrammetry with a Leica Camera in the Punjab Himalaya," *Photogrammetric Record*, Vol. IV (1964), p. 321.

STRASSER, G. J. "Photogrammetric Engineering with a Wild Phototheodolite," *Photogrammetric Engineering*, Vol. XIX (1953), p. 834.

THOMPSON, E. H. "Photogrammetry In the Restoration of Castle Howard," *Photogrammetric Record*, Vol. IV (1962), p. 95.

THOMPSON, J. J. "Application of Terrestrial Photogrammetry to Multiplex Heighting in Canada," *Photogrammetric Engineering*, Vol. XIV (1948), p. 29.

THOMPSON, M. M. "Photogrammetric Mapping of Sand Beds in a Hydraulic Test Flume," *Photogrammetric Engineering*, Vol. XXIV (1958), p. 468.

VON GRUBER, O. *Photogrammetry* (Boston: American Photographic Publishing Co., 1942), Chapter 7.

WADDELL, J. H. "Photogrammetry and the Photography of Motion," *Photogrammetric Engineering*, Vol. XXII (1956), p. 351.

WHITTLESEY, J. H. "Bipod Camera Support," *Photogrammetric Engineering*, Vol. XXXII (1966), p. 1005.

ZELLER, M. *Textbook of Photogrammetry* (London: H. K. Lewis and Co., Ltd., 1952), Chapter 2.

Problems

14–1. The azimuth of a backsight line is 129° 15′ 22″. The phototheodolite shown in Fig. 14–1 is used to take a round of photographs about the field station. Each time the camera is pointed for a new exposure, the theodolite telescope is used to sight the backsight station, and the horizontal circle is read. The circle readings are 22° 16′ 23″, 358° 38′ 50″, 320° 42′ 06″, 204° 00′ 08″, and 91° 19′ 51″. Determine the azimuth of the camera for each of these five exposures.

14–2. If the camera in Prob. 14–1 is to be pointed due north, what must be the horizontal-circle reading for the backsight?

14–3. Compute the position of the horizon line of a terrestrial photograph taken with the phototheodolite of Fig. 14–1 for each of the five positions of the tilt-setting bar, if the camera focal length is 165.60 mm.

14–4. When a camera similar to that shown in Fig. 14–7 is calibrated, the following results are obtained: $f=165.06$ mm; $S=150.2$; $D=326.8$; $H=326.6$; $S_u=260.0$; $S_L=39.9$. Determine the position, on the photograph, of the horizon line for each of the following scale readings: 218.6; 175.0; 150.2; 69.5; 51.7.

14–5. Determine the horizontal angles formed between lines directed to three points A, B, and C, and the principal plane of a photograph whose camera axis is horizontal at the time of exposure. The focal length is 135.00 mm. The plate coordinates, with respect to the horizon line as the x-axis, are $x_a=+8.22$ mm and $y_a=-1.87$ mm; $x_b=+74.21$ mm and $y_b=-26.58$; $x_c=-15.61$ mm and $y_c=-3.16$ mm.

14–6. Using the data of Prob. 14–5, but assuming that the camera axis is elevated by an angle of $6°\ 18'$, compute the horizontal angles formed between the three lines and the principal plane of the photograph.

14–7. Compute the vertical angles to the three points of Prob. 14–5.

14–8. Compute the vertical angles to the three points of Prob. 14–6.

14–9. Using the data of Prob 14–5, but assuming that the camera axis is depressed by an angle of $18°\ 54'$, compute the vertical angles to the three points.

14–10. Plot the coordinates of the points in Prob. 14–5 with respect to a set of axes drawn on a sheet of drafting paper, and solve Probs. 14–6 and 14–8 graphically.

14–11. From a plot of the positions of the points of Prob. 14–5, solve Prob. 14–9 graphically.

14–12. The azimuth of the line from the exposure station to point A of Prob. 14–5 is $159°\ 35'$. Compute the camera azimuth and the azimuths of the lines from the exposure station to points B and C.

14–13. The ground-survey coordinates of L_1 and L_2 of Fig. 14–29 are given in Example 14–6. From measurements on a pair of terrestrial photographs, the azimuths from L_1 and L_2 to a point Q are found to be $\alpha_{L_1Q}=48°\ 20'$ and $\alpha_{L_2Q}=265°\ 16'$. Compute the ground-survey coordinates of point Q.

14–14. The vertical angle from L_1 to Q of Prob. 14–13 is $3°\ 36'$. The elevation of Q is 775.4 ft. Determine the elevation of L_1.

14–15. If the elevation of L_2 of Fig. 14–29 is 591.8 ft, and the vertical angle to point P of Example 14–5 is $-1°\ 21'$, what is the elevation of P?

14–16. Two camera stations at the ends of a 200.00 ft base are at the same elevation. Exposures are made with each camera axis normal to the base and horizontal at the time of exposure. The camera focal length is 170.00 mm. The elevation of both camera lenses at the time of exposure is 452.7 ft. The coordinates of two field points A and B, as measured on the resulting photographs, are as follows:

Point	x (mm)	y (mm)	x' (mm)	y' (mm)
a	+45.30	+6.71	−21.20	+6.71
b	+60.20	−1.25	+ 4.16	−1.25

Compute the elevations of the two points and the length of the line AB to the nearest tenth of a foot.

14–17. In Prob. 14–16, the azimuth of the camera axis at each end of the base is 156° 35′. The ground-survey coordinates of the left end of the base are $X_{L_1} = 112,145.1$ ft and $Y_{L_1} = 25,540.6$ ft. Compute the ground-survey coordinates of A and B.

14–18. Determine the direction cosines of the lines aL_1, bL_1, aL_2, and bL_2 of Prob. 14–16, with respect to the photographic coordinate axes.

14–19. By means of the orientation matrix of Eq. 14–55, and applying Eq. 14–54, compute the direction cosines of the lines AL_1, BL_1, AL_2, and BL_2 of Prob. 14–18 with respect to the ground-survey axes. The azimuth of each camera is 156° 35′.

14–20. Compute the ground-survey coordinates of the right end of the base line of Prob. 14–17. Using the results of Prob. 14–19, compute the space coordinates of A and B by means of Eq. 3–70. Compare these values with the answers to Prob. 14–16 and 14–17.

14–21. The plate coordinates of two points lying on the horizon line of a terrestrial photograph are as follows: $x_a = -71.50$ mm and $y_a = -3.85$ mm; $x_c = +48.66$ mm and $y_c = -0.78$ mm. The camera focal length is 168.50 mm. Compute the elevation (or depression) angle and the swing of the photograph.

14–22. If the azimuth of the line from the exposure station of Prob. 14–21 to point A is 95° 30′, what is the camera azimuth?

14–23. A fixed-focus camera with a focal length of 132.58 mm is set for infinity focus. This camera is to be used to photograph an object 8 ft away from the camera lens. How far out must the lens be shimmed in order to achieve critical focus? If focussing is to be obtained by means of an auxiliary lens, what must be the power of the auxiliary lens, expressed in diopters?

14–24. A camera with a fixed 76.00-mm focal length and a 2¼ by 3¼ in. focal plane (3¼ in. dimension horizontal) is used to take a pair of photographs from the ends of a 4-ft base. The area of critical interest lies 8 ft from the camera base. At the time of each exposure, the camera axis was approximately normal to the base and in a generally horizontal position. Balplex 760 diapositives are prepared from the resulting negatives. At what scale, in representative-fraction form, should the stereoscopic model be measured?

14–25. In Prob. 14–24, what will be the distance between the nodal points of the projector lenses?

14–26. What distance in the object space, in inches, will the depth of focus represent in Prob. 14–24?

14–27. What will be the enlargement (or reduction) factor when the diapositives of Prob. 14–24 are prepared?

14–28. At the optimum projection distance of Prob. 14–24, what dimensions, in feet, will be covered stereoscopically in the object space of the photography?

14–29. At the minimum projection distance of Prob. 14–24, what dimensions, in feet, will be covered stereoscopically in the object space of the photography?

14–30. An area is photographed in the normal case from the ends of a 50-meter base. The area of interest lies between 150 meters and 500 meters from the base. The left camera position is 3.65 meters higher than the right. What base settings, in mm, are required in the Autograph A7 in order to realize the largest single instrument scale which will accommodate the range to be measured?

14–31. If a Stereoplanigraph C8 is to be used to plot from the photographs of Prob 14–30, compute the required base settings.

Index

ABC (Airborne Control), 133

Absolute orientation
Autograph A7, 375
Autograph A8, 367
Multiplex plotter, 323–336
Stereoplanigraph, 383

Accessories, aerial camera, 35–36

Adhesive, mosaic, 299

Adjustment
of horizontal bridging, 340–343
of radial line plot, 152
of vertical bridging, 349–354

Aerial camera
accessories for, 35–36
arrangement for
Canadian grid photography, 430
convergent photography, 439–442
trimetrogon photography, 420
body, 25–26
calibration of, 37–46
component parts of, 21
cone, 26–27
continuous strip, 33
description of, 20
drive mechanism, 28
filter, 26
focal plane, 21, 26, 27, 29, 30
interior orientation, 27
intervalometer for, 35–36
lens assembly, 21, 22–26
lenses, 24-25
magazine, 28–29
mount, 35, 440
precision, 21, 29
reconnaissance, 32
shutter, 26
U. S. Coast and Geodetic Survey
nine-lens, 2, 33–34, 400
vacuum back, 29

Aerial photogrammetry, 1

Aerial photography
classification of, 2–5
planning for, 104–118, 295–296

Aerotar lens, 25

Aerotriangulation, 338

Air base
definition of, 191
determination of, 213–216

Airborne Control (ABC), 133

Altimeter, 59, 418

Altimetry, barometric; *see* Barometric
altimetry

Altitude; *see* Flying height

Anaglyph viewing, 310

Analytical
determination of
horizontal position of a point, 95,
98, 478–481
space position of a point, 95, 98,
496–499
photogrammetry, 5, 80–98
plotter, 389–392
solution for exterior orientation, 235–
248, 257–263, 509

ANDERSON, RALPH O., 235

Aneroid barometer, 137–139

Angle
apparent depression, 403
azimuth, 55
between fiducial marks, 38
break, of trimetrogon photography,
421
depression, 404, 449, 454
dip, 402
elevation, 411–449
horizontal
from measurements on oblique photograph, 409–410, 411–413
from measurements on terrestial
photograph, 17, 461–468
using photoalidade, 17, 415–416
using rectoblique plotter, 413–415
on vertical photograph, 144–145
interlocking, of trimetrogon photography, 422
measurement of
with goniometer, 14
with photoalidade, 17, 415–416
parallactic, 175, 489
of swing, 54, 422–423, 451, 454, 497,
507
of tilt, 54, 422–423, 451, 454, 496
vertical
from measurements on oblique
photograph, 410–411
from measurements on terrestial
photograph, 468–472
using photoalidade, 17, 415–416

Angular coverage, 4–5, 112–114, 488

Annex point on trimetrogon photography, 425

Apparent
depression angle, 403
horizon, 3, 401

Army Corps of Engineers, U. S., control, 139